SMALL TRACTOR
SERVICE MANUAL

(Seventh Edition)
Vol. 1

• TRAC

•

RVICE

P.

©Copyright 1988 by   tates of America.
Lib

All instructions and diagrams have been checked for accuracy and ease of application;
however, success and safety in working with tools depend to a great extent upon individual accuracy, skill and caution. For this reason, the publishers are not able to guarantee the result of
any procedure contained herein. Nor can they assume responsibility for any damage or injury to
persons occasioned from the procedures. Persons engaging in the procedures do so entirely at
their own risk.

CONTENTS

DUAL DIMENSIONS

This service manual provides specifications in both the U.S. Customary and Metric (SI) systems of measurement. The first specification is given in the measuring system perceived by us to be the preferred system when servicing a particular component, while the second specification (given in parenthesis) is the converted measurement. For instance, a specification of "0.011 inch (0.28 mm)" would indicate that we feel the preferred measurement, in this instance, is the U.S. system of measurement and the metric equivalent of 0.011 inch is 0.28 mm.

ALLIS-CHALMERS

CONDENSED SPECIFICATIONS

MODELS

	B206, Home-steader 6	Home-steader 7	B208, Homesteader 8	B210	B212
Engine Make	B&S	B&S	B&S	B&S	B&S
Model	146707	170702	190701	243431	300421
Bore	2¾ in.	3 in.	3 in.	3-1/16 in.	3-7/16 in.
	(69.8 mm)	(76.2 mm)	(76.2 mm)	(77.8 mm)	(87.3 mm)
Stroke	2⅜ in.	2⅜ in.	2¾ in.	3¼ in.	3¼ in.
	(60.3 mm)	(60.3 mm)	(69.8 mm)	(82.5 mm)	(82.5 mm)
Piston Displacement	14.11 cu. in.	16.79 cu. in.	19.4 cu. in	23.94 cu. in.	30.16 cu. in.
	(231 cc)	(275 cc)	(318 cc)	(392 cc)	(494 cc)
Horsepower	6	7	8	10	12
Slow Idle Speed – Rpm	1750	1750	1750	1200	1200
High Idle Speed (No Load) – Rpm	3600	3600	3600	3600	3600
Full Load Speed – Rpm	3000	3000	3000	3240	3240
Crankcase Oil Capacity	2¼ pints	2¼ pints	2¼ pints	3 pints	3 pints
	(1L)	(1L)	(1L)	(1.4L)	(1.4L)
Weight –					
Above 32°F (0°C)			SAE 30		
0°F (−18°C) to 32°F (0°C)			SAE 10W		
Below 0°F (−18°C)			SAE 5W-20		
Transmission Oil Capacity	1½ pints	1½ pints	1½ pints	3 pints	3 pints
	(0.7L)	(0.7L)	(0.7)	(1.4L)	(1.4L)
Weight			SAE 90 EP		
Bevel Gear Housing Oil Capacity	....	....	....	1 pint	1 pint
				(0.5L)	(0.5L)
Weight	....	....	....	SAE 90 EP	SAE 90 EP

MODELS

	HB212	310, 310D	312, 312D	312H	314, 314
Engine Make	B&S	Kohler	Kohler	Kohler	Kohler
Model	300421	K241S	K301S	K301S	K321S
Bore	3-7/16 in.	3¼ in.	3⅜ in.	3⅜ in.	3½ in.
	(87.3 mm)	(82.5 mm)	(85.7 mm)	(85.7 mm)	(88.9 mm)
Stroke	3¼ in.	2⅞ in.	3¼ in.	3¼ in.	3¼ in.
	(82.5 mm)	(73.0 mm)	(82.5 mm)	(82.5 mm)	(82.5)
Piston Displacement	30.16 cu. in.	23.9 cu. in.	29.07 cu. in.	29.07 cu. in.	31.27 c
	(494 cc)	(392 cc)	(476 cc)	(476 cc)	(512)
Horsepower	12	10	12	12	1
Slow Idle Speed – Rpm	1200	1200	1200	1200	12
High Idle Speed (No Load) – Rpm	3600	3600	3600	3600	3
Full Load Speed – Rpm	3240	3240	3240	3240	3
Crankcase Oil Capacity			4 pints (1.9L)		
Weight –					
Above 32°F (0°C)			SAE 30		
0°F (−18°C) to 32°F (0°C)			SAE 10W		
Below 0°F (−18°C)			SAE 5W-20		
Transmission Oil Capacity			1 pint (0.5L)		
Weight			SAE 90 EP		
Bevel Gear Housing Oil Capacity			1 pint (0.5L)		
Weight			SAE 90 EP		
Gear Reduction Housing Oil Capacity	3 pints	....	....	3 pints	
	(1.4L)			(1.4L)	
Weight	SAE 90 EP	....	....	SAE 90 EP	

Allis-Chalmers

MODELS

	608	608LT	610	611LT	710-3 spd. 710-6 spd.
Engine Make	B&S	B&S	B&S	B&S	Kohler
Model	191707	191707	251707	252707	K241S
Bore	3 in. (76.2 mm)	3 in. (76.2 mm)	3-7/16 in. (87.3 mm)	3-7/16 in. (87.3 mm)	3¼ in. (82.5 mm)
Stroke	2¾ in. (69.8 mm)	2¾ in. (69.8 mm)	2⅝ in. (66.7 mm)	2⅝ in. (66.7 mm)	2⅞ in. (73.0 mm)
Piston Displacement	19.44 cu. in. (318 cc)	19.44 cu. in. (318 cc)	24.36 cu. in. (399 cc)	24.36 cu. in. (399 cc)	23.9 cu. in. (392 cc)
Horsepower	8	8	10	11	10
Slow Idle Speed – Rpm	1800	1800	1750	1750	1700
High Idle Speed (No Load) – Rpm	3600	3600	3600	3600	3600
Full Load Speed – Rpm	3400	3400	3400	3400	3240
Crankcase Oil Capacity	2¼ pints (1L)	2¼ pints (1L)	2¾ pints (1.3L)	3 pints (1.4L)	4 pints (1.9L)
Weight – Above 32°F (0°C)			SAE 30		
0°F (–18°C) to 32°F (0°C)			SAE 10W		
Below 0°F (–18°C)			SAE 5W-20		
Transmission Oil Capacity	3½ pints (1.6L)	1½ pints (0.7L)	3½ pints (1.6L)	1½ pints (0.7L)	4½ pints (2.1L)
Weight			SAE 90 EP		
Bevel Gear Housing Oil Capacity	....	....	....	....	1 pint (0.5L)
Weight	....	....	....	....	SAE 90 EP

MODELS

	314H	410, 410S	414S	416S	416H
....	Kohler	Kohler	Kohler	Kohler	Kohler
....	K321S	K241S	K321S	K341S	K341S
....	3½ in. (88.9 mm)	3¼ in. (82.5 mm)	3½ in. (88.9 mm)	3¾ in. (95.2 mm)	3¾ in. (95.2 mm)
....	3¼ in. (82.5 mm)	2⅞ in. (73.0 mm)	3¼ in. (82.5 mm)	3¼ in. (82.5 mm)	3¼ in. (82.5 mm)
....	31.27 cu. in. (512 cc)	23.9 cu. in. (392 cc)	31.27 cu. in. (512 cc)	35.89 cu. in. (588 cc)	35.89 cu. in. (588 cc)
....	14	10	14	16	16
....	1200	1700	1700	1700	1700
(Load) – Rpm	3600	3600	3600	3600	3600
....	3240	3240	3240	3240	3240
....			4 pints (1.9L)		
....			SAE 30		
(0°C)			SAE 10W		
....			SAE 5W-20		
....	3½ pints (1.6L)	3 pints (1.4L)	3 pints (1.4L)	3 pints (1.4L)	3½ pints (1.6L)
....	Dexron ATF	SAE 90 EP	SAE 90 EP	SAE 90 EP	Dexron ATF
Capacity			1 pint (0.5L)		
....			SAE 90 EP		
Oil Capacity	3 pints (1.4L)	....	....	....	3 pints (1.4L)
....	SAE 90 EP	....	....	....	SAE 90 EP

4

CONDENSED SPECIFICATIONS

MODELS

	712S	712H	716-6 spd.	716H	716H*
Engine Make	Kohler	Kohler	Kohler	Kohler	B&S
Model	K301S	K301S	K341S	K341S	326437
Bore	3⅜ in.	3⅜ in.	3¾ in.	3¾ in.	3-9/16 in.
	(85.7 mm)	(85.7 mm)	(95.2 mm)	(95.2 mm)	(90.5 mm)
Stroke	3¼ in.	3¼ in.	3¼ in.	3¼ in.	3¼ in.
	(82.5 mm)	(82.5 mm)	(82.5 mm)	(82.5 mm)	(82.5 mm)
Piston Displacement	29.07 cu. in.	29.07 cu. in.	35.89 cu. in.	35.89 cu. in.	32.4 cu. in.
	(476 cc)	(476 cc)	(588 cc)	(588 cc)	(531 cc)
Horsepower	12	12	16	16	16
Slow Idle Speed – Rpm	1700	1700	1700	1700	1700
High Idle Speed (No Load) – Rpm	3600	3600	3600	3600	3600
Full Load Speed – Rpm	3240	3240	3240	3240	3240
Crankcase Oil Capacity			4 pints (1.9L)		
Weight –					
Above 32°F (0°C)			SAE 30		
0°F (–18°C) to 32° (0°C)			SAE 10W		
Below 0°F (–18°C)			SAE 5W-20		
Transmission Oil Capacity	4½ pints	6 pints	4½ pints	6 pints	6 pints
	(2.1L)	(2.8L)	(2.1L)	(2.8L)	(2.8L)
Weight	SAE 90 EP	Dexron ATF	SAE 90 EP	Dexron ATF	Dexron ATF
Bevel Gear Housing Oil					
Capacity			1 pint (0.5L)		
Weight			SAE 90 EP		

*Tractors with S.N.16902115465 through 16902116155.

MODELS

	808GT	810GT	811GT	T-811
Engine Make	B&S	B&S	B&S	B&S
Model	191707	251707	252707	252707
Bore	3 in.	3-7/16 in.	3-7/16 in.	3-7/16 in.
	(76.2 mm)	(87.3 mm)	(87.3 mm)	(87.3 mm)
Stroke	2¾ in.	2⅝ in.	2⅝ in.	2⅝ in.
	(69.8 mm)	(66.7 mm)	(66.7 mm)	(66.7 mm)
Piston Displacement	19.44 cu. in.	24.36 cu. in.	24.36 cu. in.	24.36 cu. in.
	(318 cc)	(399 cc)	(399 cc)	(399 cc)
Horsepower	8	10	11	11
Slow Idle Speed – Rpm	1750	1750	1750	1750
High Idle (No Load) – Rpm	3600	3600	3600	3600
Full Load Speed – Rpm	3400	3400	3400	3400
Crankcase Oil Capacity	2¼ pints	3 pints	3 pints	3 pints
	(1L)	(1.4L)	(1.4L)	(1.4L)
Weight –				
Above 32°F (0°C)		SAE 30		
0°F (–18°C) to 32° (0°C)		SAE 10W		
Below 0°F (–18°C)		SAE 5W-20		
Transmission Oil Capacity		3½ pints (1.6L)		
Weight		SAE 90 EP		A-C Power Fluid 821

	MODELS				
	912-6 spd.	**912H**	**914S**	**914H**	**916H**
Engine Make	Kohler	Kohler	Kohler	Kohler	Kohler
Model	K301S	K301S	K321S	K321S	K341S
Bore	3⅜ in.	3⅜ in.	3½ in.	3½ in.	3¾ in.
	(85.7 mm)	(85.7 mm)	(88.9 mm)	(88.9 mm)	(95.2 mm)
Stroke	3¼ in.	3¼ in.	3¼ in.	3¼ in	3¼ in.
	(82.5 mm)	(82.5 mm)	(82.5 mm)	(82.5 mm)	(82.5 mm)
Piston Displacement	29.07 cu. in.	29.07 cu. in.	31.27 cu. in.	31.27 cu. in.	35.89 cu. in.
	(476 cc)	(476 cc)	(512 cc)	(512 cc)	(588 cc)
Horsepower	12	12	14	14	16
Slow Idle Speed – Rpm	1500	1500	1500	1500	1500
High Idle Speed (No Load) – Rpm	3600	3600	3600	3600	3600
Full Load Speed – Rpm	3400	3400	3400	3400	3400
Crankcase Oil Capacity			4 pints (1.9L)		
Weight –					
Above 32°F (0°C)			SAE 30		
0°F (−18°C) to 32°F (0°C)			SAE 10W		
Below 0°F (−18°C)			SAE 5W-20		
Transmission Oil Capacity	4½ pints	6 pints	4½ pints	6 pints	6 pints
	(2.1L)	(2.8L)	(2.1L)	(2.8L)	(2.8L)
Weight			A-C Power Fluid 821		
Bevel Gear Housing Oil Capacity			1 pint (0.5L)		
Weight			A-C Power Fluid 821		

FRONT AXLE SYSTEM

AXLE MAIN MEMBER

Models B206 – Homesteader 6- Homesteader 7

The front axle main member is supported by a pivot bolt in tractor frame. To remove front axle assembly, support front of tractor and disconnect drag link from steering arm (2 – Fig. AC1). Remove pivot bolt (5) and roll front axle assembly from tractor.

Models B208-Homesteader 8- 608-610

The front axle main member on Models B208, Homesteader 8, 608 and 610 is welded to tractor frame. Renewal

of frame assembly is necessary if axle cannot be repaired. Refer to Fig. AC2 for exploded view of frame and axle assembly.

Models 310-310D-312-312D- 312H-314-314D-314H

Axle main member is mounted in main frame and pivots on bolt (10 – Fig. AC3). To remove axle assembly, support front of tractor frame and disconnect tie rods from steering spindle arms. Remove pivot bolt (10) and roll axle assembly away from tractor.

Models 410-410S-414S-416S-416H

Axle main member is mounted in main frame and pivots on pin (10 – Fig. AC4). To remove front axle assembly, disconnect tie rod ball joint ends (7) from steering spindle arms. Remove bolt (11) and using a jack under frame behind axle, support front of tractor. Drive out pivot pin (10), raise front of tractor and roll axle assembly from tractor.

Models 608LT-611LT-808GT- 810GT-811GT-T811

The axle main member and stabilizer is a welded assembly. The unit pivots on a center mounting bolt and a flange bearing at rear of stabilizer. To remove front axle assembly, raise front of tractor and block securely. Disconnect drag link from steering arm (11 – Fig. AC5). Remove center mounting bolt and pull axle assembly out of flange bearing.

Models B210-B212-HB212-700 Series and 900 Series

The axle main member and stabilizer

is a welded assembly. The unit pivots on a center mounting bolt and rear of stabilizer. To remove front axle assembly, disconnect drag link ball joint end

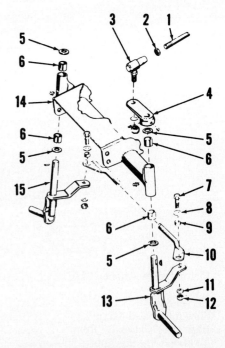

Fig. AC2 – Exploded view of front axle assembly used on Models B208, 608, 610, and Homesteader 8.

1. Drag link
2. Locknut
3. Ball joint
4. Steering arm
5. Washer
6. Bushing
7. Bolt
8. Washer
9. Spacer
10. Tie rod
11. Washer
12. Nut
13. Steering spindle L.H.
14. Axle & frame assy.
15. Steering spindle R.H.

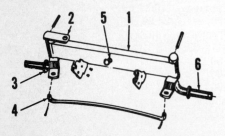

Fig. AC1 – Exploded view of front axle assembly used on Models B206, Homesteader 6 and Homesteader 7.

1. Main axle member
2. Steering arm
3. Steering spindle L.H.
4. Tie rod
5. Pivot bolt
6. Steering spindle R.H.

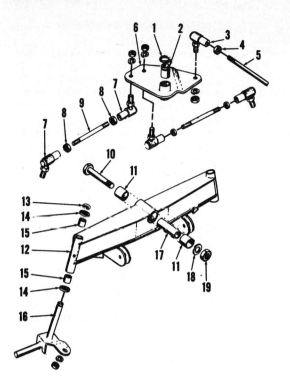

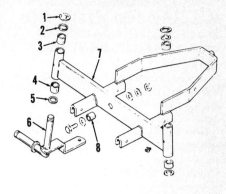

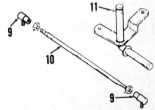

Fig. AC3 — Exploded view of front axle and steering plate assembly used on Models 310, 310D, 312, 312D, 312H, 314, 314D and 314H.

1. Snap ring
2. Bushing
3. Ball joint
4. Locknut
5. Drag link
6. Steering plate
7. Ball joint
8. Locknut
9. Tie rod
10. Pivot bolt
11. Bushing
12. Axle main member
13. "E" ring
14. Washer
15. Bushing
16. Steering spindle
17. Sleeve
18. Lockwasher
19. Nut

Fig. AC5 — Exploded view of front axle assembly used on Models 608LT, 611LT, 808GT, 810GT, 811GT and T811. Some models use a flanged bushing in place of washer (2) and bushing (3).

1. Retaining ring
2. Washer
3. Bushing
4. Bushing
5. Washer
6. Steering spindle R.H.
7. Axle main member
8. Spacer
9. Tie rod end
10. Tie rod
11. Steering spindle L.H.

(16 – Fig. AC6) from steering arm (15). Raise front of tractor and remove cap screw (38) and spacer (13) from center of axle. Lower front of axle and pull forward to slide stabilizer out of frame angle. The frame angle is bolted to main frame and can be renewed if stabilizer pivot hole is excessively worn.

TIE ROD

Models 310-310D-312-312D-312H-314-314D-314H-410-410S-414S-416S-416H

Dual tie rods are used on these models. Tie rods are adjustable and should be adjusted so there is approxi-

mately ⅛-inch (3 mm) toe-in. To adjust toe-in, disconnect tie rod ball joints from steering spindles, loosen locknuts, and turn tie rod ball joints in or out as required.

Models 608LT-611LT-808GT-810GT-811GT-T811

A Single tie rod is used on these models. To adjust toe-in, disconnect tie rod ball joints from steering spindles, loosen locknuts and turn tie rod ball joints in or out as required. Toe-in should be 1/16 to ⅛-inch (1.5-3.0 mm).

All Other Models

The tie rod is non-adjustable and can be removed after disconnecting tie rod from steering spindles.

STEERING SPINDLES

Models B206-Homesteader 6-Homesteader 7

To remove steering spindles, raise and support front of tractor and remove front wheels. Disconnect tie rod from spindles and drag link from steering arm (2 – Fig. AC1). Drive out pin holding steering arm; remove arm and lower left spindle (3) out of axle. Remove retaining pin and lower right spindle (6) out of axle.

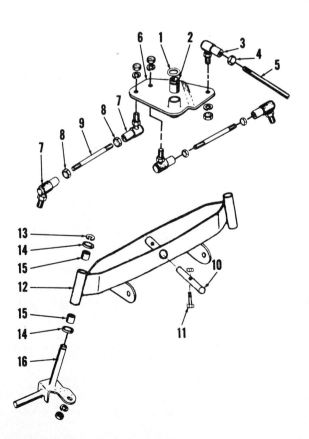

Fig. AC4 — Exploded view of front axle and steering plate assembly used on Models 410, 410S, 414S, 416S and 416H.

1. Snap ring
2. Bushing
3. Ball joint
4. Locknut
5. Drag link
6. Steering plate
7. Ball joint
8. Locknut
9. Tie rod
10. Pivot pin
11. Bolt
12. Axle main member
13. "E" ring
14. Washer
15. Bushing
16. Steering spindle

Models 310-310D-312-312D-312H-314-314D-314H-410-410S-414S-416H-416S-608LT-808GT-810GT-811GT-T811

To remove steering spindles, support front of tractor and remove front wheels. Disconnect tie rod ends from spindles. Remove "E" ring (13 – Fig. AC3 or AC4) or (1 – Fig. AC5) from top of steering spindle and lower spindle out of axle main member. All models are equipped with renewable spindle bushings. Lubricate with multi-purpose lithium base grease.

All Other Models

To remove steering spindles, refer to Fig. AC2 or AC6, support front of tractor and remove front wheels and tie rod. Remove steering arm and key from left spindle and slide spindle down out of axle main member. Remove retaining pin from right steering spindle and lower spindle from axle. Inspect spindle bushings and renew if necessary. Lubricate with multi-purpose lithium base grease.

STEERING GEAR

R&R AND OVERHAUL

Models B210-B212-HB212

To remove steering gear, remove hood, side panels and battery. Disconnect electrical wires from voltage regulator and remove fuel tank. Loosen set screw and remove steering wheel

and key. Unbolt and remove dash assembly and lay same to left side of tractor. Remove collar from steering shaft; then, unbolt and remove battery support. Disconnect "U" joint (3 – Fig. AC7) from gear and yoke assembly (5) and remove steering shaft. Disconnect the rear drag link ball joint from steering arm (10). Remove nut and washers from steering arm shaft and remove steering gear (8) as steering arm and shaft is withdrawn. Remove nut, lockwasher and set screw from lower end of eccentric pin (4) and withdraw eccentric pin with gear and yoke assembly (5). Unbolt and remove steering bracket (7).

Check needle bearings (9) and bushing (6) and renew as necessary.

When reassembling, lubricate needle bearings, bushing and gear teeth with multi-purpose grease. Before attaching, drag link or assembling "U" joint, adjust gear backlash as follows: With eccentric pin nut and set screw loose, rotate eccentric pin to obtain a minimum backlash between gears. Tighten nut and set screw, then rotate gears to make certain gears do not bind. If binding condition exits, increase backlash slightly.

Complete balance of reassembly by reversing disassembly procedure.

Models B206-Homesteader 6-Homesteader 7

The B206 is equipped with a steering arm at the end of steering column which transfers steering motion using two drag links and a pivot arm to steering spindle arm. Disassembly is self-evident upon inspection.

Models B208-Homesteader 8-608-610

To remove steering gear, first remove hood and steering wheel. Disconnect ignition wire and choke and throttle cables. Unbolt and lift off dash assembly and upper steering shaft support. Raise front of tractor and disconnect drag link (17 – Fig. AC8) from steering gear (16). Unbolt and remove steering gear. Remove nut securing steering pinion (12) to frame and remove upper steering shaft, "U" joint and steering pinion.

When reassembling steering units, move steering gear (16) closer to steering pinion (12) to remove excessive steering wheel play. To reassemble, reverse disassembly procedure.

Models 310-310D-312-312D-312H-314-314D-314H-410-410S-414S-416S-416H

To remove steering gear, first remove steering wheel and loosen clamp bolts at instrument panel. Disconnect drag link from steering gear arm and remove bolts securing steering gear housing (5 –

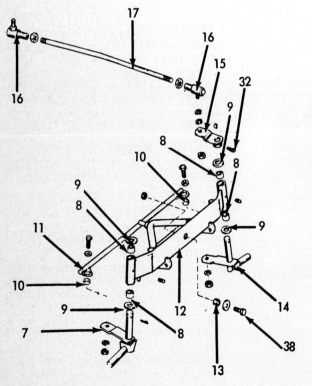

Fig. AC6 — Exploded view of front axle assembly used on Models B210, B212, HB212, 700 series and 900 series tractors.

7. Steering spindle R.H.
8. Steering spindle bearings
9. Washers
10. Tie rod spacers
11. Tie rod
12. Axle main member
13. Pivot bolt spacer
14. Steering spindle L.H.
15. Steering arm
16. Drag link ends
17. Drag link
32. Set screw
38. Axle pivot pin

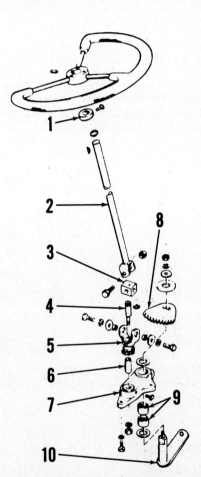

Fig. AC7 — Exploded view of steering gear used on Models B210, B212, and HB212.

1. Collar
2. Steering shaft
3. "U" joint
4. Eccentric pin
5. Gear & yoke assy.
6. Bushing
7. Steering bracket
8. Steering gear
9. Needle bearings
10. Steering arm & shaft

Fig. AC9) to frame. Raise tractor and lower steering gear and shaft out underside of tractor.

Disassembly of steering gear is self-evident after inspecting unit and referring to Fig. AC9. When reassembling steering gear, tighten plug (12) to 10-14 ft.-lbs. (14-19 N·m). Check to see that steering shaft turns freely after plug is installed.

Install lever and bolt assembly (15) with seal (18) and retainer (17). Loosen locknut (14) and back off follower stud (16) two turns. Adjust nuts (9) so seal (18) is in full contact with housing (5); but do not compress seal. Locate steering lever in mid-position (half way between full left and full right turn). Turn follower stud (16) in to obtain zero backlash and tighten locknut (14). Steering shaft should turn from full right to full left turn position without binding. Lubricate unit with approximately ¼-pound (120 mL) of multi-purpose grease.

Models 608LT-611LT-808GT-810GT-811GT-T811

To remove steering gear, tilt hood and remove upper dash, fuel tank, lower dash and steering wheel. On early

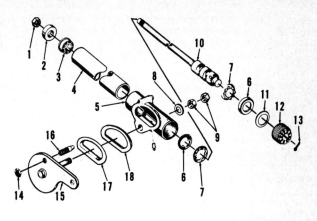

Fig. AC9 — Exploded view of steering gear used on Models 310, 310D, 312, 312D, 312H, 314, 314D, 314H, 410, 410S, 414S, 416S and 416H.

1. Nut
2. Dust seal
3. Bearing
4. Steering tube
5. Housing
6. Bearing cup
7. Bearing
8. Washer
9. Nuts
10. Steering shaft
11. Belleville washer
12. Plug
13. Cotter pin
14. Locknut
15. Lever & bolt
16. Follower stud
17. Seal retainer
18. Seal

Models 608LT and 611LT, remove steering support. Late Models 608LT, 611LT, 808GT, 810GT, and T811 are not equipped with support. Disconnect drag link from steering rod. Unbolt and remove steering plate and steering shaft. Remove base plate (11 – Fig. AC10), sector gear (10) and steering rod (8) as an assembly. To remove sector gear, remove two set screws and use a suitable puller or press to force steering rod from gear.

When reassembling sector gear and steering rod, install key with rounded end towards bent end of steering rod. Inspect bushings in base plate and steering plate for wear or damage and renew as necessary.

Models 710-3 spd.-710-6 spd.-712S-712H-716-6 spd.-912-6 spd.-912H-914H-914S-916H

To remove steering gear, remove steering wheel and battery. Disconnect drag link from steering arm (13 – Fig. AC11) and turn steering arm to allow access to mounting bolts. Remove mounting bolts and move steering gear assembly forward until casting lug clears edge of frame opening and lower entire assembly.

To disassemble steering gear, clamp support casting in a vise and remove locknut (B – Fig. AC12) and washer. Use a plastic mallet to remove steering arm from bevel drive gear and casting. Position steering shaft in a vise. Remove re-

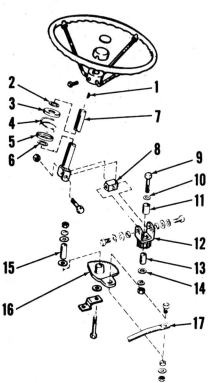

Fig. AC8 — Exploded view of steering gear used on Models B208, 608, 610 and Homesteader 8.

1. Key
2. Washer
3. Cup
4. Spring
5. Cup
6. Washer
7. Steering shaft
8. "U" joint
9. Bolt
10. Washer
11. Spacer
12. Gear & yoke assy.
13. Bushing
14. Washer
15. Sleeve
16. Quadrant gear
17. Drag link

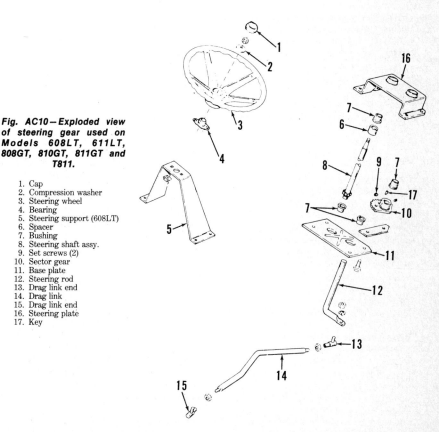

Fig. AC10 — Exploded view of steering gear used on Models 608LT, 611LT, 808GT, 810GT, 811GT and T811.

1. Cap
2. Compression washer
3. Steering wheel
4. Bearing
5. Steering support (608LT)
6. Spacer
7. Bushing
8. Steering shaft assy.
9. Set screws (2)
10. Sector gear
11. Base plate
12. Steering rod
13. Drag link end
14. Drag link
15. Drag link end
16. Steering plate
17. Key

taining ring (E) and use a piece of hard-wood to drive pinion gear off shaft. Remove key from shaft and slide shaft out of bushing. Loosen locknuts and remove adjusting cap screws, adjusting plate and bushing. Use a bearing puller to remove needle bearings from support casting.

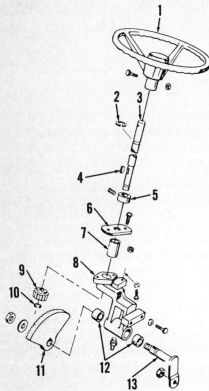

Fig. AC11—Exploded view of steering gear used on Models 710-3 spd., 710-6 spd., 712S, 712H, 716-6 spd., 716H, 912-6 spd., 912H, 914S, 914H and 916H.

1. Steering wheel
2. Retaining ring
3. Steering shaft
4. Key
5. Set collar
6. Steering plate
7. Bushing
8. Casting
9. Pinion
10. "E" ring
11. Bevel gear
12. Needle bearings
13. Steering arm assy.

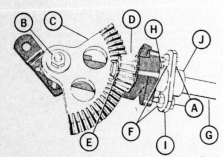

Fig. AC12—View of steering assembly removed from tractor. Refer to text for disassembly procedures.

A. Adjusting cap screws
B. Locknut & flat washer
C. Bevel gear
D. Pinion
E. "E" ring
F. Locknuts
G. Steering shaft
H. Bushing
I. Steering plate
J. Set collar

During reassembly, press needle bearings into each end of bore with end of bearing marked "Torrington" facing outward. The bearing at gear end must be ⅛-inch (3 mm) below surface of casting. The bearing at steering arm end must fit flush with casting. Install bushing (H—Fig. AC12) and adjusting plate assembly and tighten adjusting plate until about 1/64-inch (0.4 mm) of bushing is above casting surface.

ENGINE

REMOVE AND REINSTALL

Models B210-B212-HB212

Engine removal requires removal of hood, grille, grille support and dash. Disconnect battery and ignition wire and remove battery. Slide flexible fuel line off tank connection, then remove fuel tank. Remove wires from starter-generator and disconnect choke and throttle control cables from engine. Remove engine oil drain pipe. Disconnect drive shaft front coupling and remove cap screws securing engine to frame. Slide engine forward and lift it out of frame.

Models B206-B208-Homesteader 6-Homesteader 7-Homesteader 8.

To remove engine on Model B206, loosen two hood hold-down knobs and tilt hood forward. On Models Homesteader 6 and Homesteader 7, unlatch rear of hood and tilt hood forward. Remove hood on Models B208 and Homesteader 8. Disconnect ignition wire, fuel line and choke and throttle cables. Remove engine drive belt on underside of tractor. Remove engine drive pulley. Remove engine mounting bolts and lift engine from tractor frame.

To reinstall engine, reverse removal procedure.

Models 310-310D-312-312D-312H-314-314D-314H-410-410S-414S-416S-416H

To remove engine, remove hood and front grille assembly, supporting brace and engine shield. Remove front pto drive belt. Disconnect battery cables and ignition wires. Disconnect throttle and choke cables. Disconnect fuel line at fuel pump. Disconnect drive shaft coupling at rear of engine. Remove engine mounting bolts. If engine cannot be moved to the side far enough to clear oil drain pipe, then drain engine oil and remove oil drain pipe. Lift engine from tractor.

Models 608 And 610

To remove engine, first remove hood and disconnect battery cables. Remove grille assembly and grille support. Disconnect throttle cable, choke cable and fuel line at engine. Mark wires for reassembly, then disconnect electrical connections at regulator and generator. Remove regulator and generator from engine. Remove drive belts and pulleys from engine crankshaft. Remove mounting cap screws and lift engine from tractor.

Models 608LT-611LT

To remove engine, tilt hood assembly forward and remove front engine brace. Disconnect battery ground cable. Remove fuel line at carburetor and drain fuel tank. Remove throttle cable, engine ground wire, charging circuit and starter wires. Set parking brake and block tractor securely. Remove cap screw and lockwasher from crankshaft pulley assembly. Use a suitable puller to remove pulley. Tap pulley with a soft hammer just below drive pulley if needed.

NOTE: Early LT tractors have small hole for crankshaft. Later models have a larger hole in the frame, allowing engine to be removed without removing pulley.

After pulley assembly is removed, remove mounting cap screws and engine assembly.

Models 710-3 spd.-710-6 spd.-712S-712H-716-6 spd.-716H-912-6 spd.-912H-914H-914S-916H

To remove engine, remove hood and front grille assembly. Disconnect fuel line from fuel pump and plug hose or drain fuel tank. Disconnect battery ground cable, all electrical wires, choke cable and throttle cable from engine. Remove flywheel to drive shaft cap screws, washers and spacers. Remove four mounting cap screws and lift engine from tractor.

Models 808GT-810GT-811GT-T811

To remove engine, set parking brake and block tractor securely. Disconnect battery ground cable from battery. Remove fuel line at carburetor and drain fuel tank. Disconnect throttle cable, choke cable, engine ground wire, charging circuit and starter wires. On 810GT tractors remove muffler assembly. Remove four mounting cap screws and lift engine from tractor.

OVERHAUL

Engine make and model are listed at the beginning of this section. To overhaul engine components and accessories, refer to Briggs & Stratton and Kohler sections of this manual.

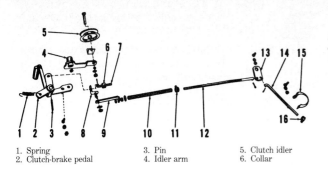

Fig. AC13 — Exploded view of B206, Homesteader 6 and Homesteader 7 clutch and brake linkage.

7. Clutch rod
8. Clip
9. Anchor
10. Spring
11. Collar
12. Brake rod
13. Pivor arm
14. Brake pivot rod
15. Brake band
16. Collar

1. Spring
2. Clutch-brake pedal
3. Pin
4. Idler arm
5. Clutch idler
6. Collar

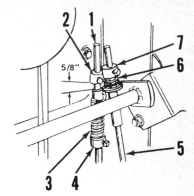

Fig. AC15 — View showing clutch and brake adjustment points on Homesteader 8 tractor.

1. Clutch rod
2. Outer collar
3. Clutch spring
4. Inner collar
5. Brake rod
6. Tapered spring
7. Collar

CLUTCH

A belt idler type clutch is used on all models. It is operated by clutch-brake pedal on right side of tractor.

ADJUSTMENT

Models B206-Homesteader 6-Homesteader 7

To adjust clutch linkage, clutch-brake pedal must be in clutch engaged position. Insert an Allen wrench through opening in right side of frame and loosen set screw in collar (6 – Fig. AC13). Position collar so it is 1/8-inch (3 mm) from angle clip (8) and tighten set screw.

Model B208

To adjust clutch, clutch-brake pedal must be in clutch engaged position. Refer to Fig. AC14. Compression spring on clutch rod should be compressed about 3/4-inch (19 mm). Loosen set screw in collar (B) and move collar to obtain correct length of spring. Turn adjusting nut (C) at end of clutch rod to adjust movement of clutch idler pulley against

drive belt. Clutch idler pulley should release drive belt when clutch-brake pedal is depressed.

Model Homesteader 8

With foot pedal up (engaged position), adjust clutch rod outer set collar (2 – Fig. AC15) to obtain 5/8-inch (16 mm) clearance between collar and clutch rod guide. Then, depress foot pedal all the way and adjust inner set collar (4) so clutch rod spring (3) is just free to rotate on rod.

Models B210-B212-310-310D-312-312D-314-314D

With clutch-brake pedal in clutch engaged position, refer to Fig. AC16 and adjust control rod locknuts (L) so there is 7/8-inch (22 mm) clearance (C) between locknuts and idler pulley pivot arm rod guide (G) with variable speed lever in "LOW" speed position.

Model HB212

To adjust clutch, clutch-brake pedal must be in clutch engaged position. Turn adjusting nuts (8 – Fig. AC17) so there is 1/8-inch (3 mm) clearance between adjusting nuts and closest end of rod guide (7).

Model 312H-314H-416H

With clutch-brake pedal in clutch engaged position, there should be 5/8-inch (16 mm) between closest nut (13 – Fig. AC18) and rod guide (14). Turn locknuts if necessary to obtain correct spacing.

Model 410

To adjust clutch idler linkage, first make certain brake linkage is properly adjusted as outlined in "BRAKE" adjustment paragraph. Then, with clutch-brake pedal in clutch engaged position, adjust jam nuts so there is 1/2-inch (13 mm) clearance between jam nuts and clutch rod guide. See Fig. AC19.

Model 410S-414S-416S

To adjust clutch idler linkage, first make certain brake linkage is properly adjusted as outlined in appropriate "BRAKE" adjustment paragraph. Then, with clutch-brake pedal in clutch engaged position, refer to Fig. AC20 and adjust jam nuts on clutch rod to obtain a clearance of 3/4-inch (19 mm) between jam nuts and clutch rod guide.

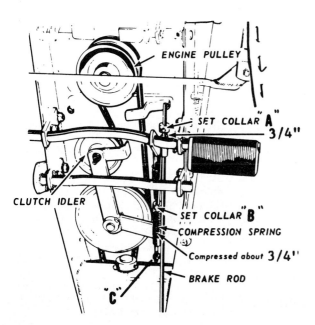

Fig. AC14 — View showing clutch and brake adjustments on Model B208.

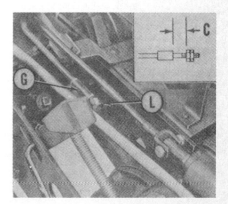

Fig. AC16 — View showing clutch rod adjustment on models with variable speed drive. Distance between rod guide (G) and rod nuts (L) should be 7/8-inch (22 mm) (C).

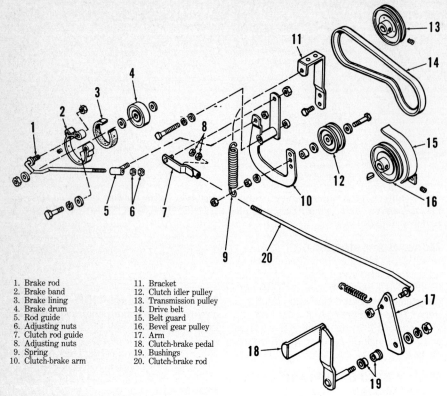

1. Brake rod
2. Brake band
3. Brake lining
4. Brake drum
5. Rod guide
6. Adjusting nuts
7. Clutch rod guide
8. Adjusting nuts
9. Spring
10. Clutch-brake arm
11. Bracket
12. Clutch idler pulley
13. Transmission pulley
14. Drive belt
15. Belt guard
16. Bevel gear pulley
17. Arm
18. Clutch-brake pedal
19. Bushings
20. Clutch-brake rod

Fig. AC17—Exploded view of clutch and brake assemblies used on Model HB212.

inner set collar until clutch rod spring is just free to rotate on rod.

NOTE: Some early models use set collars in place of locknuts, but adjustment procedure is the same.

Models 608LT-611LT

To adjust clutch, pedal must be in engaged (up) position and idler pulley tight against drive belt. On early models, adjust set collar (Fig. AC22) on clutch rod until clutch rod spring length is 2¼ inches (57 mm). Collar can be re-located more easily if foot pedal is depressed, but 2¼ inches (57 mm) dimension must be measured with clutch fully engaged. With clutch rod spring set, adjust jam nuts at end of clutch rod to obtain ⅜-inch (9.5 mm) clearance between rod guide and nuts as shown.

On late models, be sure foot pedal is released (up) and idler pulley is tight against drive belt. Adjust nuts at front of clutch rod to obtain ½-inch (13 mm) clearance (Fig. AC22A) between adjusting nut and rod guide. Then, fully depress clutch-brake pedal, loosen collar set screw and move collar against clutch rod spring until spring is compressed ½-inch (13 mm). Tighten set screw and check clutch operation.

Models 710-3 spd.-710-6 spd.-712S-712H-716-6 spd.-716H-912-6 spd.-912H-914H-914S-916H

With clutch-brake pedal in engaged position, turn adjusting nuts (Fig. AC23) until clearance ("A") between front nut and clutch rod guide is ⅜-inch (9.5 mm) on Models 710-3 spd., 710-6 spd. 716-6 spd. and 912-6 spd. or ¼-inch (6 mm) on all other models.

Models 808GT-810GT-811GT

To adjust clutch idler linkage, first make certain brake linkage is properly adjusted as outlined in appropriate "BRAKE" adjustment paragraph. On all models, be sure clutch-brake pedal is in engaged (up) position when adjusting linkage. On early models, press idler pulley against drive belt to remove slack in belt. Measure gap between adjusting nut (A – Fig. AC24) and clutch rod guide (C); gap should be 7/16 to 9/16-inch (11-14 mm) as shown. Adjust nut (A) as required. To adjust clutch rod spring tension, fully depress pedal and engage parking brake. Clutch rod spring (B) should be compressed 7/16 to ½-inch (11-13 mm). If not, loosen set screw and move collar (D) to compress spring to recommended distance.

On late models, distance between set collar (D – Fig. AC25) and rod guide (B) should be ½ to ⅝-inch (13-16 mm) with pedal in engaged position. Adjust by loosening set screw (E) and moving collar to obtain correct measurement.

Models 608-610

With foot pedal up (engaged position), adjust clutch rod locknut (Fig. AC21) to obtain ⅜-inch (9.5 mm) clearance between nut and clutch rod guide. Then, depress foot pedal all the way and adjust

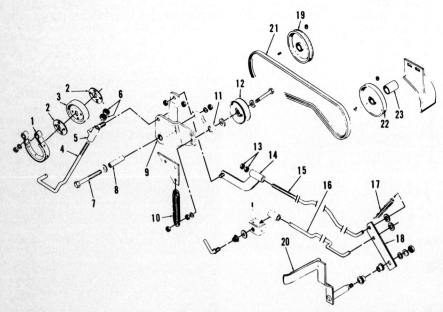

1. Brake band
2. Washers
3. Brake drum
4. Brake rod
5. Rod guide
6. Adjusting nuts
7. Pivot bolt
8. Bushing
9. Clutch-brake arm
10. Spring
11. Bushing
12. Clutch idler pulley
13. Adjusting nuts
14. Rod guide
15. Clutch-brake rod
16. Parking brake rod
17. Spring
18. Arm
19. Transmission pulley
20. Clutch-brake pedal
21. Drive belt
22. Bevel gear pulley
23. Bushing

Fig. AC18—Exploded view of clutch and brake assemblies used on Models 312H, 314H and 416H.

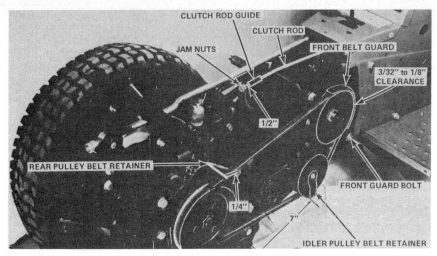

Fig. AC19—View showing clutch rod adjustment on Model 410 tractors. Distance between rod guide and jam nuts should be ½-inch (13 mm). Note positions of belt guard and belt retainers.

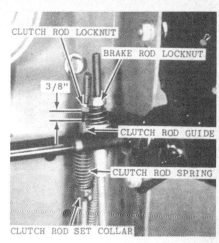

Fig. AC21—View of brake and clutch linkage used on Models 608 and 610. Early models are slightly different but adjustment procedure is basically the same.

Model T811

On Model T811, variable speed control and clutch are adjusted together. Place speed control lever up in full speed position, then loosen shoulder bolt (4—Fig. AC26). With transmission in neutral, start engine, depress clutch pedal, set parking brake and stop engine. Unlatch parking brake and allow pedal to come up slowly, then measure distance from pedal shaft to forward edge of foot rest. Distance should be 5½ inches ((140 mm); if not, adjust nut (2—Fig. AC27) towards spring to increase measurement or loosen nut to decrease measurement. Place speed control lever down in low speed position, then pull upper handle (1—Fig. AC26) only upward and hold to lock lever in position. push bar (3) down and tighten shoulder bolt.

BRAKE

On all models except 608LT and 611LT, brake consists of a contracting band on a drum located on a shaft at left side of transmission on gear drive models and on right side of reduction housing on hydrostatic drive models. On Models 608LT and 611LT, brake consists of a caliper, disc brake pads and a rotor on a shaft at right side of transmission. Brake is operated by clutch-brake pedal on right side of tractor on all models.

ADJUSTMENT

Models B206-Homesteader 6-Homesteader 7

To adjust brake, position clutch-brake pedal in clutch engaged position and compress spring (10—Fig. AC13) to a length of 5½ inches (140 mm). Position collar (11) against spring and tighten set screw. Position collar (16) on brake rod (14) so brake is engaged when clutch-brake pedal is depressed but does not drag on drum when pedal is released.

Model B208

To adjust brake, depress clutch-brake pedal until brake is fully engaged, then lock parking brake and release clutch-

brake pedal. Adjust set collar (A—Fig. AC14) so it is ¾-inch (19 mm) from rod guide.

Model Homesteader 8

To adjust brake, foot pedal must be in released (up) position. Position brake rod set collar (7—Fig. AC15) against tapered spring (6) making sure spring is not compressed. Fully depress foot pedal; on early models (prior to S.N. 26401001), pedal should stop 1¼ inches (32 mm) from pedal stop stud and on late models (S.N. 26401001 and after), pedal should stop 2½ inches (63 mm) from front edge of foot rest. Adjust set collar (7) as necessary to obtain desired measurement.

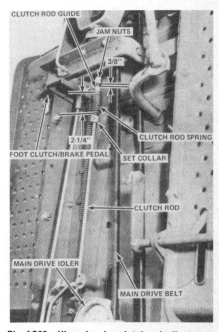

Fig. AC22—View showing clutch rod adjustment on early Models 608LT and 611LT. Distance between rod guide and jam nuts should be ⅜-inch (10 mm). Refer to text for details.

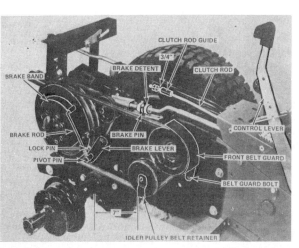

Fig. AC20—View of clutch idler linkage adjustment on Models 410S, 414S and 416S tractors. Distance between rod guide and jam nuts should be ¾-inch (19 mm).

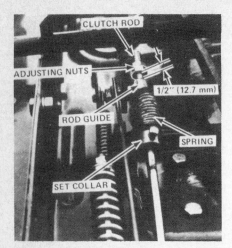

Fig. AC22A—Clutch rod adjustment points on late Models 608LT and 611LT.

Models B210-B212-310-310D-312-312D-314-314D

Adjust brake by first checking clutch adjustment as outlined in "CLUTCH" adjustment paragraph. Tighten adjusting nuts on brake band assembly until drive belt on variable speed pulley creeps when engine is running and clutch-brake pedal is depressed. Then, loosen brake adjusting nuts gradually until creeping motion of drive belt stops when engine is running and pedal is depressed.

CAUTION: To prevent possible injury, engine should be stopped while turning brake adjusting nuts.

Models HB212-312H-314H

Brake should be adjusted so brake is fully engaged when clutch-brake pedal is depressed. With hydrostatic control lever in neutral position, turn brake adjusting nuts (6–Fig. AC17 or AC18) until brake band is tight against brake drum. With clutch-brake pedal released, brake band should not drag against brake drum.

Models 410-410S-414S-416S

To adjust brake, refer to Fig. AC28. Adjust jam nuts on brake rod until forward edge of clutch arm is ⅝-inch (16 mm) from rear corner of bevel gear housing when clutch-brake pedal is firmly depressed. Make certain clutch idler releases belt tension properly before brake is applied.

Model 416H

To adjust brake, loosen jam nut at front of parking brake rod, then turn handle and rod end until brake is tight when parking brake handle is pulled up against fender. With parking brake engaged and foot pedal released, adjust nuts on foot brake rod to provide ½-inch (13 mm) clearance between nuts and brake rod guide. Refer to Fig. AC29.

Models 608-610

To adjust brake, first loosen jam nut on parking brake rod and turn rod end until brake is tight when park brake handle is in upright position. Then, with parking brake engaged and foot pedal released, adjust brake rod locknut until it just contacts tapered coil spring (Fig. AC21). Depress foot pedal fully and adjust locknut as necessary until forward edge of foot pedal stops 2½ inches (63 mm) from forward edge of foot rest.

Models 608LT-611LT

With foot pedal in released (up) position, adjust brake as follows: On all models, push brake cam lever (Fig. AC30) forward by hand to remove slack in linkage and check gap between rear of cam lever and cam lever stop with a feeler gage. Adjust nuts on brake arm if necessary to obtain ⅛-inch (3 mm) gap.

Adjust brake rod springs as follows: On early models, hold foot brake rod (Fig. AC31) forward to remove slack. Adjust jam nuts on front of brake rod to obtain clearance of ⅝ to ¾-inch (16-19 mm) between nuts and spring. Adjust nuts on rear of hand brake rod to just

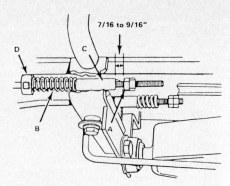

Fig. AC24—Clutch adjustment point for early Models 808GT, 810GT and 811GT. Refer to text for details.

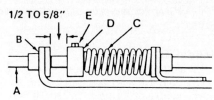

Fig. AC25—Clutch adjustment point for late Models 808GT and 811GT.

A. Clutch rod
B. Rod guide
C. Spring
D. Collar
E. Set screw

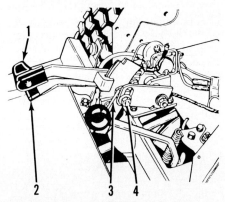

Fig. AC26—View of variable speed control linkage used on Model T811.

1. Control lever
2. Handle
3. Bar
4. Shoulder bolt

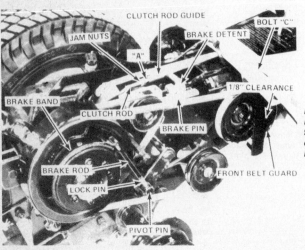

Fig. AC23—View of clutch rod adjustment on 700 and 900 series tractors. Tractor equipped with shuttle clutch is shown; other models are similar.

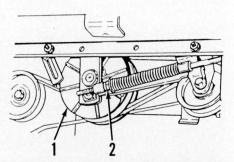

Fig. AC27—Variable speed pulley (1) and clutch rod used on Model T811. Adjusting nut (2) is used to adjust clutch. Refer to text.

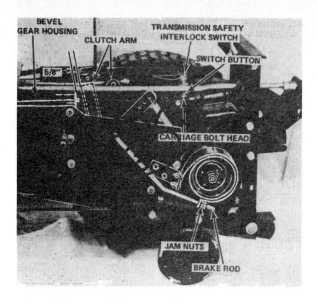

Fig. AC28 — View showing brake adjustment on Models 410, 410S, 414S and 416S. Refer to text for adjusting procedure.

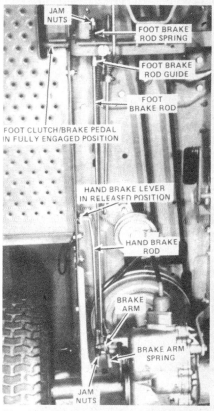

Fig. AC31 — Underside view of brake linkage used on early Models 608LT and 611LT.

Fig. AC29 — View of brake linkage adjustment points on Model 416H tractor.

hold spring against rod guide without moving brake arm away from stop. For final adjustment check, apply brake and measure brake rod springs. Springs must not be less than 7/8-inch (22 mm) and not more than 15/16-inch (24 mm) long. Readjust jam nuts if necessary to bring springs within limits.

On late models, push brake rod guide forward so mounting cap screw is at rear of slot in rod guide. Then, adjust jam nuts until brake rod spring is just snug between rod guide and nuts.

Models 710-3 spd.-712S-914S

To adjust brake, adjust jam nuts on rear end of brake rod until front edge of clutch arm (Fig. AC32) is 5/8-inch (16 mm) from lift cable guide when pedal is fully depressed and brake is locked. When parking brake lever is pulled upward against fender, brake should be locked. If not, loosen jam nut on parking brake rod and turn brake lever and rod end until parking brake operation is correct.

Models 712H-716H-912H-914H-916H

To adjust brake, loosen jam nut on front end of parking brake rod (Fig. AC33) and turn handle and rod end until parking brake is tight when brake han-

Fig. AC30 — View of caliper-disc brake used on Models 608LT and 611LT.

dle is against fender in brake lock position. With parking brake engaged and foot pedal released, adjust jam nuts on front of brake rod to obtain 3/4-inch (19 mm) clearance between jam nut and rod guide.

Models 716-6 spd. And 912-6 spd.

To adjust brake, depress pedal and move dual range lever until cam lever (Fig. AC34) is under gate finger. Insert

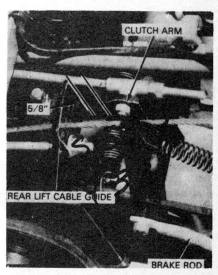

Fig. AC32 — View showing brake adjustment on Models 710-3 spd., 712S and 914S. Refer to text for adjusting procedure.

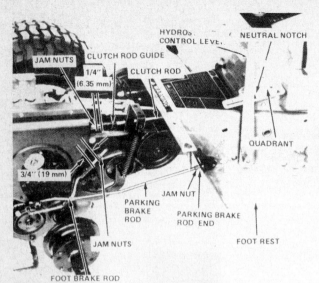

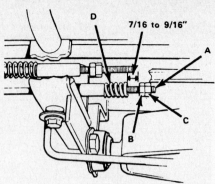

Fig. AC33 — View showing clutch and brake rod adjustments for Models 712H, 716H, 912H, 914H and 916H.

Fig. AC35 — Brake rod adjustment point for early Models 808GT, 810GT and 811GT. Distance between rod spring and jam nuts should be 7/16 to 9/16-inch (11-14 mm). Refer to text for details.

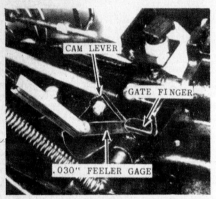

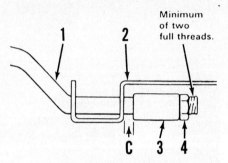

Fig. AC34 — On 716-6 spd. and 912-6 spd. tractors, insert 0.030 inch (0.762 mm) feeler gage between cam lever and gate finger when adjusting brakes.

CAUTION: A minimum of two threads must extend through nut.

Model T811

To adjust brake, place transmission in neutral and start engine. Move variable speed control lever to full speed position and shut off engine. Shift transmission into gear without depressing clutch-brake pedal. Pull forward on brake band (2 – Fig. AC36) to remove slack and measure gap (C) between spacer (3) and brake band which should be 5/8 to 3/4-inch (16-19 mm). Adjust nut (4) if necessary to obtain correct measurement.

Fig. AC36 — On late Models 808GT and 811GT and all Model T811 tractors, adjust nut (4) to obtain specified gap at (C) when adjusting brake. Refer to text for details.

CAUTION: A minimum of two threads must extend through nut.

0.030 inch (0.762 mm) feeler gage between lever and finger, then release pedal so spring pressure will hold gage in place. Loosen jam nut on front end of parking brake rod and turn lever and rod end until tension is felt when moving lever into engaged position. Retighten jam nut. With parking brake engaged, turn jam nut on rear of brake rod until front nut just contacts brake band, then turn additional 1/3-turn.

Models 808GT-810GT-811GT

To adjust brake on early models, release parking brake and push brake rod (A – Fig. AC35) forward to seat brake band on drum. The gap between nut (B) and spring (D) should be 7/16 to 9/16-inch (11-14 mm); if not, adjust nut (B) as required and lock in place with nut (C).

To adjust brake on late models, release parking brake and push brake rod (1 – Fig. AC36) up slightly. Measure gap (C) between spacer (3) and brake band (2) which should be 9/16 to 11/16-inch (14-17 mm). Adjust nut (4) to obtain correct measurement.

POWER TAKE-OFF

All Models Except 700 And 900 Series Tractors

ADJUSTMENT. On models equipped with pto, a springloaded idler is used to apply tension to pto belt. Correct belt tension is maintained by adjusting idler tension spring length. Tension of idler pulley against drive belt should be sufficient to drive implement without belt slippage. Excessive tension will cause premature failure of belts and pulley bearings.

Models 710-712-716-912-914-916

ADJUSTMENT. All models use a mechanical, friction-type pto clutch. Belt tension is adjusted by changing position of idler pulley. Pto clutch is properly adjusted when clutch pulley (Fig. AC37) moves away from clutch cone, as shown at "B", 1/8-inch (3 mm) on Models 710, 712 and 716 or 1/16-inch (1.5 mm) on

Models 912, 914 and 916 when clutch is disengaged. Turn adjusting nuts "A" on pto clutch rod clockwise to increase pulley travel or counter-clockwise to decrease travel.

Fig. AC37 — View of pto clutch used on Models 710, 712, 716, 912, 914 and 916. Adjust clutch to obtain dimension "B", 1/8-inch (3 mm) on 700 series tractors or 1/16-inch (1.5 mm) on 900 series tractors.

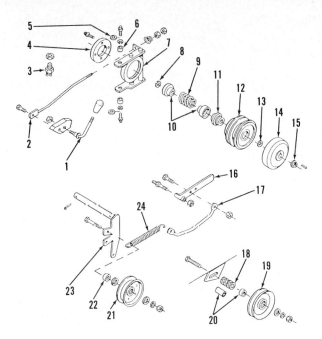

Fig. AC38 — Exploded view of pto clutch and idler pulley assembly used on 700 and 900 series tractors.

1. Clutch control handle
2. Control rod
3. Interlock switch
4. Brake disc
5. Spring washer (2)
6. Spacer (2)
7. Pivot assy.
8. Retaining ring
9. Spring
10. Spring guides
11. Bearing
12. Pulley
13. Retaining ring
14. Clutch plate
15. Retaining nut
16. Tensioning lever
17. Tension rod
18. Washers (4)
19. Rear idler pulley
20. Spacers
21. Front idler pulley
22. Spacer
23. Pivot arm
24. Tension spring

R&R AND OVERHAUL CLUTCH.

Remove drive belt from pto pulley. Remove retaining nut (15 – Fig. AC38) and withdraw clutch plate (14). Protect threads on pto shaft and pry key out of shaft keyway.

CAUTION: Pto pulley is spring loaded. Install C-clamp (Fig. AC39) as shown to compress spring and hold pulley before attempting to remove pulley retaining ring.

Compress pulley internal spring with a C-clamp (Fig. AC39) as shown, then remove retaining ring. Remove pivot assembly retaining screws. Slowly release clamp and remove pto clutch assembly. Remove cotter pin retaining idler pivot to right side plate, then withdraw idler assembly.

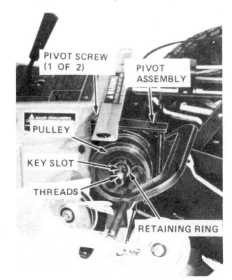

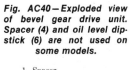

Fig. AC39 — When disassembling pto clutch, compress pulley internal spring with C-clamp as shown, then remove retaining ring and slowly release spring pressure.

Check pto shaft runout at outer retaining ring groove with a dial indicator. If runout exceeds 0.010 inch (0.254 mm), shaft should be renewed or straightened. Refer to BEVEL GEARS paragraphs. Inspect all parts for excessive wear or other damage and renew as necessary.

Reassemble in reverse order of disassembly procedure. Be sure bearing (11 – Fig. AC38) is installed with locking groove facing outward. If clutch plate retaining nut (15) is ¾-inch, tighten to 70 ft.-lbs. (95 N·m) torque; if ½-inch nut is used, tighten to 50 ft.-lbs. (68 N·m). Adjust clutch as previously outlined.

BEVEL GEARS

REMOVE AND REINSTALL

Model B210-B212

To remove bevel gear unit, first remove dash and top frame cover. Remove

seat and fender assembly. Support tractor under main frame just ahead of bevel gear housing. Disconnect brake linkage, clutch-brake rod and transmission shift rod. On variable speed drive models, disconnect fork from transmission pulley. Remove pto drive belt on models so equipped. Remove transmission drive belt and cap screws securing transmission rearward away from tractor. Disconnect drive shaft and remove drive shaft flange from bevel gear shaft. Remove cap screws securing bevel gear housing to frame and lift off bevel gear assembly.

Model HB212

To remove bevel gear drive unit, first remove steering wheel, dash assembly and top frame cover as necessary. Remove seat deck and fender assembly. Support tractor under main frame just ahead of bevel gear housing and also under gear reduction housing. Remove left rear wheel and hub assembly. Remove bevel gear pto belt pulley and disconnect pto tension spring. Unbolt belt guard and remove drive belt and pulley from right end of bevel gear shaft. Disconnect drive shaft coupling from bevel gear input shaft. Unbolt and remove left side plate. Remove remaining cap screws securing bevel gear unit to frame, then lift unit from tractor.

Reinstall bevel gear unit by reversing removal procedure. Adjust clutch and brake linkage as necessary.

Models 310-312-314-410-414-416

To remove bevel drive unit, first unbolt and remove seat deck and fender assembly. Raise and support tractor main frame just ahead of bevel gear housing. Remove left rear wheel and hub assembly. On models so equipped, remove bevel gear pto belt pulley and disconnect pto tension spring. On variable drive models, disconnect fork from drive pulley on right end of bevel

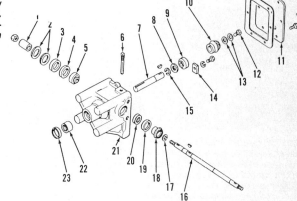

Fig. AC40 — Exploded view of bevel gear drive unit. Spacer (4) and oil level dipstick (6) are not used on some models.

1. Spacer
2. Shims
3. Oil seal
4. Spacer
5. Bearing
6. Dipstick
7. Input shaft
8. Washer
9. Bearing
10. Bevel gear (drive)
11. Cover
12. Cap screw
13. Washers
14. Clamp plate
15. Retaining ring
16. Output shaft
17. Retaining ring
18. Bevel gear (driven)
19. Oil seal
20. Bearing
21. Housing
22. Bearing
23. Oil seal

gear shaft, then remove belt and pulley. On all other models, unbolt belt guard, then remove drive belt and bevel gear pulley. On all models, unbolt and remove left side plate. Disconnect drive shaft rear coupling from bevel gear input shaft. Unbolt and remove bevel gear unit from tractor.

When reinstalling bevel gear unit, install sufficient thickness of shims on right side so shims extend 0.010 to 0.015 inch (0.254-0.381 mm) past outside machined surface of gear case. Reinstall unit by reversing removal procedure.

Models 710-712-716-912-914-916

To remove bevel gear unit, complete drive unit, pulleys and belts must first be removed. Refer to appropriate transmission section for removal procedure. Refer to POWER TAKE-OFF paragraphs and remove pto clutch assembly and idler pulley assembly. Remove pulley from right side of bevel gear unit. Disconnect drive shaft from bevel gear input shaft. Remove cap screws securing gear box to side plates. Pull side plates apart and withdraw bevel gear unit.

Reinstall bevel gear unit in reverse order of removal.

OVERHAUL

All Models So Equipped

To disassemble bevel gear unit, remove housing cover (11 – Fig. AC40) and drain lubricant. Drive output shaft (16) to the left until key is free of bevel gear (18). Remove key and disengage snap ring (17) from groove in shaft. Remove bevel gear and snap ring as shaft is withdrawn from housing. Remove cap screw and bearing clamp plate (14), then bump input shaft assembly rearward out of housing. Remove cap screw (12) and washers (13) and withdraw bevel gear (10) and bearing (9) from input shaft (7). Bearings (5, 20 and 22) and oil seals (3,

19 and 23) can now be removed from housing (21).

Clean and inspect all parts and renew any showing excessive wear or other damage. Using new oil seals and gasket, reassemble by reversing disassembly procedure. Be sure to install washers (13) with concave side facing head of cap screw (12); tighten cap screw to 27 ft.-lbs. (37 N·m) torque. Fill unit to level plug or dipstick with recommended oil.

SHUTTLE DRIVE

Models 410S-414S-416S-712S-914S

A forward-reverse shuttle drive is used on Models 410S, 414S, 416S, 712S and 914S. The transaxles used on these models are equipped with four forward gears. The shuttle drive control lever, located on right side of tractor, has three positions; forward, neutral and reverse. This allows tractor to be driven in forward or reverse direction in any of the four transaxle gears. Transaxle gears can be shifted when shuttle drive control lever is in neutral position or when clutch-brake pedal is depressed. When shuttle drive control lever is in neutral position, a brake pad is applied against transaxle input shaft pulley. This stops input shaft from turning to facilitate gear shifting.

ADJUSTMENT. To adjust shuttle drive linkage, either unbolt and remove seat deck and fender assembly or tilt seat forward, lift out tool tray, support rear of tractor and remove right rear wheel. Place shuttle drive control lever in neutral position and adjust transmission safety interlock switch (3 – Fig. AC41) so carriage head bolt contacts and closes switch. Be sure bolt does not touch switch when shift lever is engaged

in any of the four gears. Refer to Fig. AC42 and loosen set screw in brake detent (5), then slide detent forward or rearward as required to center detent groove on brake pin (4). Tighten set screw. Move control lever to full forward position. Loosen locknut on pulley brake pad stud and adjust brake pad (1 – Fig. AC41) to obtain 1/8-inch (3 mm) clearance (A) between brake pad and forward drive pulley flange (2) as shown. Tighten locknut.

Place control lever in neutral position and loosen set screw in set collar (2 – Fig. AC42). Move rod guide (7) forward until slack is removed from forward drive belt (1). Hold rod guide forward, then move set collar and spring (8) forward and tighten screw in set collar. Move control lever to full forward drive position and measure distance between rear of set collar and rear leg of rod guide. This distance should be 1/8-inch (3 mm) as shown in Fig. AC42; if not, relocate set collar to obtain this dimension.

Place control lever in neutral position. Refer to Fig. AC43, then unpin and remove swivel (A) from hole (B). Rotate until reverse drive brake band (C) is snug on shuttle planetary carrier when swivel is reconnected in hole (B).

Reassemble tractor and test operation of shuttle drive. If operation is unsatisfactory, refer to the following problems and their possible causes:
A. Will not pull forward with full power.
  Caused by: Incorrect adjustment of set collar (Fig. AC42) resulting in low tension on forward drive belt.
B. Tractor creeps forward when control lever is in neutral position:
  Caused by: Too much tension on forward drive belt.
C. Will not pull with full power in reverse.
  Caused by: Reverse drive brake band (C – Fig. AC43) adjustment too loose.
D. Tractor creeps rearward when control lever is in neutral position.

Fig. AC41—On models equipped with shuttle drive, adjust transmission interlock switch (3) so carriage head bolt contacts and closes switch when control lever is placed in neutral position. Adjust brake pad (1) to provide 1/8-inch (3 mm) clearance (A) in forward drive position.

A. 1/8-inch (3 mm) clearance
1. Brake pad
2. Drive pulley
3. Interlock switch

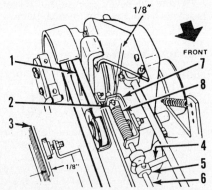

Fig. AC42—With shuttle control in forward drive position, adjust control rod set collar (2) to provide 1/8-inch (3 mm) gap as shown.

1. Forward drive belt
2. Set collar
3. Drive pulley & brake pad
4. Brake pin
5. Brake detent spool
6. Shuttle control rod
7. Rod guide
8. Spring

Fig. AC43—With shuttle control lever in neutral position, adjust swivel (A) until reverse brake band (C) is snug when swivel is reconnected in hole (B).

Caused by: Reverse drive brake band (C – Fig. AC43) adjustment too tight.

E. Cannot shift gears without grinding when shuttle control lever is in neutral position.

Caused by: Brake detent (C – Fig. AC42) not positioned correctly or clearance of brake pad (Fig. AC41) not adjusted properly.

R&R AND OVERHAUL. To remove forward-reverse shuttle drive unit, support rear of tractor and remove right rear wheel. Disconnect and remove reverse drive planetary brake (23

through 26 – Fig. AC44). Remove drive belts (28 and 29). Using a screwdriver, pry cap (5) from planetary cover (6). Remove nut (7) and gear (8). Carefully withdraw planetary assembly.

To disassemble unit, remove nuts from bolts (14) and planetary shafts (3). Remove cover (6), seal ring (9) and bearing (10). Needle bearings (1), planetary pinions (2), sleeves (4) and planetary carrier (11) can now be removed. Remove gear (15), seal ring (16), bearing (17), seal ring (18), pulley (19), inner race (20), thrust washer (21) and forward drive

pulley half (22) from transaxle input shaft.

Clean all parts and renew any showing excessive wear or other damage. Using new seal rings, reassemble by reversing disassembly procedure. Tighten nuts on cap screws (14) and planetary shafts (3) to a torque of 12-15 ft.-lbs. (16-20 N·m). Tighten planetary retaining nut (7) to a torque of 75 ft.-lbs. (102 N·m). Pack unit with No. 2 lithium base grease. Adjust shuttle drive linkage as necessary.

VARIABLE SPEED PULLEY

Models B210-B212-310-310D-312-312D-314-314D

ADJUSTMENT. Do not attempt to move variable speed control lever when engine is stopped or clutch-brake pedal is depressed. Place variable speed control lever in "HIGH" position and remove drive belt and guards. Loosen attaching bolt or ball joint locknut between control rod (4 – Fig. AC45) and rocker arm (17) and push rocker arm as far forward as possible so inside hubs of drive pulley sheaves (13 and 14) make contact. Retighten rocker arm bolt or nut. Reinstall drive belt and guards. With control lever in "HIGH" position, clearance should be 3/16-inch (5 mm) between drive belt and front guard. Move variable speed control lever to "LOW" position. Front edge of idler pulley belt stop (19) should be 9¼ inches (235 mm) from outer surface of rear axle tube. To make adjustment, loosen nut which retains idler pulley. With control lever in "LOW" position, top of drive belt should be approximately ⅛-inch (3 mm) below rim of driven pulley halves (24 and 26). Make belt adjustment by turning turnbuckle (18).

R&R AND OVERHAUL. To remove variable pulley assembly, first support right rear axle and remove right rear wheel. Remove drive belt guards and drive belt. Remove drive pulley retaining nut (16 – Fig. AC45) and withdraw drive pulley assembly. Disconnect control rod (4) from rocker arm (17) and remove rocker arm (17) by unscrewing retaining nut. Unscrew bolt holding driven pulley fork (30) and remove driven pulley fork (30), connecting bolts and turnbuckle (18) and drive pulley arm (9). Unscrew retaining nut (31) and remove driven pulley assembly.

Inspect assembly for damaged or excessively worn components. Be sure pulley sheaves are straight and run true. After reassembly, check adjustment as outlined in preceding paragraph.

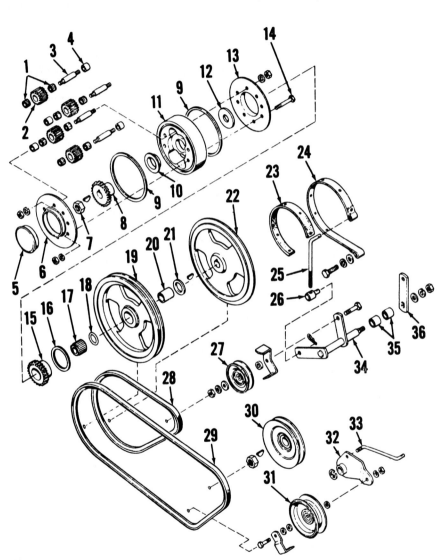

Fig. AC44 – Exploded view of forward-reverse shuttle drive unit used on Models 410S, 414S, 416S, 712S and 914S.

1. Needle bearings	15. Gear	26. Swivel
2. Planetary pinions	16. Seal	27. Forward drive idler pulley
3. Planetary shafts	17. Roller bearing	28. Forward drive belt
4. Sleeves	18. Seal ring	29. Main drive belt
5. End cap	19. Pulley	30. Pulley (bevel gear driven)
6. Cover (outer)	20. Inner race	31. Clutch idler pulley
7. Nut	21. Thrust washer	32. Idler arm
8. Gear	22. Forward drive pulley half	33. Clutch link
9. Seal ring	23. Brake lining	34. Shuttle drive lever & shaft assy.
10. Flange bearing	24. Reverse drive brake band	35. Bushings
11. Planetary carrier	25. Rod	36. Lever
12. Thrust washer		
13. Cover (inner)		
14. Through-bolts (4 used)		

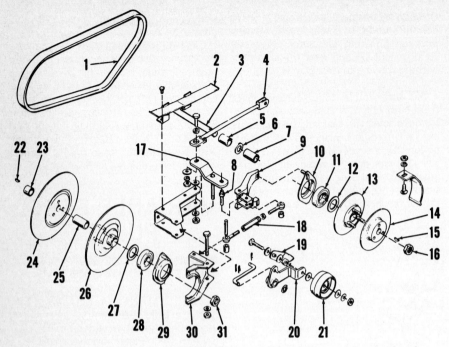

Fig. AC45 — Exploded view of typical variable speed drive used on models so equipped.

1. Drive belt	12. Retainer	22. Key
2. Belt guard	13. Movable pulley	23. Spacer
3. Bevel gear shaft	sheave	24. Fixed pulley sheave
4. Control rod	14. Fixed pulley sheave	25. Spacer
5. Spacer	15. Key	26. Movable pulley
6. Washer	16. Nut	sheave
7. Spacer	17. Lever	27. Retainer
8. Rod	18. Turnbuckle	28. Ball bearing
9. Fork	19. Belt guide	29. Bearing retainer
10. Bearing retainer	20. Idler arm	30. Fork
11. Ball bearing	21. Clutch idler pulley	31. Nut

unbolt and remove shift support and shift fork assembly. Loosen set screws in collar (3) and withdraw Hi-Lo pulley assembly.

To disassemble unit, remove six cap screws from outer edge of covers.

NOTE: Mark location of special nuts (19 and 20) for aid in reassembly.

Separate covers (6 and 18) and remove shift ring (25) and reduction gear assembly. Remove spider bolts (24), pinions (16) and needle bearings (17).

Check all parts for excessive wear and renew as necessary. When reassembling, lubricate with multi-purpose lithium base grease. Reinstall assembly by reversing removal procedure.

DUAL RANGE 6 SPEED

The dual-range 6 speed tractors have 3 forward gears and one reverse with a dual range pulley system. To select Hi or Lo range, tractor must be stopped and clutch-brake pedal fully depressed. Move range lever forward for Hi or backward for Lo.

Models 710-6 spd.-716-6 spd.-912-6spd.

PULLEY AND BELT RENEWAL. To renew pulleys or belts, remove front belt guard. However, idler pulley can be

HI-LO RANGE PULLEY

The Hi-Lo two speed transmission input pulley is used on some early models to provide lower ground speeds without altering pto rpm. When shifted to low range, ground speeds will be reduced to approximately ⅓ of standard (high range) ground speeds.

All Models So Equipped

R&R AND OVERHAUL. To remove two speed pulley assembly, first unbolt shift rod support (9 – Fig. AC46). Then,

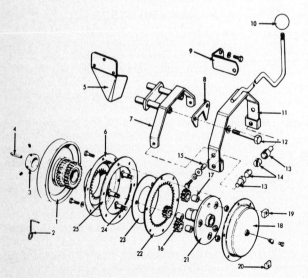

Fig. AC46 — Exploded view of Hi-Lo Range pulley assembly used on some models.

1. Pulley assy.
2. Belt stop
3. Collar
4. Key
5. Guard
6. Cover (inner)
7. Support
8. Shift stop
9. Shift rod support
10. Knob
11. Shift fork
12. Cap screw
13. Pivots
14. Pivot bearings
15. Spacers
16. Pinions
17. Needle bearings
18. Cover (outer)
19. Special nut
20. Special nut
21. Spider assy.
22. Ring gear
23. Spider plate
24. Spider bolts
25. Shift ring

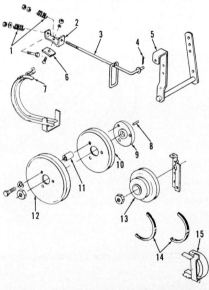

Fig. AC47 — Exploded view of dual range pulley system used on Models 710-6 spd., 716-6 spd. and 912-6 spd.

1. Spring	9. Pulley hub
2. Pulley brake strap	10. Pulley
3. Brake rod assy.	11. Spacer (3 used)
4. Cotter pin	12. Pulley
5. Lever pivot assy.	13. Drive pulley
6. Brake pad	14. Drive belts
7. Rear belt guard	15. Front belt guard
8. Key	

renewed without removal of belt guards and belts. Depress clutch-brake pedal and remove belt from pulley. Remove locknut and pulley. Remove cotter pin from pulley brake rod (3 – Fig. AC47). Do not remove brake rod from rear belt guard unless it is to be renewed. Remove rear belt guard and pulley brake rod assembly. To renew drive pulleys, remove center nut and pulleys from bevel gear box cross shaft. To renew driven pulleys, remove three cap screws, spacers (11) and pulleys. The driven pulley hub (9) is keyed on input shaft and is removed by removing locknut on input shaft. Reinstall assembly by reversing removal procedure.

ADJUSTMENTS. Adjust rear belt guard to obtain ⅛-inch (3 mm) clearance between guard and edge of pulley. To adjust idler pulley height, depress clutch-brake pedal, move range lever into Hi range and release pedal. With outside belt resting on front and rear belt guards, adjust idler pulley so there is a minimum of ⅛ inch (3 mm) clearance between outside belt and pulley. To adjust pulley brake, engage clutch-brake pedal and move range lever to Hi or Lo range. Set coil length of rear spring (Fig. AC48) to 1⅜ inch (35 mm). Set front spring compressed length of 1¾ inch (45 mm) between jam nut and rod guide. If drive belt slips under load, move idler spring into next higher hole of lever pivot (5 – Fig. AC47) to increase belt tension.

HYDROSTATIC TRANSMISSION

LUBRICATION

Models HB212-312H-314H-416H-712H-716H-912H-914H-916H

A Vickers T66 hydrostatic drive unit is used on Models HB212, 312H, 314H, and 416H; a Sundstrand Series 15 "U" type hydrostatic transmission is used on all other models.

The oil level of system reservoir should be checked periodically by removing inspection plug on side of reservoir. On Models HB212, 312H, 314H and 416H, an external oil reservoir with filter (Fig. AC51) is used. Oil should be changed and filter renewed if there is evidence of dirt in system. Recommended oil is Dexron automatic transmission fluid. On all other models, oil reservoir is integral with reduction gear housing and a screw-on type oil filter is

used. Recommended oil is Dexron ATF on Models 712H and 716H and A-C

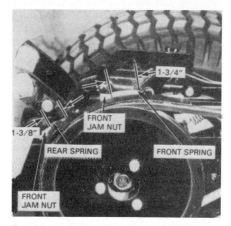

Fig. AC48 – Pulley brake adjustment points on Models 710-6 spd., 716-6 spd. and 912-6 spd. Refer to text for adjustment procedure.

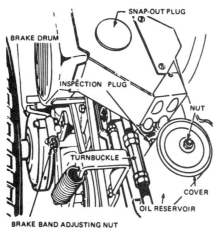

Fig. AC49 – View of hydrostatic control linkage adjustment points on Models HB212, 312H, 314H and 416H. Refer to text.

Fig. AC50 – View showing adjustment points for Models 712H, 716H, 912H, 914H and 916H with hydrostatic transmission. Refer to text for adjusting procedures.

Power Fluid 821 (or equivalent) on Models 912H, 914H and 916H.

ADJUSTMENT

Models HB212-312H-314H-416H

To adjust hydrostatic control linkage, block up under rear of tractor so wheels do not touch ground. Start engine and operate at ⅓ full speed. Then, with clutch engaged move hydrostatic control lever to forward position then into neutral position. Rear wheels should not rotate when control lever is in neutral position. Loosen locknuts at both ends of turnbuckle on control rod shown in Fig. AC49. Turn turnbuckle as required until wheels stop turning when control lever is in neutral position. Tighten locknuts and recheck adjustment.

Models 712H-716H-912H-914H-916H

To adjust hydrostatic control linkage, park tractor on level ground, shift control lever to neutral notch and set parking brake. Raise seat deck and check centering mark on hydrostatic control cam (Fig. AC50). If mark is not centered, loosen bolt (A) and move control cam in hydrostatic control strap until mark is centered. Lower seat deck, start engine and release parking brake. If tractor still creeps in neutral, note direction and reset parking brake. Loosen jam nut (B) on cam pivot shaft. If tractor creep was in reverse, turn adjusting nut (C) ⅛ to ¼ turn clockwise (viewed from R.H. side). If creep was forward, turn adjusting nut ⅛ to ¼ turn

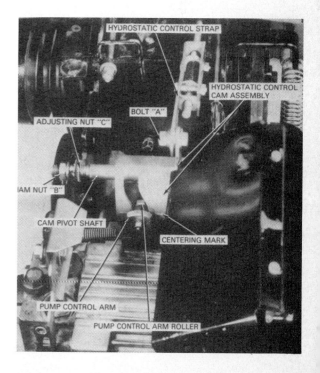

counterclockwise. Tighten jam nut and recheck adjustment.

REMOVE AND REINSTALL

Models HB212-312H-314H-416H

To remove hydrostatic transmission, first remove seat and fender assembly. Remove fender support braces and oil cooler support bracket. Disconnect transmission control rod. Remove drive belt from transmission pulley. Drain lubricant from transmission oil reservoir and disconnect transmission oil lines. Remove oil cooler fan, shroud and oil cooler assembly. See Fig. AC51. Remove cap screws securing transmission to gear reduction housing and remove transmission.

To reinstall transmission, reverse removal procedure. Use following procedure to refill transmission with oil: Before installing transmission in tractor, fill pump and motor with recommended oil through case drain openings. With transmission and cooling system installed and oil lines connected, position hydrostatic control lever in neutral position and fill reservoir with oil to correct level. Disconnect engine coil wire and at short intervals turn engine over with starter. Recheck and add oil if necessary to oil reservoir. Connect engine coil wire and run engine at idle speed. Recheck oil level. Make several short runs at a slow speed in forward and in reverse and recheck oil level. Transmission oil should now be purged of air.

Model 712H-716H-912H-914H-916H

To remove hydrostatic transmission, remove seat and fender assembly. Sup-

port left rear side of tractor and remove left rear wheel. Remove transmission fan and shroud and deflector. Loosen and remove drive belt, input pulley and fan. Disconnect pump control arm spring. Remove bolt, control arm roller, lockwasher and nut. Remove oil filter and drain lubricant from reduction gear housing. Disconnect hydraulic hoses at oil filter assembly. Remove mounting bolts and slide transmission out of gearcase.

To reinstall transmission, reverse removal procedure. Use following procedure to refill and prime transmission. While holding relief valve up, add recommended oil until oil is visible in filler tube. Remove spark plug wire. Raise rear wheels off the ground, set speed control lever halfway forward and crank engine. When wheels start to move, stop cranking. Reconnect spark plug wire, start and run tractor for 1-2 minutes. Stop engine and hold relief valve in up position. Add oil until oil is within ⅛ inch (3 mm) of top of filler tube. Recheck oil level after 5 hours operation.

OVERHAUL

Models HB212-312H-314H-416H

All models are equipped with a Vickers Model T66 hydrostatic transmission. Refer to Vickers Model T66 section in HYDROSTATIC TRANSMISSION SERVICE section for overhaul procedure.

Models 712H-716H-912H-914H-916H

All models are equipped with a Sundstrand Series 15 "U" type hydrostatic

transmission. Refer to Sundstrand Series 15 "U" type section in HYDROSTATIC TRANSMISSION SERVICE section for overhaul procedure.

GEAR REDUCTION UNIT

A gear reduction unit is used on all models equipped with a hydrostatic transmission. On Models HB212, 312H, 314H and 416H, a sliding drive gear is used in gear reduction unit so tractor may be moved manually. When gear shift lever (4 – Fig. AC61) is in vertical position, drive gear (21) will be engaged with reduction gear (43). To disengage gears, turn shift lever away from reduction housing.

CAUTION: Tractor brakes are inoperative when shift lever is in disengaged position.

All Models So Equipped

REMOVE AND REINSTALL. To remove gear reduction unit, support tractor under main frame just ahead of bevel gear housing. Remove seat deck and fender assembly. Drain reduction unit housing. Remove rear wheels, hubs, differential assembly and axle shaft. Remove bevel gear pto belt pulley and disconnect pto tension spring. Support gear reduction housing and remove left side plate. Drain hydrostatic transmission reservoir (models so equipped), disconnect oil lines and control rod, then unbolt and remove reservoir, oil cooler, shroud and cooler fan (models so equipped). Unbolt and remove hydrostatic transmission and brake band. Remove cap screws securing gear reduction unit to right side plate and lift unit from tractor.

Reinstall by reversing removal procedure. On Models HB212, 312H, 314H and 416H, fill reduction unit to level plug opening with SAE 90 EP gear oil and fill hydrostatic reservoir with Dexron Type "A" automatic transmission fluid. On all other models, reduction gear housing also serves as reservoir for hydrostatic transmission. Dexron Type "A" automatic transmission fluid is recommended for 712H and 716H models and A-C Power Fluid 821 is recommended for 912H, 914H and 916H models.

OVERHAUL. To disassemble gear reduction unit, remove brake drum and clean all paint, burrs and rust from keyed end of axle tube (37 – Fig. AC61). Unbolt and remove cover (40) from case

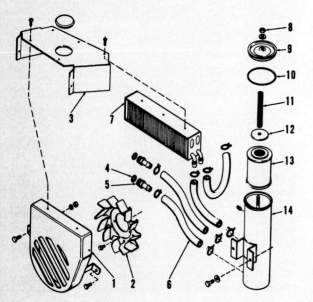

Fig. AC51 – Exploded view of hydrostatic cooling system and oil reservoir used on Models HB212, 312H, 314H and 416H.
1. Fan housing
2. Fan
3. Shroud
4. "O" ring
5. Fitting
6. Hydraulic hose
7. Oil radiator
8. Nut
9. Cap
10. "O" ring
11. Spring
12. Washer
13. Oil filter
14. Oil reservoir

(17). Remove washer (27) and first reduction gear (23). Remove snap ring (14), then withdraw output gear and axle tube assembly (41 through 45). On Models HB212, 312H, 314H and 416H, loosen set screw (46) and remove as a unit, shift fork and rail assembly (7 through 10) and, on all models, brake shaft assembly (18 through 22). Use caution when removing shift rail (10) from shift fork (9) as poppet ball and spring (7 and 8) will be released. Loosen locknut (5), remove shifter stem (6) and withdraw shift lever (4). Oil seals and needle bearings can now be removed from case and cover as required.

Reassemble in reverse order of disassembly procedure. When renewing bearings, always press against end stamped with manufacturers name or number. Press bearings into housing until 1/8 inch (3 mm) below inside machined surface of housing. Axle tube bearings (16 and 35) should be pressed in until outside edge of bearing is flush with outside edge of small bore in housing.

TRANSAXLE

Models B206-Homesteader 6-Homesteader 7-608LT-611LT

REMOVE AND REINSTALL. To remove transaxle, support rear of tractor and remove drive belt from transaxle input pulley. Remove rear wheels and remove gear shift knob. Remove cap screws securing transaxle to frame brackets. Remove axle mounting "U" bolts. Remove transaxle from tractor by tilting transaxle so shift lever passes through frame and brake drum clears brake band.

To reinstall transaxle, reverse removal procedure.

OVERHAUL. All models are equipped with a Peerless 600 series transaxle. Refer to Peerless Series 600 section in TRANSAXLE SERVICE section for overhaul procedure.

Models B208-Homesteader 8

REMOVE AND REINSTALL. To remove transaxle, remove drive belt from transaxle pulley and remove brake band. Remove gear shift lever knob. Support rear of tractor frame and remove axle "U" bolts. Roll transaxle away from tractor.

To reinstall, reverse removal procedure.

OVERHAUL. All models are equipped with a Peerless 1200 series transaxle. Refer to Peerless Series 1200 section in TRANSAXLE SERVICE section for overhaul procedure.

Models 608-610-808GT-810GT-811GT-T811

REMOVE AND REINSTALL. To remove transaxle, remove seat and fender assembly. Disconnect brake rod from brake band and clutch rod from idler bracket. Remove drive belt and

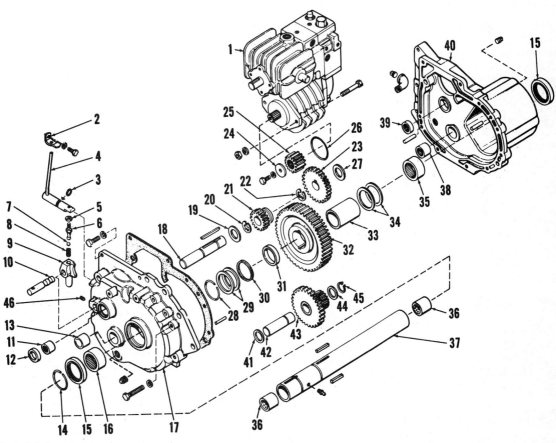

Fig. AC61 — Exploded view of gear reduction unit used on Models HB212, 312H, 314H and 416H. Gear reduction unit used on Models 712H, 716H, 912H, 914H and 916H is similar except shift assembly (2 through 10) and sliding gear (21) are not used.

1. Hydrostatic transmission	10. Shift rail	19. Washer
2. Lever latch	11. Bearing	20. "E" ring
3. "O" ring	12. Oil seal	21. Sliding gear
4. Gear shift lever	13. Bearing	22. "E" ring
5. Nut	14. Snap ring	23. Gear
6. Shift stem	15. Oil seal	24. Washer
7. Ball	16. Bearing	25. Input gear
8. Spring	17. Case	26. "O" ring
9. Shift fork	18. Brake shaft	27. Washer

28. Snap ring	37. Axle tube	
29. Washers	38. Bearing	
30. Washer	39. Bearing	
31. Spacer	40. Cover	
32. Ring gear	41. Washer	
33. Spacer	42. Shaft	
34. Washers	43. Pinion & gear	
35. Bearing	44. Washers	
36. Bushing	45. Snap ring	
	46. Set screw	

transaxle pulley. Unbolt and remove shift lever assembly. On Models 608 and 610, loosen set screws on set collar and slide transaxle rearward until it is free. On all other models, remove "U" bolt clamp from right axle and remove frame support and transaxle support bolts. Lower transaxle and slide it clear of tractor.

To reinstall transaxle, reverse removal procedure.

OVERHAUL. All models are equipped with a 3-speed transaxle manufactured by Simplicity Manufacturing Company. Refer to Simplicity 3-Speed section in TRANSAXLE SERVICE section for overhaul procedure.

GEAR TRANSMISSION

All Models So Equipped

REMOVE AND REINSTALL. The gear transmission used on tractors equipped with forward-reverse shuttle drive, is equipped with four forward gears. Reverse gear is not required in this transmission since reverse drive, in any gear, is provided by forward-reverse shuttle drive unit. The transmis-

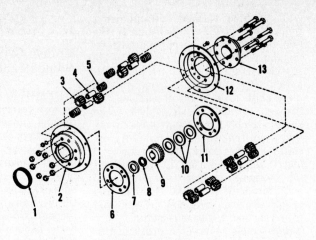

Fig. AC73—Exploded view of late type differential assembly. Early type does not use spacer plates (6 and 11) and has a spacer in place of spring (5).

1. Seal
2. Differential cover (R.H.)
3. Pinion
4. Spindle
5. Spring
6. Spacer plate
7. Axle washer
8. Snap ring
9. Differential gear
10. Axle washers
11. Spacer plate
12. Differential cover (L.H.)
13. Carrier

sion used on other gear drive models has three forward gears and one reverse. The differential is located at right rear wheel hub on all models.

To remove transmission, raise rear of tractor to a point where rear wheels are free. Support tractor under frame just ahead of bevel gear housing. Remove seat deck and fender assembly and disconnect brake linkage and transmission shift rod. Remove rear wheels, hubs, differential assembly and axle shaft. Remove forward-reverse shuttle drive unit on models so equipped. On other models, remove transmission input pulley. Then, on all models, placed a jack or blocks under transmission housing,

unbolt transmission from side plates and lift unit from tractor.

To reinstall transmission, reverse removal procedure.

OVERHAUL. All models are equipped with a 3-speed or 4-speed transmission manufactured by Simplicity Manufacturing Company. Refer to Simplicity 3-Speed And 4-Speed With Shuttle Drive section in GEAR TRANSMISSION SERVICE section for overhaul procedure.

DIFFERENTIAL

All Models So Equipped

R&R AND OVERHAUL. To remove differential, block up rear of tractor and remove rear wheels. Remove set screws from left hub and remove hub and key. Loosen set screws and remove set collar and washers from axle on left side of transmission. Remove right hub, differential and axle assembly. It may be necessary to tap on the edge of differential hub to remove it from axle tube.

To disassemble differential, remove set collar from right end of axle shaft. Remove bolts from outer edge of differential case. Remove nuts from inner row of cap screws and separate case halves, leaving cap screws in position to stabilize pinions, spacers and washers (or springs). Identify all parts to aid in reassembly. The rest of disassembly is evident upon inspection of unit and reference to Fig. AC72 or AC73.

When reinstalling assembled unit, make sure axle and differential are properly seated so seal between differential and wheel hub is compressed. The axle is held in this position by the set collar on axle shaft at left side of transmission case.

TRACTION ADJUSTMENT. Some models are equipped with controlled traction adjusters shown in Fig. AC74.

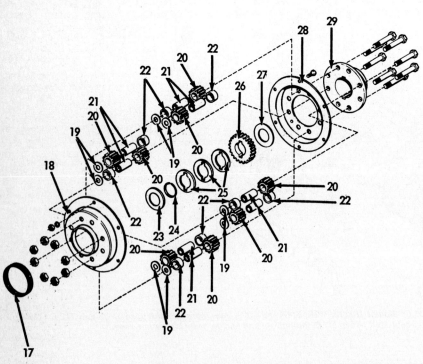

Fig. AC72—Exploded view of early differential unit with right differential gear and hub and axle shaft removed.

17. Seal
18. Differential cover (R.H.)
19. Washers
20. Pinions
21. Spindles
22. Spacers
23. Washers
24. Snap ring
25. Axle washers
26. Differential gear (L.H.)
27. Washer
28. Differential cover (L.H.)
29. Differential carrier

Adjustment of traction differential is made by tightening cap screws (2) within right rear wheel hub to 20 ft.-lbs. (27 N·m).

NOTE: Under torque will allow excessive wheel slippage and over torque will cause hard steering due to lack of differential action.

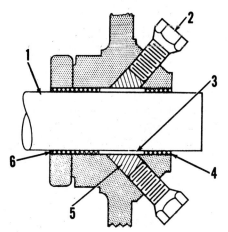

Fig. AC74 — Cross-sectional view of right rear wheel hub showing controlled traction adjusters.

1. Axle shaft
2. Adjusting screws
3. Nylon bearing
4. Bushing
5. Nylon plug
6. Bushing

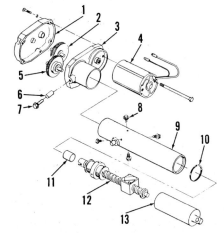

Fig. AC75 — Exploded view of typical electric lift assembly used on some models.

1. Cover
2. Intermediate gear
3. Housing
4. Motor
5. Clutch gear assy.
6. Drive pin
7. Cap screw
8. Cap screw (4)
9. Outer tube
10. Seal ring
11. Sleeve
12. Screw & brake assy.
13. Inner tube

ELECTRIC LIFT

All Models So Equipped

OVERHAUL. To disassemble, remove cap screws securing electric motor (4 – Fig. AC75) to gearcase and withdraw motor. Motor is serviced as a complete unit. To remove tube assembly, remove cap screw (7) from gearcase and withdraw tube with a rotating motion. On late models, screw and brake assembly (12) and tube (9) are serviced as an assembly. On early models, screw assembly is serviced separately and can be removed by removing four retaining screws (8), then pull inner tube (13) and screw (12) out of outer tube.

To disassemble gearcase, unbolt and remove end cover (1) and withdraw intermediate gear assembly (2). Remove outer tube and screw assembly; then, using a suitable punch, drive brake drive pin (6) out of clutch gear shaft (5). Using C-clamps or vise grips, compress Belleville washers (Fig. AC76) and remove snap ring from clutch gear shaft. Disassemble clutch gear assembly and inspect for excessive wear or other damage. Renew complete assembly if service is required.

Reassemble by reversing removal procedure. Lubricate with multipurpose grease.

HYDRAULIC LIFT

All Models So Equipped

Late Model 912H, 914H and 916H tractors are equipped with hydraulic implement lift. Hydraulic power supply is hydrostatic transmission charge pump. The hydraulic cylinder is serviced as an assembly. Two different control valves

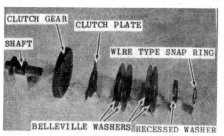

Fig. AC76 — Exploded view of electric lift overload clutch and gear assembly. Note position of Belleville washers when disassembling clutch. Only three Belleville washers are used in some clutches.

have been used. Refer to Fig. AC77 and AC78. If valve spool (4) or body (3) is excessively worn or damaged, complete valve assembly must be renewed.

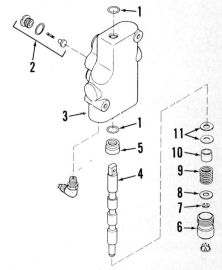

Fig. AC77 — Exploded view of CESSNA lift control valve used on some models equipped with hydraulic lift.

1. "O" rings
2. Check valve assy.
3. Valve body
4. Valve spool
5. Bushing
6. End cap
7. Retaining ring
8. Washer
9. Spring
10. Spool
11. Washers

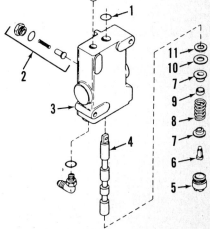

Fig. AC78 — Exploded view of AICO lift control valve used on some models.

1. "O" ring
2. Check valve assy.
3. Valve body
4. Valve spool
5. End cap
6. Spool stem
7. Spring seats
8. Spring
9. Spool stop
10. Washer
11. Quad ring

ARIENS

CONDENSED SPECIFICATIONS

MODELS

	13989, 13990	13948, 913002, 913003	GT12	GT14	GT16
Engine Make	Tecumseh	B&S	Kohler	Kohler	Kohler
Model	VH70	191707	K301S	K321S	K341S
Bore	2¾ in. (69.8 mm)	3 in. (76.2 mm)	3⅜ in. (85.7 mm)	3½ in. (88.9 mm)	3¾ in. (95.2 mm)
Stroke	2-17/32 in. (64.3 mm)	2¾ in. (69.8 mm)	3¼ in. (82.5 mm)	3¼ in. (82.5 mm)	3¼ in. (82.5 mm)
Piston Displacement	15.0 cu. in. (246 cc)	19.44 cu. in. (319 cc)	29.07 cu. in. (476 cc)	31.27 cu. in. (512 cc)	35.89 cu. in. (588 cc)
Horsepower	7	8	12	14	16
Slow Idle Speed – Rpm	1800	1750	1800	1800	1800
High Idle Speed (No Load) – Rpm	3750	4000	Note 2	Note 3	Note 4
Crankcase Oil Capacity	1½ pints (0.7L)	2¼ pints (1L)	4 pints (1.9L)	4 pints (1.9L)	4 pints (1.9L)
Weight –					
Above 32°F (0°C)			———— SAE 30 ————		
0°F (–18°C) to 32°F (0°C)			———— SAE 10W ————		
Below 0°F (–18°C)			———— SAE 5W-20 ————		
Transmission Oil Capacity	2 pints (0.9L)	2 pints (0.9L)	7 pints (3.3L)	7 pints (3.3L)	7 pints (3.3L)
Weight	SAE 90 EP	SAE 90 EP	———— SAE 10W-30 ————		

MODELS

	S-8 Gear	S-8 Hydro	S-10 Gear	S-12 Hydro	S-14 Gear
Engine Make	B&S	B&S	Kohler	Kohler	Kohler
Model	191707	191707	K241S	K301S	K321S
Bore	3 in. (76.2 mm)	3 in. (76.2 mm)	3¼ in. (82.5 mm)	3⅜ in. (85.7 mm)	3½ in. (88.9 mm)
Stroke	2¾ in. (69.8 mm)	2¾ in. (69.8 mm)	2⅞ in. (73.0 mm)	3¼ in. (82.5 mm)	3¼ in. (82.5 mm)
Piston Displacement	19.44 cu. in. (319 cc)	19.44 cu. in. (319 cc)	23.9 cu. in. (392 cc)	29.07 cu. in. (476 cc)	31.27 cu. in. (512 cc)
Horsepower	8	8	10	12	14
Slow Idle Speed – Rpm	1750	1750	1600	1600	1600
High Idle Speed (No Load) – Rpm	3500	3500	Note 1	Note 2	Note 3
Crankcase Oil Capacity	2¼ pints (1L)	2¼ pints (1L)	4 pints (1.9L)	4 pints (1.9L)	4 pints (1.9L)
Weight –					
Above 32°F (0°C)			———— SAE 30 ————		
0°F (–18°C) to 32°F (0°C)			———— SAE 10W ————		
Below 0°F (–18°C)			———— SAE 5W-20 ————		
Transmission Oil Capacity	2¾ pints (1.3L)	....	4 pints (1.9L)	7 pints (3.3L)	4 pints (1.9L)
Weight	SAE 90 EP	ATF Type "A"	SAE 90 EP	SAE 10W-30	SAE 90 EP
Differential Oil Capacity	....	2 pints	....	....	....
Weight	....	SAE 90 EP	....	....	....

MODELS

	S-14 Hydro	S-16 Hydro	YT8	YT10	YT11
Engine Make	Kohler	Kohler	Tecumseh	Tecumseh	B&S
Model	K321S	K321S	VM80	TVM220	252707
Bore	3½ in.	3¾ in.	3-5/16 in.	3-5/16 in.	3-7/16 in.
	(88.9 mm)	(95.2 mm)	(84.2 mm)	(84.2 mm)	(87.3 mm)
Stroke	3¼ in.	3¼ in.	2¾ in.	2-17/32 in.	2⅝ in.
	(82.5 mm)	(82.5 mm)	(69.8 mm)	(64.31 mm)	(66.7 mm)
Piston Displacement	31.27 cu. in.	35.89 cu. in.	23.75 cu. in.	21.82 cu. in.	24.36 cu. in.
	(512 cc)	(588 cc)	(389 cc)	(358 cc)	(399 cc)
Horsepower	14	16	8	10	11
Slow Idle Speed – Rpm	1600	1600	1800	1800	1800
High Idle Speed (No Load) – Rpm	Note 3	Note 4	3250	3250	3250
Crankcase Oil Capacity	4 pints	4 pints	2 pints	2 pints	3 pints
	(1.9L)	(1.9L)	(0.9L)	(0.9L)	(0.9L)
Weight –					
Above 32°F (0°C)			SAE 30		
0°F (–18°C) to 32°F (0°C)			SAE 10W		
Below 0°F (–18°C)			SAE 5W-20		
Transmission Oil Capacity	7 pints	7 pints	24 oz.	24 oz.	24 oz.
	(3.3L)	(3.3L)	(710mL)	(710mL)	(710mL)
Weight	SAE 10W-30	SAE 10W-30	Lithium Grease	Lithium Grease	Lithium Grease

NOTE 1: Engine S.N. 7541007 and below – 3600 rpm; S.N. 7541008 and above – 3250 rpm.
NOTE 2: Engine S.N. 8173991 and below – 3600 rpm; S.N. 8173992 and above – 3250 rpm.
NOTE 3: Engine S.N. 8117916 and below – 3600 rpm; S.N. 8117917 and above – 3250 rpm.
NOTE 4: Engine S.N. 8119833 and below – 3600 rpm; S.N. 8119834 and above – 3250 rpm.

FRONT AXLE AND STEERING SYSTEM

AXLE MAIN MEMBER

Models 13948, 13989, 13990, 913002, 913003

To remove axle main member (1 – Fig. A1), first disconnect steering drag link (6) from steering arm (7). Support front end of tractor with a hoist or jack and remove axle pivot bolt (17). Raise front of tractor and roll front axle assembly from tractor. Inspect pivot bolt bushing (19) and bolt and renew if necessary.

Models S-8G And S-8H

To remove front axle, disconnect tie rod ends (4 – Fig. A2) from steering spindles. Detach drag link (1) from link (3), unbolt link clamps (2) and remove link (3). Support front of tractor, unscrew pivot pin retaining bolt and withdraw pivot pin (18). Raise front of tractor and roll front axle assembly along with mower bracket (19) away from tractor.

Models S-10G, S-12H, S-14G, S-14H, S-16H, GT12, GT14, GT16

Front axle is supported by pto drive housing tube. To remove front axle, remove any pto driven accessories from pto drive shaft and disconnect drag link

from steering arm (4 – Fig. A3). Unscrew bolts securing pto drive housing to frame bracket. Support front of tractor and withdraw pto drive towards front of tractor until axle is clear of pto

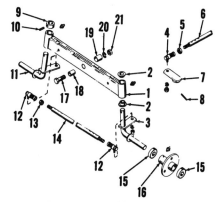

Fig. A1 – Exploded view of front axle main member assembly used on Models 13948, 13989, 13990, 913002 and 913003.

1. Main member
2. Bushing
3. Steering spindle L.H.
4. Ball joint
5. Nut
6. Drag link
7. Steering arm
8. Roll pin
9. Collar
10. Roll pin
11. Steering spindle R.H.
12. Ball joint
13. Nut
14. Tie rod
15. Ball bearing
16. Wheel hub
17. Pivot bolt
18. Spacer
19. Bushing
20. Lockwasher
21. Nut

drive shaft. Raise front of tractor and roll front axle assembly away from tractor.

Models YT8, YT10, YT11

To remove axle main member (10 – Fig. A4), disconnect tie rod ends at steering spindles (11 and 15). Support front of tractor, remove axle pivot bolt and roll axle assembly away from tractor.

TIE ROD

Models 13948, 13989, 13990, 913002, 913003

The adjustment tie rod (14 – Fig. A1) can be removed after first removing nuts securing ball joint ends to steering arms. To adjust front wheel toe-in, remove tie rod, loosen locknuts and turn ball joint ends in or out as required to obtain ⅛-inch (3 mm) toe-in.

Models S-8G And S-8H

These models are equipped with individual tie rods from tie rod connecting link (3 – Fig. A2) to steering spindles. To adjust toe-in, turn steering wheel until rear edge of connecting link (3) is perpendicular to tractor frame. Loosen jam

Ariens

nuts on tie rods and detach ends of tie rods from steering spindles. Adjust length of tie rods and attach to steering spindles. Desired toe-in is 1/16 to ⅛-inch (1.5-3 mm). Repeat procedure until desired toe-in is obtained and tighten jam nuts.

Models S-10G, S-12H, S-14G, S-14H, S-16H, GT12, GT14, GT16

The adjustable tie rod (14–Fig. A3) can be removed after first removing nuts securing ball joint ends (12) to steering spindle arms. To adjust front wheel toe-in, loosen locknuts (13), then rotate tie rod as required to obtain ⅛-inch (3 mm) toe-in. Tighten locknuts.

Models YT8, YT10, YT11

These models are equipped with individual tie rods connecting steering pivot (7–Fig. A4) to steering spindles (11 and 15). To adjust toe-in, disconnect tie rods at steering spindles. Loosen locknuts and turn ball joint ends in or out until ⅛ to ¼-inch (1.5-3 mm) toe-in is obtained.

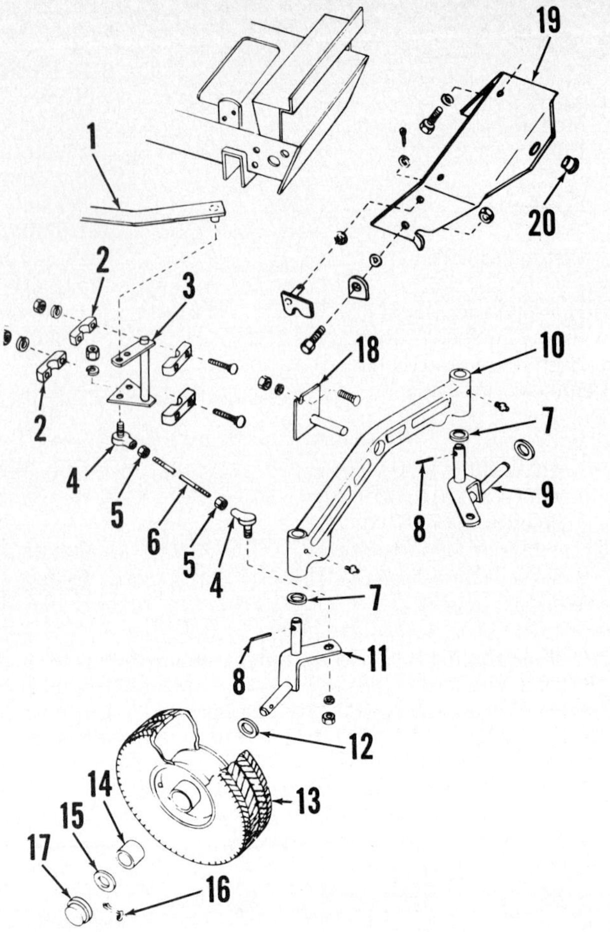

STEERING SPINDLES

All Models

Spindles on all models are retained by a pin in upper end of spindle, except on Models S-10G, S-12H, S-14G, S-14H, S-16H, GT12, GT14 and GT16 which have right spindle retained by steering arm (4–Fig. A3). To remove spindles, support front of tractor and remove wheels. Disconnect tie rod and drag link. On Models S-10G, S-12H, S-14G, S-14H, S-16H, GT12, GT14 and GT16, unscrew clamp bolt in steering arm. On all models, drive roll pins out of upper end of spindle and remove spindle from axle.

All models except Model S-8 are equipped with renewable spindle bushings. Reassemble by reversing disassembly procedure. Lubricate with multi-purpose grease.

STEERING GEAR

Models 13948, 13989, 13990, 913002, 913003

R&R AND OVERHAUL. To remove steering gear, first remove hood and disconnect drag link from steering arm (18–Fig. A5). Unscrew nut (10) at end of cross shaft (13). Drive roll pin (11) out of quadrant gear (12) and shaft and remove gear and shaft. Drive out roll pin (5) to remove pinion gear (8).

Inspect bushings and renew as needed. Lubricate bushings and gear teeth with light coat of multi-purpose grease. To reassemble, reverse removal procedure making sure wheels are in straight ahead position when pinion

Fig. A2 – Exploded view of Model S-8G or Model S-8H front axle assembly.

1. Drag link
2. Clamp
3. Steering link
4. Tie rod end
5. Nut
6. Tie rod
7. Washer
8. Pin
9. Steering spindle L.H.
10. Front axle main member
11. Steering spindle R.H.
12. Washer
13. Wheel
14. Bushing
15. Washer
16. Cotter pin
17. Grease cap

gear (8) is centered in quadrant gear (12).

Models S-8G, S-8H, YT8, YT10, YT11

R&R AND OVERHAUL. To remove steering gear, first drive out roll pin retaining steering wheel to shaft and remove steering wheel. Raise hood, disconnect wires from ignition switch, remove throttle lever knob and detach dash panel from tractor. Unscrew sector gear clamp bolts (14–Fig. A6). Discon-

nect drag link (17) from steering arm (19) and remove cotter pin (5) from shaft (6). Remove cotter pin from steering arm (19), then drive shaft down out of sector gear (15). Drive roll pin (8) out of pinion gear (7) and withdraw steering shaft, pinion gear and sector gear.

Inspect bushings for wear or other damage and renew as necessary. Reassemble by reversing removal procedure making sure wheels are in straight ahead position and pinion gear is centered in sector gear. Lubricate bushings

Fig. A3 – Exploded view of Models S-10G, S-12H, S-14G, S-14H, S-16H, GT12, GT14 and GT16 front axle assembly.

1. Drag link
2. Nut
3. Ball joint
4. Steering arm
5. Bolt
6. Bushing
7. Front axle
8. Collar
9. Bushing
10. Washer
11. Steering spindle L.H.
12. Ball joint
13. Nut
14. Tie rod
15. Steering spindle R.H.
16. Grease cap
17. Castle nut
18. Washer
19. Bearing
20. Bearing cup
21. Seal

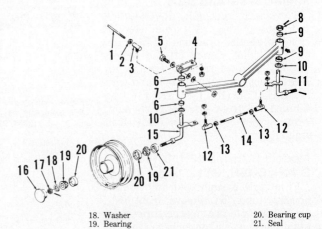

28

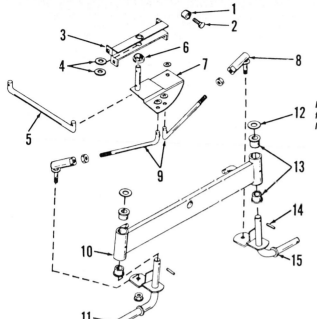

Fig. A4—Exploded view of front axle assembly used on Models YT8, YT10 and YT11.

1. Spacer
2. Pivot bolt
3. Steering pivot channel
4. Washer
5. Steering link
6. Flange bushing
7. Steering pivot
8. Ball joint
9. Tie rods
10. Axle assy.
11. Steering spindle R.H.
12. Washer
13. Bushing
14. Roll pin
15. Steering spindle L.H.

and gears with light coat of multi-purpose grease.

Models S-10G, S-12H, S-14G, S-14H, S-16H, GT12, GT14, GT16

R&R AND OVERHAUL. To remove steering gear, first remove steering wheel retaining nut and steering wheel. Remove steering arm (5–Fig. A7) from steering gear shaft, and unbolt and remove steering gear bracket (4). Raise front of tractor to allow steering gear and shaft to be removed from bottom of

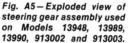

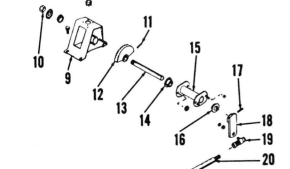

tractor. Loosen clamp (2) and slide steering shaft and gear out through bottom of tractor.

To disassemble steering gear, remove lever and shaft assembly (11–Fig. A8). Remove bearing adjuster plug (17) and bump steering cam (15) out of steering tube (4). Steering cam (15) is not available separately; if renewal is necessary, complete steering gear assembly must be replaced. Inspect bearings and races for wear or other damage and renew if necessary.

When reassembling unit, bearing adjuster plug (17) should be tightened to remove all end play; but, cam (15) must

Fig. A5—Exploded view of steering gear assembly used on Models 13948, 13989, 13990, 913002 and 913003.

1. Shaft extension
2. Bearing
3. Steering shaft
4. Wave washer
5. Roll pin
6. Bushing
7. Washer
8. Pinion gear
9. Bracket
10. Nut
11. Pin
12. Quadrant gear
13. Cross shaft
14. Bushing
15. Support
16. Bushing
17. Pin
18. Lever
19. Ball joint
20. Drag link

still rotate freely. Install lever and shaft assembly (11), seal (8), retainer (9), washer (7) and one nut (6). Be sure cam follower (10) engages steering cam (15) but does not bind when making following adjustment. Tighten adjusting nut (6) until there is 0.100 inch (2.54 mm) clearance between steering shaft plate (11) and gasket retainer (9), then install jam nut (5) to lock in position. Locate cam in mid-position (half way between full right and full left turn). Tighten cam follower screw (10) finger tight and secure with jam nut (12). Steering cam must turn from full right to full left turn without binding. Lubricate with approximately ¼-pound (120mL) of multi-purpose grease.

ENGINE

REMOVE AND REINSTALL

Models 13948, 13989, 13990, 913002, 913003

To remove engine, remove hood and on electric start models, disconnect battery cables and starter wire. On Model 13990, disconnect three prong ignition wire connector. On other models, disconnect ignition wires at engine. Disconnect carburetor choke and throttle cables. Close fuel valve beneath fuel tank and disconnect fuel line at carburetor. Release belt tension and remove engine drive belt. Unbolt engine mounting bolts and lift engine from tractor.

To reinstall engine, reverse removal procedure.

Models S-8G, S-8H, YT8, YT10, YT11

The engine may be removed by using following procedure: Tilt hood forward, disconnect fuel line and remove fuel tank and tank bracket. Disconnect battery cables, ignition and starter wires and throttle cable. Remove drive belts from engine pulleys and remove pulleys. Unscrew engine mounting bolts and remove engine.

Models S-10G, S-12H, S-14G, S-14H, S-16H, GT12, GT14, GT16

To remove engine, disconnect wires to headlights and remove hood, heat duct, grille and side panels from front of tractor. Hood, grille and side panels can be removed as a unit. Remove pto belts and disconnect wire to pto clutch at front of engine. Disconnect battery cables and electrical wires to engine. Disconnect choke and throttle cables from engine. Detach fuel line from carburetor. Unscrew drive coupling screws and engine mounting bolts. Using a suitable hoist, lift engine towards front and remove engine.

OVERHAUL

All Models

Engine make and model are listed at the beginning of this section. To overhaul engine components and accessories, refer to Briggs & Stratton, Kohler or Tecumseh sections of this manual.

CLUTCH

Models 13948, 13989, 13990, 913002, 913003

OPERATION. The clutch is a belt idler type that is spring loaded. Two belts are used between right angle drive pulley (21–Fig. A9) and transmission pulley (7). A Hi-Lo speed range is provided by positioning clutch idler pulley (2) on desired drive belt (5 or 8). The clutch idler is positioned by moving control rod (18) on left side of tractor in or out.

ADJUSTMENT. The clutch idler pulley is spring loaded and does not require adjustment. Renew drive belts if excessively worn. To renew drive belts, remove frame top cover in front of seat, then remove front belt cover (22–Fig. A9. Remove rear hitch and rear belt cover (6). Depress clutch to release belt tension and remove drive belts.

Model S-8G

OPERATION. Refer to Fig. A10 for drawing illustrating belt drive used on Model S-8G. Refer to Fig. A 11 for exploded view of belt drive components. Depressing clutch-brake pedal will pull spring loaded pulley (11–Fig. A10) away from transmission drive belt thereby allowing belt to slip. Spring loaded pulley (11) will tighten belt when clutch-brake pedal is released.

ADJUSTMENT. Clutch free travel is adjusted by turning adjusting nuts (A–Fig. A12) until there is 3/16-inch (5 mm) movement before bolt (B) contacts front of slot in clutching link when clutch-brake pedal is depressed.

Transmission belt drive idler must be adjusted if belt slips or idler spring no longer pulls against idler with clutch-brake pedal released. To adjust belt idler, loosen bolt (A–Fig. A13) and move idler shaft in idler hole to increase tension on belt and spring. Position belt guide approximately ⅛-inch (3 mm) from belt and tighten bolt (A). Belt guide (B) should be approximately ⅛-inch (3 mm) away from transmission belt where belt enters transmission pulley. Loosen bolt (C) to reposition belt guide. Check operation of belt by depressing and

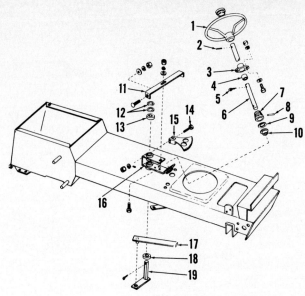

Fig. A6—Exploded view of steering mechanism used on Models S-8G, S-8H, YT8, YT10 and YT11.

1. Steering wheel
2. Spring pin
3. Flange bearing
4. Spacer
5. Cotter pin
6. Steering shaft
7. Pinion gear
8. Pin
9. Washer
10. Bushing
11. Bracket
12. Washer
13. Bushing
14. Bolt
15. Sector gear
16. Steering bracket
17. Drag link
18. Bushing
19. Steering arm

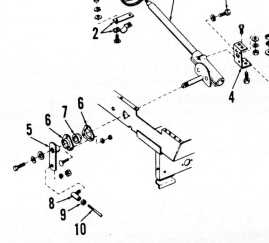

Fig. A7—Exploded view of steering mechanism used on Models S-10G, S-12H, S-14G, S-14H, S-16H, GT12, GT14 and GT16. See Fig. A8 for exploded view of steering gear assembly (1).

1. Steering gear & shaft
2. Clamp
3. Cap screw
4. Bracket
5. Steering arm
6. Bearing flange
7. Bearing & collar
8. Ball joint
9. Nut
10. Drag link

releasing clutch-brake pedal. Adjustment of transmission belt idler may affect clutch free travel which should be rechecked.

Intermediate shaft drive belt tension must be adjusted if belt slips or idler

bracket shown in Fig. A14 contacts stop bolt. Adjust belt tension by loosening bolts (A) and bolts at right end of shaft and move shaft rearward to increase belt tension. Keep shaft parallel to rear of tractor frame and move shaft rear-

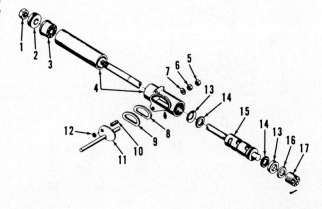

Fig. A8—Exploded view of steering gear assembly used on Models S-10G, S-12H, S-14G, S-14H, S-16H, GT12, GT14 and GT16.

1. Nut
2. Dust seal
3. Bearing
4. Housing
5. Jam nut
6. Nut
7. Washer
8. Oil seal
9. Seal retainer
10. Cam follower screw
11. Lever
12. Nut
13. Bearing race
14. Bearing
15. Steering cam & shaft
16. Belleville washer
17. Adjusting plug

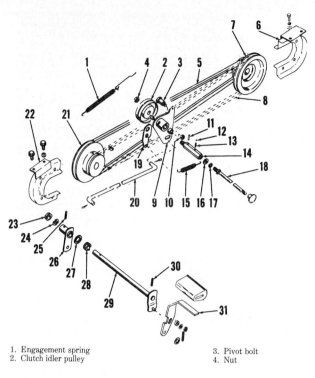

Fig. A9 – View of early clutch system. Move rod (18) in or out to position clutch idler pulley on desired drive belt for Hi or Lo range speeds. Clutch pedal must be depressed before moving rod.

5. Hi-range drive belt
6. Rear belt cover
7. Transmission pulley
8. Lo-range drive belt
9. Plate
10. Nut
11. Roll pin
12. Ball
13. Spring
14. Shift rod
15. Spring
16. Washer
17. Lockwasher
18. Control rod
19. Lever
20. Clutch rod
21. Right angle drive pulley
22. Front belt cover
23. Bushing
24. Wave washer
25. Roll pin
26. Lever
27. Washer
28. Bushing
29. Shaft
30. Roll pin
31. Clutch pedal

1. Engagement spring
2. Clutch idler pulley
3. Pivot bolt
4. Nut

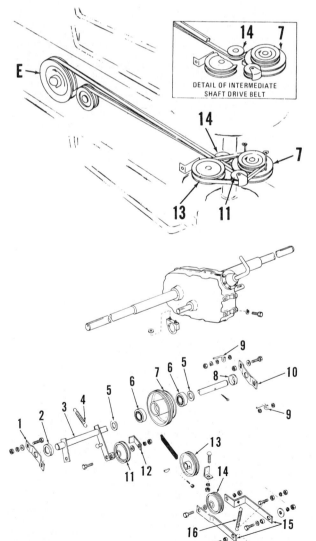

Fig. A10 – View of Model S-8G belt drive system. Engine drive pulley is denoted (E). Refer to Fig. A11 for identification of remaining pulleys.

DETAIL OF INTERMEDIATE SHAFT DRIVE BELT

Fig. A11 – Exploded view of belt drive system used on Model S-8G. Refer to Fig. A10 for pictorial view of belt drive.

1. Support
2. Nylon bearing
3. Idler pivot
4. Spring
5. Spacer
6. Bearing
7. Intermediate pulley
8. Nylon bearing
9. Belt guide
10. Support
11. Clutch pulley
12. Belt guide
13. Transmission pulley
14. Idler pulley
15. Idler bracket
16. Spring

ward until front edge of idler bracket is flush with plate (C). Shaft must be parallel to rear of tractor frame to within 1/16-inch (1.5 mm). Locate belt guides (D and E) approximately 1/8-inch (3 mm) away from transmission drive belt and tighten bolts (A). Recheck clutch free play.

Models YT8, YT10, YT11

OPERATION. The clutch is a spring loaded belt idler type. The drive belt is used to transfer power from crankshaft pulley to jackshaft and a traction belt transfers power from jackshaft to trans-axle pulley. The spring loaded clutch idler (11–Fig. A15) applies tension on drive belt.

ADJUSTMENT. The clutch idler pulley is spring loaded and does not require adjustment. Renew drive belts if excessively worn. To renew traction belt (4–Fig. A15), lift rear deck assembly and rotate belt guards away from trans-axle pulley and clutch arm. Depress clutch pedal and remove belt.

To renew drive belt, lift rear deck and remove traction belt. Disconnect spring (16–Fig. A15) from clutch arm (19). Disconnect main idler spring (13) from frame. Disconnect pto linkage and remove three cap screws mounting pto spindle to frame. Raise assembly about 1/2-inch (13 mm) and tip pulleys toward center of tractor. Note path of belt and remove belt. Reinstall belts by reversing removal procedures.

BRAKE

Models 13948, 13989, 13990, 913002, 913003

ADJUSTMENT. Brake adjustment is accomplished by turning hex nut (11–Fig. A16) at end of brake band rod. Turning nut clockwise will increase brake band tension while turning nut counter-clockwise will release tension. Brake should be adjusted so braking action begins when brake pedal is depressed one inch.

After adjusting brake band, loosen rear brake rod jam nut (Fig. A17) and depress brake pedal. Be sure pedal does not bottom against foot rest. Turn rear brake rod adjusting nut until brake lock clears tab by 1/16 to 1/8-inch (1.5-3 mm). Retighten jam nut. Turn front brake rod adjusting nut so brake pedal is at least 3/16-inch (5 mm) away from foot rest when fully depressed.

Models S-8G And S-8H

ADJUSTMENT. Depress clutch-brake pedal on Model S-8G or brake

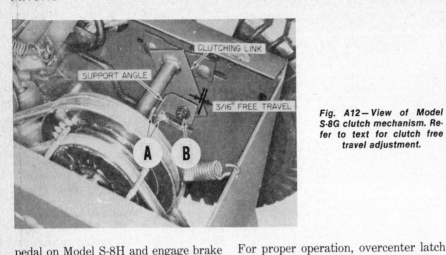

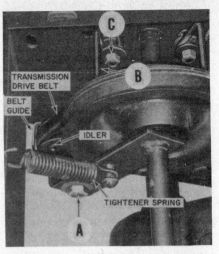

Fig. A12 — View of Model S-8G clutch mechanism. Refer to text for clutch free travel adjustment.

Fig. A13 — View of Model S-8G clutch idler and belt pulleys. Refer to text for adjustment.

pedal on Model S-8H and engage brake lock. Tighten nuts (B–Fig. A19) until spring is compressed to 1¾ inches (45 mm). Nuts (B) must be at least 1/16-inch (1.5 mm) away from support during this portion of adjustment. Release brake lock and allow brake or clutch-brake pedal to return to normal position against stop. Turn nuts (C) to obtain a spring length of 1-15/16 inches (49 mm) for S-8G models or 2⅛ inches (54 mm) for S-8H models. Clutch free travel may require adjustment after brake is adjusted and should be checked as outlined in CLUTCH section.

Models S-10G And S-14G

ADJUSTMENT. Braking is provided by drum-type brakes located on outer axle ends. Brakes should be adjusted when pedal can be depressed over two inches.

To adjust brakes, raise and support rear of tractor, then remove rear wheels. Insert screw-driver through slot provided in brake drum and turn star washer (Fig. A20) until brake locks; then, back star washer off one turn. Reinstall wheels.

Models S-12H, S-14H, S-16H, GT12, GT14, GT16

ADJUSTMENT. Dynamic braking is provided by moving hydrostatic transmission control lever to neutral position. All models are equipped with a neutral return pedal which will return transmission to neutral for emergency braking when depressed. Some models are also equipped with wheel brakes located on rear axles to prevent tractor from rolling when transmission is in neutral. All models utilize a park-lock pin which engages reduction gear in differential housing to provide positive braking when tractor is parked.

The overcenter latch pin (4–Fig. A21) prevents accidental engagement of park-lock pin (3) through a combination of slots in pivot plate and frame plate.

For proper operation, overcenter latch should be actuated when control lever is moved approximately ½-⅔ ot its travel in "PARK-START" slot and park-lock

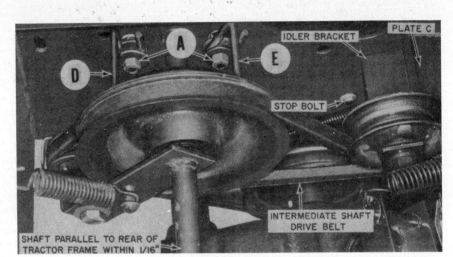

Fig. A14 — View of Model S-8G belt drive. Refer to text for intermediate belt adjustment.

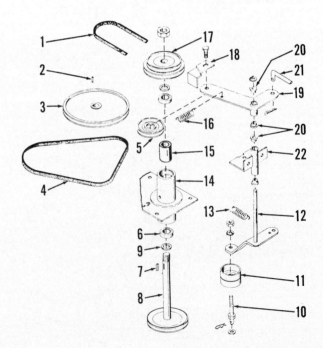

Fig. A15 — Exploded view of belt drive system used on Models YT8 and YT11.

1. Main drive belt
2. Key
3. Transaxle pulley
4. Traction belt
5. Idler pulley
6. Bearing
7. Key
8. Jackshaft spindle
9. Washer
10. Idler mounting bolt
11. Clutch idler pulley
12. Idler arm
13. Drive spring
14. Spindle housing
15. Spacer
16. Spring
17. Pulley
18. Belt retainer
19. Clutch arm
20. Bushing
21. Clutch rod
22. Idler pivot

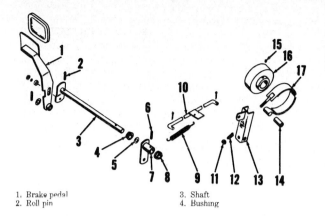

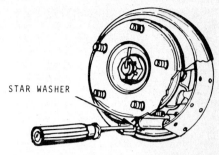

Fig. A16—Exploded view of brake assembly used on Models 13948, 13989, 13990, 913002 and 913003.

5. Washer
6. Roll pin
7. Lever
8. Bushing
9. Spring
10. Brake rod
11. Nut
12. Spring
13. Bracket
14. Spacer
15. Set screw
16. Brake drum
17. Brake band

1. Brake pedal
2. Roll pin
3. Shaft
4. Bushing

STAR WASHER

Fig. A20—Drum-type brakes, located on axle ends, are used on some early models. Refer to text.

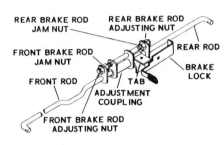

REAR BRAKE ROD JAM NUT
REAR BRAKE ROD ADJUSTING NUT
REAR ROD
FRONT BRAKE ROD JAM NUT
BRAKE LOCK
FRONT ROD
TAB
ADJUSTMENT COUPLING
FRONT BRAKE ROD ADJUSTING NUT

Fig. A17—View of brake rod assembly used on Models 13948, 13989, 13990, 913002 and 913003. Refer to text for adjustment procedure.

pin engaged after ¾ of lever travel. Refer to Fig. A22. Overcenter latch pin will "click" when actuated.

Overcenter latch pin actuation is adjusted by turning nuts (A – Fig. A21) to move cable housing until desired operation of latch pin is obtained. Tightening or loosening nut (A – Fig. A23) will adjust park-lock brake to hold control lever at rear of "PARK-START" slot when starting tractor engine.

The tractor wheel brakes (models so equipped) require adjustment if brake pedal can be depressed more than two

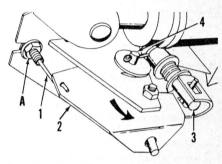

Fig. A21—View of parking brake mechanism on Models S-12H, S-14H, S-16H, GT12, GT14 and GT16. Refer to text for adjustment.

A. Adjusting nut
1. Control cable
2. Pivot plate
3. Park-lock pin
4. Overcenter latch pin

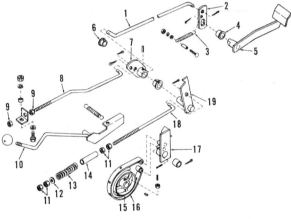

Fig. A18—Exploded view of brake mechanism used on Models S-8G and S-8H. Clutch rod is used only on Model S-8G.

1. Clutch-brake rod
2. Lever
3. Spring
4. Bushing
5. Clutch-brake pedal
6. Bushing
7. Clutch arm
8. Clutch rod
9. Nut
10. Parking brake lever

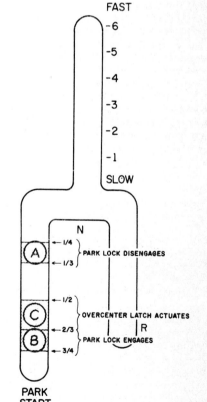

FAST
-6
-5
-4
-3
-2
-1
SLOW

N
A   1/4   PARK LOCK DISENGAGES
        1/3

C   1/2   OVERCENTER LATCH ACTUATES
        2/3   R
B   3/4   PARK LOCK ENGAGES

PARK START

Fig. A22—View of gear shift pattern showing positions of parking brake engagement and disengagement on Models S-12H, S-14H, S-16H, GT12, GT14 and GT16.

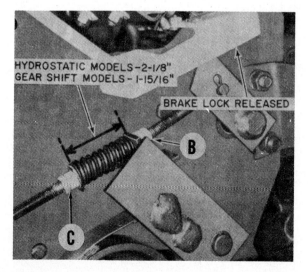

HYDROSTATIC MODELS –2-1/8"
GEAR SHIFT MODELS – 1-15/16"

BRAKE LOCK RELEASED

B

C

Fig. A19—Brake on Models S-8G and S-8H is adjusted by turning nuts (C and B). Refer to text.

Fig. A23 – View of hydrostatic shift control fork.

Fig. A25 – Models YT8, YT10 and YT11 are equipped with a caliper-disc brake located on lower right side of transaxle.

1. Brake rod
2. Disc
3. Adjusting screw
4. Brake jaw assy.

inches. To adjust brakes, proceed as follows: Raise and support rear of tractor so wheels are free to turn. Open transmission free-wheeling valves, located on top of transmission, by rotating cam up. On models equipped with disc-type brakes, tighten brake adjusting nuts (Fig. A24) evenly until brake just starts to drag, then back each nut off 1/8-turn. Adjust brake on opposite wheel using same procedure. On models equipped with drum-type brakes, remove wheel and insert screwdriver in slot provided in brake drum (Fig. A20). Adjust star washer until brake locks, then back washer off one turn. Adjust brake on opposite wheel using same procedure.

Models YT8, YT10, YT11

ADJUSTMENT. All models are equipped with a caliper-disc brake located on lower right side of transaxle assembly. To adjust brake, position tractor on level surface and place shifter lever in neutral. Adjust set screw (3 – Fig. A25) in brake jaw assembly (4) until brake starts to lock with pedal up; then, back set screw off 1/2-turn counter-clockwise.

Tension on brake pedal is adjustable. If pedal does not return or feels loose, adjust nut on end of brake rod just inside frame next to parking brake slot. Tighten nut until spring is 1 1/4 inches (32 mm) long.

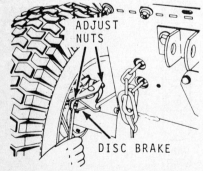

ADJUST NUTS

DISC BRAKE

Fig. A24 – View of typical caliper-disc brake used on some models. Adjust nuts as shown until brake begins to drag, then back nuts off 1/8-turn.

RIGHT ANGLE DRIVE

All Models So Equipped

R&R AND OVERHAUL. To remove right angle drive unit, release idler pulley tension and slide engine drive belt off of lower right angle drive pulley. Remove lower pulley from right angle drive. Remove frame cover in front of seat and remove front belt cover. Depress clutch and remove drive belts

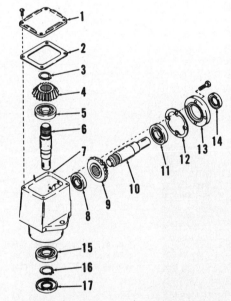

Fig. A26 – Exploded view of typical right angle drive used on some models.

1. Cover
2. Gasket
3. Snap ring
4. Input gear
5. Bearing
6. Input shaft
7. Case
8. Bearing
9. Output gear
10. Output shaft
11. Bearing
12. Gasket
13. Seal retainer
14. Oil seal
15. Bearing
16. Snap ring
17. Oil seal

from upper pulley of right angle drive. Remove right angle drive and pulley from tractor then remove pulley from right angle drive shaft.

To disassemble right angle drive unit, remove cover (1 – Fig. A26), gasket (2) and lubricant. Unbolt and remove seal retainer (13) with oil seal (14) and gasket (12). Withdraw output shaft (10) with bearing (11). Remove output gear (9). Remove oil seal (17) and snap ring (16). Drive input shaft (6) with gear (4) and bearing (5) out cover opening of case (7). Bearings (8 and 15) can now be removed from case. Remove snap ring (3) and remove drive gear (4) and bearing (5) from input shaft. Remove bearing (11) from output shaft (10).

Clean and inspect all parts and renew any showing excessive wear or other damage. Reassemble by reversing disassembly procedure and fill unit with 4 ounces (120mL) of Moly EP lithium grease.

PTO DRIVE

Models 13948, 13989, 13990, 913002, 913003

Pto clutch tension is adjusted by turning two nuts located on pto clutch rod under dash. Turning nut (N – Fig. A27) clockwise will increase tension. Refer to Fig. A27 for correct dimensions with clutch engaged.

Models S-8G And S-8H

Pto control mechanism should be adjusted if pto slips or rear nuts (B – Fig. A28) contact pivot block (P). Engage pto and tighten nuts (C) until spring length (D) is 2 5/8 inches (67 mm). It may be necessary to turn nuts (B) away from pivot block (P) so they are not in contact with pivot block when measuring spring length. With pto clutch disengaged, turn nuts (B) to obtain 1/4-inch (6 mm) clear-

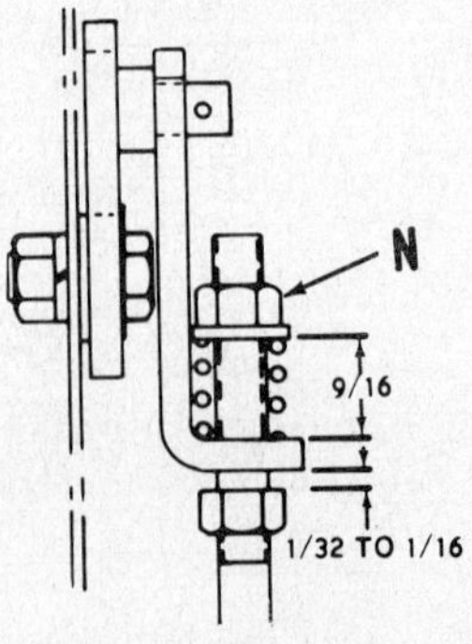

N

9/16

1/32 TO 1/16

(WITH PTO ENGAGED)

Fig. A27 – Adjust pto clutch tension on Models 13948, 13989, 13990, 913002 and 913003 by turning nuts on clutch rod to obtain dimensions shown above. Turning nut (N) clockwise increases tension.

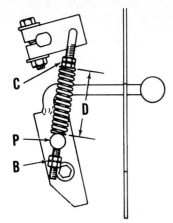

Fig. A28—View of Model S-8G or S-8H pto control lever in engaged position. See text.
PTO ENGAGED

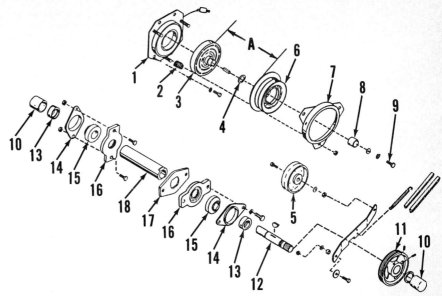

Fig. A30—Exploded view of electro-magnetic pto clutch and pto shaft assembly used on Models GT12, GT14 and GT16.

1. Field assy.	7. Brake flange	13. Locking collar
2. Spring	8. Spacer	14. Flangettes
3. Rotor assy.	9. Retainer screw	15. Bearing
4. Shim	10. Rubber cover	16. Flange
5. Idler pulley	11. Driven pulley	17. Anti-pivot plate
6. Drive pulley	12. Pto shaft	18. Tube

ance (M) between control lever and rear of lever slot as shown in Fig. A29.

Models GT12, GT14, GT16

Models GT12, GT14 and GT16 are equipped with an electro-magnetic clutch mounted on engine crankshaft. The pto shaft (12 – Fig. A30) rides in bearings and a tube (18), which also supports front axle assembly. Belt tension is automatically adjusted by spring loaded idler pulley (5).

To disassemble electro-magnetic clutch, unbolt and remove brake flange (7). Remove cap screw (9) and spacer (8); then, using a suitable puller, remove clutch pulley (6) and rotor (3). Unbolt and remove field assembly (1).

Field, rotor and armature are not available separately. If renewal is necessary complete clutch must be renewed. When reassembling clutch, check clear-

ance "A" between rotor and armature. Add or remove shims (4) as required to obtain 0.060-0.125 inch (1.524-3.175 mm) clearance. Complete reassembly in reverse of disassembly. Tighten retaining cap screw (8) to 25 ft.-lbs. (34 N·m) torque.

Adjust clutch as follows: With clutch disengaged, check clearance (C – Fig. A31) using a feeler gage through four slots (1) in brake flange. Clearance must be 0.010-0.015 inch (0.254-0.381 mm); tighten or loosen brake flange mounting nuts (5) to obtain correct gap.

To disassemble pto drive shaft assembly, remove shaft covers (10 – Fig. A30), belts, pto pulley (11) and bearing lock collars (13). Support front of tractor and unbolt bearing flanges, then withdraw shaft, bearings and tube.

Reassemble pto drive shaft assembly by reversing disassembly procedure. Lock bearing locking collars (13) to bearings (15) by turning collars in direction of shaft rotation, then lock collars to pto shaft (12) with set screws.

Models S-10G, S-12H, S-14G, S-14H, S-16H

An electro-magnetic pto clutch, mounted on engine crankshaft, is used on these models. The pto shaft (1 – Fig. A32) rides in bearings in pto housing (3) which also supports front axle assembly. Belt tension is automatically adjusted by spring loaded idler pulley (7).

To remove electro-magnetic clutch, remove retaining screw (17) and spacer (15), then pull rotor assembly (14) off

crankshaft. Unbolt and remove field assembly (13). Field and rotor are not available separately; if renewal is necessary, complete clutch must be replaced.

Reinstall clutch in reverse of disassembly procedure. Tighten studs retain-

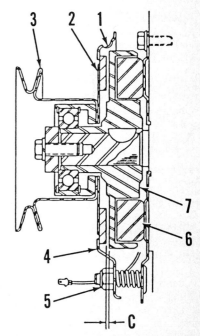

Fig. A31—Cross-sectional view of typical electro-magnetic pto clutch used on "S" and "GT" models. Adjust nuts (5) to provide 0.010-0.015 inch (0.254-0.381 mm) clearance (C) with clutch disengaged. Refer to text.

1. Adjustment slot (4)	5. Locknut
2. Armature-brake assy.	6. Field assy.
3. Pulley	7. Rotor assy.
4. Brake flange	

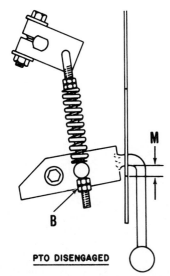

Fig. A29—View of Model S-8G or S-8H pto control lever in disengaged position. See text.

PTO DISENGAGED

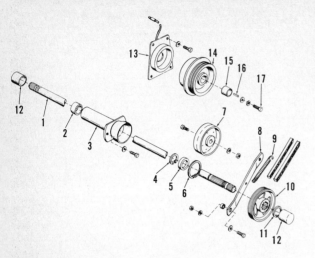

Fig. A32 — Exploded view of pto clutch and shaft assembly used on Models S-10G, S-12H, S-14G, S-14H and S-16H. Pto housing (3) supports front axle.

1. Pto shaft
2. Needle bearing
3. Housing
4. Snap ring
5. Bearing
6. Snap ring
7. Idler pulley
8. Idler arm
9. Spring
10. Driven pulley
11. Snap ring
12. Cover
13. Electric clutch field
14. Clutch & drive pulley
15. Sleeve
16. Key
17. Cap screw

ing field assembly to 30 ft.-lbs. (41 N·m). Tighten cap screw retaining rotor-armature assembly to 25 ft.-lbs. (34 N·m). When reinstalling brake flange (4 – Fig. A31), adjust locknuts (5) to provide 0.010-0.015 inch (0.254-0.381 mm) gap (C) with clutch disengaged. Gap can be checked by inserting feeler gage through four slots (1) in brake flange.

To disassemble pto shaft, remove covers (12 – Fig. A32), belts and pulley (10). Support front of tractor and remove cap screws retaining pto housing (3) to frame bracket, then withdraw pto drive towards front of tractor. Remove snap rings, shaft and bearings. Reassemble unit by reversing removal procedure.

Models YT8, YT10, YT11

All models are equipped with a spring loaded idler pto clutch. No adjustment is required. If belt slips, renew belt or idler spring.

HYDROSTATIC TRANSMISSION

EATON

Model S-8H

DRIVE RELEASE. The tractor may be moved short distances with engine stopped by rotating cam arm shown in Fig. A34 rearward to force free wheeling valve rod down into transmission. Opening free-wheeling valve relieves oil pressure in transmission and rear wheels are free to turn. The free-wheeling cam arm must be returned to its forward position to operate tractor with engine running.

LUBRICATION. Type of oil recommended for hydrostatic transmission used on Models S-8H is Type "A" ATF. Oil level is indicated on oil reservoir tank

next to transmission and should indicate reservoir is half full. Care should be used when filling reservoir to prevent contamination of fluid.

If air enters transmission fluid, system must be bled to remove air using following procedure: Unscrew nut from left end of free-wheeling cam shaft and move shaft to right until cam is clear of free-wheeling valve as shown in Fig. A35. Clean dirt and debris from free-wheeling valve and reservoir. Loosen nut (B) and unscrew free-wheeling valve rod (C). Do not allow dirt or other foreign material to enter transmission. Remove reservoir fill cap and add Type "A" ATF until reservoir is half full. Raise rear of tractor, start engine and run engine at slow idle speed. Move speed control lever to forward and

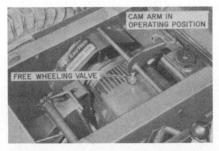

Fig. A34 — View showing location of free-wheeling valve and cam on Model S-8H.

Fig. A35 — Cam assembly on Model S-8H must be moved as shown to remove free-wheeling valve so transmission can be bled.

reverse positions until oil appears at free-wheeling valve hole. Stop engine and screw rod (C) into transmission and tighten nut (B) to 30 in.-lbs. (3 N·m). Be careful not to damage "O" rings in transmission. Install cam assembly and screw nuts on left end of shaft to position cam in center of free-wheeling rod. Recheck oil level in reservoir and fill with fluid until half full.

ADJUSTMENT. Model S-8H is equipped with a neutral-brake pedal on right side of tractor which returns transmission to neutral when pedal is depressed. To adjust neutral-brake pedal, place transmission shift lever in "PARK-START" (neutral) slot of shift quadrant and loosen bolt (A – Fig. A37). Depress pedal and apply brake lock. Tighten bolt (A). Check operation by placing shift lever in forward position and depress pedal. Shift lever should return to "PARK-START". Repeat check with shift lever in reverse position. Do not move shift lever and depress neutral-brake pedal simultaneously as control linkage may be bent or mis-adjusted.

Tractor wheels should not move when transmission shift lever is in "PARK-START" (neutral) position. If tractor creeps in neutral, proceed as follows: Adjust neutral-brake pedal as previously outlined. Place shift lever in "PARK-START" (neutral) position and note position of bolt (B – Fig. A37) in control cam. Centerline of bolt head should be aligned with timing mark. If bolt and mark are not aligned, loosen bolt (C) and move control cam up or down to align centerline of bolt head (B) with timing mark. Tighten bolt (C). Support rear of tractor so rear tires can rotate without touching ground. Start engine and run at full throttle. Loosen bolt (B) slightly and with a screwdriver inserted in slots (S) of pintle lever and friction plate, pivot pintle left or right until rear tires stop turning. Tighten bolt (B).

Friction brake shown in Fig. A37 may be adjusted by turning nut (D) to increase friction against friction plate and maintain speed settings of shift lever.

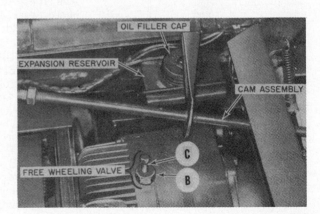

REMOVE AND REINSTALL. To remove hydrostatic transmission, remove outer fan shield attached to frame. Unscrew cap screw and remove fan, drive pulley and drive belt. Unscrew free-wheeling cam shaft nuts and remove cam assembly shown in Fig. A34. Disconnect shift linkage from transmission shift shaft. Disconnect oil line from reservoir to transmission and remove reservoir. Plug all openings in oil line and transmission to prevent contamination. Unscrew cap screws securing transmission to differential, move transmission to left and lift transmission out of tractor.

Reinstall by reversing removal procedure. Bleed air from system and adjust linkage as previously outlined.

OVERHAUL. Model S-8H is equipped with an Eaton Model 6 hydrostatic transmission. Refer to Eaton Model 6 section in HYDROSTATIC TRANSMISSION SERVICE section for overhaul procedure.

VICKERS

All Models So Equipped

DRIVE RELEASE. Free-wheeling valve located on left side of transmission and shown in Fig. A40 may be depressed to move tractor with engine stopped. Depressing free-wheeling valve relieves oil pressure and allows motor to turn.

LUBRICATION. The hydrostatic transmission, differential and hydraulic system, if so equipped, use a common oil reservoir in the differential housing. Recommended oil is SAE 10W-30 detergent type automotive engine oil having API classification SE. Maintain oil level at lowest edge of filler pipe threads with tractor on level ground. Capacity is approximately 7 pints (3.3L). Oil filter located under control console should be changed after every 500 hours of operation or every two years.

ADJUSTMENT. Transmission shift linkage must be adjusted if tractor creeps or moves forward or rearward when shift lever is in neutral slot.

Fine adjustment of transmission control linkage may cure creeping problem. To perform fine adjustment, raise and support rear of tractor so rear wheels are free to turn. Place transmission control lever in "PARK-START" position and raise rear deck. Start engine and move control lever to neutral slot. Increase engine speed to approximately full throttle. Loosen clamp bolt (B – Fig. A41) until cam follower is free to rotate and turn eccentric in either direction as required to stop rear wheel rotation. Retighten clamp bolt (B). Check adjustment by moving shift control lever into forward and reverse positions and back to neutral. Rear wheels should not turn with shift control lever in neutral.

If fine adjustment of cam follower eccentric does not stop rear wheel rotation in neutral, or if shift linkage has been disassembled, it will be necessary to use the following procedure for neutral adjustment: Raise and support rear of tractor so rear wheels are free to turn. Move shift control lever to "PARK-START" position and raise rear deck.

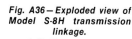

Fig. A36 – Exploded view of Model S-8H transmission linkage.

1. Bushing
2. Washer
3. Shift control cam
4. Washer
5. Plate
6. Bushing
7. Spacer
8. Washer
9. Friction plate
10. Pintle arm
11. Spring
12. Front friction pad
13. Rear friction pad
14. Bracket
15. Roller
16. Spacer
17. Neutral link
18. Pin
19. Spring
20. Shift arm
21. Shift lever
22. Bushing
23. Washer
24. Shift rod
25. Spacer
26. Shift link
27. Washer
28. Shim
29. Cam arm

Fig. A40 – View showing location of free-wheeling valve (V) on models equipped with Vickers transmission. Knob must be pushed in to move tractor with engine stopped.

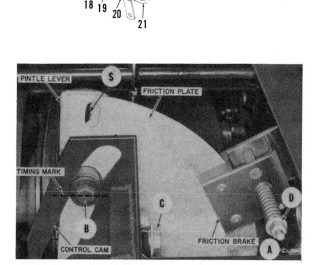

Fig. A37 – View of shift mechanism adjustment points on Model S-8H. Refer to text.

Fig. A41 – View of shift mechanism used on models equipped with Vickers transmission.

Loosen clamp bolt (B–Fig. A42) and rotate eccentric until cam follower roller is in lowest portion of neutral section in cam slot as shown in Fig. A42. Neutral section of cam slot is portion of cam slot which will not move pintle arm when cam is moved up and down. Retighten clamp bolt (B). Move shift control lever to position cam follower roller in middle of neutral section of cam slot. Loosen pintle arm clamp bolts (A–Fig. A42) so pintle shaft can slip in pintle arm. Move shift control lever to "PARK-START" position and start engine. Operate engine between 2/3 and full throttle speed. Transmission will seek its neutral position. Stop engine and check to be sure cam roller is still in center of neutral section in cam slot. Carefully tighten pintle arm clamp bolts (A) to 30-35 ft.-lbs. (41-47 N·m). Cam or pintle arm must not be disturbed when tightening bolts. Loosen shift control fork bolt (D–Fig. A43). Hold cam to prevent movement of cam follower roller in cam slot and move control fork until it is aligned with neutral slot in control shift pattern. Tighten bolt (D).

If necessary, additional fine adjustment can now be made by adjusting eccentric roller using procedure previously outlined.

The shift lever fork slides between two friction plates which can be adjusted to increase or decrease friction as desired. The friction plates are held together by two screws and springs. There should be sufficient spring pressure on friction plates to hold control lever at any selected setting. Raise rear deck and insert a screwdriver through access holes in left side of control console to adjust screws.

Fig. A43 – View of hydrostatic shift control fork. Adjust park lock brake at "A." Loosen bolt "D" to adjust neutral position of control fork.

If neutral return pedal does not shift hydrostatic control lever to neutral position from either forward or reverse position when pedal is depressed, adjust length of neutralizer rod by means of nuts (E–Fig. A41).

REMOVE AND REINSTALL. To remove hydrostatic transmission, mark and disconnect hydraulic hoses. Plug or cap openings to prevent entrance of dirt or other foreign material. Remove plate directly above drive shaft and disconnect drive shaft rear coupler. Detach coupler half from transmission input shaft. Remove pintle arm from transmission. Unbolt and remove supporting brace between crossmember and transmission. Unbolt transmission and lift transmission from tractor. Drain lubricant and clean exterior of transmission.

Reinstall hydrostatic transmission by reversing removal procedure. Fill reduction drive and differential housing to proper level with SAE 10W-30 oil. Refer to LUBRICATION paragraph.

OVERHAUL. A Vickers Model T66Z hydrostatic transmission is used. Refer to Vickers Model T66 section in HYDROSTATIC TRANSMISSION SERVICE section for overhaul procedure.

SUNDSTRAND

All Models So Equipped

LUBRICATION. The hydrostatic transmission shares a common reservoir in gear reduction and differential unit. Recommended oil is SAE 10W-30 engine oil having API classification SE. If ambient temperature is above 80°F (27°C) and tractor will be in heavy load conditions, change transmission oil to SAE 30. Maintain oil level at top of filler plug pipe elbow (3–Fig. A50). Check oil level with tractor on level surface and engine running at fast idle. Care should

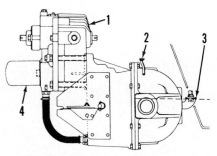

Fig. A50 – Recommended transmission oil is SAE 10W-30 engine oil for models equipped with Sundstrand hydrostatic transmission. Fill to top of filler plug pipe elbow (3).

1. Hydrostatic transmission
2. Breather
3. Oil level & filler plug
4. Oil filter

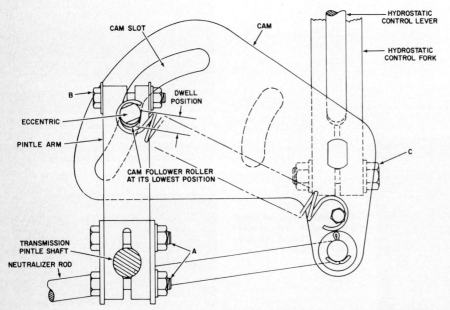

Fig. A42 – Diagram of typical shift mechanism used on models equipped with Vickers transmission. Refer to text for adjustment.

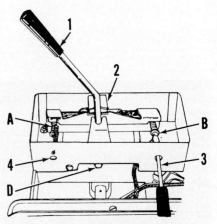

Fig. A51 – View of control lever friction adjustment screws (A and B). Top of console is removed for ease of viewing.

1. Control lever
2. Control fork
3. Screwdriver
4. Access holes

be used when filling reservoir to prevent contamination of fluid. The oil and oil filter (4) should be changed every 500 hours of operation or once a year, whichever comes first. Be sure transmission breather (2) is not plugged.

ADJUSTMENT. If tractor creeps when hydrostatic control lever is in neutral slot, shift linkage must be adjusted.

Proper friction adjustment on control lever is necessary for proper operation. Control lever friction plates must be adjusted so control lever (1–Fig. A51) will remain at any selected setting under normal operating conditions. Friction plate spring pressure is adjusted by tightening screws at "A" and "B." Raise rear deck and insert screwdriver through access holes (4) as shown. Friction plates must remain parallel, check and adjust screws evenly. If tractor has a tendency to speed up, tighten screw "A" slightly more than "B." If tractor slows down, tighten screw "B" slightly more than "A."

EARLY MODELS. To adjust control linkage, proceed as follows: Raise and support rear of tractor so wheels are free to turn. Start engine and place control lever in neutral position. With engine speed at full throttle, loosen clamp bolt (B–Fig. A52) and turn eccentric as required until rear wheels stop turning. Retighten clamp bolt (B). Check adjustment by moving lever into forward and reverse positions and back to neutral. Wheels should not turn with shift lever in neutral.

If fine adjustment of cam follower eccentric does not stop rear wheel rotation in neutral, or if shift linkage has been disassembled, it will be necessary to use following procedure for neutral adjustment: Raise and support rear of tractor so wheels are free to turn. Loosen clamp bolt (B–Fig. A52) and turn eccentric until flats on eccentric are parallel with cam slot as shown, then retighten clamp bolt. Move cam to align cam follower roller with cam dwell center mark. Loosen pintle lever clamp bolt (A) so pin-

tle shaft can rotate freely in pintle lever. Start engine and place control lever in neutral position. Move pintle lever as required until wheels stop turning. Be sure cam follower roller is still aligned with cam dwell center mark, then shut off engine. Carefully tighten bolt (A) making sure cam or pintle lever position is not disturbed. Loosen adjusting nuts on shift rod and neutralizer rod, then depress neutralizer pedal. Make sure cam follower roller is aligned with cam dwell center mark, and adjust nuts snug against neutralizer plate. Loosen shift control fork bolt (D–Fig. A51). Hold cam to prevent movement of cam follower roller in cam slot and move control fork until it is aligned with neutral slot in control console. Retighten nut (D).

If wheels still creep when in neutral, loosen clamp bolt (B–Fig. A52) and adjust eccentric roller until wheels stop. Retighten clamp bolt (B).

LATE MODELS. To adjust control linkage, proceed as follows: Raise and support rear of tractor so wheels are free to turn. Remove floor plate, then disconnect shift rod yoke (2–Fig. A53) from neutralizer rod (3). If shift lever does not return to neutral position when neutral return pedal is depressed, adjust length of neutralizer rod using adjusting nuts (4). Loosen locking nut (1–Fig. A54) so eccentric (2) can be turned with a wrench. Start engine and move shift lever to neutral position. With engine running at full throttle, adjust eccentric until wheels stop turning and tighten locking nut. Shut off engine and adjust shift rod yoke until shift rod (7) is centered in slot in transmission lever (6).

REMOVE AND REINSTALL. To remove hydrostatic transmission, first disconnect battery and drain lubricant. Remove rear deck and fuel tank. Disconnect drive shaft rear coupler and remove coupler half from transmission input shaft. Disconnect hydraulic hoses and plug or cap all openings to prevent entrance of dirt. Disconnect control linkage from transmission. Unbolt

transmission and remove from rear axle differential assembly.

Reinstall hydrostatic unit in reverse of removal. Fill reservoir with clean 10W-30 engine oil. Prime transmission by removing implement relief valve, located on top of unit between directional valves, and pour in one pint (0.5L) of 10W-30 oil. Reinstall relief valve but do not tighten valve plug. Start engine and run until oil runs past threads of plug, then tighten plug.

OVERHAUL. A Sundstrand Series 15 "U" type hydrostatic transmission is used. Refer to Sundstrand Series 15 "U" Type section in HYDROSTATIC TRANSMISSION SERVICE section for overhaul procedure.

TRANSAXLE

LUBRICATION

All Models

Models 13948, 13989, 13990, 913002, 913003 and S-8 are equipped with Peerless 1200 series transaxle. Models

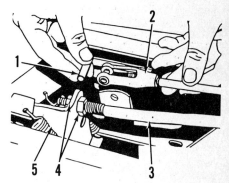

Fig. A53 – To adjust hydrostatic shift linkage on late models, shift rod (2) must be disconnected from neutralizer rod (3). Refer to text.
1. Pin
2. Shift rod
3. Neutralizer rod
4. Adjusting nuts
5. Neutralizer plate

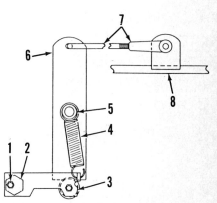

Fig. A54 – View of hydrostatic shift linkage used on late models. Refer to text for adjustment.
1. Locking nut
2. Eccentric
3. Bearing
4. Spring
5. Pintle arm
6. Pintle lever
7. Shift rod & yoke
8. Neutralizer rod

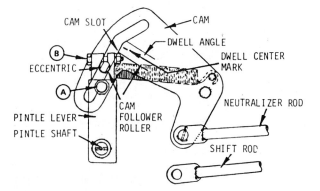

Fig. A52 – Diagram of typical mechanism used on early models equipped with hydrostatic transmission. Refer to text for adjustment.

Ariens

TRACTOR

S-10G and S-14G are equipped with Peerless 2300 series transaxle. Models YT8, YT10 and YT11 are equipped with Foote Model 4000-5 transaxle. Refer to CONDENSED SPECIFICATIONS at the beginning of this section for transaxle lubricating fluid type and capacity for model being serviced.

REMOVE AND REINSTALL

Model S-8G

To remove transaxle, remove brake band and shift linkage. Remove transaxle drive belt. Unscrew two front mounting cap screws. Support rear of tractor and unscrew axle retaining "U" bolts. Raise rear of tractor and roll transaxle away from tractor.

To reinstall transaxle, reverse removal procedure.

Models YT8, YT10, YT11

To remove transaxle, raise rear deck and remove traction belt. Remove shift lever knob and place transmission in neutral. Disconnect and remove range selector lever linkage. Disconnect brake linkage. Remove rear hitch plate and support tractor under frame. Use a floor jack to support front of transmission. Remove four cap screws from transaxle mount and "U" bolts from axle housing. Roll transaxle away from tractor.

Remove rear wheels, clean case and place on bench.

To reinstall transaxle, reverse removal procedure.

All Other Models So Equipped

To remove transaxle, remove rear hitch plate from rear of frame and frame top cover in front of seat. Remove rear drive belt cover, depress clutch and remove drive belts from transaxle pulley. Disconnect brake rod from brake band. Unscrew transaxle retaining cap screws located beneath seat. Support rear of tractor and remove retaining axle brackets. Roll transaxle assembly from tractor. Remove input pulley, brake assembly and wheels and hubs from transaxle.

To reinstall transaxle, reverse removal procedure.

OVERHAUL

All Models

Models 13948, 13989, 13990, 913002, 913003 and S-8 are equipped with a Peerless 1200 series transaxle. Models S-10G and S-14G are equipped with a Peerless 2300 series transaxle. Models YT8, YT10 and YT11 are equipped with a Foote Model 4000-5 transaxle. Refer to the appropriate Peerless or Foote section in TRANSAXLE SERVICE section for overhaul procedure.

REDUCTION GEARS AND DIFFERENTIAL

Model S-8H

R&R AND OVERHAUL. Model S-8 Hydro is equipped with a Peerless Model 1309 reduction gear and differential unit. To remove rear axle assembly, remove hydrostatic transmission as previously outlined. Unscrew front mounting screws and axle "U" bolts. Raise rear of tractor and roll rear end assembly away from tractor.

Remove wheel and hub assemblies from axles. Remove brake disc from brake shaft. Clean axle shafts and remove any burrs on shafts. Unscrew cap screws and drive out dowel pins in cover (29 – Fig. A64). Lift cover off case and axle shaft. Withdraw brake shaft (5), input gear (4) and thrust washers (3 and 6) from case. Remove output shaft (11), output gear (10), spacer (9), thrust washer (8) and differential assembly from case. Axle shaft housings (20 and 22) must be pressed from case and cover.

To disassemble differential, unscrew four cap screws and separate axle shaft and carriage assemblies from ring gear (28). Drive blocks (25), bevel pinion gears (26) and drive pin (27) can now be removed from ring gear. Remove snap rings (12) and slide axle shafts (18 and 23) from axle gears (13) and carriages (16 and 24).

Clean and inspect all parts and renew any parts damaged or excessively worn. When installing needle bearings, press bearings in from inside of case or cover until bearings are 0.015-0.020 inch (0.381-0.508 mm) below thrust surfaces. Be sure heads of differential cap screws and right axle shaft (18) are installed in right carriage housing (16). Right axle shaft is installed through case (1). Tighten differential cap screws to 7 ft.-lbs. (9 N·m) and cover cap screws to 10 ft.-lbs. (14 N·m). Differential assembly and output shaft (11) must be installed in case at same time. Remainder of assembly is reverse of disassembly procedure. Fill unit with approximately two pints (0.9L) of SAE 90 EP gear lube.

Models S-12H, S-14H, S-16H, GT12, GT14, GT16

R&R AND OVERHAUL. To remove gear reduction and differential unit, remove hydrostatic transmission as outlined in previous paragraph and proceed as follows: Detach parking pawl assem-

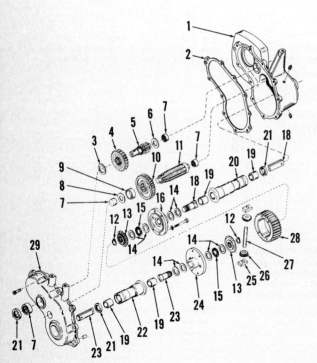

Fig. A64 — Exploded view of gear reduction and differential unit used on Model S-8H.

1. Case
2. Gasket
3. Washer
4. Idler gear
5. Brake shaft
6. Washer
7. Bearing
8. Washer
9. Spacer
10. Output gear
11. Output shaft
12. Snap ring
13. Bevel gear
14. Thrust washers
15. Thrust bearing
16. Differential carrier
18. Axle shaft (R.H.)
19. Bushing
20. Axle housing
21. Oil seal
22. Axle housing
23. Axle shaft (L.H.)
24. Differential carrier
25. Drive block
26. Drive pinion
27. Drive pin
28. Ring gear
29. Cover

bly from housing and disconnect brake control rods. Support rear of tractor and unbolt axle brackets from frame. Roll unit forward until oil filter pipe is clear of rear hitch plate, raise tractor and roll assembly rearward from tractor.

To disassemble unit, drain lubricant from housing, then remove wheels and hubs (1–Fig. A65) from axles (6). Unbolt axle bearing retainer and withdraw axle and bearing assemblies from rear housing (7). Unbolt and separate front and rear housings (23 and 7). Be sure differential bearing caps are marked for correct reassembly as they are matched to front housing. Unbolt and remove bearing caps, then pry differential assembly out of housing. Drive a pointed punch through pinion shaft expansion plug (20) and pry plug out of housing. Remove snap ring (19) and shim (18) from end of pinion shaft. Remove side cover (25) and place a screwdriver blade under edge of reduction gear (24) to prevent gear from binding, then press pinion gear (13) out of housing and remove outer bearing (21), spacer (17) and reduction gear (24). Press pinion shaft out of inner bearing (14). Press bearing cups (15 and 22) out of housing.

To disassemble differential, drive lock pin (2) out of pinion shaft (3) as shown in Fig. A66; then, drive pinion shaft (3) from housing. Rotate pinion gears (27–Fig. A65) 90 degrees to openings in differential case and remove pinion gears (27), side gears (28) and thrust washers (26 and 29). To remove differ-

ential case bearings (9), use a suitable puller inserting puller jaws into indentations provided in differential case. Remove cap screws securing ring gear (12) to case, then drive ring gear off case using a hammer and wood block.

Clean and inspect all parts and renew any parts damaged or excessively worn.

Reassemble in reverse of disassembly procedure. When installing inner bearing cup (15) in original housing (23), reuse original shim pack (16). If housing (23) is being renewed, determine proper shim pack as follows: Install bearing cup (15) in housing without shims. Press bearing cone (14) on pinion shaft and position shaft and bearing in housing. Using a depth measuring tool similar to one shown in Fig. A67, measure distance from bottom of bearing cradles to pinion gear surface. Subtract measured dimension from 1.2097 and difference will be required shim pack thickness. Remove inner bearing cup, install required shim pack and reinstall cup into housing.

Position pinion gear, reduction gear (chamfered side of splines towards pinion gear) and spacer in housing. Press outer bearing cone onto pinion shaft until a slight drag is felt when gear is turned by hand, then install thickest shim (18–Fig. A65) possible which will still allow installation of snap ring (19). Use sealer when installing expansion plug (20) and side cover (25).

Position ring gear (12) on differential case (11) and pull gear into place by

tightening retaining cap screws evenly. Final torque on cap screws should be 50-55 ft.-lbs. (68-75 N·m).

Press bearing cones (9) on original differential case (11) using original shims (10). If differential case is being renewed, install 0.020 inch shim pack under each bearing. Position differential assembly in front housing with ring gear facing same side as reduction gear cover. Install bearing caps in their original positions and tighten cap screws to 40-45 ft.-lbs. (54-61 N·m).

Using a dial indicator, check for proper ring gear to pinion backlash of 0.003-0.007 inch (0.076-0.178 mm). If necessary, adjust backlash by moving shims (10) from one side to the other until correct backlash is obtained. To check gear teeth contact pattern, paint teeth with gear pattern compound, then rotate pinion while applying light load to ring gear. Compare contact area on teeth with patterns illustrated in Fig. A68 and correct if necessary. Desired tooth contact pattern on ring gear is shown at "A." To move toe pattern "B" towards heel, shim ring gear away from pinion, within 0.003-0.007 inch (0.076-0.178 mm) backlash limits. To move heel pattern "C" towards toe, shim ring gear closer to pinion, within backlash limits. If pattern is low "D", remove shims located under pinion inner bearing

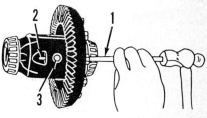

Fig. A66–To disassemble differential, use a long, thin punch (1) to drive retaining pin (2) out of pinion shaft (3), then drive pinion shaft out of differential case.

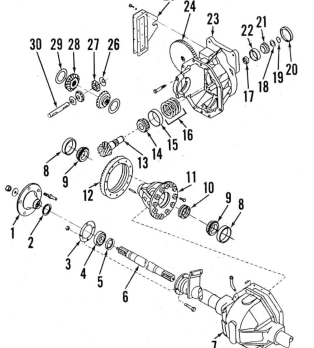

Fig. A65–Exploded view of gear reduction, differential and rear axle unit used on Models S-12H, S-14H, S-16H, GT12, GT14 and GT16.

1. Hub
2. Felt seal
3. Retainer
4. Axle bearing
5. Oil seal
6. Axle
7. Rear housing
8. Bearing cup
9. Bearing cone
10. Shims
11. Differential case
12. Ring gear
13. Pinion gear
14. Bearing cone (inner)
15. Bearing cup (inner)
16. Shims
17. Spacer
18. Shim
19. Snap ring
20. Expansion plug
21. Bearing cone (outer)
22. Bearing cup (outer)
23. Front housing
24. Reduction gear
25. Cover
26. Thrust washer (2)
27. Pinion gear (2)
28. Side gear (2)
29. Thrust washer (2)
30. Pinion shaft

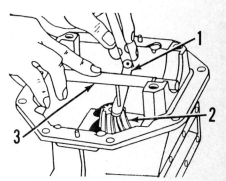

Fig. A67–If front housing is renewed, measure from bottom of bearing cradles to pinion gear surface as shown to determine pinion shaft shim pack thickness. Refer to text.

1. Feeler gage
2. Pinion shaft
3. Depth measuring tool

cup. If pattern is high "E", increase shim pack under pinion inner bearing cup.

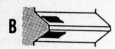

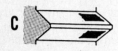

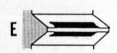

Fig. A68—Illustration of typical gear teeth contact patterns encountered when checking ring gear and pinion. "A" pattern desired; "B" too close to toe; "C" too close to heel; "D" contact too low; "E" contact too high. Refer to text and correct as necessary.

Assemble front housing to rear housing and tighten retaining screws to 18-23 ft.-lbs. (24-32 N·m).

HYDRAULIC LIFT

All Models So Equipped

OPERATION. The hydrostatic transmission charge pump supplies oil flow to operate hydraulic lift cylinder. Oil flow is controlled by a hand operated control valve with four positions: Up, Hold, Down and Float. Hydraulic system pressure should be 500-800 psi (3448-5516 kPa) at full engine rpm.

CYLINDER OVERHAUL. To disassemble cylinder, first remove adapter fittings from cylinder body (8–Fig. A69), then remove rod cap (2) from body. Withdraw piston rod (4) and piston (5) from body. Unscrew retaining screw (7) to remove piston from rod.

Inspect cylinder body, piston and rod for scoring or other damage and renew as needed. Renew all "O" ring seals. Coat all parts with clean oil when reassembling.

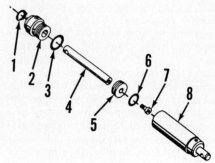

Fig. A69—Exploded view of hydraulic lift cylinder used on models so equipped.

1. "O" ring
2. Rod cap
3. "O" ring
4. Piston rod
5. Piston
6. "O" ring
7. Cap screw
8. Cylinder body

BOLENS

CONDENSED SPECIFICATIONS

MODELS

	730	733	736	G9, 853	LT8, G8	G10*
Engine Make	B&S	B&S	B&S	B&S	B&S	Tecumseh
Model	170702	170701	170701	190401	191707	HH100
Bore	3 in.	3 in.	3 in.	3 in.	3 in.	3-5/16 in.
	(76.2 mm)	(76.2 mm)	(76.2 mm)	(76.2 mm)	(76.2 mm)	(84.1 mm)
Stroke	2⅜ in.	2⅜ in.	2⅜ in.	2¾ in.	2¾ in.	2¾ in.
	(60.3 mm)	(60.3 mm)	(60.3 mm)	(69.8 mm)	(69.8 mm)	(69.8 mm)
Piston Displacement	16.79 cu. in.	16.79 cu. in.	16.79 cu. in.	19.44 cu. in.	19.44 cu. in.	23.7 cu. in.
	(275 cc)	(275 cc)	(275 cc)	(319 cc)	(319 cc)	(389 cc)
Horsepower	7	7	7	8	8	10
Slow Idle Speed – Rpm	1750	1750	1750	1750	1750	1200
High Idle Speed (No Load) – Rpm.	3600	3600	3600	3600	3600	3600
Full Load Speed – Rpm	3250	3250	3250	3250	3250	3250
Crankcase Oil Capacity	2¼ pints	2¼ pints	2¼ pints	2¾ pints	2¼ pints	3 pints
	(1L)	(1L)	(1L)	(1.3L)	(1L)	(1.4L)
Weight –						
Above 32°F (0°C)				SAE 30		
0°F (–18°C) to 32°F (0°C)				SAE 10W-30		
Below 0°F (–18°C)				SAE 5W-20		
Transmission Oil Capacity	3 pints	3 pints	....	5 pints	1½ pints	5 pints
	(1.4L)	(1.4L)		(2.4L)	(0.7L)	(2.4L)
Weight	SAE 90 EP	SAE 90 EP	Type "A"	SAE 90 EP	SAE 90 EP	SAE 90 EP

MODELS

	1053, 1054	G11	G11XL	H11XL	LT11	1225, 1256
Engine Make	Wisconsin	B&S	B&S	B&S	B&S	Wisconsin
Model	TR-10D	252417	253417	253417	252707	TRA-12D
Bore	3⅛ in.	3-7/16 in.	3-7/16 in.	3-7/16 in.	3-7/16 in.	3½ in.
	(79.3 mm)	(87.3 mm)	(87.3 mm)	(87.3 mm)	(87.3 mm)	(88.9 mm)
Stroke	2⅝ in.	2⅝ in.	2⅝ in.	2⅝ in.	2⅝ in.	2⅞ in.
	(66.7 mm)	(66.7 mm)	(66.7 mm)	(66.7 mm)	(66.7 mm)	(73.0 mm)
Piston Displacement	20.2 cu. in.	24.36 cu. in.	24.36 cu. in.	24.36 cu. in.	24.36 cu. in.	27.66 cu. in.
	(331 cc)	(399 cc)	(399 cc)	(399 cc)	(399 cc)	(453 cc)
Horsepower	10	11	11	11	11	12
Slow Idle Speed – Rpm	1000	1750	1750	1750	1750	1000
High Idle Speed (No Load) – Rpm.	3800	3600	3600	3600	3600	3860
Full Load Speed – Rpm	3450	3300	3300	3300	3300	3600
Crankcase Oil Capacity	2 pints	3 pints	3 pints	3 pints	3 pints	2 pints
	(0.9L)	(1.4L)	(1.4L)	(1.4L)	(1.4L)	(0.9L)
Weight –						
Above 32°F (0°C)				SAE 30		
0°F (–18°C) to 32°F (0°C)				SAE 10W-30		
Below 0°F (–18°C)				SAE 5W-20		
Transmission Oil Capacity	5 pints	5 pints	3 pints	16 pints	1½ pints	....
	(2.4L)	(2.4L)	(1.4L)	(7.6L)	(0.7L)	
Weight	SAE 90 EP	SAE 90 EP	SAE 90 EP	**	SAE 90 EP	Type "A"

MODELS

	1254	G12,1253	G12XL	H12XL	1257
Engine Make	Wisconsin	Tecumseh	Tecumseh	Tecumseh	Tecumseh
Model	TRA-12D	HH120	OH120	OH120	HH120
Bore	3½ in.	3½ in.	3⅛ in.	3⅛ in.	3½ in.
	(88.9 mm)	(88.9 mm)	(79.3 mm)	(79.3 mm)	(88.9 mm)
Stroke	2⅞ in.	2⅞ in.	2¾ in.	2¾ in.	2⅞ in.
	(73.0 mm)	(73.0 mm)	(69.8 mm)	(69.8 mm)	(73.0 mm)
Piston Displacement	27.66 cu. in.	27.66 cu. in.	21.1 cu. in.	21.1 cu. in.	27.66 cu. in.
	(453 cc)	(453 cc)	(346 cc)	(346 cc)	(453 cc)
Horsepower	12	12	12	12	12
Slow Idle Speed–Rpm	1000	1200	1200	1200	1200
High Idle Speed (No Load)–Rpm	3860	3600	3600	3600	3600
Full Load Speed-Rpm	3600	3200	3200	3200	3200
Crankcase Oil Capacity	2 pints	3 pints	3 pints	3 pints	3 pints
	(0.9L)	(1.4L)	(1.4L)	(1.4L)	(1.4L)
Weight–					
Above 32°F (0°C)			SAE 30		
0°F (–18°C) to 32°F (0°C)			SAE 10W-30		
Below 0°F (–18°C)			SAE 5W-20		
Transmission Oil Capacity	5 pints	5 pints	3 pints	16 pints	....
	(2.4L)	(2.4L)	(1.4L)	(7.6L)	
Weight	SAE 90 EP	SAE 90 EP	SAE 90 EP	**	Type "A"

MODELS

	1455, 1476, 1477	G14	G14XL	H14	H14XL
Engine Make	Wisconsin	Tecumseh	Tecumseh	Tecumseh	Tecumseh
Model	S-14D	HH140	OH140	HH140	OH140
Bore	3¾ in.	3-5/16 in.	3-5/16 in.	3-5/16 in.	3-5/16 in.
	(95.2 mm)	(84.1 mm)	(84.1 mm)	(84.1 mm)	(84.1 mm)
Stroke	3 in.	2¾ in.	2¾ in.	2¾ in.	2¾ in.
	(76.2 mm)	(69.8 mm)	(69.8 mm)	(69.8 mm)	(69.8 mm)
Piston Displacement	33.1 cu. in.	23.75 cu. in.	23.75 cu. in.	23.75 cu. in.	23.75 cu. in.
	(542 cc)	(389 cc)	(389 cc)	(389 cc)	(389 cc)
Horsepower	14	14	14	14	14
Slow Idle Speed-Rpm	1000	1200	1200	1200	1200
High Idle Speed (No Load)–Rpm	3680	3600	3600	3600	3600
Full Load Speed–Rpm	3400	3200	3200	3200	3200
Crankcase Oil Capacity	4 pints	3 pints	3 pints	3 pints	3 pints
	(1.9L)	(1.4L)	(1.4L)	(1.4L)	(1.4L)
Weight–					
Above 32°F (0°C)			SAE 30		
0°F (–18°C) to 32°F (0°C)			SAE 10W-30		
Below 0°F (–18°C)			SAE 5W-20		
Transmission Oil Capacity	20 pints	5 pints	3 pints	20 pints	16 pints
	(9.5L)	(2.4L)	(1.4L)	(9.5L)	(7.6L)
Weight	Type "A"	SAE 90 EP	SAE 90 EP	Type "A"	**

	MODELS				
	1556	G16XL	H16	H16XL	QS16
Engine Make	Tecumseh	Tecumseh	Tecumseh	Tecumseh	Kohler
Model	HH150	OH160	HH160	OH160	K341
Bore	3½ in. (88.9 mm)	3½ in. (88.9 mm)	3½ in. (88.9 mm)	3½ in. (88.9 mm)	3¾ in. (95.2 mm)
Stroke	2⅞ in. (73.0 mm)	2⅞ in. (73.0 mm)	2⅞ in. (73.0 mm)	2⅞ in. (73.0 mm)	3¼ in. (82.5 mm)
Piston Displacement	27.66 cu. in. (453 cc)	27.66 cu. in. (453 cc)	27.66 cu. in. (453 cc)	27.66 cu. in. (453 cc)	35.89 cu. in. (588 cc)
Horsepower	15	16	16	16	16
Slow Idle Speed – Rpm	1200	1200	1200	1200	2350
High Idle Speed (No Load) – Rpm	3600	3600	3600	3600	3600
Full Load Speed – Rpm	3200	3200	3200	3200	3400
Crankcase Oil Capacity	3 pints (1.4L)	3 pints (1.4L)	3 pints (1.4L)	3 pints (1.4L)	4 pints (1.9L)
Weight –					
Above 32°F (0°C)	SAE 30				
0°F (–18°C) to 32°F (0°C)	SAE 10W-30				
Below 0°F (–18°C)	SAE 5W-20				
Transmission Oil Capacity	20 pints (9.5L)	3 pints (1.4L)	20 pints (9.5L)	16 pints (7.6L)	20 pints (9.5L)
Weight	Type "A"	SAE 90 EP	Type "A"	**	Type "F"

*Early Model G10 with S.N.0100101-029999 uses a Tecumseh HH100 engine.
Late Model G10 beginning with S.N.0300101 uses a B&S 251417 engine.

**Refer to HYDROSTATIC DRIVE UNIT paragraphs for recommended transmission oil.

FRONT AXLE AND STEERING SYSTEM

AXLE MAIN MEMBER

Models G8-LT8-LT11

The axle main member (16 – Fig. B1) is mounted directly to front main frame and pivots on bolt (18). To remove front axle assembly, disconnect drag link (15) from steering arm. Using a suitable jack or hoist, raise front of tractor. Remove pivot bolt and roll front axle assembly from tractor.

Models 730-733-736

To remove front axle main member, place pto control lever in disengaged position and remove pto drive belt from groove of pto driven pulley shown in Fig. B3. Disconnect drag link from steering arm (14 – Fig. B2). Support front of tractor. Remove pto pulley retaining cap screw (S – Fig. B3) and axle pivot bolt and nut (N). Let pto pulley drop down on its spindle far enough for axle to be lowered and removed from tractor. Renew pivot bushing and bolt if excessive wear is indicated.

Models G9-G10-G11-G12-G14-H14-H16-1053-1054-1225-1253-1254-1256-1257-1556

The axle main member (11 – Fig. B4) is mounted in axle support (7) and pivots on pin (6). To remove front axle assembly, first unbolt and remove pto support from front axle support (7). Disconnect drag link ball joint end (12) from steering spindle arm (10). Support front of tractor using a jack or hoist, and after removing roll pin, drive pivot pin (6) forward out of axle support. Raise front of tractor and roll front axle assembly from under tractor.

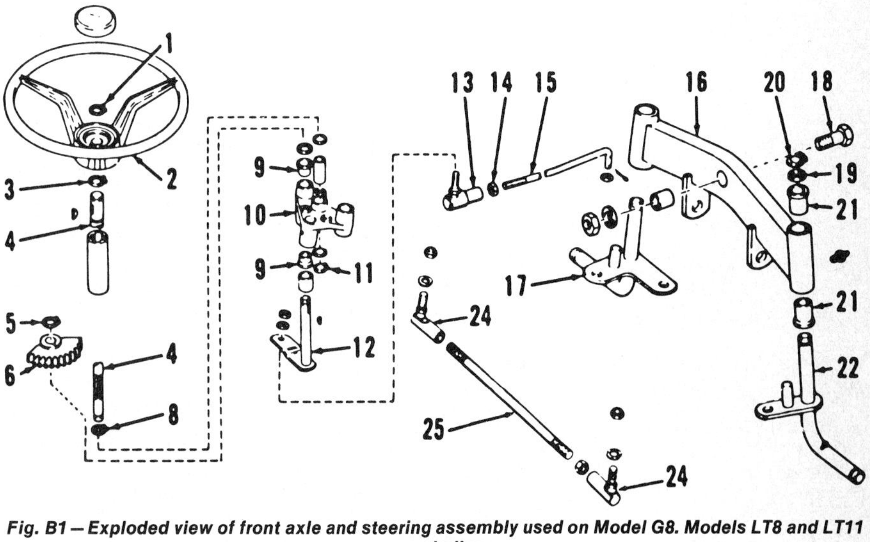

Fig. B1 – Exploded view of front axle and steering assembly used on Model G8. Models LT8 and LT11 are similar.

1. Snap ring
2. Steering wheel
3. Snap ring
4. Shaft
5. Snap ring
6. Quadrant gear
8. Snap ring
9. Bushing
10. Steering support
11. Snap ring
12. Steering arm
13. Ball joint
14. Jam nut
15. Drag link
16. Axle main member
17. Steering spindle L.H.
18. Pivot bolt
19. Washer
20. Snap ring
21. Bushing
22. Steering spindle R.H.
24. Ball joint ends
25. Tie rod

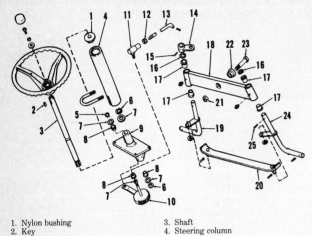

Fig. B2—Exploded view of front axle and steering gear assemblies used on Models 730, 733 and 736.

5. Snap ring
6. Snap ring
7. Washer
8. Bushing
9. Steering support
10. Quadrant gear
11. Ball joint
12. Jam nut
13. Drag link
14. Steering arm
15. Pin
16. Washer
17. Bushing
18. Axle main member
19. Steering spindle L.H.
20. Tie rod
21. Nut
22. Bushing
23. Pivot bolt
24. Steering spindle R.H.
25. Pin

1. Nylon bushing
2. Key
3. Shaft
4. Steering column

connect ball joint (12–Fig. B6) at forward end of drag link from right hand steering arm (16). Raise and support front of tractor under frame rails so pivot pin (17) can be removed, then raise front of tractor so axle assembly will clear and can be rolled forward from under frame. If heavy wear is evident, renew pivot pin (17) and its bushings (19).

Model QS16

Axle main member (13–Fig. B7) pivots on pin (6) supported by axle bolster (5). To remove, disconnect forward end of drag link (15) from left steering arm (14). When tractor has been raised and blocked up safely, remove roll pin from pivot pin (6), push out to rear and axle can be lowered and rolled forward from under tractor. Axle pivot parts are unbushed. Severe wear will call for renewal.

TIE ROD

Models 730-733-736

Removal of tie rod is self-evident after inspection of unit. Toe-in is not adjustable on these models. Tie rod ends should be inspected for wear and repaired as necessary to retain original wheel alignment.

All Other Models

The adjustable tie rod can be removed after first removing nuts securing ball joint ends to steering arms. To adjust front wheel toe-in, loosen locknuts and turn ball joint ends in or out as required to obtain ⅛ to ⅜-inch (3-9 mm) toe-in.

Fig. B3—On Models 730, 733 and 736, unscrew cap screw (S) and allow pto pulley to drop down enough so axle can be removed after removing pivot bolt nut (N).

Models G11XL-G12XL-G14XL-G16XL-H11XL-H12XL-H14XL-H16XL

The front axle assembly (25–Fig. B5) is mounted in axle support (16) and pivots on bolt (21). To remove axle assembly, unbolt and remove pto idler pulley assembly from front axle support (16). Disconnect drag link (27) from steering arm (26). Support front of tractor with jack or hoist. Remove pivot bolt and axle support mounting bolt. Remove axle support and roll axle assembly away from tractor.

Models 1455-1476-1477

To remove front axle assembly, first release and remove pto drive belts. Dis-

STEERING SPINDLES

Models G8-LT8-LT11

To remove steering spindles, support tractor under axle main member and remove front wheels. Disconnect drag link from left steering spindle. Remove tie rod. Remove snap rings (20–Fig. B1) retaining steering spindles and remove steering spindles.

Models 730-733-736

To remove steering spindles, first support tractor under axle main member and remove front wheels. Disconnect drag link at steering arm (14–Fig. B2), remove tie rod (20), drive out roll pin (15) and remove steering arm (14). Left hand steering spindle may now be removed. Drive out roll pin (25) and remove right hand steering spindle (24).

Models G9-G10-G11-G12-G14-H14-H16-1053-1054-1225-1254-1256-1257-1556

To remove steering spindles (10 and 14–Fig. B4), block up under axle main member and remove front wheels. Disconnect drag link ball joint end from

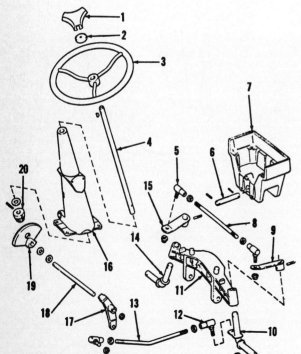

Fig. B4—Exploded view of typical front axle and steering system used on Models G9, G10, G11, G12, G14, H14, H16, 1053, 1054, 1225, 1253, 1254, 1256, 1257 and 1556.

1. Cover
2. Washer
3. Steering wheel
4. Steering shaft
5. Tie rod end
6. Pivot pin
7. Axle support
8. Tie rod
9. Steering arm R.H.
10. Steering spindle R.H.
11. Axle main member
12. Drag link end
13. Drag link
14. Steering arm L.H.
15. Steering arm L.H.
16. Steering support
17. Quadrant arm
18. Cross shaft
19. Quadrant gear
20. Pinion gear

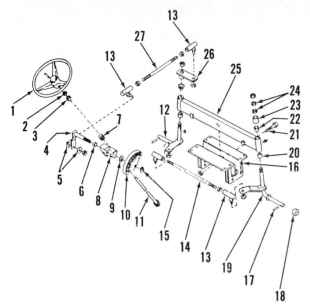

Fig. B5—Exploded view of
front axle and steering sys-
tem used on Models G11XL,
G12XL, G14XL, G16XL,
H11XL, H12XL, H14XL and
H16XL.

1. Steering wheel
2. Washer
3. Bearing
4. Steering arm
5. Spacers
6. Spacer
7. Flange bushing
8. Support bracket
9. Shim
10. Sector gear
11. Steering shaft assy.
12. Spindle L.H.
13. Ball joint ends
14. Tie rod
15. Snap ring
16. Axle support
17. Roll pin
18. Wheel bearing
19. Spindle R.H.
20. Bronze bearing
21. Pivot bolt
22. Flange bushing
23. Hub
24. Flat washers
25. Axle main member
26. Steering arm
27. Drag link

steering spindle arm. Drive out roll pins securing tie rod steering arms (9 and 15) to steering spindles. Bump spindles downward out of steering arms and axle main member.

Models G11XL-G12XL-G14XL-G16XL-H11XL-H12XL-H14XL-H16XL

To remove steering spindles, support front axle assembly and remove front wheels. Disconnect drag link (27—Fig. B5) and remove tie rod (14). Remove locknut and spindle arm (26). Left hand spindle can now be removed. Remove locknut, flat washers, steering hub (23), and withdraw right hand spindle. Check flange bearings (22) and bronze bearings (20) for excessive wear and renew as necessary.

Models 1455-1476-1477

To remove either steering spindle from these models, block up under front axle and remove wheel with bearings and seals from spindle. Disconnect tie rod (11—Fig. B6) and drag link (13). Remove clamp bolt from steering arm (14 or 16) and pull steering arm from spindle (24). Remove key and lower steering spindle out of axle end. Clean and inspect bearing parts (20 through 23) making necessary renewal as called for by wear or damage. Lubricate spindle bearings and wheel bearings with multi-purpose grease (Bolens 16020) during reassembly and recheck toe-in before returning to service.

Model QS16

To remove steering spindles, raise and block under front axle for wheel removal. With this design, removal of drag link and tie rod from steering arms is optional. Steering spindle (9—Fig. B7)

can be separated from steering arm (7) after backing out cap screw at top. Remove Woodruff key after lifting off steering arm and lower steering spindle from axle. Inspect, clean and lubricate all bearing parts. Renew parts as necessary.

STEERING GEAR

Models G8-LT8-LT11

To remove steering gear, disconnect drag link from steering arm (12—Fig. B1). Remove quadrant gear snap ring (5) and remove quadrant gear (6) and steering arm (12). Remove snap ring (1) or roll pin and lift off steering wheel. Remove snap rings (8 and 11) and withdraw steering shaft (4). Check steering support bushings (9) for wear and renew if necessary.

During reassembly, position steering wheel and front wheels in straight ahead position and install quadrant gear so it is centered on steering shaft pinion. Adjust left and right turn angles by adjusting ball joint end (13) on drag link.

Models 730-733-736

To remove steering gear, first disconnect drag link from arm of quadrant gear (10—Fig. B2). Remove left engine side panel. Remove quadrant gear retaining snap ring (5) and withdraw quadrant gear (10) from underside of tractor. Unscrew cap screw retaining steering wheel and remove steering wheel. Remove two snap rings (6) holding steering shaft in support (9) and remove steering shaft (3). It may be necessary to remove or deflect drive belt for access to lower snap ring.

Check bushings for wear and renew if necessary. During reassembly, position steering wheel and front wheels in straight ahead position. Install quadrant gear (10) so it is centered on pinion of steering shaft. Drag link can be adjusted to provide equal left and right turn angles by adjusting drag link end (11).

Models G9-G10-G11-G12-G14-H14-H16-1053-1054-1225-1254-1256-1257-1556

The steering gear used is a pinion and quadrant gear type. To remove steering gear, first disconnect rear drag link ball joint end from quadrant arm (17—Fig. B4). Remove foot rest from left side of tractor and remove pins from cross shaft (18). Using a long thin punch, drive cross shaft towards left side of tractor and remove steering arm and quadrant gear (19). Drive roll pin from pinion gear (20) and withdraw steering shaft (4) from steering support (16).

When reassembling, minor wear in

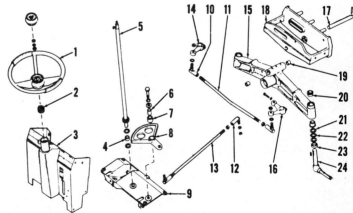

Fig. B6—Exploded view of front axle and steering system used on Models 1455, 1476 and 1477.

1. Steering wheel
2. Bearing
3. Steering column
4. Bushing
5. Steering shaft
6. Spacer
7. Bushing
8. Quadrant gear
9. Steering support
10. Tie rod end
11. Tie rod
12. Drag link end
13. Drag link
14. Steering arm L.H.
15. Axle main member
16. Steering arm R.H.
17. Pivot pin
18. Axle support
19. Pivot bushing
20. Flange bearing
21. Thrust race
22. Thrust bearing
23. Dust seal
24. Steering spindle

teeth of tapered pinion and gear sector can be compensated for by use of more or thicker spacer washers. Do not mesh too tight; just eliminate looseness.

When reinstalling steering gear, place front wheels in straight ahead position and then center quadrant gear on pinion. The drag link (13) can be lengthened or shortened as required so front wheels will have equal angle for left and right turns.

Models G11XL-G12XL-G14XL-G16XL-H11XL-H12XL-H14XL-H16XL

To remove steering gear, disconnect drag link from steering arm (4–Fig. B5). Remove snap ring (15) from steering arm (4). Keep track of all shims and their locations during disassembly. Remove steering arm shaft, shims and quadrant gear. Remove roll pin from steering wheel and withdraw steering shaft from bottom side of tractor. It may be necessary to tap steering shaft down until flange bushing is pushed out of steering support (8).

Check bushings and gears for wear and renew as necessary. Reassemble steering gear by reversing disassembly procedure. If pinion and quadrant gears do not engage fully, adjust shims between quadrant gear and steering support. Adjust drag link as required to have equal turning angle on right or left turns.

Models 1455-1476-1477

To remove steering gear, disconnect rear ball joint of drag link (13–Fig. B6) from lever portion of quadrant gear (8). Remove logo plate from center of steering wheel followed by retaining nut and washers so steering wheel can be pulled off steering shaft (5). Take care not to lose Woodruff key from tapered portion of shaft. Remove cotter key from lower end of steering shaft (5) below support plate (9) so shaft can be lifted up to

disengage its pinion from quadrant (8) and clear of support plate. Tip shaft and column so shaft can be lowered out of tube down past rear edge of support plate (9) and out from under tractor. Take care not to damage self-aligning bearing (2) and protect bronze bushing (4) from dirt. Back out pivot bolt and remove quadrant gear (8).

Thoroughly clean and inspect gears and bushings for wear and damage. All parts are serviced for individual renewal as needed.

When reinstalling, set steering wheel and tractor front wheels in straight ahead position and reinstall quadrant gear (8) properly centered on steering pinion of shaft (5). Engine oil is specified as correct lubricant for steering shaft, bushings and drag link ends.

Steering radius stops which limit right and left movement of quadrant gear are fitted in right side frame rail. Be sure adjusters (square-head set screws) are set to limit turning radius to prevent wheel interference with under-tractor attachments and locknuts are secure.

When drag link is being reconnected to lever arm portion of quadrant gear, its overall length should be measured. On Models 1455, 1476 and 1477, this length should be 24-9/16 inches (623.9 mm). Adjust as needed.

Model QS16

To remove steering gear assembly, first remove logo cap from hub of steering wheel, back off retainer nut and remove wheel. Remove Woodruff key from tapered portion of upper shaft assembly (4–Fig. B7). Disconnect ball joint (23) from pitman arm (22) to separate drag link. Remove nut from inboard end of sector shaft (16) and bump shaft out of steering sector (17). Then, while holding sector in one hand, grasp pitman arm (22) and pull shaft clear of steering support casting (20) with pitman arm attached. If shaft (16) is to be

renewed, remove pitman arm (22).

To remove upper and lower steering shafts (4 and 18), remove retaining rings (1) from each shaft so shafts can be separated at swivel coupling at lower end of upper shaft. Take care not to lose Woodruff key. Remove lower shaft (18) with pinion from under tractor.

Clean and inspect shaft bearings (3 and 19). Renew as necessary. If bushings (21) require renewal, unbolt and remove steering support (20) for set up in a shop press to drive old bushings out and press new ones into bushing bores.

Lubricate during reassembly. Set front wheels straight ahead and center quadrant gear on pinion. Then, adjust length of drag link by its threaded ends to equalize turning radius each way from centered position of steering wheel.

ENGINE

REMOVE AND REINSTALL

Models G8-LT8-LT11

To remove engine, detach drive belts from engine pulley and remove pulley from engine crankshaft. Tilt engine hood forward and disconnect battery cables, starter and alternator or starter-generator wires, ignition wires, choke and throttle cables. Close fuel valve under fuel tank and disconnect fuel line. Unscrew engine mount bolts and lift engine from tractor.

Models 730-733-736

Before removing engine, remove drive belts from engine drive pulley, then remove engine drive pulley. Unscrew retaining screws and remove hood. Disconnect battery cables and remove battery. Disconnect starter-generator wires, ignition wires, choke and throttle cables. Close fuel valve under fuel tank and disconnect fuel line. Unscrew engine mount bolts; move engine towards rear so engine clears fuel tank, then lift engine from tractor.

Models G9-G10-G11-G12-G14-H14-H16-1053-1054-1225-1254-1256-1257-1556

To remove engine, raise hood and disconnect hood stop rod. Remove cap screws securing hood and grille hinge to tractor frame and lift off hood and grille assembly. Disconnect battery cables, wires from starter-generator, ignition wire and choke and throttle control cables. Release belt tension and remove drive belt or belts. Remove pto belt guide and with pto lever in neutral position, remove pto belt or belts. Unbolt engine, slide it forward and lift it from tractor frame.

To reinstall engine, reverse removal procedure.

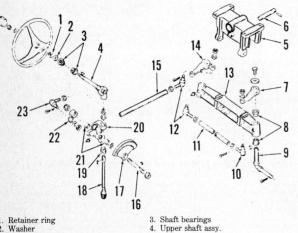

Fig. B7–Exploded view of front axle and steering system used on Model QS16.

5. Axle bolster
6. Pivot pin
7. Steering arm R.H.
8. Bearing set
9. Spindle R.H.
10. Tie rod end R.H.
11. Tie rod
12. Ball joints (L.H. thread)
13. Tie rod end L.H.
14. Steering arm L.H.
15. Drag link
16. Sector shaft
17. Steering sector
18. Lower shaft & pinion
19. Flange bushing
20. Support casting
21. Bushings
22. Pitman arm
23. Ball joint (R.H. thread)

1. Retainer ring
2. Washer
3. Shaft bearings
4. Upper shaft assy.

Models G11XL-G12XL-G14XL-G16XL-H11XL-H12XL-H14XL-H16XL

To remove engine, remove hood and side panels. Disconnect battery cables, starter, alternator and ignition wires. Disconnect choke and throttle cables. Close fuel tank shut-off valve and disconnect fuel line at filter. Remove drive shaft bolts at engine. Disconnect pto clutch wire. Scribe a line on front engine supports along frame for ease in reinstalling engine. Remove engine mount bolts and lift engine out.

Reinstall engine by reversing removal procedure. Align scribed lines (made during removal) on engine front supports with frame, then install front mounting bolts. Insert proper engine mount spacers to obtain specified clearance between frame and bottom surface of engine support. On Models G11XL and H11XL, clearance should be 3/16 to ¼-inch (5-6 mm), and on all other models 7/16 to ½-inch (11-13 mm).

NOTE: Front and rear rubber engine mounts are not interchangeable. The rear mounts are softer than front mounts; press down on center of mounts to identify for correct installation.

When reinstalling drive shaft, make sure drive hub on hydrostatic models is 5/16-inch (8 mm) from face of transmission. On gear drive models, hub on right angle gear box should be bottomed against end of shaft splines.

Models 1455-1476-1477

To remove engine, proceed in this sequence: Disconnect battery cables. Remove bolt and set screw at forward end of drive shaft. Disconnect headlight wiring then unlatch and unbolt hood at hinge and stop arm for removal. Close shut off valve under fuel tank and disconnect fuel line. Remove support bolts from gas tank-battery platform and lift out as an assembly. Identify and remove carburetor control cables and interfering wiring from engine, then unbolt engine mounts. Release and remove pto belts from engine pulley. For security, attach hoist, to engine then slip engine forward to disengage from drive shaft and lift engine out of frame. Reverse these steps to reinstall.

Model QS16

To remove engine, open hood, loosen three screws at bottom of each side panel and release two quarter-turn fasteners at top of each panel for removal. Disconnect headlight wiring connector plugs and hood lanyard from muffler support and hood can be lifted off and set aside.

Disconnect battery cables and remove battery clamp so battery can be removed. Shut off fuel valve at tank and

remove line at carburetor or at fuel filter. Disconnect control cables at carburetor. Release and remove pto drive belts. Remove cable from starter motor, uncouple leads to regulator/rectifier and disconnect orange primary lead at ignition coil. Separate rear of engine crankshaft from driveshaft by removing through-bolt and Woodruff key (when used). When bolts are removed from engine mounts, engine can be raised, shifted forward and lifted clear of engine compartment.

Reinstall engine by reversal of this order, taking care that battery connection is not made until just before replacing engine hood and grille assembly.

OVERHAUL

All Models

Engine make and model are listed at the beginning of this section. To overhaul engine components and accessories, refer to appropriate engine sections of this manual.

DRIVE BELTS

REMOVE AND REINSTALL

Models G8-LT8-LT11

To remove drive belt (15 – Fig. B8), move clutch idler pulley away from belt and remove belt from engine pulley. Slide belt off transmission pulley (16). Place transmission end of drive belt through gear shift lever slot in floor of tractor. Move belt over end of gear shift lever and pull belt back through floor and remove from tractor.

Models G9-G10-G11-G12

To remove drive belt, depress clutch-brake pedal and slip belt from engine and drive shaft pulleys. When renewing

drive belt, make certain idler pulley (5 – Fig. B9) is in outside hole of idler control arm (4).

Models G11XL-G12XL-G14XL-G16XL

To remove drive belt (B – Fig. B10), loosen belt guides. Depress clutch pedal, remove idler pulley and slip belt from transaxle and gear box pulleys. After installing new belt, adjust belt guides to clearances as follows: Idler pulley belt guide (G) ⅛-inch (3 mm), transaxle pulley (H) 3/32-inch (2 mm) and gear box pulley (F) 1/16-inch (1.5 mm) clearance.

Models 730-733-736

To remove drive belts, unbolt idler support (29 – Fig. B11), move idler pulleys away from drive belts and slide drive belts off pulleys. When installing new drive belt, be sure idler pulley is working against drive belt.

Models 853-1053-1054-1253-1254-G14

To remove drive belts, refer to Fig. B12 or B13 and remove belt guide on models so equipped. On Model 853, place speed range lever between high and low range. This will position belt tightener between high and low range belts and remove belt tension. On all other models, tie idler pulley away from belts with wire. Unscrew nut from front end of drive shaft and remove washers. Remove four cap screws holding drive shaft support to mounting plate and remove support by sliding forward. Drive belts may now be removed. Install drive belts by reversing removal procedure.

Models 1225-1256-1257-1556-H14-H16

To remove drive belts, pull idler pulley away from drive belts. Loosen belt guide retaining bolts and move belt guides

Fig. B8 – Exploded view of clutch-brake assembly used on Models G8, LT8 and LT11.

1. Clutch-brake pedal
2. Brake lock assy.
3. Brake lock arm
4. Nylon bushing
5. Brake arm
6. Key
7. Crankshaft pulley
8. Clutch rod
9. Brake rod
10. Pivot blocks
11. Idler arm assy.
12. Spring
13. Idler pulley
14. Belt guard
15. Drive belt
16. Transaxle pulley
17. Wing nut
18. Spacer
19. Brake pads
20. Brake disc
21. Brake pad holder
22. Lever
23. Spacer
24. Plate

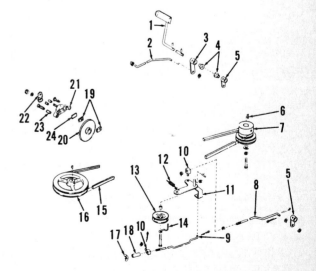

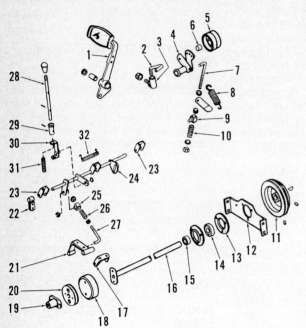

1. Clutch-brake pedal
2. Clutch rod
3. Ball joint end
4. Idler arm
5. Clutch idler pulley
6. Spacer
7. Brake rod
8. Clutch spring
9. Pivot block
10. Spring
11. Drive shaft pulley
12. Bearing support
13. Bearing retainer
14. Bearing
15. Collar
16. Drive shaft
17. Bracket
18. Brake drum
19. Coupling flange
20. Coupling
21. Brake shoe (drive shaft)
22. Brake shoe (transmission)
23. Brackets
24. Brake shaft
25. Pivot block
26. Spring
27. Brake rod
28. Park brake lever
29. Brake lock
30. Pivot
31. Spring
32. Torsion spring

proximately ½-inch (13 mm) free travel.

The clutch brake plate (3–Fig. B14), used on all models except Model 853, mechanically stops rotation of drive shaft when clutch is disengaged to prevent gear clash when shifting gears. With clutch in fully engaged position, there should be 3/32-inch (2.4 mm) clearance "C" between rear clutch flange (2) and brake plate friction surface. To adjust, move brackets (27–Fig. B13) forward or back in slotted holes provided in brackets. Lubricate splined area of drive shaft to insure free movement of rear clutch flange.

On Model 853, brake drum (45–Fig. B12) and brake shoe (43) are used to stop drive shaft when clutch is disengaged. Refer to BRAKES section for adjustment procedure.

NOTE: After clutch adjustment is completed, be sure switch actuator (14–Fig. B13) engages interlock switch (11) correctly. Switch should begin to actuate with pedal at halfway point. Adjust by repositioning bracket (12) in its mounting slots.

All Other Models (So Equipped)

On models having a spring loaded clutch idler pulley, adjustment is not necessary. Renew drive belt or idler spring when idler pulley does not take up drive belt slack and slippage occurs.

away from drive belts. Slip drive belts off driven pulley then off drive pulley and remove through bottom of tractor.

CLUTCH

ADJUSTMENT

Models G9-G10-G11-G12

The clutch on these models is belt idler type. The only adjustment consists of changing belt tension. To increase belt tension, move idler pulley (5–Fig. B9) from outside hole to center hole in idler control arm (4).

Models 853-1053-1054-1253-1254-G14

A double-plate, disc type clutch is used on these models. Refer to Fig. B12 or B13. A pedal on left side of tractor operates clutch and also activates service brake.

Clutch should be disengaged when clutch pedal is approximately 2/3 depressed. If not, adjust nuts (A and B– Fig. B14) on clutch rod (5) until clutch disengages properly and pedal has ap-

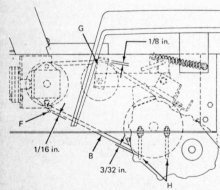

Fig. B10—Models G11XL, G12XL, G14XL and G16XL use a spring loaded idler pulley for main drive clutch. Adjust belt guides to clearances shown.

B. Drive belt
F. Gear box belt guide
G. Idler pulley belt guide
H. Transaxle belt guides

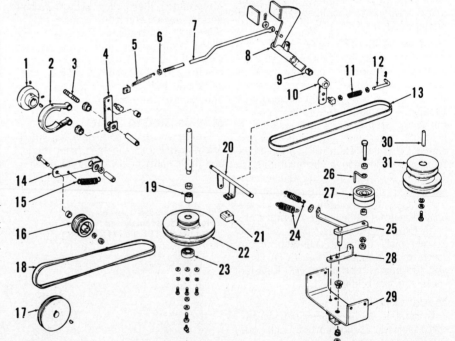

Fig. B11—Exploded view of clutch-brake system used on Models 730 and 733. Model 736 uses same clutch system. Refer to text for 736 brake system.

1. Brake drum
2. Brake band
3. Stud
4. Brake arm
5. Spring
6. Adjusting nut
7. Brake rod
8. Clutch-brake pedal
9. Bushing
10. Lever
11. Spring
12. Brake rod
13. Drive belt
14. Lever
15. Spring
16. Idler pulley
17. Transmission pulley
18. Drive belt
19. Bearing
20. Shaft
21. Pulley brake pad
22. Pulley
23. Bearings
24. Springs
25. Clutch arm
26. Belt guide
27. Clutch pulley
28. Spring mount
29. Mount plate
30. Key
31. Engine pulley

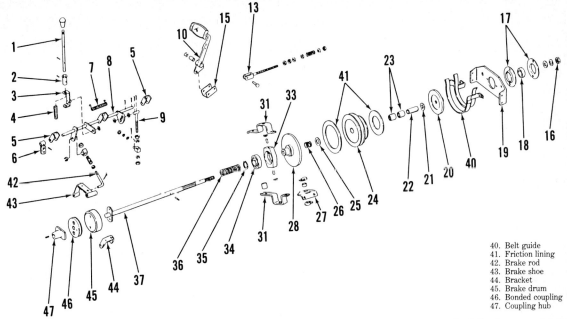

Fig. B12—Exploded view of clutch-brake system used on Model 853. Refer to Fig. B13 for legend except for following components.

40. Belt guide
41. Friction lining
42. Brake rod
43. Brake shoe
44. Bracket
45. Brake drum
46. Bonded coupling
47. Coupling hub

R&R AND OVERHAUL

Models 853-1053-1054-1253-1254-G14

To remove clutch assembly, first release drive belt tension. On models equipped with 2-speed drive belt arrangement, belt tension is released by placing speed range lever between high and low range. This will position belt tightener between high range and low range belts. On all other models, unhook drive belt tension spring or tie idler pulley away from drive belt with wire. Refer to Fig. B12 or B13 and disconnect clutch rod (13) from release bearing yoke (31). Disconnect coupling at rear of drive shaft. Unbolt brackets (27) and front bearing support (19) from frame and remove clutch and drive shaft assembly from tractor.

To disassemble clutch unit, clamp drive shaft in a vise and remove nut, washers, bearing and front support from drive shaft. Remove front clutch plate (20) which is threaded on end of drive shaft.

CAUTION: Remove this plate carefully as all parts following it are under tension from clutch pressure spring (36).

The remaining parts can now be removed from drive shaft.

All parts are individually renewable. To renew drive pulley clutch facings, first remove old friction lining and clean each side of pulley (24). Cement new friction linings to pulley and place front and rear clutch flanges (20 and 28) on top of friction linings. Firmly clamp together pulley and flange assembly and place in oven, preheated to 400°F

(200°C), for a minimum of 15 minutes.

Reassembly procedure is reverse of disassembly. Reinstall assembly on tractor and, on Model 853, adjust drive belt tension by moving bearing support (19) up or down on mounting bracket until desired tension is obtained. Drive belt

tension is correct when belt tightener pulley moves 2 inches (50 mm) from disengaged position to full engaged position. Other models require no drive belt adjustment since a spring loaded belt tightener is used. Adjust clutch as previously outlined.

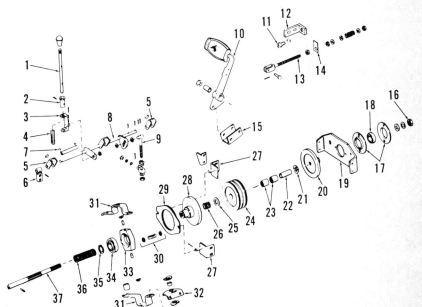

Fig. B13—Exploded view of typical clutch-brake system of Models 1053, 1054, 1253, 1254 and G14. Transmission brake drum, mounted on front of transaxle wormshaft, is not shown. It is engaged by brake shoe (6). See text.

1. Parking brake lever	11. Interlock switch
2. Brake lock	12. Switch bracket
3. Lever pivot	13. Clutch rod
4. Spring	14. Switch actuator
5. Bracket (2)	15. Link
6. Brake shoe	16. Locking nut
7. Torsion spring	17. Bearing flanges
8. Brake shaft	18. Bearing
9. Brake rod	19. Bearing support
10. Clutch-brake pedal	

20. Clutch flange-front	29. Brake plate
21. Bowed washer	30. Spring/washer set (2)
22. Spacer	31. Bearing yoke halves
23. Needle bearings (2)	32. Bracket
24. Sheave & facing	33. Bearing retainer
25. Thrust race	34. Release bearing
26. Spring	35. Retainer
27. Bracket assy. (2)	36. Spring
28. Clutch flange (rear)	37. Drive shaft

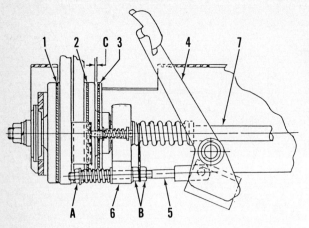

Fig. B14—View of double plate, disc type clutch used on Models 1053, 1054, 1253, 1254 and G14. Model 853 is similar except brake plate (3) is not used. Refer to text for adjustment procedure.

A. Adjusting nut
B. Adjusting nuts
C. 3/32-inch (2.4 mm) clearance
1. Front clutch flange
2. Rear clutch flange
3. Brake plate
4. Clutch-brake pedal
5. Clutch rod
6. Yoke
7. Drive shaft

BRAKES

ADJUSTMENT

Models G8-LT8-LT11

A disc type brake is used on these models. To adjust brake, turn wing nut (17–Fig. B8) at end of brake control rod. Adjust brake so it is not effective before clutch is disengaged. If brake cannot be adjusted to give full braking action, renew brake pads.

Models G9-G10-G11-G12

To adjust brakes, refer to Fig. B9 and depress clutch-brake pedal (1) until clutch is disengaged. Then, adjust nuts, moving pivot block (9) on brake rod (7), until brake shoe (22) is tight against brake drum on transaxle wormshaft. The brake on drive shaft can now be adjusted by moving pivot block (25) on brake rod (27) so brake shoe (21) will contact drive shaft brake drum (18) immediately after clutch is disengaged.

Models 730-733

A band type brake is used on these models. To adjust brake, turn adjusting nut (6–Fig. B11) on brake rod (7) so brake band is tight on drum when clutch-brake pedal is fully depressed. Brake band should not drag on drum until clutch is disengaged by clutch-brake pedal.

Model 736

Model 736 is equipped with a disc brake as shown in Fig. B15. To adjust

brake, turn adjusting nut (5) so brake pads will be tight against disc when brake pedal is depressed. Be sure brake pads do not drag against disc when brake pedal is not applied.

Model 853

To adjust main brake, located on transaxle wormshaft, refer to Fig. B12 and depress clutch-brake pedal until clutch is disengaged. Adjust nuts, moving pivot block on brake rod (9), until brake shoe (6) is tight against brake drum on transaxle wormshaft. The brake on drive shaft (37) can now be adjusted by moving pivot block on brake rod (42) until brake shoe (43) contacts brake drum (45) immediately after clutch is completely disengaged.

Models 1053-1054-1253-1254-G14

To adjust drive shaft brake, loosen nuts and move brackets (27–Fig. B13) to obtain 3/32-inch (2 mm) gap between lining on brake plate (29) and rear clutch plate (28) with clutch engaged. Retighten nuts on brackets. Then adjust nuts, moving pivot block on brake rod (9), until brake shoe (6) contacts brake drum on transaxle immediately after clutch is completely disengaged. Brake must be fully applied when pedal (10) is depressed to within one inch of pedal stop.

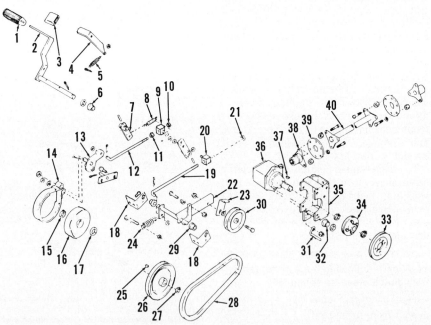

Fig. B16—Exploded view of clutch and brake system used on Models G11XL, G12XL, G14XL and G16XL.

1. Pedal pad	11. Adjusting nut	21. Locknut	31. Belt guide
2. L.H. pedal assy.	12. Brake rod	22. Idler shaft assy.	32. Bushing
3. Grip	13. Brake arm assy.	23. Belt guide	33. Pulley
4. Brake lock	14. Brake band	24. Spring	34. Hub assy.
5. Spring	15. Snap ring	25. Key	35. Gear box support
6. Bushing	16. Brake drum	26. Transaxle pulley	36. Gear box assy.
7. Control arm	17. Thrust washer	27. Snap ring	37. Key
8. Spring	18. Idler arm support	28. Drive belt	38. Hub
9. Pivot block	19. Clutch rod	29. Bushing	39. Coupling disc
10. Locknut	20. Pivot block	30. Idler pulley	40. Drive shaft

Fig. B15—Exploded view of Model 736 brake system. Refer to Fig. B11 for clutch mechanism.

1. Clutch-brake pedal	10. Carrier
2. Brake rod	11. Brake arm
3. Pivot block	12. Cam arm
4. Spring	13. Washer
5. Adjusting nut	14. Caliper
6. Spring	15. Brake pads
7. Snap ring	16. Rivet
8. Washer	17. Spacer
9. Spring	18. Brake disc

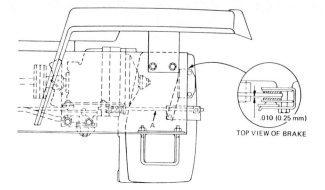

Fig. B17 — To adjust brake on Models H11XL, H12XL, H14XL and H16XL, turn brake rod (A) until there is 0.010 inch (0.254 mm) between brake disc and pad.

.010 (0.25 mm)

TOP VIEW OF BRAKE

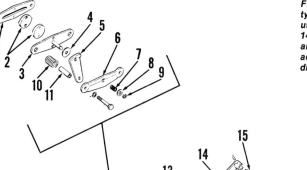

Fig. B18 — Exploded view of typical disc brake assembly used on Models 1256, 1257, 1455, 1476, 1477, 1556, H14 and H16. On some models, actuating linkage may be different from that shown.

1. Carrier (inner)
2. Brake pads
3. Carrier (outer)
4. Washer
5. Cam
6. Cam actuator
7. Spring
8. Washer
9. Snap ring
10. Spring
11. Spacer
12. Pivot block
13. Brake rod
14. Brake arm
15. Brake pedal
16. Pad
17. Spacer
18. Brake disc

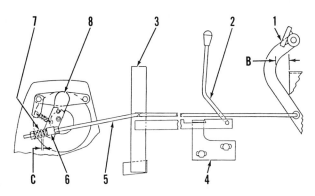

Fig. B19 — View of brake control linkage used on some late Models 1256, 1257, 1556, H14 and H16. Refer to text for adjustment procedure.

B. ½-⅝-inch (13-16 mm)
C. 0.010 inch (0.254 mm) clearance
1. Brake pedal
2. Park brake lever
3. Brake arm
4. Park brake stop
5. Brake rod
6. Pivot block
7. Spring
8. Disc brake assy.

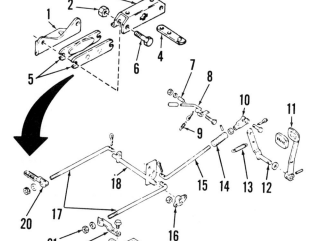

Fig. B20 — Exploded view of brake system used on Model QS16.

1. Brake support
2. Locknut
3. Bracket
4. Lever
5. Pad plates
6. Bolt
7. Spacer
8. Latch
9. Extension spring
10. Clevis
11. Pedal
12. Brake arm
13. Return spring
14. Ratchet
15. Adjusting rod
16. Flange bearing
17. Brake rods (2)
18. Transfer shaft
19. Arm extension R.H.
20. Arm extension L.H.
21. Locknut
22. Brake assy. R.H.

Models G11XL-G12XL-G14XL-G16XL

A band type brake is used on these models. To adjust brake, turn adjusting nuts (10 and 11 — Fig. B16) to reposition pivot block (9) until brake band is tight on drum when pedal is depressed. Brake band should not drag on drum until pedal is depressed.

Models H11XL-H12XL-H14XL-H16XL

A disc type brake is used on these models. To adjust brake, release parking brake and turn brake rod (A — Fig. B17) until there is 0.010 inch (0.254 mm) clearance between brake disc and pad. When brake pedal is fully released, brake disc must turn freely.

Models 1256-1257-1455-1476-1477-1556-H14-H16

These hydrostatic drive models are equipped with a mechanically actuated caliper disc brake with its single disc fixed to input pinion shaft of tractor's reduction gear and differential unit. See Fig. B18. Some minor differences in linkages occur among models, but service is identical. Actual function of disc brake is to serve as a parking brake or when towing or pushing tractor in freewheeling. Dynamic braking of hydrostatic transmission is service brake for these models.

Before adjusting disc brake it is advisable to inspect brake caliper assembly for damaged spacers, springs or cam levers and to renew badly worn pads or carriers. With brake rod disconnected, brake assembly is easily unbolted from axle housing for disassembly and necessary parts renewal. All parts are serviced.

Basic adjustment calls for setting linkage length to limit pedal travel. On early models, adjust operating length of brake control rod (13 — Fig. B18) to obtain a maximum of 1½ inch (38 mm) free pedal travel before brake engagement. On late models, engage parking brake, then adjust parking brake stop (4 — Fig. B19) to provide ½ to ⅝-inch (13-16 mm) clearance (B) between pedal and pedal stop. With pedal in "Park" position, loosen front adjusting nut on brake rod (5) and tighten rear nut to compress spring (7) until there is a 0.010 inch (0.254 mm) gap (C) between middle coils of spring. Turn front adjusting nut up to pivot block (6), then back off ½-turn.

Model QS16

On Model QS16, brake discs are mounted on axle shafts just inboard of wheel hubs. See Fig. B20 for exploded view of parts and typical linkage.

Brake pad clearance is checked and adjusted as shown in Fig. B21. When

Bolens

TRACKTOR

Fig. B21 — When adjusting brake on Model QS16, clearance at "A" must never exceed 0.010 inch (0.254 mm). Adjust at locknut "B" with parking brake released.

measurement between pad face and disc at point "A" exceeds 0.010 inch (0.254 mm) with brake pedal relaxed, adjust brake by turning nut "B" as required. If pads are in serviceable condition, acceptable clearance from disc surface may be from 0 to 0.010 inch (0-0.254 mm), **equal** on both axles. If brake pads are worn to excess, remove brake rod (17 – Fig. B20) from brake arm (19 or 20) and unbolt brake assembly from tractor axle housing for removal. With one pad retainer bolt (6) removed, pads (5) can be removed for renewal.

PTO DRIVE

Models 730-733-736-G8-LT8-LT11

Pto clutch uses a spring loaded idler. No adjustment is required. If belt slips, renew belt or idler spring. Bearings in pto drive pulley are renewable.

Models G11XL-G12XL-G14XL-G16XL-H11XL-H12XL-H14XL-H16XL

ADJUSTMENT. All models are equipped with an electro-magnetic clutch mounted on engine crankshaft. Belt tension is controlled by adjustable idler pulleys. To adjust belt tension, proceed as follows:

On early models, turn adjuster knob (1 – Fig. B22) until indicator wire (A) is between adjustment lines on side of idler support. On late models, turn adjuster

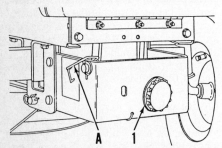

Fig. B22 — To adjust pto belt tension on early "XL" models, turn adjuster knob (1) until indicator wire (A) is between adjustment lines on side of idler support.

knob (1 – Fig. B23) until indicators (B) are even with one another. On all models, both idlers should be in line after adjustment is completed.

The only adjustment necessary on pto clutch is clutch-brake clearance (C – Fig. B24) which should be 0.010 to 0.015 (0.254-0.381 mm) with clutch disengaged. Check clearance at four slots (1) provided in brake flange (4) using a feeler gage. If necessary, adjust brake flange locknuts (5) to obtain specified clearance at each slot.

TESTING. If clutch does not engage, check the following: Check voltage at clutch lead which should be 10 volts minimum. Clutch coil resistance should be between 3.0 and 2.3 ohms. A reading outside these values indicates a faulty coil. Current draw should be 4.17 amps. Individual components of clutch are not serviced separately; renew as complete unit if necessary.

REMOVE AND REINSTALL. Disconnect battery ground cable, then remove hood, side panels and front frame cross plate. Slip belt off pulley. Disconnect electrical connector. Remove locknuts retaining brake flange (4 – Fig. B24) and withdraw flange and springs. Unscrew mounting cap screw from crankshaft and remove pulley and armature assembly (2) and rotor assembly (7). Unbolt and remove coil assembly (6).

Reinstall in reverse order of removal. On models equipped with Briggs and Stratton engines, be sure spacers (8 – Fig. B24) are installed at coil mounting cap screws and on crankshaft as shown. Tighten rotor retaining cap screw to 25 ft.-lbs. (34 N·m) torque. Adjust brake as previously outlined.

Models QS16

ADJUSTMENT. To adjust pto actuating linkage and brake shoe proceed as follows: Loosen control cable bracket retaining screws located on left side of console, then move bracket down in slots to increase tension on belts. To adjust pto brake, loosen cap screws (4 – Fig. B25) and move brake shoe (3) in slots to

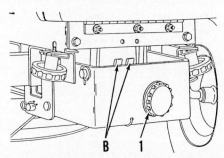

Fig. B23 — On late "XL" models, turn adjuster knob (1) until indicators (B) are parallel to adjust pto belt to correct tension.

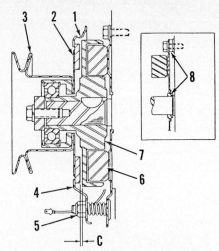

Fig. B24 — An electro-magnetic pto clutch is used on all "XL" models. Spacers (8) are used only on tractors with a Briggs & Stratton engine. Four slots (1) are provided in brake flange (4) to check clutch-brake clearance (C). Refer to text.

C. 0.010-0.015-inch (0.254-0.381 mm) clearance
1. Adjustment slot (4)
2. Armature/brake assy.
3. Drive pulley
4. Brake flange
5. Locknut (4)
6. Coil assy.
7. Rotor assy.
8. Spacers

obtain 0.012 inch (0.305 mm) clearance between brake shoe and rim of drive pulley.

REMOVE AND REINSTALL. To remove pto drive belts, first remove hood. Place pto control lever in "On" position and remove brake shoe pivot pin (2 – Fig. B25). Move control lever to "Off" position and disconnect springs (5 and 6). Slip belts off pulleys and reinstall new belts by reversing removal procedure. Adjust as previously outlined.

Models 1455-1476-1477

ADJUSTMENT. To adjust pto control linkage, disconnect control rod (3 – Fig. B26) from pto lever (1). Adjust position of clevis yoke (4) on control rod until desired belt tension is obtained. With

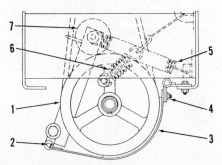

Fig. B25 — View of pto driven pulley and idler used on Model QS16. Adjust brake shoe (3) to provide 0.012 inch (0.305 mm) clearance between shoe and rim of pulley.

1. Pto pulley
2. Pin
3. Belt guide & brake shoe assy.
4. Nut (2)
5. Idler spring
6. Extension spring
7. Idler pulley

54

pto lever in "On" position, adjust upper belt guide (7) to obtain ⅛ to ¼-inch (3-6 mm) clearance between belts and guide. Adjust lower belt guide (14) to 3/32 to ⅛-inch (2-3 mm) clearance between belts and guide.

REMOVE AND REINSTALL. To renew drive belts, place pto lever in "Off" position and remove lower belt guide. Slip old belts off pulleys and install new belts; adjust as previously outlined.

The pto shaft (17 – Fig. B26) is supported by renewable bearings (18) located in front axle main member (19). The pto idler pulley (6) is also equipped with a renewable ball bearing.

All Other Models

ADJUSTMENT. To adjust pto drive belts, loosen three cap screws securing

pto support (7 – Fig. B27) to front axle support (12). Raise or lower pto support to obtain desired belt tension. Check adjustment of lower belt guide; there should be ⅛-inch (3 mm) clearance between pulley and guide when pto is engaged.

On some late models, a pto brake is used. To adjust brake, place pto lever in disengaged position. Adjust lower nut (2 – Fig. B28) until bowed washer (1) is fully compressed. Adjust upper nut (5) to obtain 1/16-inch (1.5 mm) gap ("G") as shown. Pulley must stop within five seconds; if not, readjust nut (2) to provide more braking pressure.

REMOVE AND REINSTALL. To renew pto belts, place belt idlers in disengaged position. Loosen or remove belt guides as necessary. Slip old belts off pulleys and install new belts. Adjust as previously outlined.

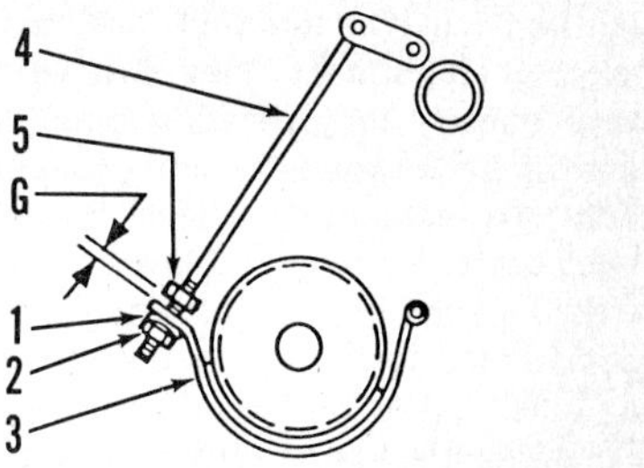

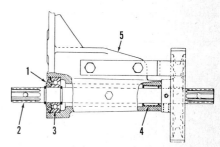

Fig. B28—On models so equipped, adjust pto brake so pulley stops within five seconds. Refer to text.

1. Bowed washer
2. Lower nut
3. Brake band
4. Control rod
5. Upper nut
G. 1/16-inch (1.5 mm) gap

The pto shaft (2 – Fig. B29) is supported by renewable bearings (3 and 4) located in pto support housing (5). When reassembling pto shaft assembly, soak nylon washer-seal (1) in hot water, 140-160°F (60-70°C), for about five minutes to make seal pliable before installation. After reassembly is complete, lubricate through fitting in housing with multi-purpose grease.

INTERLOCK SWITCHES

For safety reasons, many models of these tractors are furnished with interlock switches which are usually wired in series with ignition and starting circuits to insure that parking brakes are applied, tractor drive is in neutral and pto controls are in their disengaged position. All such safety switches are covered here because their adjustment for proper operation concerns simultaneous adjustment of other mechanical systems as brakes and transmission linkages.

IMPORTANT NOTE: If tractor cannot be started, the occasional failure of one of these switches may be misjudged as the failure of another working circuit such as that of starter solenoid, ignition switch or

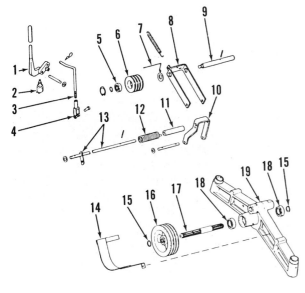

Fig. B26—Exploded view of pto control linkage used on Models 1455, 1476 and 1477. Pto shaft (17) is supported by renewable bearings (18) located in front axle main member (19).

1. Pto lever
2. Interlock switch
3. Control rod
4. Clevis yoke
5. Bearing
6. Idler pulley
7. Belt guide
8. Idler shaft bracket
9. Idler shaft
10. Control arm
11. Sleeve
12. Torsion spring
13. Control shaft
14. Belt guide
15. Snap ring
16. Pto pulley
17. Pto shaft
18. Bearings
19. Axle main member

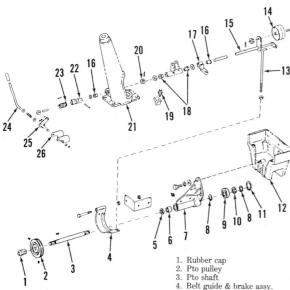

Fig. B27—Exploded view of typical pto shaft assembly and control linkage used on Models G9, G10, G11, G12, G14, H14, 1054, 1225, 1253, 1254, 1256, 1257 and 1556. Some early models are not equipped with interlock switch (19) or brake band (4).

5. Seal
6. Needle bearing
7. Pto support
8. Snap rings
9. Ball bearing
10. Nylon washer-seal
11. Snap ring
12. Axle support
13. Control rod
14. Idler pulley
15. Control shaft
16. Nylon bearings
17. Shaft support
18. Flanged bushings
19. Interlock switch
20. Switch actuator cam
21. Steering support
22. Pivot arm
23. Spring
24. Control lever
25. Control pivot
26. Support bracket

1. Rubber cap
2. Pto pulley
3. Pto shaft
4. Belt guide & brake assy.

Fig. B29—When renewing nylon washer-seal (1) in pto support, soak seal in hot water for about five minutes to make seal pliable before installation.

1. Nylon washer-seal
2. Pto shaft
3. Ball bearing
4. Needle bearing
5. Pto support

ignition coil. If all interlock switches are in correct adjustment, they can be tested very quickly for operating condition by use of an inexpensive self-powered test light. To make such a test, first disconnect battery ground cable to prevent accidental short circuit which might damage solid state ignition or rectifier-regulator as used on recent production engines. Then, isolate switch terminals at connector. With test light connected across interlock switch leads or terminals, manually operate switch and check for clean "ON" and "OFF" action. If continuity through closed switch is at all doubtful, it should be renewed.

ADJUSTMENT

Models G8-LT8-LT11-736

These models have interlock switches operated by clutch-brake pedal and pto actuating linkage. Some late models also use an interlock switch located under operator's seat. Be sure switches are being engaged properly by movement of clutch-brake pedal, pto lever and seat. Check continuity if starting problems are encountered.

Models G9-G10-G11-G12-G14-1054-1254

All models use two interlock switches, and some models are also equipped with a third switch actuated by sitting on operator's seat.

Pto switch is operated by a cam (2– Fig. B30) located on pto control shaft. With pto lever in "OFF" position, flat of cam should be in vertical position as shown and actuator spring (3) should just contact switch button. Check switch operation and adjust as necessary.

The clutch-brake pedal interlock switch (4–Fig. B31) should begin to close when pedal is halfway depressed. To adjust, move switch mounting bracket so actuator spring (3) contacts switch (4) properly.

On models equipped with seat interlock switch (2–Fig. B32), be sure switch is activated when seat is depressed.

Models 1225-1256-1257-1556-H14-H16

These models use two interlock switches connected in series with start terminal of ignition key switch and switch terminal of starter solenoid.

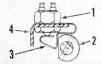

Fig. B30—View of interlock switch, actuator spring and pto linkage cam used on Models G9, G10, G11, G12, G14, 1054 and 1254.

1. Interlock switch
2. Pto cam
3. Actuator spring
4. Transmission cover

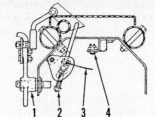

Fig. B31—View of typical parking brake interlock switch used on Models G9, G10, G11, G12, G14, 1054 and 1254.

1. Clutch-brake pedal
2. Brake rod
3. Actuating spring
4. Interlock switch

One switch is operated by a cam located on pto control shaft. To adjust switch, move pto lever to "OFF" position. Refer to Fig. B33 and set clearance of 1/64 to 3/64-inch (0.4-1.2 mm) between switch button and cam by loosening mounting cap screws (A) and shifting switch bracket (B) up or down in its slots.

The brake interlock switch (B–Fig. B34) is actuated by a cam located on park brake control rod on early models. To adjust, place park lock lever in "Park" position and loosen switch bracket cap screws (A). Move bracket (B) in or out to obtain 1/64 to 3/64-inch

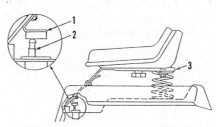

Fig. B32—View of seat interlock switch location typical of all models so equipped.

1. Actuating bracket
2. Interlock switch
3. Seat support

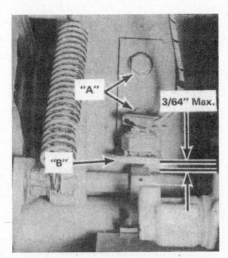

Fig. B33—View of pto interlock switch used on Models 1225, 1256, 1257, 1556, H14 and H16. With pto OFF, loosen cap screws "A" and shift mounting bracket "B" to set required clearance from cam.

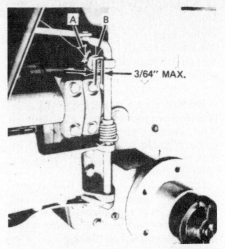

Fig. B34—On some early model hydrostatic drive tractors, brake interlock switch is activated by a cam on park brake control rod.

(0.4-1.2 mm) clearance between switch and cam. On some late models, switch is actuated by parking brake linkage as shown in Fig. B35. This switch requires no adjustment; however, it should be tested if doubtful.

Models 1455-1476-1477

On these tractors, two interlock switches are used. One is mounted on reduction gear housing cover behind hydrostatic unit and is engaged by the

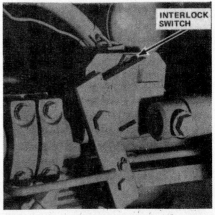

Fig. B35—On some late model hydrostatic drive tractors, brake interlock switch is activated when brake pedal is depressed. Switch requires no adjustment.

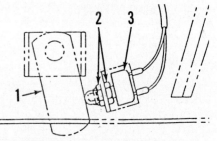

Fig. B36—On "XL" models, brake interlock switch is actuated by brake control arm (1) when brake pedal is depressed.

1. Brake control arm
2. Adjusting nuts
3. Interlock switch

oil relief spool when transmission is set in neutral or park. It is not adjustable, but should be checked for continuity if starting trouble is encountered. Another interlock switch is engaged by movement of pto control lever to "OFF" position. Be sure contact is made and if necessary, check action of switch by use of a test light to determine continuity.

Models G11XL-G12XL-G14XL-H11XL-H12XL-H14XL-H16XL

All models are equipped with a brake interlock switch, located inside the frame behind brake pedal, and a seat switch, located under seat support.

When brake is applied, interlock switch button (3–Fig. B36) should be depressed approximately 3/32 inch (2 mm). To adjust, loosen nuts (2) and move switch forward or back as required.

The seat switch should be activated when back edge of seat support is depressed 5/8 inch (16 mm). Loosen and move bracket (1–Fig. B32) to obtain proper switch adjustment.

Model QS16

Two microswitches, one on parking brake rod, another on pto control serve as safety interlocks on this model. They are spring-actuated and nonadjustable.

If brake interlock should be disconnected, be sure its spring clip is reinstalled at a mid-point on brake rod between ratchet and threaded portion.

Test for continuity if a tractor starting problem develops.

TRANSAXLE

LUBRICATION

All Models

Refer to CONDENSED SPECIFICATIONS at the beginning of this section for transaxle lubricating fluid type and capacity for model being serviced.

REMOVE AND REINSTALL

Models G8-730-733-LT8-LT11-G11XL-G12XL-G14XL-G16XL

To remove transaxle assembly, remove transmission drive belt and brake assembly from transaxle. Remove rear axle retaining bolts, support rear of tractor and roll transaxle assembly from tractor.

To reinstall transaxle, reverse removal procedure.

All Other Models

To remove transaxle assembly, remove seat and fenders. On models equipped with disc type brake, remove brake assembly. On Models G10, G12, G14, 853, 1053, 1054, 1253 and 1254, remove park brake lever. On all models, support rear of tractor and disconnect drive shaft. Unbolt retaining bolts and roll transaxle assembly from tractor.

To reinstall transaxle, reverse removal procedure.

OVERHAUL

All Models

Models G8, LT8 and LT11 are equipped with a Peerless 600 series transaxle. Models 730 and 733 are equipped with a

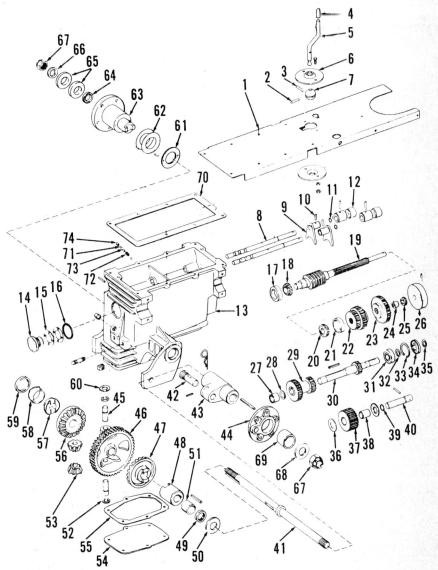

Fig. B41 — Exploded view of transaxle assembly used on Models G9, G10, G11 and 853.

1. Transaxle cover
2. Dowel pin
3. Drive pin
4. Knob
5. Shift lever
6. Retainer
7. Pivot ball
8. Shifter rail
9. Shifter fork
10. Roll pin
11. Seal ring
12. Connector
13. Transaxle case
14. Bearing retainer cap
15. Shim
16. "O" ring
17. Bearing cup
18. Bearing cone
19. Wormshaft
20. Bearing cone
21. Bearing cup
22. Second & third sliding gear
23. First & reverse sliding gear
24. Bearing
25. Oil seal
26. Brake drum
27. Bearing
28. Snap ring
29. Cluster gear
30. Input shaft
31. Ball bearing
32. Snap ring
33. Retainer ring
34. Oil seal
35. Snap ring
36. Thrust washer
37. Reverse idler gear
38. Bushing
39. Seal ring
40. Idler shaft
41. Axle shaft
42. Free-wheeling pin
43. Hub drive coupling
44. Hub (R.H.)
45. Differential pinion shaft
46. Wormwheel
47. Side gear (R.H.)
48. Side gear drive
49. Oil seal
50. Thrust bearing
51. Bushing
52. Snap ring
53. Differential pinion gear
54. Bottom cover
55. Gasket
56. Side gear (L.H.)
57. Side gear coupling
58. Bushing
59. Oil seal
60. Washer
61. Thrust bearing
62. Shim
63. Wheel hub
64. Oil seal
65. Thrust bearing
66. Special washer
67. Axle nut
68. Washer
69. Bearing
70. Gasket
71. Ball
72. Spring
73. Pin
74. Set screw

Peerless 1200 series transaxle. Models G11XL, G12XL, G14XL and G16XL are equipped with a Peerless 2300 series transaxle with a limited-slip differential. Models G9, G10, G11 and 853 are equipped with a three-speed transaxle manufactured for Bolens. Models G12, G14, 1053, 1054 and 1254 are equipped with a three-speed transaxle plus a Hi-Lo range contained within the transaxle case manufactured for Bolens. On models equipped with a Peerless trans-axle, refer to the appropriate Peerless section in TRANSAXLE SERVICE section for overhaul procedure. On all other models, refer to the following paragraphs for transaxle overhaul procedure.

Models G9-G10-G11-853

After removing transaxle assembly, remove rear wheels and unbolt and re-

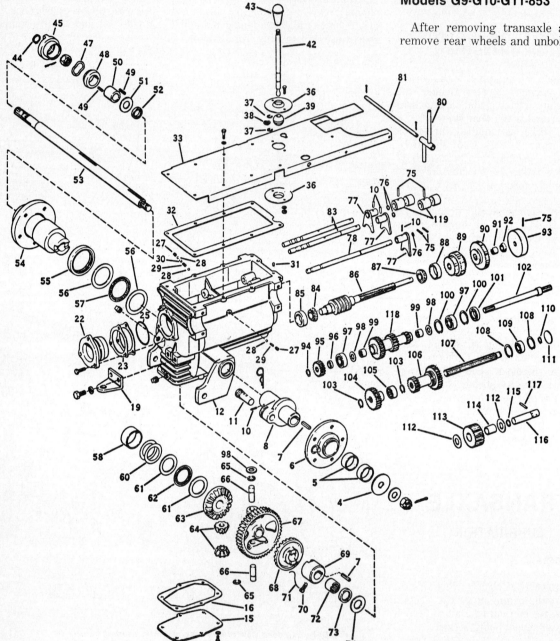

Fig. B42 — Exploded view of transaxle assembly used on Models G12, G14, 1053, 1054, 1253 and 1254.

4. Thrust washer	30. Interlock pin	51. Washer
5. Bushing	31. Breather	52. Oil seal
6. Hub (R.H.)	32. Gasket	53. Axle shaft
7. Key	33. Transaxle cover	54. Hub (L.H.)
8. Hub drive coupling	36. Retainer	55. Oil seal
10. Roll pin	37. Snap ring	56. Thrust washer
11. Free-wheeling pin	38. Seal ring	57. Thrust bearing
12. Transaxle case	39. Pivot ball	58. Bushing
15. Bottom cover	42. Shift lever	60. Shim
16. Gasket	43. Knob	61. Thrust washer
19. Hitch plate	44. Snap ring	62. Thrust bearing
22. Bearing retainer cap	45. Handwheel	63. Side gear (L.H.)
23. Shim	47. Spring washer	64. Differential pinion
25. "O" ring	(4 used)	gear
27. Plug	48. "Posi-Traction--cone	65. Snap ring
28. Detent ball	49. Key	66. Differential pinion
29. Spring	50. Cone drive hub	shaft

67. Wormwheel	87. Bearing cone	102. Input shaft
68. Side gear (R.H.)	88. Bearing cup	103. Snap ring
69. Side gear drive hub	89. Second & third	104. Input driven gear
70. Set screw	sliding gear	105. Bearing
71. Lock wire	90. First & reverse	106. Hi-Lo range gear
72. Bearing	sliding gear	107. Splined shaft
73. Bearing	91. Bearing	108. Retainer ring
74. Washer	92. Oil seal	109. Ball bearing
75. Roll pin	93. Brake drum	110. Snap ring
76. Seal ring	94. Snap ring	111. Expansion plug
77. Shifter fork	95. Input gear	112. Thrust washer
78. Range shifter rail	96. Spacer	113. Reverse idler gear
80. Range shift lever	97. Ball bearing	114. Bushing
81. Cross shaft	98. Washer	115. Seal ring
83. Shifter rails	99. Bearing	116. Idler shaft
84. Bearing cone	100. Retainer ring	117. Roll pin
86. Wormshaft	101. Oil seal	118. Cluster gear

move top cover assembly (1–Fig. B41). Remove cotter pin and castellated nut from left end of axle shaft. Then, drive out 3/16 inch shearproof pin located next to right side gear drive hub (48). Move axle shaft to the right until side gear drive hub key can be removed. Remove left wheel hub (63), shims (62) and thrust washer (61). Unbolt and remove transaxle bottom cover (54), then withdraw axle shaft from right side of case while holding differential and wormwheel assembly. Remove differential and side gears through bottom opening of case.

To remove shifter rails (8) and forks (9), first drive out roll pins holding forks to rails. After removing plug from interlock pin bore on left side of case, pull left shifter rail forward out of case.

NOTE: Hold hand over interlock pin bore to catch detent balls, spring and interlock pin. Remove right shifter rail and lift out both shifter forks.

Drive out roll pin and remove brake drum (26) from wormshaft (19). Remove cap screws from bearing retaining cap (14) and bump wormshaft out rear of case. Bearing retainer cap (14), shims (15) and rear bearing cup (17) will be removed from rear of case and sliding gears (22 and 23) will be removed from inside of case as wormshaft is removed. Remove drive shaft coupling flange, key and snap ring, pry out front seal (34) and remove bearing retainer ring (33). Bump input shaft (30) forward until ball bearing (31) is free of case. Remove snap ring (28) from rear of input shaft, withdraw input shaft and lift cluster gear (29) from inside of case. Drive out roll pin securing reverse idler shaft in case and remove shaft (40), reverse idler gear (37) and thrust washers.

Reassemble unit by reversing disassembly procedure, and making the following adjustments. When reinstalling wormshaft, add or remove shims (15) as required to obtain 0.004-0.008 inch (0.120-0.203 mm) end play. After reassembling differential and axle shaft in case, adjust left axle nut tight enough so differential will operate without binding. Then, adjust right axle nut to obtain minimum end play but do not bind axle.

Apply a light coat of Prussian Blue to several teeth on wormwheel (46). Rotate wormshaft and check wear pattern on painted wormwheel teeth (area where blue is removed). If pattern is not centered on wormwheel, add or remove shims (62) at left hub as required to center pattern.

NOTE: One 0.005 inch (0.127 mm) shim equals approximately 1/16 inch (1.59 mm) shift of wormwheel wear pattern.

Readjust differential and axle end play as outlined before.

Models G12-G14-1053-1054-1253-1254

Remove transaxle unit, then remove rear wheels. Unbolt and remove bottom cover (15–Fig. B42) and top cover assembly (33). Remove snap ring (44), adjusting handwheel (45), cotter pin, castellated nut, four spring washers (47), "Posi-Traction" drive cone (48), cone drive hub (50) and two straight keys (49), in this order, from left end of axle shaft. After removing set screw (70) from side gear drive hub (69), move axle shaft to the right until drive hub key can be removed. Remove left wheel hub (54) and while holding wormwheel and differential assembly, withdraw axle shaft (53) from right side of case. Remove differential assembly, side gears, thrust bearings and shims through bottom opening of case.

Drive out roll pins securing shifter forks (77) to shifter rails (83). Remove plug from interlock pin bore on left side of case. Pull left shifter rail forward out of case while holding hand over interlock pin bore to catch detent balls, spring and interlock pin. Remove right shifter rail and lift shifter forks from wormshaft sliding gears. Remove roll pin and brake drum (93) from front of wormshaft (86) and unbolt bearing retainer at rear of case. Bump wormshaft rearward, removing bearing retainer cap (22), shims (23), rear bearing cup (85) and sliding gears (89 and 90) as shaft is withdrawn from case. Remove roll pin from range shifter fork and rail and remove

plug, spring and detent ball from right side of case. Withdraw range shifter rail (78) and lift out shifter fork. Remove expansion plug (111) and bearing retainer ring (108) from front of case and remove snap ring and gear (104) from splined shaft (107). Bump splined shaft forward until bearing is free from case. Remove snap ring from rear of splined shaft, withdraw shaft and lift Hi-Lo range sliding gear (106) from case. Pry oil seal (101) from case and remove bearing retainer ring (100). Remove snap ring, input gear (95) and spacer from input shaft (102) and then, remove cluster gear (118) and washers as input shaft is withdrawn from case. Drive roll pin from idler shaft and remove idler shaft (116), reverse idler gear (113) and thrust washers.

Reassembly procedure is reverse of disassembly. When reinstalling wormshaft, add or remove shims (23) at bearing retainer cap to obtain 0.004-0.008 inch (0.102-0.203 mm) wormshaft end play. After reassembling differential and axle shaft in case, adjust left axle nut tight enough so differential will operate without binding. Then, adjust right axle nut to obtain minimum end play but do not bind axle.

Apply a light coat of Prussian Blue to several wormwheel teeth. Rotate wormshaft and check wear pattern on painted wormwheel teeth (area where blue is removed). If wear pattern is not centered on wormwheel, add or remove shims (60) as required to center pattern. One 0.005 inch (0.127 mm) shim will shift wear pattern approximately 1/16 inch (1.59 mm). Readjust differential and axle end play as previously outlined.

RIGHT ANGLE DRIVE UNIT

R&R AND OVERHAUL

Models G11XL-G12XL-G14XL-G16XL

To remove right angle drive unit, remove idler pulley and slide drive belt off right angle drive pulley. Remove pulley from right angle drive. Remove frame

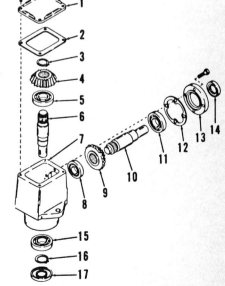

Fig. B44 – Exploded view of right angle drive used on Models G11XL, G12XL, G14XL and G16XL.

1. Cover	
2. Gasket	
3. Snap ring	10. Output shaft
4. Input gear	11. Bearing
5. Bearing	12. Gasket
6. Input shaft	13. Seal retainer
7. Case	14. Oil seal
8. Bearing	15. Bearing
9. Output gear	16. Snap ring
	17. Oil seal

cover in front of seat and remove front belt cover. Remove right angle drive from tractor.

To disassemble right angle drive unit, remove cover (1–Fig. B44), gasket (2) and lubricant. Unbolt and remove seal retainer (13) with oil seal (14) and gasket (12). Withdraw output shaft (10) with bearing (11). Remove output gear (9). Remove oil seal (17) and snap ring (16). Drive input shaft (6) with gear (4) and bearing (5) out the cover opening of case (7). Bearings (8 and 15) can now be removed from case. Remove snap ring (3) and remove drive gear (4) and bearing (5) from input shaft. Remove bearing (11) from output shaft (10).

Clean and inspect all parts and renew any showing excessive wear or other damage. Reassemble by reversing disassembly procedure and fill unit with 4 ounces (120 mL) of Moly EP lithium grease.

HYDROSTATIC TRANSMISSION

LUBRICATION

Model 736

The manufacturer recommends that oil in reservoir be renewed once a year when operating under normal conditions. If tractor is operated frequently in extremely dusty conditions, renew oil in reservoir once each month. To renew oil, disconnect oil line at reservoir. Plug line to prevent entrance of dirt and oil loss from transmission. Remove, clean and dry reservoir, then reassemble on tractor. Fill reservoir at "FULL" mark on dipstick using Bolens #171-9650 hydraulic oil or Type "A" automatic transmission fluid.

Models 1225-1256-1257-1556-H14-H16-H11XL-H12XL-H14XL-H16XL

Maintain hydraulic oil level at "FULL" mark on reservoir dipstick. Use Bolens #171-9650 hydraulic oil or Type "A" automatic transmission fluid on all models except "XL" models. On "XL" models, recommended oil is as follows: If tractor is used under constant heavy load conditions in hot weather, use SAE 30 oil with API classification, SC, SD or SE. Under normal load conditions and temperatures above 20° F (−7°C), use SAE 20 oil with API classification SC, SD or SE. When temperatures are 20° F (−7°C) and below, use Type "F" automatic transmission fluid.

The hydraulic oil and oil filter should be renewed each 250 hours of operation or once a year under normal operating conditions, or more often if operating under constant heavy load conditions or extremely dusty conditions.

Models 1455-1476-1477

The manufacturer recommends renewing hydraulic oil filter and transmission oil each 300 hours of operation or once each year. The capacity of reduction gear and differential housing (also hydraulic reservoir) is 10 quarts (9.5 L). Fill only with Bolens #171-9650 hydraulic oil or Type "A" automatic transmission fluid.

Model QS16

Weekly or 25 hour checks are recommended for transmission fluid with filter changes at 200 hour intervals. Recommended oil is Type "F" automatic transmission fluid. Approximate capacity is 20 pints (9.5 L). Always change transmission fluid when discolored or contaminated.

LINKAGE ADJUSTMENT

Model 736

To adjust hydrostatic drive linkage, block up rear wheels so they do not touch ground. Start engine with travel pedal in neutral position. Rear wheels should not rotate. If wheels rotate, loosen nut (A–Fig. B49) and cap screw (B). Move bracket (C) either forward or backward until rear wheels stop turning. Retighten nut (A) and cap screw (B) and recheck adjustment of travel pedal.

Models 1225-1256-1257

Before making neutral adjustment, be sure parking pawl engages transmission drive gear when selector lever is placed in PARK position. With transmission in PARK position, differential should be locked. If differential is not locked, proceed as follows: Remove clevis pin (A–Fig. B50). Turn adjusting block (B) to lengthen stud (C) until pawl (D) correctly engages transmission gear (E).

NOTE: Do not turn pawl (D) as mesh between pawl and transmission gear will be misaligned.

To accomplish neutral adjustment, first raise and support rear of tractor so wheels are off ground. Refer to Fig. B51 and loosen cap screws (A). Start engine; if wheels rotate forward, move bracket (B) forward until wheels stop and noise in hydrostatic transmission ceases. If wheels rotate in reverse, tap bracket (B) towards rear. Retighten cap screws (A).

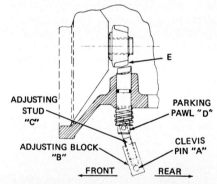

Fig. B50 – View of parking pawl and transmission gear on Models 1225, 1256 and 1257. Refer to text for parking pawl adjustment.

Fig. B51 – View of hydrostatic control cam assembly used on Models 1225, 1256 and 1257.

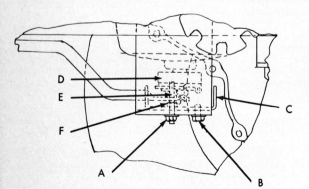

Fig. B49 – View of neutral adjustment points on Model 736. Refer to text for procedure.

A. Nut
B. Cap screw
C. Bracket
D. Control arm
E. Stud
F. Nut

Models 1455-1476-1477

Hydrostatic linkage for Eaton Model 12 transmission used on these models is adjusted as follows:

With selector lever in DRIVE position, all linkages should move freely. Loosen two jam nuts on control rod away from swivel block, then place selector lever in PARK position. See Fig. B52. Parking pawl should be fully meshed in bull gear. Push spool of unloader assembly back into PARK detent position. (Front detent groove inside casting.) Adjust two jam nuts up against swivel block (3). Place selector lever in NEUTRAL position. Push tractor forward and backward to be sure tractor free-wheels freely in this position. Place selector lever in DRIVE and activate travel pedal. Check to see that pin in transaxle control linkage moves freely into upper and lower slot of interlock plate. If interference is evident, readjust jam nuts to eliminate interlock-slot pin interference.

Fig. B52—View of adjustment points on Eaton Model 12 transmission in Models 1455, 1476 and 1477. Note location of interlock switch. See adjustment procedure in text.

1. Unloader valve (oil relief) assy.
2. Parking pawl link rod
3. Swivel block
4. Interlock plate

Models 1556-H14-H16

When tractor "creeps" either forward or back in neutral, then neutral control of hydrostatic unit (Model 10) requires adjustment. Be sure transmission fluid level is correct before undertaking adjustment, then proceed as follows:

With engine turned off, release parking brake, set travel pedal in full reverse and check under right side of tractor to determine if pin ("A"–Fig. B53) is snug in corner "B" of locking lever "C." If not, loosen cap screw "D" and shift locking lever "C" until pin is in position shown. Tighten cap screw.

Now, raise and block under rear of tractor so drive wheels are clear and start engine, setting throttle for one-quarter speed, control pedal in neutral. Refer to Fig. B53 and slightly loosen cap screws "E" which hold adjusting bracket "G" through elongated holes to control support "H." Hold neutral arms "F" in contact with pin "K", then shift adjusting bracket "G" forward if creep is in forward direction, or back if creeping is to the rear until wheel rotation and hydrostatic noise stops.

NOTE: Edge of adjustment bracket "G" must be kept parallel to edge of control support "H."

IMPORTANT: Pin "A" must enter slot "J" of locking lever "C" without contacting sides of slot. If contact is made, loosen cap screw "D" and readjust until pin "A" travels length of slot "J" freely. Be sure to retighten cap screw "D."

Models H11XL-H12XL-H14XL-H16XL

To adjust hydrostatic drive linkage, block up rear of tractor so rear wheels clear ground. Start engine with travel pedal in neutral position. If rear wheels creep, loosen cap screws (A–Fig. B54) and move support plate (1) forward if wheels rotate forward or toward rear of

tractor if wheels rotate in reverse. Secure support plate when wheels stop rotating. Stop engine and lock brake. Loosen jam nuts (B) and move rod (4) until pin lightly contacts slot (C) of neutral plate.

Model QS16

To perform linkage neutral adjustment on tractor equipped with Sundstrand hydrostatic unit, proceed as follows:

Remove seat and fender assemblies. Be sure free-wheeling valve on left side of unit is closed, and fluid level is correct. Jack up tractor and block securely under axle so rear wheels are clear. With travel pedal in neutral, start engine and release parking brake. Refer to Fig. B55 and loosen nuts "B" at rear end of rod "C." If wheels creep in forward direction, shorten rod "C" working length by tightening outer nut until rotation stops. If creep is to rear, increase length of rod "C" by tightening inner nut until backward rotation is halted. Tighten both sides securely, then check performance.

REMOVE AND REINSTALL

Model 736

To remove hydrostatic transmission, disconnect hydraulic reservoir hose and remove reservoir. Plug openings to prevent entrance of dirt into system. Unbolt and remove seat and fenders. Remove backplate or hitch assembly from frame. Remove disc brake assembly. Unbolt and remove fan screen and cooling fan. Disconnect control rod from lever on hydrostatic transmission. Remove drive belt and transmission input pulley. Support tractor frame, remove cap screws from top of frame and "U" bolt from axle supports. Roll reduction gear and differential assembly with hydrostatic transmission rearward

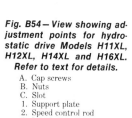

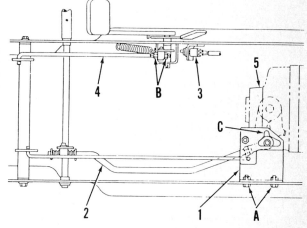

Fig. B54—View showing adjustment points for hydrostatic drive Models H11XL, H12XL, H14XL and H16XL. Refer to text for details.
A. Cap screws
B. Nuts
C. Slot
1. Support plate
2. Speed control rod
3. Interlock switch
4. Brake rod
5. Hydrostatic unit

Fig. B53—View of transmission linkage adjustment to eliminate creeping in neutral on Models 1556, H14 and H16. Refer to text for procedure.

from tractor. Place unit on left wheel and tire (right axle pointing upward). Remove right rear wheel, then unbolt and remove hydrostatic transmission.

Reinstall hydrostatic transmission by reversing removal procedure. Use new mounting gasket and tighten four hydrostatic transmission mounting cap screws to 200 in.-lbs. (22.6 N·m). Fill hydraulic reservoir to dipstick full mark with approved fluid. Fill reduction gear and differential housing to level plug opening with SAE 90 EP gear oil. Check and adjust linkage as necessary.

Models 1225-1256-1257-1556-H14-H16-H11XL-H12XL-H14XL-H16XL

To remove hydrostatic transmission from these models, first unbolt and remove seat and fender assemblies. Disconnect and remove hydraulic fluid reservoir hose and reservoir (if so equipped) along with all auxiliary hydraulic hoses. Plug or cap all openings as soon as disconnect is made. Disconnect disc brake linkage and remove brake assembly. Disconnect hydrostatic control rod from control linkage, but do not remove control arm from control shaft until later.

NOTE: Be sure all hydraulic assembly parts and hoses are adequately identified to eliminate error in reinstallation.

Raise and support rear of tractor frame and disconnect drive shaft. On all models except "XL" models, place scribe marks on frame tubes and reduction gear housing to aid realignment during reassembly. On "XL" models, scribe a line on left hand frame rail at rear edge of quadrant support plate. When

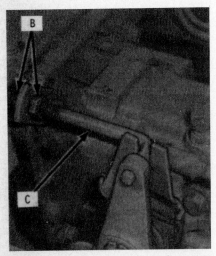

Fig. B55—Linkage neutral adjustment of Sundstrand hydrostatic unit on Model QS16 is made by changing length of rod "C" by shifting nuts "B." Refer to text.

reinstalling transaxle, plate must be parallel with frame. On all models, remove retaining screws and clamps and roll assembly rearward from tractor frame.

Remove control arm and levers from control shaft using suitable puller. Do not attempt to pry or drive control arm off shaft, as internal damage can occur. Rotate reduction drive housing so input shaft of hydrostatic transmission points upward and block securely; transmission can now be unbolted and lifted off.

Reinstall transmission on reduction and differential housing, using a new gasket, and tighten cap screws to 20 ft.-lbs. (27 N·m). Reinstall assembly on tractor by reversing removal procedure. Fill hydraulic reservoir to dipstick full mark with approved hydraulic fluid. Operate engine at ⅓ throttle and shift hydrostatic drive to forward and reverse several times to purge air from system. Recheck fluid level and adjust linkage as necessary.

Models 1455-1476-1477

To remove hydrostatic transmission from tractors in this model group, first, drain automatic transmission fluid (ATF) from reservoir. Remove seat and fender asemblies which includes deck assembly forward of operator's seat. Support rear of tractor under frame rails, disconnect and remove brake control linkage. Disconnect and remove transmission control linkages. Remove hoses for hydraulic system (if so equipped) and tape or otherwise protect open lines or connection fittings. Be sure to identify removed items for ease of reassembly. Remove oil filter, then unbolt attaching bolts so entire assembly can be rolled rearward away from tractor frame.

Tip transmission back and rest on a six inch (15.2 cm) block. Remove hydraulic oil lines. Remove control arm from hydrostatic control shaft using a suitable puller. Do not pry or drive control arm off shaft, as internal damage can occur. Unbolt and lift off hydrostatic transmission.

Reinstall hydrostatic transmission by reversing removal steps. Refill unit with Type "F" automatic transmission oil. Adjust linkage as needed.

Model QS16

To remove hydrostatic transmission begin by unbolting and removing seat and fender assemblies.

NOTE: If service to hydrostatic assembly only is intended, it is not necessary to remove rear axle and reduction gear housing. If removal of rear axle will be required,

see REDUCTION AND DIFFERENTIAL section following.

Drain and discard fluid from transaxle. At forward end of drive shaft, loosen set screw and remove bolt which attaches front universal joint to engine crankshaft so drive shaft can slide forward for removal from input shaft of hydrostatic unit. Uncouple and remove hydraulic lines from top of pump section housing. This will require removal of forward ends of these lines at hydraulic control valve so lines are not damaged. Tape over or cap openings. Uncouple external pickup tube from pump section and at front of reduction gear housing just under hydrostatic motor section. Leave elbow fittings in place after plugging or capping against dirt entry. Remove fluid filter from under pump section. Remove cap screw holding mounting tab for neutral adjustment rod (see Fig. B55) so rod can be disengaged and removed. Drive out roll pin which holds control linkage on control shaft and remove linkage assembly. Remove mounting cap screws and lift out hydrostatic transmission.

To reinstall hydrostatic transmission, the reverse of preceding steps applies with these additional steps and cautions:

Be sure filter mount (stud tube) is securely staked so as not to turn when filter is installed. Use grease to hold gasket in place on motor end flange, then use three **shorter** cap screws to mount hydrostatic unit against reduction gear housing, leaving **longer** cap screw for attaching neutral adjustment rod tab. Tighten all cap screws to 31 ft.-lbs. (42 N·m). When drive shaft is reinstalled, check for ⅛ inch (3 mm) clearance between drive shaft end and pump input shaft. Loosen engine mounts to adjust, if necessary. Fill new filter with Type "F" automatic transmission fluid and screw on hand tight. Use about 8 quarts (7.5 L) of new fluid to charge reduction gear housing. Loosen pickup tube at pump (front) end and retighten when fluid appears at fitting. Remove spark plug and crank engine for 15-20 seconds to fill unit with fluid, then reinstall spark plug. Start engine and operate at low throttle engaging hydraulic lift lever so lift system will fill with fluid. Block up rear axle and perform linkage neutral adjustment as previously covered. Check fluid level on dipstick and top off to level mark.

OVERHAUL

All Models

Model 736 is equipped with an Eaton Model 6 hydrostatic transmission.

Models 1225, 1256, 1257, 1556, H14 and H16 are equipped with an Eaton Model 10 hydrostatic transmission. Models H11XL, H12XL, H14XL and H16XL are equipped with an Eaton Model 11 hydrostatic transmission. Models 1455, 1476 and 1477 are equipped with an Eaton Model 12 hydrostatic transmission. Model QS16 is equipped with a Sundstrand Series 15 "In-Line" type hydrostatic transmission. Refer to the appropriate Eaton or Sundstrand section in HYDROSTATIC TRANS-MISSION SERVICE section for overhaul procedure.

REDUCTION GEARS AND DIFFERENTIAL

REMOVE AND REINSTALL

Model 736

To remove reduction gear and differential assembly, disconnect hydraulic reservoir hose and remove reservoir. Plug openings to prevent entrance of dirt into system. Unbolt and remove seat and fenders. Remove backplate or hitch assembly from frame. Remove disc brake assembly. Unbolt and remove fan screen and cooling fan. Disconnect control rod from lever on hydrostatic transmission. Remove drive belt and transmission input pulley. Support tractor frame, remove cap screws from top of frame and "U" bolt from axle supports. Roll reduction gear and differential assembly with hydrostatic transmission rearward from tractor. Place unit on left wheel and tire (right axle pointing upward). Remove right rear wheel, then unbolt and remove hydrostatic transmission.

Reinstall transaxle unit by reversing removal procedure. Use new mounting gasket and tighten four hydrostatic transmission mounting cap screws to 200 in.-lbs. (22.6 N·m). Fill hydraulic reservoir to dipstick full mark with approved fluid. Fill reduction gear and differential housing to level plug opening with SAE 90 EP gear oil. Check and adjust linkage as necessary.

Models 1225-1256-1257-H11XL-H12XL-H14XL-H16XL

To remove reduction gear and differential assembly, first unbolt and remove seat and fender assemblies. Disconnect and remove hydraulic fluid reservoir hose and reservoir (if so equipped) along with all auxiliary hydraulic hoses. Plug or cap all openings immediately. Identify hoses to ensure correct reassembly. Disconnect brake linkage and remove disc brake assembly. Disconnect speed control linkage. On "XL" models, scribe a line on left hand frame rail at rear edge of quadrant support plate, then unbolt plate. On all other models, put scribe marks on frame tubes and reduction gear housing to aid realignment during reassembly. On all models, remove retaining screws and clamps and roll assembly rearward from

tractor. Hydrostatic transmission can now be separated from reduction drive housing.

Reinstall unit on tractor by reversing removal procedure. Tighten hydrostatic retaining screws to 20 ft.-lbs. (27 N·m). Fill hydraulic reservoir with approved hydraulic fluid. Operate engine at ⅓-throttle and shift hydrostatic transmission to forward and reverse several times to purge air from system. Recheck fluid level and adjust linkage as required.

Models 1455-1476-1477

To remove axle-differential assembly from tractors in this model group, first, drain transmission fluid from reservoir. Remove seat and fender assemblies which includes deck assembly forward of operator's seat. Support rear of tractor under frame rails, disconnect and remove brake control linkage. Disconnect and remove transmission control linkages. Remove hoses for hydraulic system (if so equipped) and tape or otherwise protect open lines or connection fittings. Be sure to identify removed items for ease of reassembly. Remove oil filter, then unbolt attaching bolts so entire assembly can be rolled rearward away from tractor frame.

Reverse this order to reinstall.

Models 1556-H14-H16

To remove rear axle, final drive and transmission unit from these tractors, disengage pto and drain axle housing oil reservoir by removing plug at bottom of side cover beneath left axle housing. Remove tractor seat, fender assembly and fender support. Disconnect and cap off hydraulic lines, storage tank, filter and lift system, taking measures to protect against dirt. Disconnect and remove hydrostatic controls at hydrostatic control shaft (under tractor) and uncouple and remove brake assembly from rear axle housing. Place solid supports beneath tractor frame rails (tubes) and unbolt frame clamps from sides of axle housing. It may be desirable to remove fan guard. Check for clearance, and roll complete drive assembly to the rear, carefully disengaging drive shaft splines from input shaft of hydrostatic

transmission. Do not force.

Reinstallation is performed in reverse of this sequence, followed by renewal of lubricant. Perform necessary adjustments.

Model QS16

To remove axle and final drive, drain oil from reservoir in housing. Drain plug is located at front of housing just below oil filter. Remove seat and fender assemblies, then disconnect transmission control linkage. Disconnect hydraulic lines from fittings above charge pump, protect from dirt, loosen or remove at hydraulic control valve and set aside. Remove set screw from front universal joint, slip drive shaft forward and disengage from hydrostatic input shaft. Disconnect brake linkage inside frame rails, and note that disc brake assembly will be released from its mount on axle when "U" bolts are removed. Support rear of tractor under frame, then remove cap screws which hold frame rails to axle housing followed by cap screws in transmission support, so entire drive assembly can be rolled rearward.

Reverse this order for reinstallation; replenish transmission fluid and perform necessary adjustments.

OVERHAUL

Model 736

Remove reduction gear and differential assembly and hydrostatic transmission from tractor. Separate hydrostatic transmission from reduction gear and differential housing. Drain lubricant from differential housing and remove brake disc from brake shaft.

To overhaul gear reduction and differential unit, refer to exploded view in Fig. B66. Clean axle shafts and remove any burrs on shafts. Unscrew cap screws and drive out dowel pins in cover. Lift cover off case and axle shaft. Remove brake shaft (5), idler gear (4) and thrust washers (3 and 6) from case. Withdraw output shaft (11), output gear (10), spacer (9), thrust washer (8) and differential assembly from case. Axle shaft housings (20 and 22) must be pressed from case and cover.

To disassemble differential, unscrew four cap screws (17) and separate axle shaft and carriage assemblies from ring gear (28). Drive blocks (25), bevel pinion gears (26) and drive pin (27) can now be removed from ring gear. Remove snap rings (12) and slide axle shafts (18 and 23) from axle gears (13) and carriages (16 and 24).

Clean and inspect all parts and renew any parts damaged or excessively worn. When installing needle bearings, press bearings in from inside of case or cover until bearings are 0.015-0.020 inch (0.381-0.508 mm) below thrust surfaces. Be sure heads of differential cap screws (17) and left axle shaft (18) are installed in left carriage housing (16). Left axle shaft is installed through case (1).

Tighten differential cap screws to 7 ft.-lbs. (9 N·m) and cover cap screws to 10 ft.-lbs. (14 N·m). Differential assembly and output shaft (11) must be installed in case at same time. Remainder of assembly is reverse of disassembly procedure.

After assembly is completed, fill transmission reservoir to full mark on dipstick with Bolens #171-9650 hydraulic oil or Type "A" automatic transmission fluid. Fill reduction and differential housing to level plug with SAE 90 EP gear lube.

Models 1225-1256-1257-1556-H14-H16

Remove reduction gear and differential assembly and hydrostatic transmission from tractor. Remove hydrostatic control plate from left side and separate hydrostatic transmission from reduction gear and differential housing. Drain lubricant from differential housing and remove brake disc from brake shaft.

To overhaul gear reduction and differential unit, remove outer snap ring, adjusting handwheel (33–Fig. B67), spring washers (34), inner snap ring, shim (35), "Posi-Traction" drive cone (36), coupling (37) and keys (38) from left end of axle. Remove left wheel hub (41), then remove cover (23) from case (8). Remove right hub nut (13) and right wheel hub (11). Withdraw axle (1) and differential components. Input shaft components (16 through 20) can now be removed.

Clean and inspect all components for damage or excessive wear. When reassembling differential, shims (5) are used to position right side gear with drive pinions (29) and also are used to adjust axle end play. Change number or size of shims (5) to obtain an end play of 0.002-0.014 inch (0.051-0.356 mm). Install left wheel hub (41), seal (40), thrust washer (39), coupling (37), cone (36) and snap ring (32). Push inward on left end of axle shaft and measure distance between coupling (37) and snap ring (32). Install shims (35) as required to reduce the gap to 0.002-0.016 inch (0.051-0.406 mm). To assemble gear reduction and differential unit, reverse disassembly procedure.

After assembly is completed, fill transmission reservoir to full mark on dipstick with Bolens #171-9650 hydraulic oil or Type "A" automatic transmission fluid. Fill reduction and differential housing to level plug with SAE 90 EP gear lube.

Models H11XL-H12XL-H14XL-H16XL

Remove reduction gear and differential assembly and hydrostatic transmission from tractor. Separate hydrostatic transmission from reduction gear and drain differential housing. Remove brake disc assembly.

To overhaul reduction gear and differential, unbolt and remove right hand transaxle cover (9–Fig. B68). Remove cluster gear assembly (14) and pinion shaft (5). Make sure thrust races (6) and bearing (7) stay with shaft (5). Unbolt and remove left hand cover (33). Lift differential assembly from housing.

To disassemble differential, unscrew four cap screws and separate ring gear (24), carrier (23) and cover (17). Remove snap ring (21), pinion shaft (22) and bevel pinion gears (20). Remove snap rings (19) and slide axles (18) out of axle gears and differential carrier assembly (17 and 23).

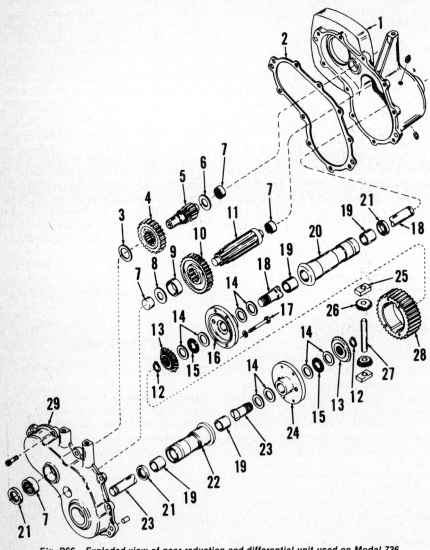

Fig. B66 — Exploded view of gear reduction and differential unit used on Model 736.

1. Case	9. Spacer	16. Differential carrier	23. Axle shaft (L.H.)
2. Gasket	10. Output gear	17. Bolt	24. Differential carrier
3. Washer	11. Output shaft	18. Axle shaft (R.H.)	25. Drive block
4. Idler gear	12. Snap ring	19. Bushing	26. Drive pinion gear
5. Brake shaft	13. Bevel gear	20. Axle housing	27. Drive pin
6. Washer	14. Thrust washers	21. Oil seal	28. Ring gear
7. Bearing	15. Thrust bearing	22. Axle housing	29. Cover
8. Washer			

Clean and inspect all parts and renew any parts damaged or excessively worn. When installing needle bearings inside covers, press pinion shaft bearings (2 and 8), cluster gear bearings (12) and axle housing bearings (10 and 32) 1/32 to 1/16 inch (0.8-1.5 mm) below machined surface. Press inner axle bearings to ¼ inch (6 mm) below machined surface. Reassemble differential and tighten cap screws to 25 to 30 ft.-lbs. (34-41 N·m). Install differential assembly and side covers and check axle end play. End play should be a minimum of 0.005-0.020 inch (0.127-0.508 mm) and is adjusted by changing shim (25). Reassemble gear reduction and differential unit and torque side cover cap screws to 30 ft.-lbs. (41 N·m).

After assembly is completed, reinstall assembly on tractor and fill with automatic transmission fluid Type "F" approximately 8 quarts (7.5 L). Adjust linkage as necessary.

Models 1455-1476-1477

After removing hydrostatic drive and differential assembly, remove wheels, hubs and drive keys from axles. Using a ⅜ inch Allen wrench, remove oil filter stud (10 – Fig. B69). Unbolt and remove unloader assembly and cover (2). Remove bearing flange (55), brake shaft (58) and coupler (52). Remove locating bolt (12), then remove hydrostatic unit from transaxle housing.

To disassemble reduction gears and differential, unbolt and remove axle housing (26). Slide differential assembly from transaxle housing (51) and lay it aside for later disassembly. Remove bowed "E" ring (47) and while holding bull gear (48), withdraw intermediate shaft (50) and spacer (49) from housing. Lift out bull gear.

Remove six cap screws (34) from differential assembly and separate axle assemblies from ring gear (37). Remove floating pinion shaft (43), pinion gears (41) and thrust washers (40) from ring gear. Side gears (39), shims (38) and covers (36 and 44) can be removed from axle shafts after first removing retaining rings (42).

Remove bushing (20) with parking pawl (24) from transaxle housing.

Inspect all parts and renew any showing excessive wear or other damage. When renewing needle bearings, press new bearings beyond machined casting

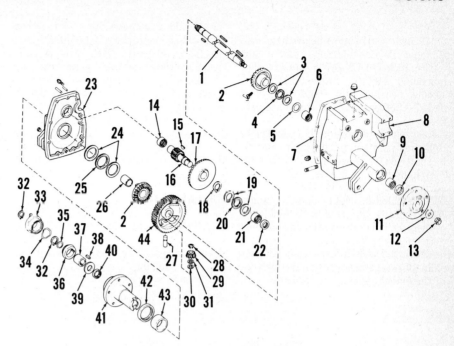

Fig. B67 — Exploded view of gear reduction and differential unit on Models 1225, 1256, 1257, 1556, H14 and H16.

1. Axle shaft	12. Washer	23. Cover	34. Spring washer
2. Side gear	13. Nut	24. Thrust washers	35. Shim
3. Thrust washers	14. Bearing	25. Thrust bearing	36. Cone
4. Thrust bearing	15. Key	26. Bearing	37. Coupling
5. Shim	16. Pinion shaft	27. Drive pin	38. Key
6. Bearing	17. Bevel gear	28. Snap ring	39. Thrust washer
7. Gasket	18. Thrust washers	29. Drive pinion	40. Oil seal
8. Case	19. Thrust washers	30. Thrust washer	41. Wheel hub
9. Bearing	20. Thrust bearing	31. Thrust washer	42. Oil seal
10. Oil seal	21. Bearing	32. Snap ring	43. Bearing
11. Wheel hub	22. Oil seal	33. Adjusting handwheel	44. Ring gear

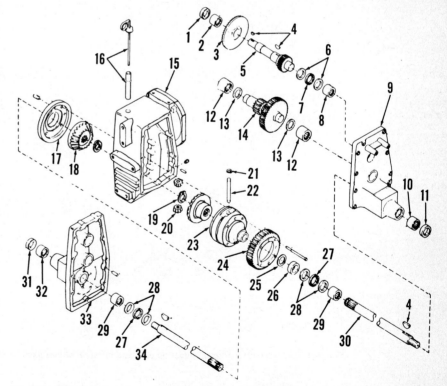

Fig. B68 — Exploded view of gear reduction and differential assembly used on Models H11XL, H12XL, H14XL and H16XL.

1. Oil seal	8. Needle bearing	
2. Needle bearing	9. Transaxle cover (R.H.)	
3. Bevel gear	10. Bearing	
4. Key	11. Oil seal	
5. Pinion shaft	12. Needle bearing	
6. Thrust race	13. Thrust race	
7. Thrust bearing		

14. Cluster gear assy.	20. Pinion gear	26. Spacer	31. Oil seal
15. Transaxle housing	21. Snap ring	27. Thrust bearing	32. Bearing
16. Dipstick assy.	22. Pinion shaft	28. Thrust race	33. Transaxle cover (L.H.)
17. Differential cover	23. Carrier	29. Needle bearing	34. Axle (L.H.)
18. Axle gear	24. Ring gear	30. Axle (R.H.)	
19. Snap ring	25. Shim		

surface as follows: Axle bearings (32) 0.040 inch (1.016 mm) below machined surface; needle bearings (28) 0.005-0.030 inch (0.127-0.762 mm) below machined surface; intermediate shaft needle bearing (46) 0.005-0.020 inch (0.127-0.508 mm) below machined surface.

Reassemble differential, keeping the following points in mind: Right hand axle shaft (45) is more than 2 inches (50 mm) longer than left axle shaft (35), and cover (44) with threaded bolt holes must be assembled on right hand axle shaft. After bolting differential assembly together, support differential on end cover (44) only with axle shaft (45) pointing downward. Insert a feeler gage between shim (38) and end cover (36) through one of the end cover slots, to measure clear-ance. Add or remove shims as required to obtain a clearance of 0.001-0.007 inch (0.025-0.178 mm). This will provide proper differential bevel gear backlash.

Renew all "O" rings, gaskets and oil seals and reassemble transaxle by reversing disassembly procedure.

Reinstall assembly on tractor; fill with Bolens #171-9650 hydraulic oil or Type "A" automatic transmission fluid and adjust linkage as necessary.

Model QS16

After removing rear axle assembly with hydrostatic drive unit, thoroughly clean entire unit to eliminate possibility of dirt entering system when hydrostatic unit is separated.

Remove plug (9 – Fig. B70) to drain fluid from system, then four mounting cap screws so hydrostatic unit can be lifted off and set aside. Continue disassembly by removal of right hand drive wheel, hub, brake disc rotor and Woodruff key (10). Back out cap screws (33) and remove right hand housing and axle sleeve (34) by sliding carefully from axle (19). Entire reduction gear set, cluster gear (8), pinion shaft (5) and input bevel gear (4) can be slipped together from housing (3). Watch for thrust races (7) during removal. Remove left side cover (25) after wheel, hub and brake disc are removed, then both axles (11 and 19) and complete bull gear (16) assembly can be removed.

Carefully inspect all thrust races (7) and thrust bearings (30) for undue wear,

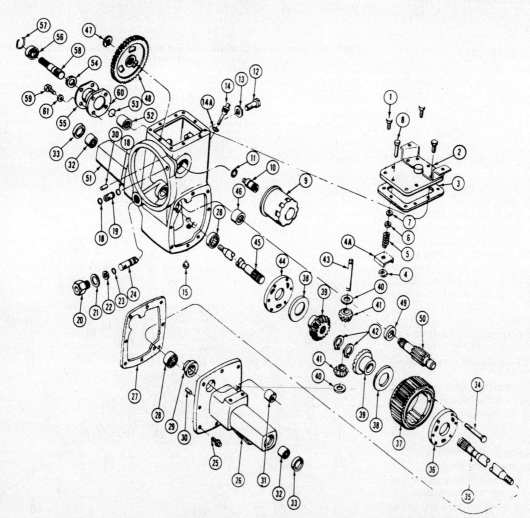

Fig. B69 — Exploded view of axle, reduction gear and differential unit used on Models 1455, 1476 and 1477.

1. Cap screw	11. "O" ring	23. "O" ring	33. Oil seal	43. Shaft	53. Snap ring
2. Cover	12. Locating bolt	24. Parking pawl	34. Cap screw	44. Cover (R.H.)	54. Oil seal
3. Gasket	13. Seal washer	25. Cap screw	35. Axle shaft (L.H.)	46. Needle bearing	55. Bearing flange
4. Speed nut	14. Dipstick	26. Axle housing	36. Cover (L.H.)	47. Bowed "E" ring	56. Ball bearing
4A. Deflector	14A. "O" ring	27. Gasket	37. Ring gear	48. Bull gear	57. Snap ring
5. Spring	15. Drain plug	28. Needle bearing	38. Shim	49. Spacer	58. Brake shaft
6. Washer	18. "O" rings	29. Spacer	39. Side gears	50. Intermediate shaft	59. Cap screw
7. Gasket	19. Tube	30. Dowel	40. Thrust washers	51. Transaxle housing	60. Gasket
8. Unloader button	20. Bushing	31. Needle bearing	41. Pinion gears	52. Coupling	61. Seal washer
9. Oil filter	21. Seal washer	32. Needle bearing	42. Retaining rings		
10. Filter stud	22. Quad ring				

galling or other damage. Remove axle seals (23) and remove and check condition of axle needle bearings (24). Renew bearings as needed, installing so they are seated from 1/32 to 1/16 inch (0.8-1.5 mm) past counterbore for axle seal. Always renew seals when axle is disassembled for any reason. Be sure to use a properly fitted seal driver.

Carefully check condition of all needle bearings (24, 27 and 28) in side housings; renew if at all doubtful. Press new bearings, identification side out, with a fitted drive to a point 1/32 to 1/16 inch (0.8-1.5 mm) below machined surface.

If there is evidence of damage or excessive wear in axle-differential assem-

bly, remove four cap screws (20) so axle and bull gear carriers (12 and 18) can be removed. Side bevel gears (13) can be removed from axles (11 and 19) after snap rings (14) are removed. Check condition of pinion gears (15) and pinion shaft (17) and renew as needed.

NOTE: When renewing any gears, be sure part numbers are properly checked out; ratios may differ.

To reassemble final drive when overhaul is complete, begin with bull gear-differential and axles. When carrier side plates (12 and 18) are set in place, cap screws (20) should be tightened to 30

ft.-lbs. (41 N·m) in even cross-sequence. Rotation should be free with no perceptible binding or roughness between pinions and side gears. Minimum of 0.010 inch (0.254 mm) axle end play is essential. Side gear should have 0.004 inch (0.102 mm) minimum clearance with bull gear carriers (12 and 18). Axle shaft end play is most easily checked by measuring between inner end of spacer (31) and carrier side plate (18) when axle is partially reassembled. Use a feeler gage, and add or remove shims to hold within limits of 0.005-0.030 inch (0.127-0.762 mm).

Backlash between all gear sets is 0.004-0.010 inch (0.102-0.254 mm).

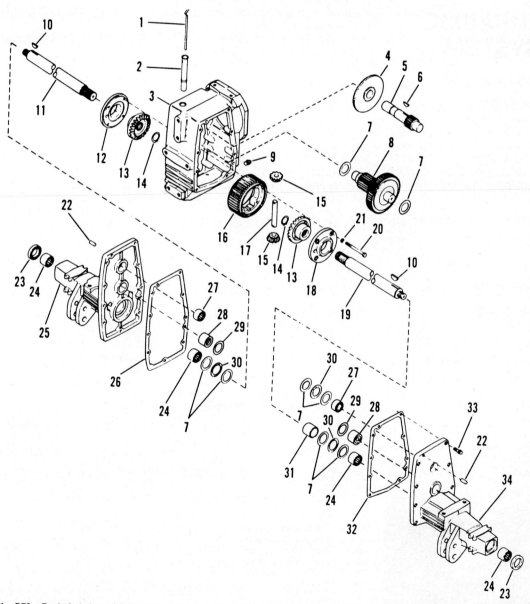

Fig. B70 — Exploded view of final drive-reduction gear and differential used with Sundstrand hydrostatic unit on Model QS16.

1. Dipstick	7. Thrust race (8)	13. Side gear (2)	18. Bull gear carrier (R.H.)
2. Fill pipe	8. Cluster gear	14. Snap ring (2)	19. Axle (R.H.)
3. Housing	9. Plug	15. Pinion gear	20. Cap screw (4)
4. Input bevel gear	10. Woodruff key (2)	16. Bull gear	21. Lockwasher
5. Pinion shaft	11. Axle (L.H.)	17. Pinion shaft	22. Dowel pin (4)
6. Woodruff key	12. Bull gear carrier (L.H.)		

23. Oil seal (2)	29. Shim(s)
24. Needle bearing (4)	30. Thrust bearing (3)
25. Housing cover (L.H.)	31. Spacer
26. Cover gasket	32. Cover gasket
27. Nedle bearing	33. Cap screw (17)
28. Needle bearing	34. Housing cover (R.H.)

Check after gears are reinstalled in case. Use new side gaskets (26 and 32). Check side clearance of cluster gear (8) between thrust washer (7) and right hand side cover. Add or remove shims (29) if not within 0.005-0.030 inch (0.127-0.762 mm) limit. Remove right hand cover to do so. When assembly is completed, torque cover cap screws to 30 ft.-lbs. (41 N·m).

Check entire reduction gear assembly for freedom of rotation before remounting hydrostatic unit. Refill axle housing with specified fluid and reassemble to tractor frame. Test and perform required adjustments.

HYDRAULIC SYSTEM

All Models So Equipped

TESTING. Hydraulic lift system pressure is provided by charge and auxiliary hydraulic pump located in hydrostatic transmission. Hydraulic lift pressure should be 450-500 psi (3100-3447 kPa) on all models except QS16, which should be 550-800 psi (3792-5516 kPa).

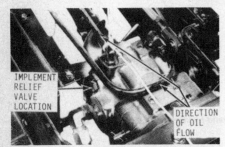

Fig. B71 — On models so equipped, hydrostatic charge pump supplies hydraulic lift system pressure. To check pressure, install a 1000 psi (7000 kPa) pressure gage in hydraulic line "A" using a tee fitting. Refer to text.

1. Hydrostatic transmission
2. Oil filter
3. Control valve
4. Hydraulic cylinder

Fig. B72 — On Model QS16, implement relief valve is located behind plug as shown. Shims are available to adjust pressure.

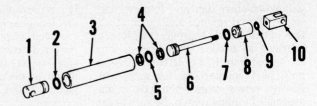

Fig. B73 — Exploded view of early style hydraulic cylinder used on some models.

1. Cylinder head
2. "O" ring
3. Cylinder tube
4. Washers
5. "O" ring
6. Piston & rod
7. "O" ring
8. Gland
9. "O" ring
10. Clevis

To check pressure on all models, proceed as follows: Using a tee fitting, install a 1000 psi (7000 kPa) pressure gage in hydraulic line (A – Fig. B71) between control valve (3) and lift cylinder (4). With oil at operating temperature and engine running at full rpm, move control lever until cylinder reaches end of its travel and observe pressure reading.

If pressure is low, check the following:
1. System low on oil.
2. Plugged hydraulic filter.
3. Hydraulic valve or cylinder leaking internally.
4. Malfunctioning implement relief valve.
5. Charge pump defective.

On Model QS16, shims are available to increase implement relief valve pressure

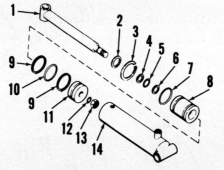

Fig. B74 — Exploded view of late style hydraulic cylinder used on some models.

1. Piston rod	8. Gland
2. Seal	9. Washer
3. Snap ring	10. "O" ring
4. Washer	11. Piston
5. "O" ring	12. Washer
6. Washer	13. Nut
7. "O" ring	14. Cylinder

setting. See Fig. B72. One 0.012 inch shim will increase pressure approximately 50 psi (345 kPa).

HYDRAULIC CYLINDER

All Models So Equipped

To remove piston rod assembly from cylinder, elbow hose fittings must first be removed from cylinder tube. Refer to appropriate Fig. B73 or B74. Then, remove cylinder gland (8) from cylinder tube and withdraw piston rod assembly from cylinder.

Inspect piston and cylinder for wear, scoring or other damage and renew as necessary. Renew all "O" rings and ring washers. Coat all "O" rings with grease to prevent damage during reassembly.

CONTROL VALVE

All Models So Equipped

To remove spool (7 – Fig. B75) from valve body (5), remove screw from end of spool, detent assembly and centering spring and guides. Withdraw spool from lever end of valve body.

If spool or valve body is damaged, renew complete valve assembly. Install new lip seal rings (6) onto spool with lip opening towards inside of spool. Coat seal rings with grease and reinstall spool into valve body from lever end.

Fig. B75 — Exploded view of typical hydraulic lift control valve. When renewing lip seals (6), lip opening goes towards inside of spool (7).

1. Detent ramp
2. Spring guides
3. Centering spring
4. Outlet
5. Valve body
6. Lip seals
7. Valve spool
8. Relief valve assy.
9. Inlet
10. Detent assy.

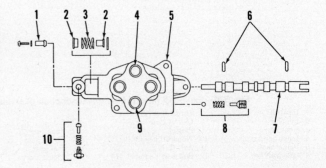

CASE/INGERSOLL

CONDENSED SPECIFICATIONS

	MODELS				
	107	**108**	**110**	**117**	**118**
Engine Make	Tecumseh	B&S	B&S	Tecumseh	B&S
Model	V70	190707	251707	V70	190707
Bore	2¾ in. (69.8 mm)	3 in. (76.2 mm)	3-7/16 in. (87.3 mm)	2¾ in. (69.8 mm)	3 in. (76.2 mm)
Stroke	2-17/32 in. (64.3 mm)	2¾ in. (69.8 mm)	2⅝ in. (66.7 mm)	2-17/32 in. (64.3 mm)	2¾ in. (69.8 mm)
Piston Displacement	15 cu. in. (246 cc)	19.44 cu. in. (319 cc)	24.36 cu. in. (399 cc)	15 cu. in. (246 cc)	19.44 cu. in. (319 cc)
Horsepower	7	8	10	7	8
Slow Idle Speed – Rpm	1000	1750	1750	1000	1750
High Idle Speed (No Load) – Rpm	3600	3600	3600	3600	3600
Full Load Speed – Rpm	3500	3500	3500	3500	3500
Crankcase Oil Capacity	1½ pints (0.7L)	2¼ pints (1L)	2¼ pints (1L)	1½ pints (0.7L)	2¼ pints (1L)
Weight –					
Above 32°F (0°C)	SAE 30				
0°F (−18°C) to 32°F (0°C)	SAE 10W-30				
Below 0°F (−18°C)	SAE 5W-20				
Transmission Oil Capacity	2 pints (0.9L)	2 pints (0.9L)	2 pints (0.9L)	....	....
Weight	SAE 90 EP	SAE 90 EP	SAE 90 EP	Type "A"	Type "A"
Differential Oil Capacity	....	....	....	2¾ pints (1.3L)	2¾ pints (1.3L)

	MODELS			
	210	**220**	**222, 442**	**224, 444**
Engine Make	Kohler	Kohler	Kohler	Kohler
Model	K241A	K241A	K301A	K321A
Bore	3¼ in. (82.5 mm)	3¼ in. (82.5 mm)	3⅜ in. (85.7 mm)	3½ in. (88.9 mm)
Stroke	2⅞ in. (73.0 mm)	2⅞ in. (73.0 mm)	3¼ in. (82.5 mm)	3¼ in. (82.5 mm)
Piston Displacement	23.9 cu. in. (392 cc)	23.9 cu. in. (392 cc)	29.07 cu. in. (476 cc)	31.27 cu. in. (512 cc)
Horsepower	10	10	12	14
Slow Idle Speed – Rpm	1000	1000	1000	1000
High Idle Speed (No Load) – Rpm	3600	3600	3600	3600
Full Load Speed – Rpm	3500	3400	3400	3500
Crankcase Oil Capacity	3 pints (1.4L)	3 pints (1.4L)	3 pints (1.4L)	4 pints (1.9L)
Weight –				
Above 32°F (0°C)	SAE 30			
0°F (−18°C) to 32°F (0°C)	SAE 10W-30			
Below 0°F (−18°C)	SAE 5W-20			
Transmission Oil Capacity	3 pints (1.4L)	10 pints (4.7L)	10 pints (4.7L)	10 pints (4.7L)
Weight –				
Above 32°F (0°C)	SAE 90 EP	SAE 20W-40	SAE 20W-40	SAE 20W-40
Below 32°F (0°C)	SAE 90 EP	SAE 5W-20	SAE 5W-20	SAE 5W-20
Differential Oil Capacity	....	6 pints (2.8L)	6 pints (2.8L)	6 pints (2.8L)
Weight	....	SAE 90 EP	SAE 90 EP	SAE 90 EP

FRONT AXLE AND STEERING SYSTEM

AXLE MAIN MEMBER

All Models

The axle main member is mounted to main frame and pivots on a pivot pin on all models. To remove axle assembly, refer to Figs. C1 or C2, then disconnect drag link from steering arm on Models 107, 108, 110, 117 and 118 or from right steering spindle on all other models. Using a suitable jack under main frame, raise front of tractor until weight is removed from front wheels. Remove pivot pin, then raise front of tractor to clear axle main member. Roll front axle assembly forward from tractor.

TIE ROD

All Models

The tie rod used on all models is adjustable and front wheel toe-in is adjusted as follows: Disconnect tie rod ball joints (5 – Fig. C1 or 10 and 12 – Fig. C2) from steering spindles, loosen locknuts, and turn tie rod ends in or out as required. The correct toe-in is $\frac{1}{8}$ to $\frac{1}{4}$-inch (3-6 mm) measured as shown in Fig. C3.

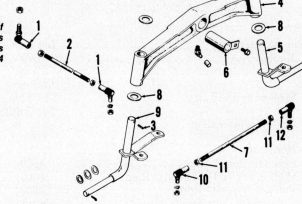

Fig. C2 – Exploded view of front axle and components used on Model 442. Models 210, 220, 222, 224 and 444 are similar.

1. Ball joint
2. Drag link
3. Roll pin
4. Axle main member
5. Steering spindle L.H.
6. Pivot pin
7. Tie rod
8. Thrust washer
9. Steering spindle R.H.
10. Ball joint
11. Locknut
12. Ball joint

STEERING SPINDLES

All Models

To remove steering spindles, block up under axle main member and remove front wheels. Disconnect drag link from right steering arm on Models 107, 108, 110, 117 and 118, or from right steering spindle on other models and remove tie rod. Remove cotter pins and washers, retaining rings or roll pins from top of steering spindles and lower steering spindles out of axle main member.

STEERING GEAR

Models 107-108-110-117-118

R&R AND OVERHAUL. Refer to Fig. C4 and remove steering wheel retaining nut (1), steering wheel and key (4). Disconnect drag link from quadrant gear (7). Using a suitable jack or hoist, raise front of tractor. Unscrew cap screws retaining pivot pin (8) and remove pin and quadrant gear (7). Withdraw steering shaft (3) through bottom of tractor. Remove and inspect bushings (2) for excessive wear.

Reinstall by reversing removal procedure. Position quadrant gear arm at a

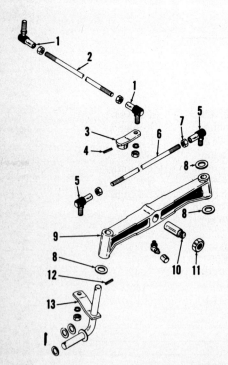

Fig. C1 – Exploded view of axle main member assembly used on Models 107, 108, 110, 117 and 118.

1. Ball joint	8. Washer
2. Drag link	9. Axle main member
3. Steering arm	10. Pivot pin
4. Roll pin	11. Nut
5. Ball joint	12. Roll pin
6. Tie rod	13. Steering spindle
7. Locknut	

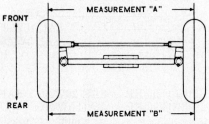

Fig. C3 – Toe-in measurement "A" should be $\frac{1}{8}$ to $\frac{1}{4}$-inch (3-6 mm) less than measurement "B" with both measurements taken at hub height.

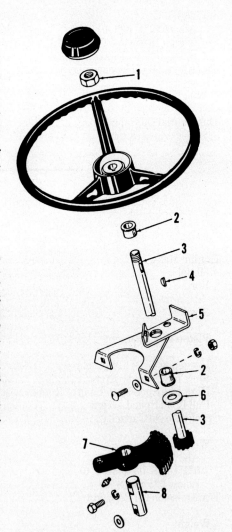

Fig. C4 – Exploded view of steering gear assembly used on Models 107, 108, 110, 117 and 118.

1. Nut	5. Bracket
2. Bushing	6. Washer
3. Steering shaft & pinion	7. Quadrant gear
4. Key	8. Steering pin

90 degree angle to drag link with front wheels in straight ahead position and connect drag link.

Models 210-220-222-224-442-444

R&R AND OVERHAUL. Refer to Fig. C5 or C6 and remove steering wheel retaining nut and steering wheel (1). On late Models 220, 222, 442 and 444 and all 224 tractors, remove key (17 – Fig. C6) and tube (16). On all models, raise front of tractor using a suitable jack or hoist and disconnect drag link from quadrant gear (11 – Fig. C5 or C6). Remove cap screw (15), lockwasher (14), washer (13), quadrant gear (11) and shims (10 and 12). Shims (10 and 12) should be kept in the order they are removed to aid in reassembly. On early Models 210, 220, 222, 442 and 444, unseat retaining ring (4 – Fig. C5) from

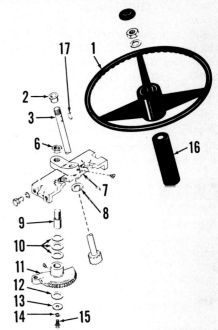

Fig. C6 – Exploded view of steering gear assembly used on late production 220, 222, 442 and 444 tractors and all 224 tractors.

1. Steering wheel	10. Shims
2. Nylon bushing	11. Quadrant gear
3. Steering shaft &	12. Shim
pinion	13. Washer
6. Locknut	14. Lockwasher
7. Steering support	15. Cap screw
8. Washer	16. Tube
9. Stub shaft	17. Key

its groove, then on all models withdraw steering shaft and pinion (3 – Fig. C5 or C6) from steering support (7) and from underside of tractor. Remove nylon bushing (2) from steering column. Unbolt and remove steering support (7). Remove locknut (6), then unscrew stub shaft (9) from support.

Clean and inspect all parts and renew any showing excessive wear or other damage. To reassemble, reverse disassembly procedure. On early Models 210, 220, 222, 442 and 444 steering shaft (3 – Fig. C5) end play is controlled by washers (5 and 8) and retaining ring (4). On late production models and all 224 tractors, tighten steering wheel retaining nut to remove excessive end play of steering shaft (3). Shims (10 – Fig. C5 or C6) are used to adjust gear backlash between quadrant gear (11) and steering shaft pinion. Adjust gear backlash by repositioning shims (10) from upper to lower side of quadrant gear (11) to decrease backlash or from lower to upper side of quadrant gear to increase backlash. Backlash should be minimal without causing binding of gears. Gears should be lubricated with good quality multi-purpose grease after every 50 hours of operation.

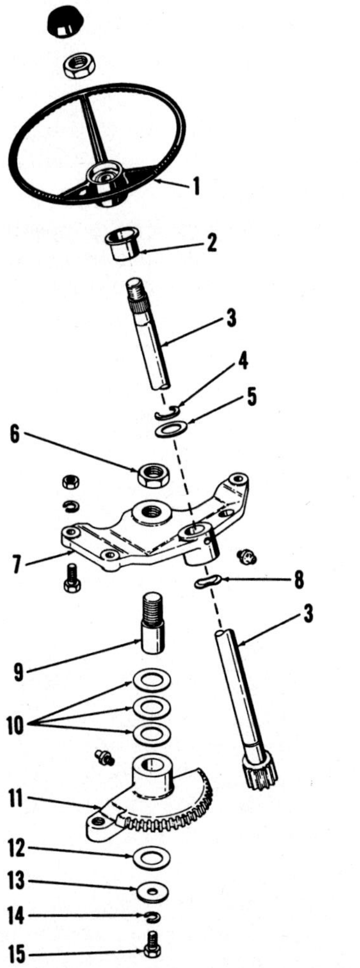

ENGINE

REMOVE AND REINSTALL

Models 107-117

To remove engine, remove hood and grille and disconnect battery cables. Disconnect fuel line, starter generator wires, ignition wire and choke and throttle control cables. Detach drive belts from engine drive pulley. Unscrew mounting bolts and lift engine from tractor.

To reinstall engine, reverse removal procedure.

Models 108-110-118

To remove engine, tilt hood and grille assembly forward, disconnect battery cables and remove battery. Disconnect starter cable, alternator wire and magneto ground wire. Disconnect fuel line and choke and throttle control cable. Remove belts from engine drive pulley. Remove four engine mounting plate bolts and lift engine and mounting plate from tractor.

Model 210

To remove engine, tilt hood and grille assembly forward and disconnect battery cables, starter-generator wires and ignition wire. Disconnect headlight wire, choke and throttle control cables and

fuel line. Unbolt and remove belt guard, then remove belt from engine drive pulley. Disconnect pto clutch linkage. Remove four engine mount cap screws and lift engine and mounting plates from tractor.

Reinstall engine assembly by reversing removal procedure.

Models 220-222-224-442-444

To remove engine, tilt hood and grille forward. Disconnect battery cables, starter-generator wires and ignition wire. Disconnect headlight wires and pull through hole in engine plate. Disconnect choke and throttle cables and fuel line. Disconnect pto clutch control rod (models so equipped). Disconnect hydraulic line at oil tank and drain oil tank. Disconnect hydraulic line leading to oil cooler. Unscrew mounting bolts securing bracket holding oil tank and oil cooler and remove as an assembly. On late production 220, 222 and 442 tractors and all 224 and 444 tractors, drain engine crankcase and remove drain tube. Disconnect oil lines from hydraulic pump, unbolt engine and lift engine and pump from tractor frame.

To reinstall engine, reverse removal procedure. Be sure crankcase and hydraulic reservoir are refilled and hydraulic hoses are properly connected before starting engine.

Fig. C5 – Exploded view of steering gear assembly used on Model 210 and early production 220, 222, 442 and 444 tractors.

1. Steering wheel	8. Wave washer
2. Bushing	9. Steering pin
3. Steering shaft &	10. Shims
pinion	11. Quadrant gear
4. Retainer ring	12. Shim
5. Washer	13. Washer
6. Nut	14. Lockwasher
7. Support plate	15. Cap screw

OVERHAUL

Engine make and model are listed at the beginning of this section. To overhaul engine components and accessories, refer to Briggs & Stratton, Kohler and Tecumseh sections of this manual.

CLUTCH AND BRAKE

Model 107

The clutch and brake mechanisms are actuated by clutch-brake pedal on right side of tractor. Refer to Fig. C7 for an exploded view of clutch and brake assemblies. Clutch is spring loaded and does not require adjustment. To adjust brake, turn adjusting nuts (11–Fig. C7) so brake will engage when clutch is disengaged.

Model 108-110

A belt idler type clutch and a disc brake are used on these tractors. The clutch idler is spring loaded and does not require adjustment. Refer to Fig. C8 for exploded view of clutch and brake assemblies. To adjust brake, disconnect eye-bolt (15) from actuating lever (23). Adjust nuts (24) until free movement at top of actuating lever does not exceed ½-inch (13 mm), then reconnect eye-bolt. Adjust nut (13) on brake rod so brake will engage when clutch is fully disengaged.

Model 117

A clutch is not used on Model 117 tractors. The control arm of hydrostatic transmission has a natural tendency to return to neutral position when there is no tension against arm. To prevent control arm from working into neutral position when speed control lever is released, a plate attached to control arm is held by a friction button on the end of brake control rod. Refer to Fig. C9. When brake is applied, the plate is released and transmission control arm is allowed to move into neutral position.

To adjust brake, turn adjusting nuts (13) to provide sufficient braking action. After adjusting brake, adjustment of neutral linkage should be checked.

Model 118

The belt idler clutch is operated by clutch-brake pedal on right side of tractor. As pedal is depressed, pin on clutch-brake pedal rotates pivot plate (8–Fig. C10) and clutch idler (7) to release tension on drive belt (2). As pedal is further depressed, brake band (16) is drawn

tight on brake drum (13). Adjust brake by turning nut (14) on brake rod. Make certain clutch is fully disengaged before brake is applied.

Model 210

The belt idler clutch is operated by clutch-brake pedal on left side of tractor. To adjust clutch, loosen locknut (8–Fig.

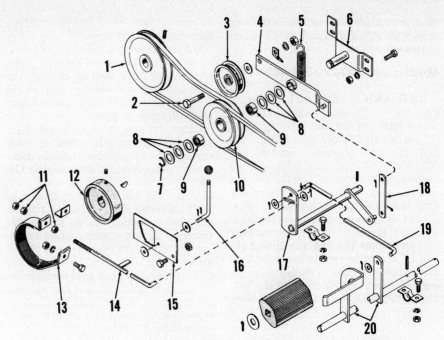

Fig. C7 – View showing clutch and brake assemblies on Model 107.

1. Transmission pulley
2. Bolt
3. Clutch idler pulley
4. Lever
5. Spring
6. Jackshaft
7. Snap ring
8. Washers
9. Bearing
10. Jackshaft pulley
11. Nuts
12. Brake drum
13. Brake band
14. Brake rod
15. Parking brake bracket
16. Parking brake lever
17. Lever
18. Idler arm
19. Clutch-brake rod
20. Pedal & shaft

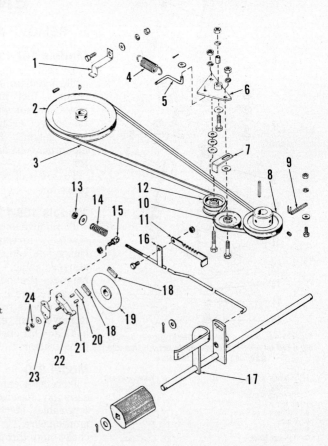

Fig. C8 – Exploded view of clutch and brake system used on 108 and 110 tractors. Spring (14) is not used on some tractors.

1. Belt keeper (2 used)
2. Transaxle input pulley
3. Drive belt
4. Clutch spring
5. Clutch rod
6. Pivot plate
7. Belt keeper
8. Engine drive pulley
9. Belt keeper (2 used)
10. Idler pulley (Vee)
11. Brake latch
12. Idler pulley (flat)
13. Nut
14. Brake return spring
15. Eye-bolt
16. Brake rod
17. Clutch-brake pedal & shaft assy.
18. Brake pads
19. Brake disc
20. Plate
21. Actuating pins
22. Carrier
23. Actuating lever
24. Nuts

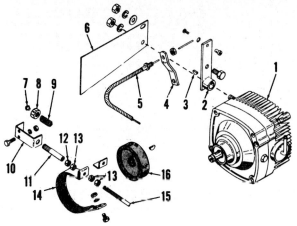

Fig. C9 — View showing brake and transmission friction plate on Model 117.

1. Transmission
2. Control arm
3. Key
4. Cable bracket
5. Speed control cable
6. Friction plate
7. Friction button
8. Nut
9. Spring
10. Bracket
11. Rod extension
12. Locknut
13. Adjusting nuts
14. Brake band
15. Brake rod
16. Brake drum

Model 117

To remove drive belt, first remove pto drive belt from engine pulley. Move spring loaded idler away from front of drive belt and slide drive belt off engine pulley and transmission pulley.

Install new drive belt by reversing removal procedure.

Model 118

To remove drive belt (2 – Fig. C10), first tilt hood forward and remove battery. Loosen retaining nuts and move belt keepers (4, 6 and 12) away from belt. Remove pto drive belt from engine pulley (5). Depress clutch-brake pedal and engage brake latch (10). Remove drive belt.

Using Fig. C10 as a guide, install new belt on pulleys as shown. Install pto drive belt on engine pulley. Release clutch-brake pedal. Adjust all belt keepers to 1/16-inch (1.5 mm) clearance from belt when pedal is in normal (up) position. Belt keeper (4) should be positioned halfway between points where belt enters and leaves Vee idler pulley (7). Reinstall battery.

Model 210

To remove primary drive belt (20 – Fig. C11), loosen retaining nut and move belt keeper (17) away from belt. Unbolt bearing flanges (25) from frame and move jackshaft assembly to the right and downward. Remove primary drive belt. Install new belt by reversing removal procedure. Adjust belt keeper (17) so there is a clearance of 1/16-inch (1.5 mm) between keeper and belt. Keeper should be centered between points where belt enters and leaves idler pulley (16).

C11) and rotate turnbuckle (7) as necessary until a clearance of 1/8-inch (3 mm) is obtained between brake latch pin on pedal arm and instrument tower side panel. Tighten locknut.

To adjust brake, turn adjusting nuts (1) on brake link (9) so clutch will fully disengage before brake is applied. With pedal in normal (up) position, compressed length of brake spring (2) should be approximately 1¼ inches (32 mm).

Models 220-222-224-442-444

To adjust brake on early production 220, 222, 442 and 444 tractors, refer to Fig. C12. Remove clevis pin (8) and turn clevis (9) until there is sufficient braking action when brake pedal is depressed. Do not over-adjust brake. When brake pedal is depressed, there must be enough brake pedal travel for neutral return spring attached to brake pedal to return speed control lever to neutral.

Later production 220, 222, 442 and 444 models, and all 224 tractors are equipped with band type brake shown in Fig. C13. To adjust brake, first adjust brake linkage mounting nuts to obtain 0.010-0.015 inch (0.254-0.381 mm) clearance between washers and brake arms. Disconnect brake rod clevis from vertical link. Place range transmission in neutral position. Tighten band adjusting nut until tractor cannot be moved manually, then back nut off 1½ turns. Hold brake vertical link in vertical position and push it rearward until all slack is removed from linkage. With brake pedal in full release (up) position, adjust clevis on linkage rod until holes in clevis are aligned with hole in vertical link. Install clevis pin.

DRIVE BELTS

REMOVE AND REINSTALL

Model 107

To remove front drive belt, remove pto drive belt from engine pulley. Move spring loaded idler away from front drive belt and slide drive belt off engine pulley and jackshaft pulley (10 – Fig. C7). To remove rear drive belt, remove front drive belt as previously outlined, disengage clutch and slide rear drive belt off jackshaft pulley (10) and transmission pulley (1).

Model 108-110

To remove drive belt (3 – Fig. C8), depress clutch-brake pedal and lock in this position with brake latch (11). Loosen retaining bolts and move belt keepers (1, 7 and 9) away from belt. Remove drive belt from pulleys.

Install new drive belt, making certain belt is positioned around idlers (10 and 12) as shown in Fig. C8. Adjust all belt keepers to 1/16-inch (1.5 mm) from belt when clutch-brake pedal is in normal (up) position. Belt keeper (7) should be positioned halfway between points where belt enters and leaves Vee idler pulley (10).

Fig. C10 — Exploded view of clutch and brake system used on Model 118 tractors.

1. Transmission input pulley
2. Drive belt
3. Flat idler (frame)
4. Belt keeper
5. Engine drive pulley
6. Belt keeper
7. Clutch idler
8. Pivot plate
9. Clutch spring
10. Brake latch
11. Flat idler
12. Belt keeper
13. Brake drum
14. Nut
15. Spring
16. Brake band
17. Brake rod
18. Clutch-brake pedal & shaft assy.

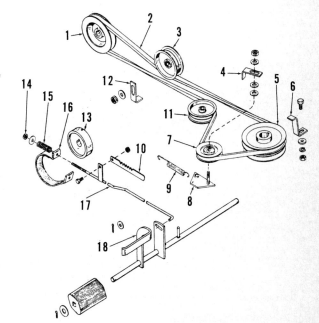

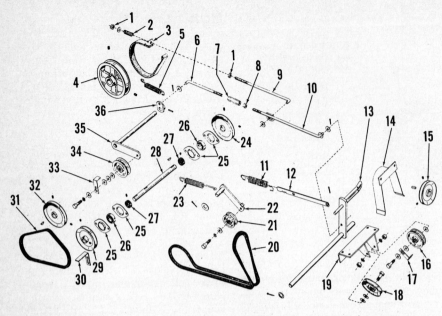

Fig. C11—Exploded view of clutch and brake system used on Model 210 tractors.

1. Brake adjusting nuts	19. Bracket	28. Jackshaft
2. Spring	20. Primary drive belt	29. Pulley
3. Brake band	21. Idler pulley	30. Belt keeper
4. Brake drum	22. Idler arm	31. Transaxle drive belt
5. Clutch spring	23. Spring	32. Transaxle input
6. Clutch link	24. Pulley	pulley
7. Turnbuckle	25. Bearing flanges	33. Belt keeper
8. Locknut	26. Bearing	34. Clutch idler pulley
9. Brake link	27. Lock collar	35. Clutch idler shaft
10. Clutch-brake rod		36. Arm
11. Return spring		
12. Brake latch		
13. Clutch-brake pedal		
& shaft assy.		
14. Belt guard		
15. Engine drive pulley		
16. Flat idler		
17. Belt keeper		
18. Vee idler		

To remove transaxle drive belt (31– Fig. C11), loosen belt keepers (30 and 33) and move them away from belt. Depress clutch-brake pedal and remove belt. Install new belt over pulleys and release pedal. Adjust belt keepers so there is a clearance of 1/16-inch (1.5 mm) between keepers and belt. Position keeper (33) so it is centered above clutch idler pulley (34) when clutch-brake pedal is depressed. Adjust clutch and brake linkage as necessary.

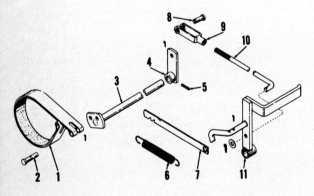

Fig. C12—Exploded view of brake assembly used on early production Models 220, 222, 442 and 444. Parking brake arrangement may differ on earlier models.

1. Brake band
2. Pin
3. Shaft
4. Arm
5. Roll pin
6. Spring
7. Parking brake latch
8. Pin
9. Clevis
10. Brake rod
11. Brake pedal

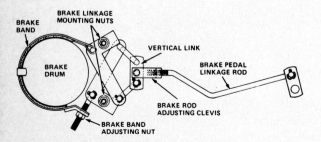

Fig. C13—Brake assembly used on late production 220, 222, 442 and 444 tractors and all 224 tractors.

CASE/INGERSOLL HYDRAULIC DRIVE

Models 220, 222, 224, 442 and 444 are equipped with a hydraulic drive system. To service system and its components, refer to following paragraphs.

OPERATION

Models 220-222-224-442-444

The three main components of hydraulic drive are hydraulic pump, control valve and hydraulic motor. The hydraulic pump draws oil from the reservoir located at front of tractor behind oil cooler. Oil is pumped to the drive control valve and when control valve is in neutral, oil passes through the valve and to the oil cooler. After flowing through the oil cooler, oil is returned to reservoir. If control valve is in forward or reverse position, oil is directed to hydraulic motor. This causes motor shaft to rotate which in turn drives range transmission input gear. Oil returning from the motor, flows through control valve, through oil cooler and to reservoir. When control lever is returned to neutral position, oil flow between valve and motor stops which stops rotation of motor shaft providing a dynamic braking action to stop tractor.

OIL FLOW AND PRESSURE CHECK

Models 220-222-224-442-444

To check oil flow and system pressure, install a "Hydra Sleuth," "Flo-Rater" or equivalent tester as shown in Fig. C14. Remove hydraulic lines from control valve to hydraulic motor and plug control valve ports, Close shut-off valve in line and fully open load valve on tester. Start and operate engine at 3600 rpm until hydraulic oil temperature is approximately 120°F (50°C). Check and record flow at 0 pressure. Slowly close tester load valve until pressure gage reading is 1000 psi (6895 kPa) and note flow reading. This flow reading must not be more than 25 percent less than previously recorded 0 pressure flow reading. If pump output flow drops more than 25 percent, pump is worn and must be overhauled or renewed.

If pump output flow drop is less than 25%, record flow at 1000 psi (6895 kPa) and continue tests. Fully open shut-off valve in line and load valve on tester. With engine still operating at 3600 rpm, move control lever in full forward or reverse position. Slowly close load valve on tester until pressure gage reading is

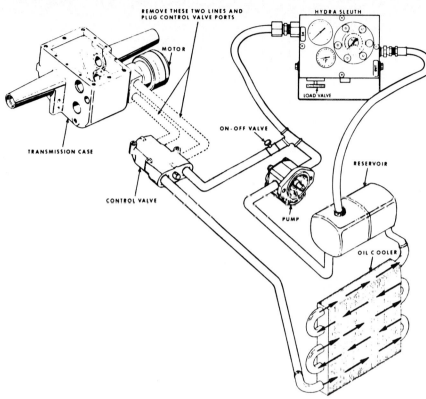

Fig. C14 — View showing "Hydra Sleuth" tester installed to check flow and pressure of hydraulic drive system on Models 220, 222, 224, 442 and 444.

1000 psi (6895 kPa) and note flow reading. This reading must not exceed ½-gpm (1.9L/min.) less than previously recorded pump gpm flow at 1000 psi (6895 kPa). If control valve internal leakage is more than ½-gpm (1.9L/min.), check and adjust relief valve pressure.

To check relief valve pressure, close load valve on tester and note pressure gage reading. The relief valve should open between 1850-2000 psi (12755-13790 kPa) on Models 220, 222 and 442. On Models 224 and 444, relief valve opening pressure should be 2050-2150 psi (14135-14825 kPa). On all models, turn adjusting plug (1–Fig. C15 or 8–Fig. C16) in to increase pressure or out to decrease pressure as required. Recheck control valve for internal leakage.

If control valve leakage still exceeds ½-gpm (1.9L/min.), valve body is excessively worn or cracked and valve must be renewed.

Remove test equipment and install original lines. If pump and control valve check out good and adequate tractor performance cannot be obtained, remove hydraulic motor and overhaul or renew motor.

CONTROL VALVE

Models 220-222-224-442-444

Early Models 220, 222, 442 and 444 tractors were equipped with a single-spool Dukes drive control valve (Fig. C15). Later production models and all 224 tractors are equipped with Dukes control valve shown in Fig. C16. Spool (3), detent assembly (11 through 18) and secondary (lift) relief valve assembly (19 through 23) are not used on models not equipped with hydraulic lift.

R&R CONTROL VALVE. To remove control valve, first drain hydraulic reservoir. Disconnect control lever linkage and hydraulic lines. Unbolt and remove control valve assembly. Plug hydraulic line openings to prevent dirt from entering system.

OVERHAUL (EARLY DUKES). To disassemble control valve, refer to exploded view in Fig. C15 and remove snap rings (7 and 13) from ends of spool (9) and withdraw spool from body. Remove quad rings at both ends of spool bore in body. Unscrew relief spring adjusting plug (1) and remove spring (3) and ball (4). Unscrew relief ball seat (5) and remove "O" ring (6).

Inspect components and renew any which are excessively worn. To reinstall spool (9), quad rings and snap rings, install quad ring (12) in spool bore. Insert spool (9) from back end of body as shown in Fig. C15. Pull spool through body until rear end of spool just clears rear quad ring groove in spool bore and install quad ring (8). Install front snap ring (13) on spool and carefully push spool into body and through rear quad ring (8). Install rear snap ring (7).

After installing control valve in tractor, check relief valve opening pressure and adjust as necessary.

OVERHAUL (LATE DUKES). To disassemble control valve, refer to Fig. C16 and proceed as follows: Remove snap rings (1) and withdraw travel spool (2).

NOTE: Some models, without hydraulic lift, are not equipped with lift spool (3), detent assembly (11 through 18) and secondary relief valve assembly (19 through 23).

On valves with two spools, remove plugs (18), springs (17) and detent balls (16), then unbolt and remove detent cover (15), withdraw lift spool assembly from valve body (5). Detent stem (14), spacer (13), centering spring (12) and washer (11) can now be removed. Unscrew cap (10) and remove gasket (9), adjusting screw (8), spring (7) and main relief ball (6). Place body (5) on a bench so drain plug (24) is pointing upward. Remove cap (19), gasket (20), adjusting screw (21), spring (22) and secondary

Fig. C15 — Exploded view of Dukes single-spool control valve used on early production 220, 222, 442 and 444 tractors.

1. Adjusting plug
2. "O" ring
3. Spring
4. Ball
5. Ball seat
6. "O" ring
7. Snap ring
8. Quad ring
9. Spool
10. Body
11. Plug
12. Quad ring
13. Snap ring

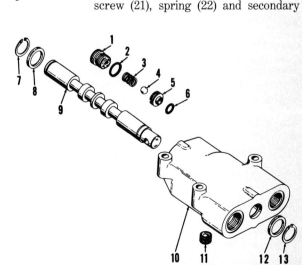

relief ball (23). Remove "O" rings (4) from valve body.

Clean and inspect all parts and renew any showing excessive wear or other damage. When installing relief valves, turn about ½ of adjusting screw threads into the valve. Install new "O" ring seals (4) in grooves in front end of valve body. Lubricate seals and insert spools (2 and 3) into correct bores at rear (relief valve) end of valve body. Push spools forward through front seals until rear seal grooves in bores are exposed. Install and lubricate rear seal rings, then move spools back to normal centered position. Install snap rings on travel spool (2) and using "Loctite" on detent stem threads, install washer (11), centering spring (12), spacer (13) and detent stem (14) on lift spool (3). Install detent cover (15), balls (16), springs (17) and plugs (18).

After installing control valve on tractor, adjust main relief valve pressure as previously outlined and secondary relief valve pressure to 575 psi (3965 kPa).

HYDRAULIC PUMP

Models 220-222-224-442-444

Wooster, Cessna and Borg-Warner hydraulic pumps have been used on these tractors. Refer to Figs. C17, C18 and C19 for identification and to following paragraphs for service procedures.

R&R PUMP. To remove hydraulic pump, drain hydraulic oil and disconnect hydraulic lines from pump. Cap or plug openings to prevent dirt from entering system. On tractors prior to S.N. 9646800, unbolt and remove side panels. Then, unbolt and remove pump and support assembly from side of tractor. On tractors with S.N. 9646800 and later, remove battery and battery tray. Unbolt and remove pump and support assembly from above.

On all models, mark position of coupling on pump shaft for aid in reassembly. Loosen set screw and remove coupling half from pump. Unbolt and remove pump from support.

Reinstall pump by reversing removal procedure. Make certain hydraulic reservoir is refilled before starting engine.

OVERHAUL (WOOSTER). To disassemble pump, refer to Fig. C17 and clamp flange of front cover (11) in a vise.

CAUTION: Do not clamp on pump body.

Scribe a line across pump covers and body for aid in reassembly. Remove cap screws from rear cover (1) and remove rear cover and seal ring (2). Remove pump body (3) with bearings (4 and 7), driven gear (5) and drive gear (6).

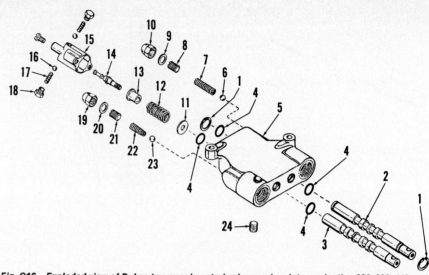

Fig. C16—Exploded view of Dukes two-spool control valve used on late production 220, 222, 442 and 444 tractors and all 224 tractors. Spool (3) and items (11 through 23) are used only on models equipped with hydraulic lift.

1. Snap rings
2. Travel spool
3. Lift spool
4. "O" rings
5. Valve body
6. Main relief ball
7. Main relief spring
8. Adjusting screw
9. Gasket
10. Cap
11. Washer
12. Centering spring
13. Spacer
14. Detent stem
15. Detent cover
16. Detent ball
17. Spring
18. Plug
19. Cap
20. Gasket
21. Adjusting screw
22. Secondary relief spring
23. Secondary relief ball
24. Drain plug

Withdraw bearings and gears from pump body. Remove brass pressure seal (8), rubber spacer (9), seal ring (10) and oil seal (12) from front cover.

Clean and inspect all parts and renew any that are excessively worn or otherwise damaged. When reassembling, renew all seals and lubricate all internal parts with clean oil. Install drive gear shaft carefully to prevent damage to lip of oil seal (12). Tighten four pump cap screws evenly to a torque of 28-32 ft.-lbs. (38-43 N·m).

OVERHAUL (CESSNA). To disassemble pump, refer to Fig. C18 and scribe a line across covers (1 and 11) and

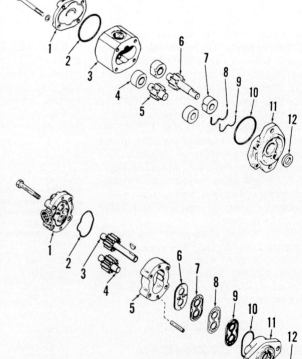

Fig. C17—Exploded view of Wooster hydraulic drive pump used on some early model tractors equipped with Case/Ingersoll hydraulic drive.
1. Rear cover
2. Seal ring
3. Pump body
4. Bearing
5. Driven gear
6. Drive gear
7. Bearing
8. Pressure seal
9. Rubber spacer
10. Seal ring
11. Front cover
12. Oil seal

Fig. C18—Exploded view of hydraulic pump similar to Cessna hydraulic pump used on some late production tractors equipped with Case/Ingersoll hydraulic drive.
1. Rear cover
2. Seal ring
3. Drive gear
4. Driven gear
5. Pump body
6. Diaphragm
7. Back-up gasket
8. Protector gasket
9. Diaphragm seal
10. Seal ring
11. Front cover
12. Oil seal

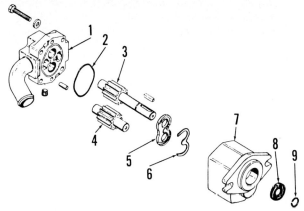

body (5) for aid in reassembly. Remove cap screws from rear cover (1) and separate rear cover and seal ring (2) from pump body. Withdraw driven gear (4) and drive gear (3). Separate body (5) from front cover (11). Note position of small pressure vent hole in diaphragm (6), gaskets (7 and 8) and diaphragm seal (9) and place a mark on adjacent area on cover. Remove diaphragm, gaskets, diaphragm seal and seal ring (10) from cover. Inspect shaft oil seal (12) and if removal is necessary, heat front cover (11) to approximately 250°F (120°C). Then, pull oil seal straight out of cover.

Clean and inspect all parts and renew any showing excessive wear or other damage. When reassembling, renew all seals, gaskets and diaphragm. Install diaphragm seal (9) with open "V" side first in cover (11) and small pressure vent hole adjacent to previously affixed mark on cover. Install gaskets (7 and 8) and diaphragm (6) aligning pressure vent holes with hole in diaphragm seal. Bronze side of diaphragm must face gears. Lubricate internal parts with clean oil. Make certain scribe marks on covers (1 and 11) and pump body (5) are aligned. Install and tighten cover cap screws to a torque of 24-26 ft.-lbs. (33-35 N·m).

OVERHAUL (BORG-WARNER). To disassemble pump, refer to Fig. C19 and scribe a line across cover (1) and pump

body (7) for aid in reassembly. Remove cap screws from rear cover and separate cover from pump body. Remove seal ring (2) and snap ring (9), then withdraw driven gear (4) and driving gear (3). Remove wear plate (5) and pressure seal (6). To remove oil seal (8), heat pump body to approximately 250°F (120°C), then pull oil seal straight out of cover.

Clean and inspect all parts and renew any showing excessive wear or other damage. When reassembling, lubricate internal parts with clean oil. Press new oil seal (8) in cover until seal is 0.188 inch (4.78 mm) below flush with end of bore. Install pressure seal (6) in wear plate (5). Install wear plate assembly in body (7). Carefully install drive gear (3) so lip of oil seal is not damaged. Install driven gear (4) with long end of shaft in body. Place new seal ring (2) in groove in cover (1), install cover assembly and align scribe marks. Install cap screws and tighten them to a torque of 24-26 ft.-lbs. (33-35 N·m). Place snap ring (9) in its groove on shaft.

HYDRAULIC MOTOR

Models 220-222-224-442-444

REMOVE AND REINSTALL. To remove hydraulic motor, place range transmission shift lever in neutral position. Block up under tractor frame and place a rolling floor jack under range

transmission and differential housing. Unbolt and remove fenders, seat and seat support. Disconnect hydraulic lines from hydraulic drive motor and plug or cap all openings. Remove cap screws securing range transmission and differential assembly to tractor frame and roll assembly rearward from tractor. Drain lubricant from transmission and differential housing, then unbolt and remove top cover. Remove left rear wheel. Unbolt hydraulic drive motor, hold range transmission sliding gear and withdraw drive motor. Let sliding gear rest in bottom of transmission housing.

When reinstalling hydraulic drive motor, use new "O" ring on motor housing. Hold range transmission sliding gear in position (shift fork between gears) and insert motor output shaft through housing and gear. Apply "Loctite" to cap screw threads and tighten motor retaining cap screws to a torque of 110-125 ft.-lbs. (149-169 N·m). The balance of installation is reverse of removal procedure. Fill transmission and differential housing to level plug opening with SAE 90 EP gear oil. Capacity is approximately 6 pints (2.8L). Fill hydraulic reservoir with new oil using SAE 5W-20 for temperatures below 32°F (0°C) or SAE 20W-40 for temperatures above 32°F (0°C). Use oil with API classification of SC, SD or SE.

Early Models 220-222

OVERHAUL HYDRAULIC MOTOR. These models are equipped with a hydraulic motor as shown in Fig. C20. Before disassembling motor, mark a line across surface of gerotor housing (18), spacer plate (15) and body (10). Also mark port side of mounting flange (1) and mark a line across front end of spool (7) bore and mounting flange (1) bore. These marks will aid in reassembly.

Unscrew cap screws (24) and remove end cap (22), "O" ring (21) and spacer (13). Remove rotor (19), rollers (20) and housing (18) as a unit. Remove "O" ring (17) and unscrew cap screws (16). Remove spacer plate (15), "O" ring (14) and drive coupling (12). Remove retaining cap screws and separate mounting flange (1) from body by tapping lightly on flange with a leather mallet. Remove washer (2), quad ring (4), "O" ring (5) and thrust washer (6) from flange (1). Withdraw spool (7) from body and drive pin (9) from body.

Inspect all parts for scratches, scoring and excessive wear. Spool (7) and body (10) are available only as an assembly. End cap (22) and spacer plate (15) may be polished but should not be grooved. Check thickness of housing (18), rotor (19) and rollers (20). Thickness of rotor and rollers must be within 0.002 inch (0.051 mm) of housing thickness. If dif-

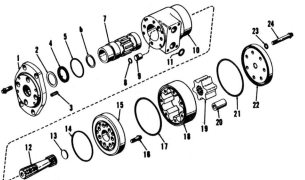

ference in thickness is greater than 0.002 inch (0.051 mm), housing (18), rotor (19) and rollers (20) must be renewed as an assembly. Seals and washers are available as an overhaul kit.

To assemble motor, install plug (9) so "O" ring end is to outside. Install components (2 through 6) in mounting flange (1) and install flange on body so marked side is on side of body ports. Tap mounting flange onto body and tighten cap screws evenly to 215 in.-lbs. (24 N·m). Make certain roll pins (3) do not protrude beyond face of mounting flange. Slide spool (7) into body (10) until it bottoms on thrust washer (6) in flange. Align marks on spool (7) and mounting flange (1). Install "O" rings (14 and 17) on spacer plate (15). Install spacer plate on body (10) so smaller "O" ring (14) is adjacent to body and marks are aligned. Secure plate with cap screws (16) and tighten to 175 in.-lbs. (19 N·m). Slide drive coupling (12), longer splined end first, through spacer plate and into spool. Install rotor, rollers and housing assembly with marks aligned. Stand motor on its mounting flange and install spacer (13) and end cap (22). Tighten cap screws (24) evenly to 175 in.-lbs. (19 N·m).

If no alignment marks were made during disassembly, or if new parts are used, it may be necessary to realign gerotor assembly to obtain proper motor operation. Reinstall motor and refill reservoir. Start engine and move control lever in forward position. Tractor should move forward; however, if tractor moves rearward with control lever in forward position, hydraulic motor is not properly aligned. To correct this condition, remove end cap (22) from motor. Index mark gerotor housing (18) to spacer plate (15) and rotor (19) to a spline on drive coupling (12). Slide rotor and housing assembly off drive coupling and rotate assembly one coupling tooth in either direction, then slide rotor back on drive coupling. Reinstall end cap (22) using new washers (23) and tighten cap screws evenly to 175 in.-lbs. (19 N·m). Recheck for correct operation.

Late Models 220-222 and All Models 224-442-444

OVERHAUL HYDRAULIC MOTOR. To disassemble hydraulic drive motor, clamp motor body port boss in a padded jaw vise with output shaft pointing downward. Remove seven cap screws (24–Fig. C21) and remove end cover (23), seal ring (22), commutator (19) and commutator ring (18). Remove sleeve (21), manifold (17) and manifold plate (16). Lift drive link (11), wear plate (12), rotor (13), rollers (14) and stator (15) off body (5). Remove output shaft (10), then remove snap ring (1), spacer (2), shim (3) and oil seal (4). Remove seal ring (9). Do not remove needle bearing (8), thrust bearing (7) or thrust washer (6) from body (5) as these parts are not serviced separately.

Clean and inspect all parts for excessive wear or other damage and renew as necessary. A seal ring and seal kit (items 2, 3, 4, 9, 20 and 22) is available for resealing motor. To reassemble motor, clamp body port boss in a padded vise with seven tapped holes upward. Insert shaft (10) and drive link (11). Install new seal ring (9) in groove on body (5). Place stator (15) on wear plate (12) and install rotor and rollers (13 and 14) with counterbore in rotor facing upward. Place wear plate and rotor assembly over drive link and onto body.

NOTE: Two cap screws, 3/8 x 4½ inches with heads removed, can be used to align bolt holes in body (5) with holes in wear plate (12), stator (15), manifold plate (16), manifold (17), commutator plate (18) and end cover (23).

Install manifold plate (16) with slots toward rotor. Install manifold (17) with swirl grooves toward rotor and diamond shaped holes upward. Place commutator ring (18) and commutator (19) on manifold with bronze ring groove facing upward. Place bronze seal ring (20) into groove with rubber side downward. Lubricate seal ring (9) and install sleeve (21) over assembled components. Install new seal ring (22) on end cover (23), lubricate seal ring and install end cover. Remove line up bolts and install seven cap screws (24). Tighten cap screws evenly to 50 ft.-lbs. (68 N·m).

Remove motor from vise and place it on bench with output shaft pointing upward. Lubricate and install new oil seal (4), shim (3), spacer (2) and snap ring (1). Lubricate motor by pouring new oil in one port and rotating output shaft until oil is expelled from other port.

HYDROSTATIC TRANSMISSION

LUBRICATION

Models 117-118

Both models are equipped with an Eaton Model 6 hydrostatic transmission. Approximate fluid capacity is 2¾ pints (1.3 L) of Type "A" automatic transmission fluid.

NEUTRAL ADJUSTMENT

Model 117

The control arm of hydrostatic transmission used on Model 117 tractors has a natural tendency to return to neutral position when there is no tension against control arm. To prevent control arm

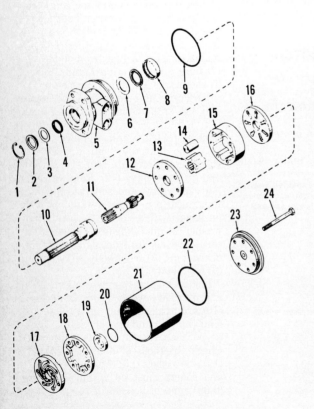

Fig. C21 — Exploded view of Ross hydraulic drive motor used on late Models 220 and 222 and all Models 224, 442 and 444.

1. Snap ring
2. Spacer
3. Shim washer (0.10 in.)
4. Oil seal
5. Body
6. Thrust washer
7. Thrust bearing
8. Needle bearing
9. Seal ring
10. Output shaft
11. Drive link
12. Wear plate
13. Rotor
14. Roller (6)
15. Stator
16. Manifold plate
17. Manifold
18. Commutator ring
19. Commutator
20. Seal ring
21. Sleeve
22. Seal ring
23. End cover
24. Cap screw (7)

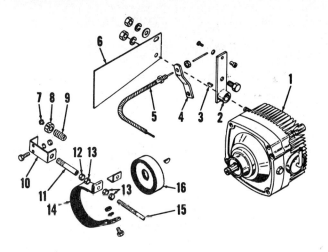

Fig. C23 — View showing brake, transmission linkage and friction plate used on Model 117 tractors.

1. Transmission
2. Control arm
3. Key
4. Cable bracket
5. Speed control cable
6. Friction plate
7. Friction button
8. Nut
9. Spring
10. Bracket
11. Rod extension
12. Locknut
13. Adjusting nuts
14. Brake band
15. Brake rod
16. Brake drum

from working into neutral position under normal operation, a plate attached to control arm is held by a friction button on end of brake control rod. Refer to Fig. C23. When brake is applied, plate is released and transmission control arm is allowed to move to neutral position.

To adjust neutral linkage, loosen locknut (12 – Fig. C23) and turn control rod extension (11) to increase or decrease friction between button (7) and plate (6). There should be sufficient friction to prevent transmission control arm from self-neutralizing when speed control lever is released, but speed control lever should not be difficult to move. Turn nut (8) to adjust spring tension on control rod so it will return to original position when brake is disengaged.

Adjust brake as necessary, then recheck adjustment of neutral linkage.

Model 118

To adjust neutral position of transmission linkage on Model 118 tractors, refer to Fig. C24 and proceed as follows: Place travel control lever (8) in neutral detent position. At this time, cam follower pin on control link (6) should be centered in S-slot of control cam (9) as shown in Fig. C25. If not, adjust nuts (10 – Fig. C24) to move "U" bolt (11) as shown in Fig. C26 until follower pin is centered in S-slot. Block up under rear of tractor so rear wheels are free to turn. With travel control lever in neutral detent position, start engine and operate at approximately half throttle. Rear wheels should remain stationary. If wheels rotate forward or rearward, loosen nut (7 – Fig. C24) and while keeping cam follower pin on control link (6) centered in S-slot as shown in Fig. C25, move control arm (4 – Fig. C24) as required to stop rotation of wheels. Retighten nut (7). Move travel control lever through forward and reverse drive ranges and recheck neutral adjustment.

REMOVE AND REINSTALL

Models 117-118

To remove hydraulic transmission, tilt seat and fender assembly forward and drain lubricant from gear reduction and differential housing.

On Model 117, disconnect control cable from transmission and detach friction plate from control arm of transmission. Remove oil expansion reservoir and mounting plate.

On Model 118, disconnect control cam from control link. Oil expansion reservoir can be removed if desired by rotating it in a clockwise direction.

CAUTION: If oil expansion reservoir is removed, precautions should be taken to prevent entrance of dirt or other foreign material into transmission.

On either model, unbolt and remove screen and cooling fan. Remove drive belt from input pulley. Unbolt transmission from gear reduction housing and lift hydraulic transmission from tractor.

Before disassembling transmission, thoroughly clean exterior of unit. Remove venting plug, invert assembly and drain fluid from unit.

Reinstall hydrostatic transmission by reversing removal procedure. Check and adjust linkage for neutral position as required. Fill reservoir ⅓ full with transmission fluid.

OVERHAUL

Models 117-118

Both models are equipped with an Eaton Model 6 hydrostatic transmission. Refer to Eaton Model 6 section in HYDROSTATIC TRANSMISSION SERVICE section for overhaul procedure.

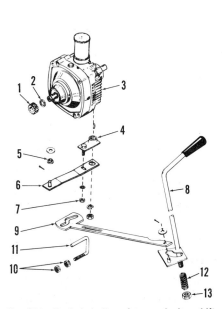

Fig. C24 — Exploded view of transmission shift linkage used on Model 118 tractors.

1. Transmission output gear
2. Spacer
3. Transmission
4. Control arm
5. Cam follower pin bushing
6. Control link
7. Adjusting nut
8. Travel control lever
9. Control cam
10. Adjusting nuts
11. "U" bolt
12. Spring
13. Nut

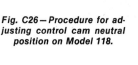

Fig. C25 — View showing correct neutral position of cam follower pin in S-slot of control cam on Model 118.

Fig. C26 — Procedure for adjusting control cam neutral position on Model 118.

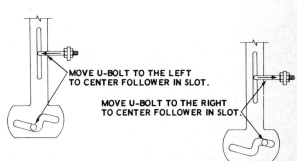

CAM FOLLOWER SHOULD BE IN THIS POSITION WHEN TRAVEL CONTROL LEVER IS IN NEUTRAL.

TRAVEL CONTROL CAM

CAM FOLLOWER

MOVE U-BOLT TO THE LEFT TO CENTER FOLLOWER IN SLOT.

MOVE U-BOLT TO THE RIGHT TO CENTER FOLLOWER IN SLOT.

TRANSAXLE

LUBRICATION

Models 107-108-110-210

Model 107 is equipped with a Peerless 1200 series transaxle. Approximate capacity is 2 pints (0.9 L) of SAE 90 EP gear lubricant. Lubricant is added through gear shift opening.

Models 108 and 110 are equipped with a Peerless 600 series transaxle. Approximate capacity is 2 pints (0.9 L) of SAE 90 EP gear lubricant. Lubricant is added through gear shift opening.

Model 210 is equipped with a Peerless 2300 series transaxle. Approximate capacity is 3 pints (1.4 L) of SAE 90 EP gear lubricant. Lubricant is added through gear shift opening.

REMOVE AND REINSTALL

Models 107-108-110-210

On Models 107, 108 and 110, disconnect brake linkage, depress clutch-brake pedal and remove drive belt from transaxle input pulley. On Model 210, unbolt and remove belt guard. Disconnect brake linkage, depress clutch-brake pedal and remove drive belt from transaxle input pulley. On all models, support tractor under frame and remove shift lever knob. Unbolt transaxle from frame, raise rear of tractor and remove transaxle assembly.

Reinstall transaxle by reversing removal procedure. Adjust clutch and brake linkage as required.

OVERHAUL

Models 107-108-110-210

Model 107 is equipped with a Peerless 1200 series transaxle. Models 108 and 110 are equipped with a Peerless 600 series transaxle. Model 210 is equipped with a Peerless 2300 series transaxle. Refer to the appropriate Peerless section in TRANSAXLE SERVICE section for overhaul procedure.

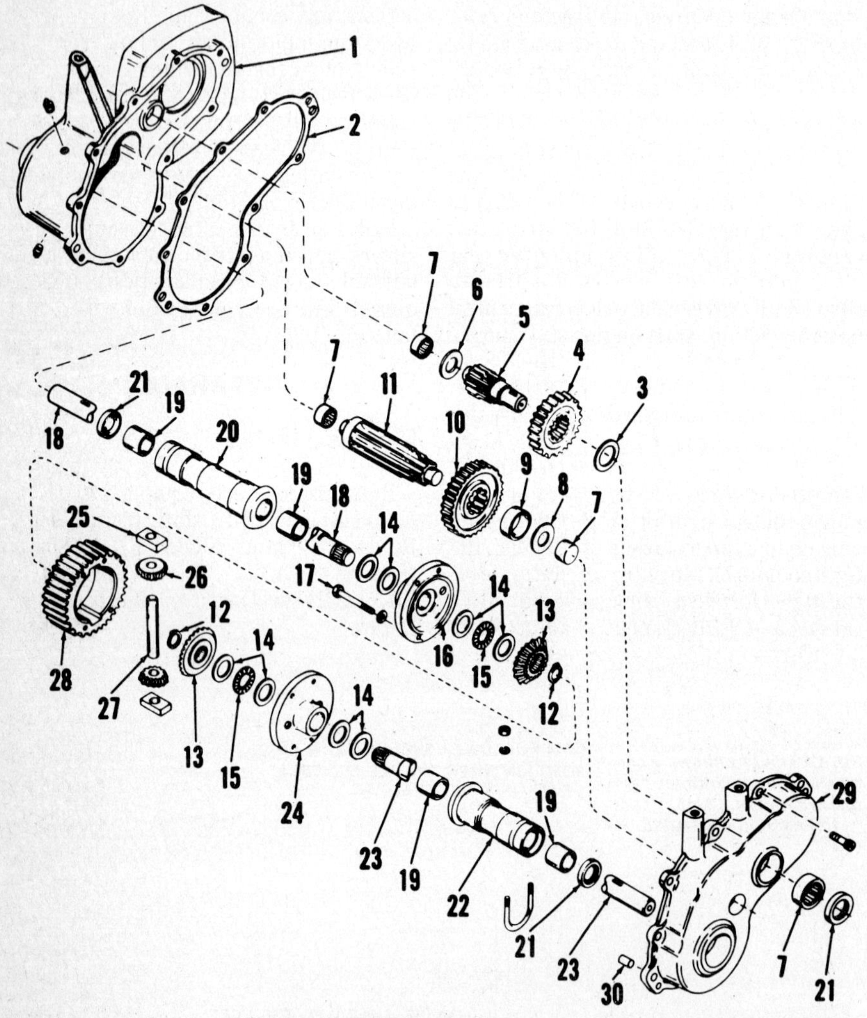

REDUCTION GEARS AND DIFFERENTIAL

Models 117-118

REMOVE AND REINSTALL. To remove reduction gears and differential assembly, tilt seat and fender assembly forward and drain lubricant from reduction and differential housing.

On Model 117, remove oil expansion reservoir and mounting plate. Plug opening to prevent dirt or other foreign material from entering hydrostatic drive unit. Disconnect control cable and detach friction plate from control arm of transmission.

On Model 118, disconnect control cam from control link on hydrostatic transmission.

On either model, unbolt and remove screen and cooling fan. Remove drive belt from input pulley, then disconnect and remove brake assembly. Support rear of tractor and unbolt reduction drive and differential assembly from tractor frame. Raise rear of tractor and remove assembly.

To reinstall reduction drive and differential assembly, reverse removal procedure. Refill reduction drive and differential housing with 2¾ pints (1.3 L) of SAE 90 EP gear oil. Fill transmission oil expansion reservoir ⅓ full with Type "A" automatic transmission fluid. Adjust control linkage and brake as required.

Models 117-118

OVERHAUL. With reduction drive and differential assembly removed as outlined in preceding paragraph, unbolt and remove hydrostatic transmission and rear wheel and hub assemblies. Clean axle shafts and remove any rust or burrs. Place unit in a vise with left axle shaft pointing downward. Remove cap screws and drive dowel pins out of cover. Lift cover (29 – Fig. C34) off case and axle shaft. Withdraw brake shaft

Fig. C34 — Exploded view of Peerless Model 1305 reduction gear and differential unit used on Models 117 and 118.

1. Case	9. Spacer	16. Differential carrier	23. Axle shaft (R.H.)
2. Gasket	10. Output gear	17. Cap screw	24. Differential carrier
3. Washer	11. Output shaft	18. Axle shaft (L.H.)	25. Drive block
4. Idler gear	12. Snap ring	19. Bushing	26. Drive pinion gear
5. Brake shaft	13. Bevel gear	20. Axle housing	27. Drive pin
6. Washer	14. Thrust washers	21. Oil seal	28. Ring gear
7. Bearing	15. Thrust bearing	22. Axle housing	29. Cover
8. Washer			30. Dowel pin

(5), idler gear (4) and thrust washers (3 and 6) from case. Remove output shaft (11), output gear (10), spacer (9) and thrust washer (8), then remove differential and axle shaft assembly. Axle shaft housings (20 and 22) can be pressed from case and cover.

To disassemble differential, remove four cap screws (17) and separate axle shaft and carrier assemblies from ring gear (28). Drive blocks (25), bevel pinion gears (26) and drive pin (27) can now be removed from ring gear. Remove snap rings (12) and slide axle shafts (18 and 23) from axle gears (13) and carriers (16 and 24).

Clean and inspect all parts and renew any showing excessive wear or other damage. When installing needle bearings, press bearings in from inside of case or cover until bearings are 0.015-0.020 inch (0.381-0.508 mm) below thrust surfaces. Be sure heads of differential cap screws (17) and left axle shaft (18) are installed in left carrier (16). Tighten differential cap screws to 7 ft.-lbs. (9 N·m) and cover-to-case cap screws to 10 ft.-lbs. (14 N·m). Differential assembly and output shaft (11) must be installed in case at the same time. Remainder of assembly is reverse of disassembly procedure.

RANGE TRANSMISSION AND DIFFERENTIAL

Models 220-222-224-442-444

A two-speed range transmission is used on all models. The range transmission and differential are contained in one case. The transmission shift lever has three positions; High, Neutral and Low. When transmission is in neutral, tractor can be moved manually.

REMOVE AND REINSTALL. To remove range transmission and differential assembly, place shift lever in neutral position. Block up under tractor frame and place a rolling floor jack under transmission and differential housing. Unbolt and remove fenders, seat and seat support. Disconnect brake rod and remove brake band. Disconnect hydraulic lines from hydraulic drive motor and plug or cap all openings to prevent entrance of dirt or other foreign material. Remove cap screws securing transmission and differential assembly to tractor frame and roll assembly rearward from tractor.

Reinstall by reversing removal procedure. Transmission and differential oil should be renewed each 500 hours of operation or once each year. Use SAE 90 EP gear oil. Capacity is approximately 6 pints (2.8 L).

OVERHAUL. To disassemble range transmission and differential assembly, drain lubricant, then remove top cover and rear wheels. Place a large drive punch against inside end of brake shaft (38 – Fig. C35) and hit drift sharply with a hammer. This will dislodge retaining ring (5) from its groove in brake shaft. Remove retaining ring and brake idler gear (4) as brake shaft is withdrawn. Unbolt hydraulic drive motor (30), hold sliding gear (14) and remove drive motor, input shaft and sliding gear. On early production models, input shaft is separate from drive motor. Unseat retaining rings (15), withdraw shift rod (31) and remove shift fork (16). Remove "C" rings (18) from inner end of axle shafts (27 and 40), withdraw axle shafts and lift out differential assembly with spacer (9) and thrust washers (10 and 24). Remove locknuts (11) and bolts (26), then remove low speed ring gear (12) and high speed ring gear (23). Separate differential case halves (13 and 22) and remove drive pin (21) with roll pin (7), thrust washers (19), pinion gears (20) and axle gears (17). Remove oil seals (28, 33 and 37). Remove plug (34) and needle bearing (35). If necessary, remove brake shaft bushings (6 and 36) and axle shaft flanged bushings (8, 25 and 29). New bushings must be reamed after installation.

Clean and inspect all parts and renew any showing excessive wear or other damage. If brake shaft bushings were removed, press new bushings into position, then ream inner bushing (6) to 1.004-1.005 inches (25.502-25.527 mm) and outer bushing (36) to 1.192-1.193 inches (30.277-30.302 mm). If axle shaft bushings were removed, install inner bushings (8 and 25) with oil groove downward, then install outer bushings (29). Ream all four axle bushings to 1.876-1.877 inches (47.650-47.675 mm). Reassemble differential and ring gears. Use new locknuts (11) and tighten them to 50 ft.-lbs. (68 N·m). Use new oil seals (28, 33 and 37), new gasket (2) and new "O" ring on drive motor flange. Use 0.015 inch thick spacers (9) as required to adjust differential unit side play until side play is 0.005-0.030 inch (0.127-0.762 mm). When installing drive motor, apply a suitable thread locking solution on cap screw threads and tighten cap screws to 110-125 ft.-lbs. (150-169 N·m). Fill transmission and differential housing to level plug opening with SAE 90 EP gear oil. Capacity is approximately 6 pints (2.8 L).

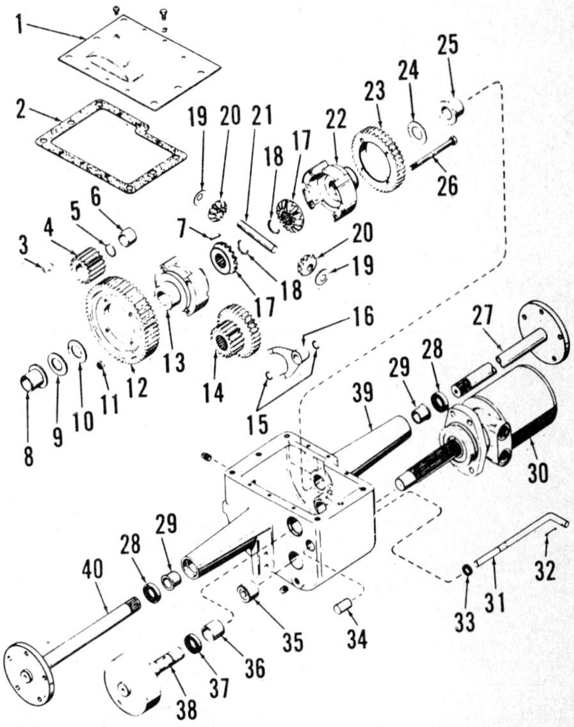

Fig. C35 – Exploded view of range transmission and differential used on Models 220, 222, 224, 442 and 444. On early production units, input shaft is separate from drive motor (30).

1. Cover
2. Gasket
3. Key
4. Brake idler gear
5. Retaining ring
6. Bushing
7. Roll pin
8. Flanged bushing
9. Spacer
10. Thrust washer
11. Locknut (4)
12. Low speed ring gear
13. Differential case half
14. Hi-Lo sliding gear
15. Retaining rings
16. Shift fork
17. Axle gears
18. "C" rings
19. Thrust washers
20. Bevel pinion gears
21. Drive pin
22. Differential case half
23. High speed ring gear
24. Thrust washer
25. Flanged bushing
26. Bolt (4)
27. Axle shaft (L.H.)
28. Oil seal (2)
29. Flanged bushing (2)
30. Drive motor
31. Shift rod
32. Roll pin
33. Oil seal
34. Plug
35. Needle bearing
36. Bushing
37. Oil seal
38. Brake drum & shaft
39. Transmission & differential housing
40. Axle shaft (R.H.)

PTO CLUTCH

Models 210, 220, 222, 224, 442 and 444 may be equipped with a dry disc pto clutch shown in Fig. C36 or C37.

Model 210

R&R AND OVERHAUL. To remove pto clutch, tilt hood forward and disconnect pto control rod from cam actuator lever (3 – Fig. C36). Remove left hand thread cap screw (2), hub spacer (8), Belleville springs (7), spacer (9), outer cam (5) with bearing (6) and cam actuator lever (3) as an assembly. Remove retaining ring (21), inner cam (16) with bearing (15), shim and spacer pack (14 and 9), pulley (12) with bearing (13) and friction disc (11). Spacers (9) and springs (10) can now be removed. Remove two machine screws (20) and lift off clutch plate (19) and grass screen (18). Unbolt and remove drive hub (17).

Clean and inspect all parts and renew any showing excessive wear or other damage. Install drive hub (17) and tighten four cap screws to 35-40 ft.-lbs. (47-54 N·m). Place screen (18) and clutch plate (19) on drive hub and tighten machine screws securely. Fit two springs (10), one spacer (9), two springs (10), one spacer (9) and two springs (10), one spacer (9), in this sequence on drive hub. Place friction disc (11) over shoulder of clutch pulley (12), then place both on drive hub. Install original shim and spacer pack (14 and 9). Measure diameter of cam (16) at each side of lever notches. One side will measure about 3 inches (76 mm) and the other about 2⅞ inches (73 mm). Install cam and bearing (16 and 15) on drive hub with shorter side of cam downward and install retaining ring (21). Place washer, hub spacer (8), Belleville springs (7) and spacer (9) on left hand thread cap screw (2). Position outer cam (5) with bearing (6) so longer diameter between notches is downward. Install cam actuating lever (3) in notches of inner cam (16), then install outer cam assembly. Tighten cap screw (2) to 35-40 ft.-lbs. (47-54 N·m).

With clutch disengaged, measure friction disc clearance using two feeler gages 180 degrees apart. Clearance should measure 0.015-0.025 inch (0.381-0.635 mm). To increase clearance, remove shims (14) or to decrease clearance, add shims (14) as required.

NOTE: If clutch will not disengage, check for incorrect assembly of cams. When correctly installed, facing notches on inner and outer cams are out of alignment when clutch is engaged or disengaged.

Models 220-222-224-442-444

R&R AND OVERHAUL. To remove pto clutch, remove tractor hood and unbolt oil cooler supports from frame. Rotate oil cooler assembly ahead for access to clutch. Disconnect pto control rod from cam actuator lever (3 – Fig. C37). Remove left hand thread cap screw (2), fan (1), hub spacer (9), Belleville springs (8), outer cam (5) with bearing (6) and cam actuator (3) as an assembly. Remove washer (4), inner cam (16) with bearing (15), spacer and shim pack (7 and 14), pulley (12) with bearing (13) and friction disc (11). Spacers (7) and springs (10) can now be removed. Remove two machine screws (20) and lift off clutch plate (19) and grass screen (18). Unbolt and remove drive hub (17).

Clean and inspect all parts and renew any showing excessive wear or other damage. Check friction disc for glaze and wear. If friction surface is glazed or if friction disc thickness measures less than ⅛ inch (3 mm), renew friction disc. Sealed bearings (6, 13 and 15) must rotate freely and quietly.

Install drive hub (17) and tighten four cap screws to 35-40 ft.-lbs. (47-54 N·m). Place screen (18) and clutch plate (19) on drive hub and tighten machine screws (20) securely. Install springs (10) and spacers (7) in same sequence as original assembly. Place friction disc (11) over shoulder of clutch pulley (12), then place

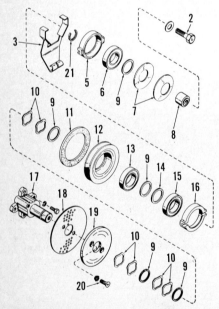

Fig. C36 – Exploded view of power take-off clutch used on Model 210 tractors.

2. Cap screw (L.H. thread)
3. Cam actuator lever
5. Outer cam
6. Bearing
7. Belleville springs
8. Hub spacer
9. Spacers (0.050 in.)
10. Springs
11. Friction disc
12. Clutch pulley
13. Bearing
14. Shim (0.010 in.)
15. Bearing
16. Inner cam
17. Drive hub
18. Grass screen
19. Clutch plate
20. Machine screw (2 used)
21. Retaining ring

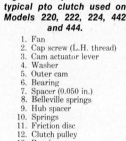

Fig. C37 – Exploded view of typical pto clutch used on Models 220, 222, 224, 442 and 444.

1. Fan
2. Cap screw (L.H. thread)
3. Cam actuator lever
4. Washer
5. Outer cam
6. Bearing
7. Spacer (0.050 in.)
8. Belleville springs
9. Hub spacer
10. Springs
11. Friction disc
12. Clutch pulley
13. Bearing
14. Shim (0.010 in.)
15. Bearing
16. Inner cam
17. Drive hub
18. Grass screen
19. Clutch plate
20. Machine screw (2)

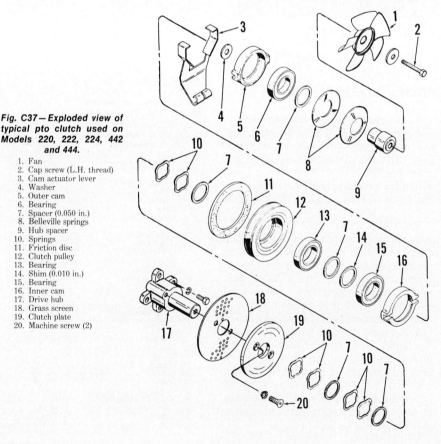

both on drive hub. Install original spacer and shim pack (7 and 14). Measure diameter of inner cam (16) at each side of lever notches. One side will measure about 3 inches (76 mm) and other about 2⅝ inches (73 mm). Install cam and bearing assembly (15 and 16) with shorter side of cam downward, on drive hub. Place washer, fan (1), hub spacer (9) and Belleville springs (8) on left hand thread cap screw (2). Position outer cam (5) with bearing (6) and washer (4) on hub spacer (9) so longer diameter of cam between notches is downward. Install cam actuating lever (3) in notches of inner cam (16), then install outer cam assembly (1 through 9). Tighten cap screw (2) to 35-40 ft.-lbs. (47-54 N·m).

With clutch disengaged, measure friction disc clearance using two feeler gages 180 degrees apart. Clearance should measure 0.015-0.025 inch (0.381-0.635 mm). To increase clearance, remove shims (14) or to decrease clearance, add shims (14) as required.

NOTE: If clutch will not disengage, check for incorrect assembly of cams (5 and 16). When correctly installed, facing notches on inner and outer cams are out of alignment when clutch is engaged or disengaged.

Bolt oil cooler supports to tractor frame and install hood.

HYDRAULIC LIFT

All Models So Equipped

The hydraulic lift system pressure is provided by hydraulic drive pump. The control valve used is two-spool Dukes valve shown in Fig. C16. Refer to appropriate paragraphs in HYDRAULIC TRANSMISSION section for service procedure on pump and control valve.

LIFT CYLINDER

REMOVE AND REINSTALL. With lift cylinder in retracted position, disconnect the two hoses. Unpin and remove cylinder assembly.

Reinstall cylinder by reversing removal procedure. Operate cylinder to full extended and retracted position several times. Then, with cylinder in retracted position, check oil level in hydraulic reservoir. Add oil as necessary. Use SAE 5W-20 oil if temperature is below 32°F (0°C) or SAE 20W-40 oil if temperature is above 32°F (0°C).

OVERHAUL (F30). Remove street elbows from cylinder tube (8–Fig. C38) and drain cylinder. Pull outward on clevis (1) and remove rod guide (2) and rod and piston assembly. Unscrew clevis from rod (5), then remove guide (2). Remove cylinder head (10) from tube (8). Remove and discard all "O" rings and back-up rings.

Clean and inspect all parts and renew any showing excessive wear, scoring or other damage. When reassembling, renew all "O" rings and back-up rings and lubricate internal parts with SAE 20W oil. Apply a suitable thread locking solution on threads of rod (5) and tighten clevis securely. Use pipe thread sealer or Teflon tape on threads and install two street elbows.

OVERHAUL (H30 or J30). Drain oil from cylinder and disassemble as follows: Clean all paint and/or rust from inside base end of cylinder tube (3–Fig. C39). Push piston and rod assembly and end plate (7 or 8) out of cylinder tube. Remove "O" ring (5) from piston, "O" ring (6) from end plate (7 or 8) and wiper seal (1) and "O" ring (2) from cylinder tube.

Clean and inspect all parts and renew any showing excessive wear, scoring or other damage. When reassembling, renew wiper seal and "O" rings which are available in a seal kit. Lubricate wiper seal and all "O" rings and use caution not to damage "O" rings during reassembly. Install end plate (7 or 8) just far enough to permit installation of cylinder mounting pin.

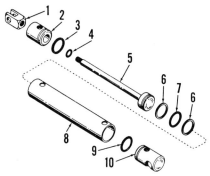

Fig. C38 — Exploded view of Model F30 hydraulic lift cylinder used on some tractors.

1. Clevis	6. Back-up rings
2. Rod guide	7. "O" ring
3. "O" ring	8. Tube
4. "O" ring	9. "O" ring
5. Rod & piston	10. Cylinder head

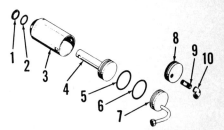

Fig. C39 — Exploded view of Model H30 or J30 hydraulic lift cylinder used on some tractors. Items 8, 9 and 10 are used on H30 cylinder.

1. Wiper seal	6. "O" ring
2. "O" ring	7. End plate (J30)
3. Cylinder tube	8. End plate (H30)
4. Rod & piston	9. Pip nipple
5. "O" ring	10. Pipe elbow

CUB CADET CORP.
CONDENSED SPECIFICATIONS

MODELS

	73	86	106,108	107,109	126,128
Engine Make	Kohler	Kohler	Kohler	Kohler	Kohler
Model	K161	K181	K241AS	K241AS	K301AS
Bore	2⅞ in.	2-15/16 in.	3¼ in.	3¼ in.	3⅜ in.
	(73 mm)	(74.6 mm)	(82.5 mm)	(82.5 mm)	(85.7 mm)
Stroke	2½ in.	2¾ in.	2⅞ in.	2⅞ in.	3¼ in.
	(63.5 mm)	(69.8 mm)	(73 mm)	(73 mm)	(82.5 mm)
Piston Displacement	16.22 cu. in.	18.6 cu. in.	23.9 cu. in.	23.9 cu. in.	29.07 cu. in.
	(266 cc)	(305 cc)	(392 cc)	(392 cc)	(476 cc)
Horsepower	7	8	10	10	12
Slow Idle Speed – Rpm	1000	1000	1000	1000	1000
High Idle Speed (No Load) – Rpm	3780	3780	3800	3800	3800
Full Load Speed – Rpm	3600	3600	3600	3600	3600
Crankcase Oil Capacity	2½ pints	2½ pints	3 pints	3 pints	3 pints
	(1.2 L)	(1.2 L)	(1.4 L)	(1.4 L)	(1.4 L)
Weight –					
Above 32°F (0°C)			SAE 30		
0°F (–18°C) to 32°F (0°C)			SAE 10W		
Below 0°F (–18°C)			SAE 5W-20		
Transmission Oil Capacity	7 pints	7 pints	7 pints	14 pints	7 pints
	(3.3 L)	(3.3 L)	(3.3 L)	(6.6 L)	(3.3 L)
Weight			IH Hy-Tran Fluid		
Transmission Type	Gear	Gear	Gear	Hydro	Gear

MODELS

	127,129	80,282	81,182 (Early)	182 (Late)	111, 382 (Early)
Engine Make	Kohler	B&S	B&S	B&S	B&S
Model	K301AS	191707	191707	191707	252707
Bore	3⅜ in.	3 in.	3 in.	3 in.	3-7/16 in.
	(85.7 mm)	(76.2 mm)	(76.2 mm)	(76.2 mm)	(87.3 mm)
Stroke	3¼ in.	2¾ in.	2¾ in.	2¾ in.	2⅝ in.
	(82.5 mm)	(69.8 mm)	(69.8 mm)	(69.8 mm)	(66.7 mm)
Piston Displacement	29.07 cu. in.	19.44 cu. in.	19.44 cu. in.	19.44 cu. in.	24.36 cu. in.
	(476 cc)	(319 cc)	(319 cc)	(319 cc)	(399 cc)
Horsepower	12	8	8	8	11
Slow Idle Speed – Rpm	1000	1800	1800	1800	1800
High Idle Speed (No Load) – Rpm	3800	3500	3500	3500	3500
Full Load Speed – Rpm	3600	3400	3400	3400	3400
Crankcase Oil Capacity	3 pints	3 pints	3 pints	3 pints	3 pints
	(1.4 L)	(1.4 L)	(1.4 L)	(1.4 L)	(1.4 L)
Weight –					
Above 32°F (0°C)			SAE 30		
0°F (–18°C) to 32°F (0°C)			SAE 10W		
Below 0°F (–18°C)			SAE 5W-20		
Transmission Oil Capacity	14 pints	*	2¾ pints	24 oz.	2¾ pints
	(6.6 L)		(1.3 L)	(710 mL)	(1.3 L)
Weight	IH Hy-Tran Fluid		SAE 90 EP	EP Lithium Grease	SAE 90 EP
Transmission Type	Hydro	Hydro	Gear	Gear	Gear

*Reduction gear and differential capacity is 2¾ pints (1.3 L) of IH Hy-Tran fluid. Hydrostatic transmission capacity is 1½ pints (0.7 L) of Hy-Tran fluid.

MODELS

	382 (Late)	382H	482, 1100	147, 149	169
Engine Make	B&S	B&S	B&S	Kohler	Kohler
Model	252707	252707	253707	K321A	K341
Bore	3-7/16 in.	3-7/16 in.	3-7/16 in.	3½ in.	3¾ in.
	(87.3 mm)	(87.3 mm)	(87.3 mm)	(88.9 mm)	(95.2 mm)

	MODELS (Cont.)				
	382 (Late)	**382H**	**482, 1100**	**147, 149**	**169**
Stroke	2⅝ in.	2⅝ in.	2⅝ in.	3¼ in.	3¼ in.
	(66.7 mm)	(66.7 mm)	(66.7 mm)	(82.5 mm)	(82.5 mm)
Piston Displacement	24.36 cu. in.	24.36 cu. in.	24.36 cu. in.	31.27 cu. in.	35.90 cu. in.
	(399 cc)	(399 cc)	(399 cc)	(512 cc)	(588 cc)
Horsepower	11	11	11	14	16
Slow Idle Speed – Rpm	1800	1800	1750	1000	1000
High Idle Speed (No Load) – Rpm	3500	3500	3600	3800	3600
Full Load Speed – Rpm	3400	3400	3500	3600	3400
Crankcase Oil Capacity	3 pints	3 pints	3 pints	3 pints	3 pints
	(1.4 L)	(1.4 L)	(1.4 L)	(1.4 L)	(1.4 L)
Weight –					
Above 32°F (0°C)	——————————————— SAE 30 ———————————————				
0°F (–18°C) to 32°F (0°C)	————————————— SAE 10W —————————————				
Below 0°F (–18°C)	—————————————— SAE 5W-20 ——————————————				
Transmission Oil Capacity	24 oz.	**	4 pints	14 pints	14 pints
	(710 mL)		(1.9 L)	(6.6 L)	(6.6 L)
Weight	EP Lithium	Hy-Tran	SAE 90 EP	Hy-Tran	Hy-Tran
	Grease	Fluid		Fluid	Fluid
Transmission type	Gear	Hydro	Gear	Hydro	Hydro

**Reduction gear and differential capacity is 2¾ pints (1.3 L) of IH Hy-Tran fluid. Hydrostatic transmission capacity is 1½ pints (0.7 L) of Hy-Tran fluid.

	MODELS			
	800	**1000**	**1200**	**1204**
Engine Make	Kohler	Kohler	Kohler	Kohler
Model	K181QS	K241AQS	K301AQS	K301
Bore	2-15/16 in.	3¼ in.	3⅜ in.	3⅜ in.
	(74.6 mm)	(82.5 mm)	(85.7 mm)	(85.7 mm)
Stroke	2¾ in.	2⅞ in.	3¼ in.	3¼ in.
	(69.8 mm)	(73.0 mm)	(82.5 mm)	(82.5 mm)
Piston Displacement	18.63 cu. in.	23.9 cu. in.	29.07 cu. in.	29.07 cu. in.
	(305 cc)	(392 cc)	(476 cc)	(476 cc)
Horsepower	8	10	12	12
Slow Idle Speed – Rpm	1800	1800	1800	1800
High Idle Speed (No Load) – Rpm	3600	3600	3600	3600
Full Load Speed – Rpm	3400	3400	3400	3400
Crankcase Oil Capacity	2½ pints	3 pints	3 pints	3 pints
	(1.2 L)	(1.4 L)	(1.4 L)	(1.4 L)
Weight –				
Above 32°F (0°C)	——————————— SAE 30 ———————————			
0°F (–18°) to 32°F (0°C)	————————— SAE 10W —————————			
Below 0°F (–18°C)	————————— SAE 5W-20 —————————			
Transmission Oil Capacity	7 pints	7 pints	14 pints	4 pints
	(3.3 L)	(3.3 L)	(6.6 L)	(1.9 L)
Weight	————— IH Hy-Tran Fluid —————			SAE 90 EP
Transmission Type	Gear	Gear	Hydro	Gear

	MODELS			
	1210, 1211	**1250**	**1450**	**1650**
Engine Make	Kohler	Kohler	Kohler	Kohler
Model	K301	K301AQS	K321AQS	K341AQS
Bore	3⅜ in.	3⅜ in.	3½ in.	3¾ in.
	(85.7 mm)	(85.7 mm)	(88.9 mm)	(95.2 mm)
Stroke	3¼ in.	3¼ in.	3¼ in.	3¼ in.
	(82.5 mm)	(82.5 mm)	(82.5 mm)	(82.5 mm)
Piston Displacement	29.07 cu. in.	29.07 cu. in.	31.27 cu. in.	35.90 cu. in.
	(476 cc)	(476 cc)	(512 cc)	(588 cc)
Horsepower	12	12	14	16
Slow Idle Speed – Rpm	1800	1800	1800	1800
High Idle Speed (No Load) – Rpm	3600	3600	3600	3600
Full Load Speed – Rpm	3400	3400	3400	3400
Crankcase Oil Capacity	3 pints	3 pints	3 pints	3 pints
	(1.4 L)	(1.4 L)	(1.4 L)	(1.4 L)

	MODELS (Cont.)			
	1210, 1211	1250	1450	1650
Weight –				
Above 32°F (0°C)	SAE 30			
0°F(–18°C) to 32°F (0°C)	SAE 10W			
Below 0°F (–18°C)	SAE5W-20			
Transmission Oil Capacity	14 pints (6.6 L)	14 pints (6.6 L)	14 pints (6.6 L)	14 pints (6.6 L)
Weight	IH Hy-Tran Fluid			
Transmission Type	Hydro	Hydro	Hydro	Hydro

FRONT AXLE SYSTEM

AXLE MAIN MEMBER

All Models

The front axle main member is mounted directly on the main frame and pivots on center mounting pivot pin or bushing. The pivot pin or bushing is retained by a nut on Models 80, 81, 111, 182, 282, 382 and 482, by a bolt on Models 1204, 1210 and 1211 and by a spring pin on all other models. To remove front axle main member assembly (2–Figs. CC1, CC2, CC3 or CC4), disconnect steering drag link from drag link arm or steering spindle. Raise and support front of tractor. Remove pivot pin or bushing retaining nut, bolt or pin and remove pivot bushing (1–Figs. CC1 and CC4) or pivot pin (1–Figs. CC2 and CC3). Lower front axle assembly and roll forward from under tractor.

TIE ROD

All Models

To adjust toe-in, disconnect tie rod ball joints from steering spindles, loosen locknuts and turn tie rod ball joints in or

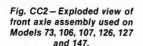

out as required. The toe-in should be 1/16 to 1/8 inch (1.5-3 mm).

STEERING SPINDLES

Models 86-108-109-128-129-149-169-482-800-1000-1100-1200-1250-1450-1650

To remove steering spindles (3 and 6–Fig. CC3), support front of tractor and remove front wheels. Disconnect drag link and tie rod ends from steering spindles. Remove nuts (10) and steering spindle bolts (9). Remove steering spindles and spacers (8).

When reassembling, tighten nuts (10) to 80 ft.-lbs. (108 N·m).

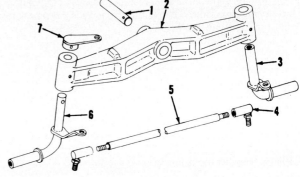

Fig. CC2 – Exploded view of front axle assembly used on Models 73, 106, 107, 126, 127 and 147.

1. Pivot pin
2. Axle main member
3. Steering spindle (R.H.)
4. Tie rod ball joint end
5. Tie rod
6. Steering spindle (L.H.)
7. Drag link arm

Models 1204-1210-1211

To remove steering spindles (3 and 6–Fig. CC4), raise and support front of tractor. Remove wheel and tire assemblies. Disconnect drag link end (10) at left spindle (3). Disconnect tie rod ends at each spindle. Remove cap screws (7) and washers (8). Slide spindles down out of axle main member.

When reassembling, tighten cap screws (7) to 33-37 ft.-lbs. (45-50 N·m).

All Other Models

To remove steering spindles (3 and 6–Fig. CC1 or CC2), raise front of tractor and remove front wheels. Disconnect tie rod ball joint ends and drag link ball joint end from steering spindles. Remove pins and/or cap screws from top of steering spindles and slide spindles down out of axle main member.

STEERING GEAR

Models 80-81-111-182-282-382

REMOVE AND REINSTALL. Disconnect and remove battery. Disconnect pto rod, spring and ignition switch. Remove solenoid mounting bolts and lay

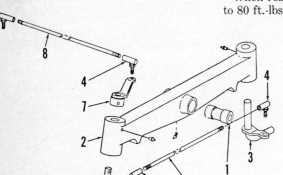

Fig. CC1 – Exploded view of front axle assembly used on Models 80, 81, 111, 182, 282 and 382.

1. Pivot bushing
2. Axle main member
3. Steering spindle (R.H.)
4. Tie rod ball joint end
5. Tie rod
6. Steering spindle (L.H.)
7. Drag link arm
8. Drag link

solenoid on frame. Disconnect throttle cable and fuel line at carburetor. Remove steering arm cover and disconnect drag link. Drive roll pin out of bottom of steering wheel and lift wheel off. Remove steering column tower. Remove cotter pin and washer from steering shaft and lift shaft out. Remove pivot bolt from steering gear assembly and slide gear rearward out of frame.

OVERHAUL. Inspect nylon bearing (5–Fig. CC5) and bushings for wear or

damage. Check for broken teeth, bent shafts or stripped threads. Renew damaged or worn parts as necessary.

To renew steering shaft bushing, carefully break bushing with a chisel. Heat new bushing in boiling water for five minutes to make it flexible. Position bushing in socket and drive it in with a wooden or rubber mallet.

Reassemble and install by reversing removal procedures. Apply "Lubriplate" or equivalent grease liberally to gear assembly, bearings and shaft.

Models 1204-1210-1211

REMOVE AND REINSTALL. To remove steering unit, first remove steering wheel center cover. Remove nut (7–Fig. CC6) and use a suitable puller to remove steering wheel. Disconnect drag link at steering arm plate (14). Remove mounting bolts retaining steering gear housing and tube. Lower steering gear housing and tube assembly through control panel and out of tractor.

OVERHAUL. Clamp steering arm plate (14–Fig. CC6) in a vise and remove nut (11) and jam nut (12). Separate housing and tube assembly

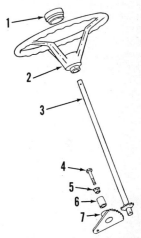

Fig. CC5—Exploded view of steering unit used on Models 80, 81, 111, 182, 282 and 382.
1. Steering wheel cap
2. Steering wheel
3. Steering shaft assy.
4. Pivot bolt
5. Bearing
6. Drag link bushing
7. Steering gear assy.

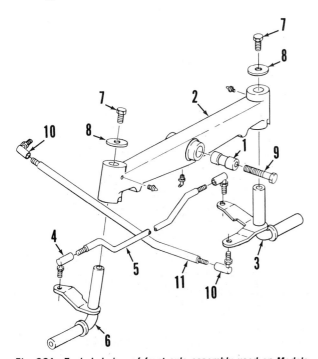

Fig. CC3—Exploded view of typical front axle assembly used on Models 86, 108, 109, 128, 129, 149, 169, 482, 800, 1000, 1100, 1200, 1250, 1450 and 1650. Some models use a pivot bolt instead of pin (1).
1. Pivot pin
2. Axle main member
3. Steering spindle (L.H.)
4. Tie rod ball joint end
5. Tie rod
6. Steering spindle (R.H.)
7. Retaining pin
8. Spacer
9. Steering spindle bolt
10. Nut

Fig. CC4—Exploded view of front axle assembly used on Models 1204, 1210 and 1211.
1. Pivot bushing
2. Axle main member
3. Left spindle
4. Tie rod end
5. Tie rod
6. Right spindle
7. Cap screw
8. Washer
9. Bolt
10. Drag link end
11. Drag link

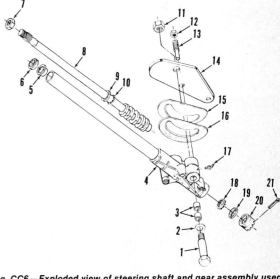

Fig. CC6—Exploded view of steering shaft and gear assembly used on Models 1204, 1210 and 1211.
1. Pivot bolt
2. Washer
3. Bushings
4. Housing & tube assy.
5. Bearing
6. Seal
7. Nut
8. Steering shaft & cam
9. Bearing race
10. Bearing
11. Nut
12. Jam nut
13. Cam adjustment bolt
14. Steering arm plate
15. Seal retainer
16. Seal
17. Grease fitting
18. Bearing & retainer
19. Bearing race
20. Adjustment plug
21. Cotter pin

from steering arm plate. Remove cotter pin (21) and adjustment plug (20). Remove steering shaft and cam assembly (8) and bearings from housing and tube assembly.

During reassembly, coat cam ends, balls and races with lithium base grease. Install balls and races on the cam ends and cover with lithium base grease. Install into housing and tube assembly. Make certain races enter housing squarely and are not cocked. Install adjustment plug (20). Screw plug inward until end play of cam is removed but shaft turns freely. Insert cotter pin (21) into nearest hole. Fill housing with lithium base grease. Loosen jam nut (12) and back cam adjustment bolt out two turns. Install seal (16), retainer (15) and steering arm plate (14). Install the washer and nut (11). Tighten the nut until there is 3/32 inch (2.4 mm) clearance between steering arm plate and housing (Fig. CC8). Install a jam nut against nut (11 – Fig. CC6) and tighten jam nut to 40 ft.-lbs. (54 N·m). Lubricate at fitting (17) until grease begins to appear between steering arm plate (14) and housing. Center steering cam by rotating

steering shaft halfway between full right and full left turn. Turn cam adjustment bolt (13) inward to eliminate backlash, then tighten jam nut (12) to 40 ft.-lbs. (54 N·m). Steering shaft should rotate smoothly with minimum backlash.

All Models Except 80-81-111-182-282-382-1204-1210-1211

REMOVE AND REINSTALL. To remove steering unit, remove steering wheel, felt seal, retainer, bearing and bearing retainer from upper end of steering column. Disconnect drag link rear ball joint from steering unit lever. Remove the two cap screws securing steering unit to frame cross member, then lower unit and remove from under side of tractor.

OVERHAUL. Remove lever and bolt assembly (11 – Fig. CC7). Remove cam bearing adjuster plug (8) and bump steering cam assembly (15) out of steering column. Remove bearings (6) and bearing races (7).

When reassembling unit, cam bearing adjuster plug should be tightened to remove all end play; but, cam (15) must still rotate freely. Stake adjuster plug or install cotter pin to prevent it from working loose. Install lever and bolt assembly (11). Install copper washer (5) and adjusting nut. Tighten adjusting nut until steering lever is 3/32 inch (2.4 mm) from cam housing. See Fig. CC8. Tighten jam nut to 40 ft.-lbs. (54 N·m). To adjust cam follower (14 – Fig. CC7), locate cam in mid-position (halfway between full right and full left turn). Turn cam follower screw in until zero backlash is obtained. Secure with locknut. Steering cam should turn from a full left to full right turn without binding. Lubricate with approximately ¼ pound (0.2 L) of multipurpose grease.

ENGINE

REMOVE AND REINSTALL

Models 80-81-111-182-282-382

To remove engine, first remove grille and hood assemblies. Disconnect battery cables, starter, charging and control module wires. Shut off fuel at fuel tank, disconnect fuel line at carburetor and remove fuel tank. Disconnect choke and throttle cables. Work mower drive and main drive belts free of engine pulley and idler pulley. Remove engine mounting bolts and lift engine out of frame.

Reinstall engine by reversing removal procedure.

Models 73-86-106-107-108-109-126-127-128-129-147-149-169

Disconnect battery ground cable. On models equipped with firewall mounted fuel tank, shut off fuel and remove fuel tank and panel extension as an assembly. On all models, disconnect and remove front pto linkage. Remove grille and hood assembly. Disconnect generator-starter wires and ignition wires. Disconnect choke and throttle cables. Raise front of tractor and remove the four engine mounting bolts (on some models, front of tractor must be raised to remove front bolts). Slide engine forward and lift from frame using a suitable hoist.

Reinstall engine in reverse order of removal.

Models 1204-1210-1211

Raise hood and unhook side panel extension spring, flat washer and wing nut on each side. Remove the two side panels. Close the fuel shut-off valve

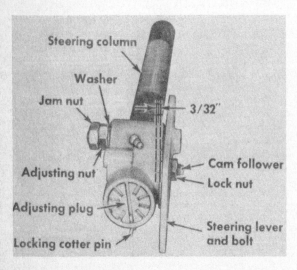

Fig. CC7 – Exploded view of typical steering unit used on all models except 80, 81, 111, 182, 282 and 382.

1. Steering wheel
2. Seal
3. Column bearing
4. Steering column
5. Copper washer
6. Retainer & ball assy.
7. Bearing race
8. Adjusting plug
9. Seal
10. Retainer
11. Lever & bolt assy.
12. Drag link ends
13. Drag link
14. Cam follower stud
15. Steering cam

Fig. CC8 – View of assembled steering unit similar to the type used on all models except 80, 81, 111, 182, 282 and 382. Tighten adjusting nut until steering lever is 3/32 inch (2.4 mm) from housing.

Steering column

Washer

Jam nut

3/32"

Adjusting nut

Cam follower

Lock nut

Adjusting plug

Steering lever and bolt

Locking cotter pin

located on the bottom left side of fuel tank and disconnect fuel line at fuel tank. Remove the two hex nuts and flat washers and remove fuel tank. Disconnect the four headlight wires at headlights and separate headlight wiring harness from grille (it may be necessary to cut plastic wire ties). Remove the four bolts and lockwashers retaining grille and hood to front of chassis and remove hood and grille assembly. Remove bolts on each side of pedestal and gas tank straps. Disconnect all electrical connections at engine and starter. Remove air cleaner cover and disconnect throttle and choke cables. Remove bolt on right side retaining heat shield and remove heat shield. Remove bolt, flat washer, star washer, ground wire and wire harness from left heat shield. Remove the self-tapping screw on bottom of coupling guard (attached to heat shield) and lift heat shield and coupling guard out of tractor. Remove drive pin at drive shaft coupling at rear of engine. Remove the two nuts securing coupling to flexible disc and slide coupling and disc back on drive shaft. Remove the two bolts retaining the self-aligning bearing on engine at drive shaft. Remove the four engine mount bolts and remove engine.

Reinstall engine by reversing removal procedure.

Models 482-800-1000-1100-1200-1250-1450-1650

Disconnect battery ground cable. Remove grille housing, hood and side panels. Disconnect starter wires, charging wires, electric clutch wires, ignition wires, ground wires and headlight wires. Remove air filter assembly, then disconnect choke and throttle linkage. Shut off fuel at tank, disconnect fuel line from carburetor and remove fuel tank and supports. Remove engine mounting

bolts (on some models, front of tractor must be raised to remove front bolts). On models so equipped, disconnect flexible drive coupler (3 – Fig. CC9) from rear of engine. On all models, use a suitable hoist and lift engine from frame.

Reinstall by reversing removal procedure.

OVERHAUL

All Models

Engine make and model are listed at the beginning of this section. To overhaul engine components and accessories, refer to Kohler and Briggs & Stratton sections of this manual.

CLUTCH

The clutch used on all gear drive models is 4½ inch (114 mm), dry disc, spring loaded type.

Models 73-86-106-108-126-128-800-1000-1200

ADJUSTMENT. To maintain correct clearance of 0.050 inch (1.27 mm) between clutch release bearing and clutch release lever, clutch pedal must have a free travel (measured at pedal return stop) of approximately 9/32 inch (7 mm) on Models 86, 108, 128, 800, 1000 and 1200 or 3/16 inch (5 mm) on Models 73, 106 and 126. It is necessary to adjust the linkage when free travel measurement becomes less than the required 3/16 or

9/32 inch (5 mm or 7 mm). To adjust linkage, turn adjusting nut (2 – Fig. CC10) on front end of clutch release rod in or out as required to obtain proper free travel.

R&R AND OVERHAUL. Complete service of clutch, clutch shaft, loading spring, release bearing and cushion spring will require moving engine forward. To remove clutch assembly, proceed as follows: Remove frame cover and clutch shield. On Models 800, 1000 and 1200, disconnect flex coupling from rear of clutch shaft. On all other models, drive roll pins out of rear coupling and slide coupling forward on clutch shaft. On models so equipped, remove electric lift cylinder and bracket. On all models, remove release lever pivot pin (2 – Fig. CC11) and hanger bracket (1), and disconnect clutch release rod from pedal arm. Remove engine mounting bolts, then slide engine forward far enough to clear clutch parts. The complete clutch can now be removed from tractor.

Using a suitable press and slotted washer, compress loading spring (Fig. CC12) and remove coiled spring pin, then release spring tension. Remove spring pins from pressure plates and withdraw clutch shaft from remaining parts. Refer to Fig. CC13 or CC14 for exploded view of clutch assembly.

Inspect clutch disc for wear and for elongated holes from drive plate pins. Inspect slotted hub of rear pressure plate; if slots are cupped, renew pressure plate. Inspect remaining parts for wear or other damage and renew as needed.

Fig. CC9 — On hydrostatic transmission models, a flexible drive coupler (3) is used. Remove cap screws (2) to disconnect. Model 1100 is shown; other models are similar.

1. Engine rear isomounts
2. Cap screws
3. Flexible coupler

Fig. CC10 — Underside view of Model 1000 brake and clutch control linkage. Other models so equipped are similar.

1. Clutch release lever
2. Adjusting nut
3. Release rod
4. Safety start switch
5. Brake rods

Fig. CC11 — View of typical main drive clutch used on gear drive models.

1. Hanger bracket
2. Pivot pin
3. Driving disc
4. Drive plate
5. Pressure plate assy.
6. Drive disc spring
7. Drive pin

Reassemble by reversing disassembly procedure. On Models 800, 1000 and 1200, one drive plate pin (7 – Fig. CC11) is longer than the other two. Drive disc spring (6) should be installed on longest pin. Be sure steel ball spacer (3 – Fig. CC14) is in place when reassembling rear flex coupling. Adjust clutch linkage as previously outlined.

BRAKES

Models 73-800-1000-1200-1250-1450-1650 (Internal)

REMOVE AND REINSTALL. The brake on these models is located in reduction gear housing. To remove

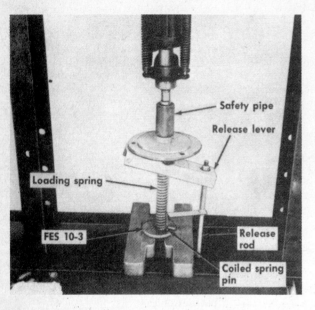

Fig. CC12 – View showing clutch loading spring compressed for coiled spring pin removal. Refer to text for details.

brake disc linings, it is necessary to detach transmission and reduction gear housing from frame. To do this, remove fenders, seat and seat support. Drive out pin from clutch shaft rear coupling or unbolt flexible coupling if so equipped. Disconnect brake rod. Support rear of frame and remove cap screws securing frame to transmission and reduction gear housings. Push down on drawbar and pull rearward on transmission. Roll rear assembly away from frame.

On gear drive models, support transmission housing and drain transmission lubricant. Remove brake adjuster screw, pivot pin, brake lever, push rod and ball from housing. Refer to Figs. CC15 and CC16. Remove reduction drive front cover, reduction gear retaining cap screw and reduction gear. The brake disc, linings and retainer can then be removed.

On hydrostatic drive models, differential, bevel pinion shaft and constant mesh gear (Fig. CC17) must be removed. Refer to DIFFERENTIAL AND REDUCTION GEAR paragraphs for procedure. After removing constant mesh gear, remove rear brake lining from housing recess and push front lining and retainer forward out of housing.

Reassemble by reversing disassembly procedure.

ADJUSTMENT. To adjust brake on gear drive models, turn adjusting screw in or out as required to obtain correct pedal travel. Brake should start to engage with pedal depressed to within 1-5/16 inches (33 mm) from pedal stop. Brake must be fully engaged when pedal is depressed to within ¾ inch (19 mm) from pedal stop.

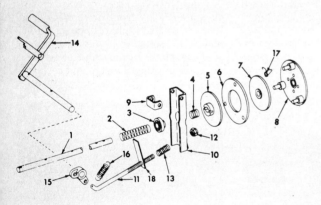

Fig. CC13 – Exploded view of disc clutch assembly used on early models equipped with a clutch.

1. Clutch shaft
2. Loading spring
3. Release bearing
4. Cushion spring
5. Pressure plate
6. Clutch disc
7. Pressure plate
8. Clutch drive plate
9. Bracket
10. Release lever
11. Rod
12. Adjusting nut
13. Spring
14. Pedal assy.
15. Clutch & brake arm
16. Pedal return spring
17. Anti-chatter spring (3)
18. Safety switch lever

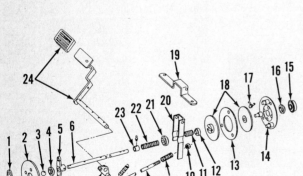

Fig. CC14 – Exploded view of disc clutch assembly used on late models equipped with a clutch. Items 15, 16 and 23 are used on tractors with serial number 612808 and after.

10. Adjusting nut
11. Teasing spring
12. Spacer
13. Clutch disc
14. Drive plate
15. Pilot hub
16. Bushing
17. Anitchatter spring (3)
18. Safety switch lever
19. Clutch lever hanger
20. Release lever
21. Throwout bearing
22. Loading spring
23. Lubricating bushing
24. Clutch pedal assy.

1. Drive shaft coupling
2. Flex disc
3. Ball
4. Bushing
5. Coupling arm
6. Clutch shaft
7. Clutch & brake arm
8. Clutch release rod
9. Spring

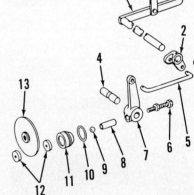

Fig. CC15 – Exploded view of internal brake assembly used on some models.

1. Clutch & brake pedal
2. Pedal arm
3. Return spring
4. Pivot pin
5. Brake rod
6. Adjusting screw
7. Brake lever
8. Push rod
9. Ball
10. "O" ring
11. Lining retainer
12. Brake linings
13. Brake disc

To adjust brake on hydrostatic drive models, support rear of tractor so rear wheels can turn freely. With brake pedal in up position, tighten brake lever adjusting screw until finger tight. Actuate brake pedal through a full stroke, then retighten adjusting screw finger tight and secure with jam nut. If brake drags with pedal in up position, loosen adjusting screw slightly.

Models 86-106-107-108-109-126-127-128-129-147-149-169-800-1000-1200-1210-1211-1250-1450-1650 (External)

The brakes on these models are mechanically actuated and located at the end of both rear axles. The brakes are disc type with brake pads contacting a disc attached to wheel hub and axle. Disassembly of brake unit is self-evident after removing rear wheel.

ADJUSTMENT. To adjust brakes, support rear of tractor so rear wheels can rotate freely. Adjust brakes by turning jam nuts at end of each brake rod (9 – Fig. CC18). Brakes must not engage before pedal is within maximum distance above pedal stop of 1-3/16 inches (30 mm) on Models 86, 108, 109, 128, 129, 149, 169, 800, 1000, 1200, 1210, 1211, 1250, 1450 and 1650; 1-5/16 inches (33 mm) on Models 106 and 126; 1-11/16 inches (43 mm) on Models 107, 127 and 147. The brakes should be fully engaged when pedal is depressed to a point ¾ inch (19 mm) above pedal stop. Brakes must have equal stopping action at both wheels. With rear wheels supported off ground, start engine and let run with transmission in third gear, or in forward position on hydrostatic models. Apply brakes. If one wheel stops sooner than other wheel, adjust brake rod on wheel that does not stop until both wheels stop simultaneously.

Models 80-81-111-182 (Early)-282-382-(Early) 482-1100-1204

The brakes on these models are mechanically actuated and are externally mounted on left side of transaxle. The brakes are disc type with brake pads contacting a disc attached to brake shaft of transaxle. Disassembly of brake unit is self-evident after removing left rear wheel, fender and foot support. See Fig. CC19.

ADJUSTMENT. To adjust brake, pedal should be in raised position. Remove all slack from linkage by moving brake arm up and pulling brake rod down. Adjust brake rod jam nuts to allow a clearance of ¼ inch (6 mm) between adjusting nut and actuating cam

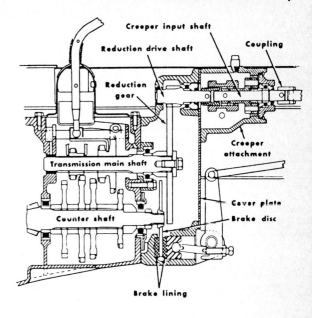

Fig. CC16 — Cross-sectional view of internal brake assembly used on some gear drive models.

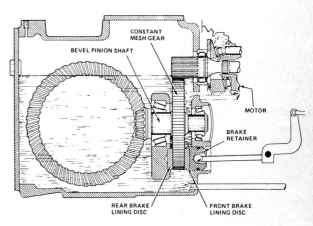

Fig. CC17 — Cross-sectional view of internal brake assembly used on some hydrostatic drive models.

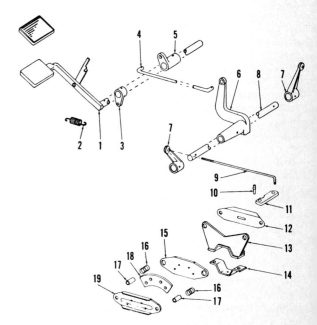

Fig. CC18 — Exploded view of typical external type disc brake assembly used on some models. Brake caliper assemblies are located at end of both rear axles. Neutral return arm (3) is used only on hydrostatic models.

1. Brake & clutch pedal
2. Return spring
3. Neutral return arm
4. Brake rod
5. Rod lever
6. Lever
7. Brake arm
8. Pivot shaft
9. Brake rod
10. Pin
11. Lever cam
12. Cam plate
13. Bracket
14. Flange
15. Carrier
16. Spring
17. Bushing
18. Brake pad (2)
19. Carrier

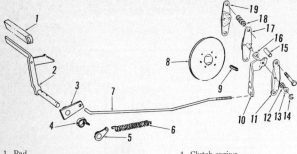

Fig. CC19 — Exploded view of external single caliper disc brake assembly used on some models equipped with transaxle.

7. Brake rod
8. Brake disc & hub assy.
9. Key
10. Cam
11. Actuator plate
12. Compression spring
13. Thrust washer
14. Retaining ring
15. Bushing
16. Thrust washer
17. Stud plate
18. Return spring
19. Rib plate assy.

1. Pad
2. Brake & clutch pedal
3. Brake rod lever
4. Clutch spring
5. Brake lever
6. Extension spring

each side. Remove creeper drive shift lever knob and breather. Disconnect front brake rod and drive out drive shaft coupling rear pin. Support tractor frame, then remove mounting bolts and roll transmission and differential assembly rearward from tractor. Drain creeper drive unit. Unbolt unit and remove from reduction drive coupling (3 – Fig. CC20).

On all models, reinstall creeper drive unit and reassemble tractor by reversing removal and disassembly procedures. Fill creeper drive unit to level plug opening, approximately ½ pint (0.2 L), with IH Hy-Tran Fluid.

(10 – Fig. CC19) on Models 80, 81, 111, 182, 282 and 382. On Models 482, 1100 and 1204, turn adjusting nut to obtain ¼ inch (6 mm) clearance between brake rod spacer and actuating cam. To check adjustment, put tractor in gear and attempt to push it while slowly depressing clutch-brake pedal. Brake should start to apply as clutch disengages. There should be no neutral zone between brake and clutch action. Readjust as necessary.

back off adjusting nut one complete turn and tighten jam nut. Recheck braking action.

OVERHAUL. To disassemble creeper drive unit, remove snap ring (22 – Fig. CC20) and withdraw shaft (14) with retainer (20), bearing (17), planet carrier and gears (12 and 13) and direct drive coupling (4). Drive out coiled spring pin securing direct drive coupling (4) to shaft and remove coupling. Slide planet carrier, gears and thrust washer from input shaft. Remove snap ring (16) and withdraw shaft and bearing from retainer (20). Bearing (17) can be pressed from shaft after snap ring (18) is removed. Remove oil seal (21) from bearing retainer.

Models (Late) 182-382

ADJUSTMENT. The disc type brake on these tractors is located on left side of transaxle. To adjust brake, pedal should be in released position. Loosen jam nut and turn adjusting nut (8 – Fig. CC19A) in until brake disc (3) is locked. Then,

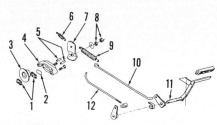

Fig. CC19A — Exploded view of disc brake assembly and control linkage used on late Model 182 and 382 tractors equipped with 5-speed transaxle.

1. Brake pads
2. Back-up plate
3. Brake disc
4. Holder
5. Pins
6. Return spring
7. Brake lever
8. Locknuts
9. Tension spring
10. Brake rod
11. Clutch-brake pedal
12. Clutch rod

To remove shifter assembly, drive shift poppet pin from shift lever shaft and remove poppet (10) and spacer (11). Move shift lever towards rear of housing and remove shift collar (2) from yoke (1). Drive pin from shift yoke and shaft, then withdraw shift lever shaft from yoke and housing. Remove "O" rings (7).

Clean and inspect all parts and renew any showing excessive wear or other damage. Use new oil seal (21) and "O" rings (7 and 19) and using Figs. CC21 and CC22 as a guide, reassemble creeper drive unit by reversing disassembly procedure.

2-SPEED CREEPER DRIVE

A 2-speed creeper drive is available for gear drive models. The creeper drive is mounted to the front of reduction drive. A speed selection lever allows shifting to standard (direct drive) speed or creeper (4 to 1 underdrive) speed as desired.

CAUTION: Do not attempt to shift creeper drive while engine clutch is engaged or while tractor is in motion.

All Models So Equipped

REMOVE AND REINSTALL. On Models 86, 108, 128, 800, 1000 and 1200, remove creeper drive shift lever knob, then unbolt and remove frame cover. Drive both roll pins from drive shaft rear coupling and slide coupling forward on shaft. Drain creeper drive unit. Unbolt and remove unit.

NOTE: Drive shaft will have to be moved slightly to the side to allow unit to slide off splined driven coupling (3 – Fig. CC20).

On all other models, disconnect battery cables and remove fenders and seat support as necessary. Drive a wooden wedge between front axle and frame on

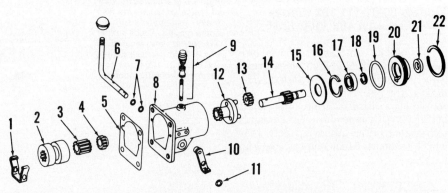

Fig. CC20 — Exploded view of 2-speed drive unit used on some gear drive models. Driven coupling (3) is pinned to reduction drive shaft.

1. Shift yoke
2. Shift collar
3. Driven coupling
4. Direct drive coupling
5. Gasket
6. Shift lever
7. "O" rings
8. Housing
9. Breather assy.
10. Shift poppet
11. Spacer
12. Planet carrier
13. Planet gear (3 used)
14. Input shaft
15. Thrust washer
16. Snap ring
17. Ball bearing
18. Snap ring
19. "O" ring
20. Bearing retainer
21. Oil seal
22. Snap ring

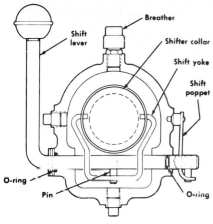

Fig. CC21 — Cross-sectional end view of creeper drive shifting components.

REDUCTION DRIVE

Models 73-86-106-108-126-128-800-1000-1200

R&R AND OVERHAUL. To remove reduction drive, first split tractor as follows: On all models, disconnect battery cables and on models with battery under the seat, remove battery. On all models except Model 73, remove fenders and seat support. On Models 86, 108, 128, 800, 1000 and 1200, remove frame cover. On all models, drive a wooden wedge between front axle and frame on each side. Disconnect front brake rod from brake lever. Disconnect clutch shaft rear coupler. Note that models with rear flexible coupling have a steel ball spacer located in coupling to properly locate clutch shaft. On models equipped with three-point hitch, remove lift lever and attaching plate. On models where necessary, remove creeper drive and transmission shift lever knobs. On all models, support tractor frame, remove mounting bolts and roll transmission and differential assembly rearward from tractor.

Drain, unbolt and remove creeper drive if so equipped. Drain transmission and differential housing. Remove brake cross shaft and levers, then unbolt and remove reduction drive front cover. Using a suitable puller, remove reduction shaft (12 — Fig. CC23) with bearing (6) and oil seal (9). Unbolt and remove reduction driven gear (2) and spacer (1). Remove cap screws securing reduction housing (5) to transmission and remove housing. Press needle bearing (11) out rear side of housing.

When reassembling, press needle bearing (11) into housing until flush with rear surface. Renew copper sealing

washers on housing mounting lower cap screws, and tighten mounting cap screws to 80 ft.-lbs. (108 N·m). Tighten reduction gear retaining screw to 55 ft.-lbs. (75 N·m). Recouple tractor in reverse order of splitting procedure.

Models 107-109-127-129-147-169-1250-1450-1650

The constant mesh reduction gear on these hydrostatic drive models is located between bevel pinion shaft mounting bearings. To remove reduction gear, refer to DIFFERENTIAL AND REDUCTION GEAR section.

Models 80-282-382H

The reduction gears on these hydrostatic drive models are contained in Peerless reduction drive and differential unit. For service procedures, refer to DIFFERENTIAL AND REDUCTION GEAR section.

TRANSAXLE

LUBRICATION

All Models

Models 73, 86, 106, 108, 126, 128, 800, 1000 and 1200 are equipped with a 3-speed transaxle manufactured for Cub Cadet by International Harvester Corporation. Transaxle fluid capacity is approximately 7 pints (3.3 L) of IH Hy-Tran fluid.

Models 81, 111 and early 182 and 382 are equipped with a Peerless 1200 series transaxle. Transaxle fluid capacity is approximately 2¾ pints (1.3 L) of SAE 90 EP gear oil.

Late Models 182 and 382 are equipped with a Peerless 800 series transaxle. Transaxle fluid capacity is approximately 24 ounces (710 mL) of lithium base grease.

Models 482, 1100 and 1204 are equipped with a Peerless 2300 series transaxle. Transaxle fluid capacity is approximately 4 pints (1.9 L) of SAE 90 EP gear oil.

REMOVE AND REINSTALL

Models 73-86-106-108-126-128-800-1000-1200

The transaxle must be removed with the reduction drive unit. To remove transaxle, refer to the previous REDUCTION DRIVE paragraphs.

Models 81-111-(Early) 182-382

Disconnect transaxle drive belt. Raise rear of tractor and support under axle housings. Remove rear wheels, drive keys and spacers. Remove left fender and foot support. Remove brake mounting bolts and brake caliper assembly, brake disc and key. Remove drawbar assembly and gear shift knob. Unbolt transaxle housing and slide frame slightly to the left to clear brake shaft. Carefully raise frame off transaxle.

Reinstall by reversing removal procedure.

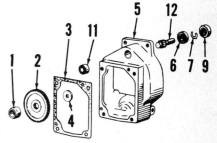

Fig. CC23 — Exploded view of reduction gear drive used on Models 73, 86, 106, 108, 126, 128, 800, 1000 and 1200.

1. Reduction gear spacer
2. Driven reduction gear
3. Gasket
4. Retainer
5. Reduction housing
6. Front bearing
7. Snap ring
9. Oil seal
11. Rear bearing
12. Reduction shaft

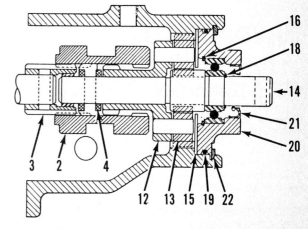

Fig. CC22 — Cross-sectional side view of creeper drive assembly with shifter collar in direct drive position. Refer to Fig. CC20 legend for identification of parts.

Models (Late) 182-382

To remove transaxle, raise and support rear of tractor and block front axle on both sides to prevent tipping. Slip drive belt off transaxle pulley. Disconnect brake linkage. Remove drawbar assembly and gear shift knob. Unbolt transaxle housing from support brackets and separate transaxle from frame. Unbolt and remove brake pad holder and brake disc. Remove rear wheel assemblies.

Reinstall by reversing removal procedure.

Models 482-1100-1204

Disconnect and remove battery. Remove fenders, foot platforms and center frame cover. Drive a block of wood between front axle and both sides of frame. Loosen drive belt guide bolts and depress clutch-brake pedal to its lowest position. Work drive belt off transaxle input pulley. Remove brake mounting bolts and brake assembly. Support rear of tractor, then remove mounting bolts and roll transaxle assembly from frame.

Reinstall by reversing removal procedure.

OVERHAUL

All Models

Models 73, 86, 106, 108, 126, 128, 800, 1000 and 1200 are equipped with a 3-speed transaxle manufactured for Cub Cadet by International Harvester Corporation. Models 81, 111 and early 182 and 382 are equipped with a Peerless 1200 series transaxle. Late Models 182 and 382 are equipped with a Peerless 800 series transaxle. Models 482, 1100 and 1204 are equipped with a Peerless 2300 series transaxle. Refer to the appropriate International Harvester or Peerless section in TRANSAXLE SERVICE section for overhaul procedure.

HYDROSTATIC TRANSMISSION

LUBRICATION

Models 107-109-127-129-147-149-169-1210-1211-1250-1450-1650

These models are equipped with Sundstrand hydrostatic transmission. Manufacturer recommends renewing oil filter and oil in hydrostatic transmission after each 150 hours of operation or once a year. Refill system with 14 pints (6.6 L) of Hy-Tran fluid.

Models 80-282-382H

These models are equipped with an Eaton Model 6 hydrostatic transmission. Periodically check fluid level and maintain level at full mark on reservoir. Transmission fluid capacity is approximately 1½ pints (0.7 L) of IH Hy-Tran fluid.

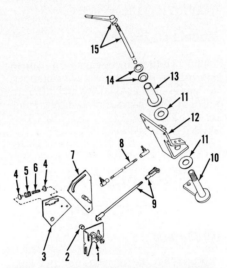

Fig. CC30—Exploded view of hydrostatic transmission control linkage used on Models 107, 127 and 147. Items 1 through 9 are similar on all models.

1. Cam pivot bracket
2. Pivot bushing
3. Damper spring plate
4. Damper spring guide pins
5. Damper spring (heavy)
6. Damper spring (light)
7. Speed control cam
8. Speed control rod
9. Neutral return rod
10. Friction adjusting
11. Friction discs
12. Support
13. Friction collar
14. Belleville washers
15. Control rod & handle

Fig. CC31—Exploded view of hydrostatic transmission control linkage used on Models 109, 129, 149 and 169. Items 20 through 24 (inset) are used on Models 109, 129 and 149 prior to serial number 426000. Items 10 through 14 are used on late Models 109, 129 and 149 and on all 169 models. Refer to Fig. CC30 legend for items 1 through 9.

10. Support shim
11. Belleville washers
12. Control shaft support
13. Friction disc
14. Control shaft & handle
20. Retaining ring
21. Control shaft
22. Spacer
23. Friction bushing
24. Control shaft support

LINKAGE ADJUSTMENT

Models 107-109-127-129-147-149-169-1210-1211-1250-1450-1650

If tractor creeps with control lever in neutral position, control lever in neutral position, control lever linkage must be adjusted. Before adjusting linkage,

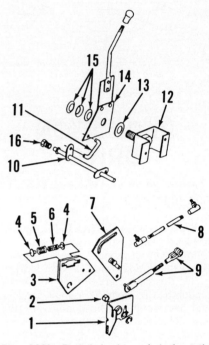

Fig. CC32—Exploded view of hydrostatic transmission control linkage used on Models 1210, 1211, 1250, 1450 and 1650. Refer to Fig. CC30 legend for items 1 through 9.

10. Control rockshaft
11. Connecting link
12. Control bracket
13. Friction washer
14. Control handle
15. Belleville washers
16. Rockshaft bearing

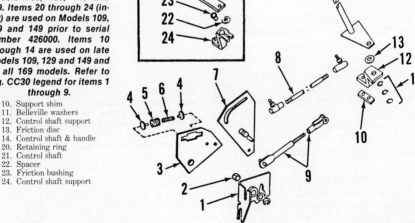

make certain foot brake is properly adjusted, then proceed as follows:

Control lever friction adjustment should be checked and adjusted first. A pull of approximately 10 pounds (5 kg) should be required to move lever in either direction. On Models 107, 127 and 147, tighten adjusting nut, located on friction adjusting shaft (10–Fig. CC30), as necessary. On Models 109, 129 and 149 prior to serial number 426000, tighten friction adjusting screw, located on control rod support (24–Fig. CC31), as needed. On Models 109, 129 and 149, serial number 426000 and after, and Model 169, friction adjusting nut is located on lower end of control shaft (14). On Models 1210, 1211, 1250, 1450 and 1650, adjust lever friction by tightening locknut, securing control handle (14–Fig. CC32) to control bracket (12), as required.

To adjust cam pivot bracket (1–Figs. CC30, CC31 or CC32), first remove seat and fender assembly on Models 107, 127 and 147; on all other models remove frame cover. On all models, raise and securely block rear of tractor so rear wheels are off the ground and block front wheels so tractor cannot move. Loosen cam bracket (1) mounting screws, then start engine and operate at half throttle. Move speed control lever to forward position, then fully depress brake pedal and lock in place. Adjust cam bracket upward or downward until wheels stop turning and any excessive noise or vibration in transmission is

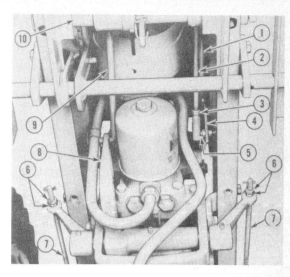

Fig. CC34—Bottom view of typical hydrostatic transmission tractor showing location of brake and transmission control rod adjusting points.

1. Neutral return rod
2. Control rod
3. Jam nut
4. Control cam
5. Ball joint
6. Brake adjusting nuts
7. Brake rods (rear)
8. Brake lever
9. Brake rod (front)
10. Brake pedal cross shaft

eliminated, then tighten cam bracket cap screws. With brake pedal fully depressed, neutral return rod (9) should not touch end of slot in speed control cam (7). If rod touches, disconnect clevis end of rod from brake cross shaft and adjust as needed. Release brake pedal and move speed control lever to forward position, then fully depress brake pedal and release it. Speed control lever should return to neutral position and wheels stop turning. If not, adjust length of speed control connecting rod (8) until speed control lever returns to neutral position when brake pedal is depressed.

Models 80-282-382H

Raise rear wheels off the ground and support rear frame securely. Adjust friction nut on linkage to obtain an 8-10 pound (3.5-4.5 kg) effort at speed control lever. With speed control lever in neutral, start and run engine at full throttle. Wheels should not turn. Adjust turnbuckle on control linkage (14–Fig. CC33) if wheels creep.

CAUTION: Stop engine before making adjustment to linkage.

The drive belt is factory preset and requires not adjustment. When belt has worn or stretched to a point where slippage occurs, a new belt should be installed.

REMOVE AND REINSTALL

Models 107-127-147

To remove hydrostatic transmission and differential assembly, first disconnect battery cables, then remove seat, seat support, fenders and air deflector. Disconnect control rod ball joint (5–Fig. CC34) from speed control cam (4). Disconnect neutral return rod (1), front brake rod (9) and drive shaft coupling. Drive a wooden wedge between front axle and frame on each side and block up under main frame. Support differential case with a rolling floor jack to prevent unit from tilting forward. Unbolt assembly from main frame, place release lever in release position and roll assembly rearward from tractor.

Reinstall assembly by reversing removal procedure. Adjust brakes and control linkage as necessary.

Fig. CC33—View of drive belts and hydrostatic transmission used on Models 80, 282 and 382H tractors.

1. Main drive belt idler
2. Mower pulley
3. Mower drive belt idler
4. Main drive pulley
5. Intermediate drive pulley
6. Main drive belt
7. Final drive belt
8. Idler pulley
9. Hydrostatic pulley
10. Gear reduction unit
11. Brake adjusting nut
12. Hydrostatic transmission
13. Fan
14. Hydrostatic adjusting rod

Models 109-129-149-169-1210-1211-1250-1450-1650

If desired, hydrostatic transmission can be removed from tractor without removing differential assembly. Disconnect battery cables and remove frame cover. Drive out dowel pin from front of drive shaft at engine drive plate hub. Unbolt and remove drive shaft coupling disc (3–Fig. CC35), then remove drive shaft. Disconnect front brake rod (1), drain differential housing and disconnect transmission suction line. Remove cam bracket mounting bolts (7) and move cam bracket and linkage up out of the way. Unbolt hydrostatic transmission from differential housing and remove unit through top opening in frame.

Reinstall hydrostatic transmission by reversing removal procedure. Adjust brakes and control linkage.

To remove hydrostatic transmission and differential as an assembly, remove battery and frame cover. Unbolt and remove seat support and fenders. Disconnect drive shaft flexible coupling. Unbolt cam bracket and move cam bracket and linkage up out of the way. Disconnect front brake rod. Drive a wooden wedge between front axle and frame on each side and block up under main frame. Place a rolling floor jack under differential housing to prevent assembly from tilting forward, unbolt assembly from main frame and roll assembly rearward from tractor.

Reinstall assembly by reversing removal procedure. Adjust brakes and control linkage.

Models 80-282-382H

To remove hydrostatic transmission, disconnect speed control rod at transmission. Remove seat and fender assembly and detach transmission clutch lever from bracket. Remove transmission cooling fan (13–Fig. CC33). Unscrew brake caliper assembly and move out of the way. Disconnect brake rod from brake lever. Pull belt idler pulley (8) away from drive belt to release tension on drive belt and remove drive belt from transmission input pulley. Unscrew differential housing retaining bolts. Block up under tractor frame, unscrew axle housing retaining bolts and remove transmission and differential assembly from tractor. Separate transmission from differential. If oil expansion reservoir is removed, precautions should be taken to prevent entrance of dirt or other foreign material into transmission.

All Models

Models 107, 109, 127, 129, 147, 149, 169, 1210, 1211, 1250, 1450 and 1650 are equipped with a Sundstrand 15 series "U" type hydrostatic transmission. Models 80, 282 and 382H are equipped with an Eaton Model 6 hydrostatic transmission. Refer to the appropriate Sundstrand or Eaton section in HYDROSTATIC TRANSMISSION SERVICE section for overhaul procedure.

AXLE SHAFTS

Models 73-86-106-107-108-109-126-127-128-129-147-149-169-800-1000-1200-1250-1450-1650

The axle carriers (4–Fig. CC36) do not have to be removed to remove axles (1). To remove axles, first drain differential housing and remove rear cover. Remove brake assembly from axle housing on models so equipped. Support transmission-differential housing with a floor jack or wood block. Remove "C" type snap rings from inner ends of axles. Slide axles out of axle carriers.

Remove cap screws securing axle carriers to differential housing and remove carriers. Replacement bushing on Model 73 must be pressed in position with oil groove at the bottom. On all other models, install needle bearing until flush with outer edge of its bore. The oil seals

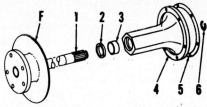

Fig. CC36–Exploded view of axle and carrier used on all models except Models 81, 111, 182, 382, 482 and 1100. Brake disc (F) is used on models equipped with external, axle mounted disc brakes. Model 73 uses a bushing instead of needle bearing (3).

1. Axle
2. Oil seal
3. Needle bearing
4. Axle carrier
5. Gasket
6. "C" ring retainer
F. Brake disc

Fig. CC35–Top view of hydrostatic transmission used on Models 109, 129, 149, 169, 1210, 1211, 1250, 1450 and 1650. Unit can be removed from tractor without removing differential. Refer to text.

1. Brake rod
2. Drive shaft
3. Flexible disc
4. Roll pin
5. Coupling arm
6. Alignment mark
7. Cam bracket cap screw

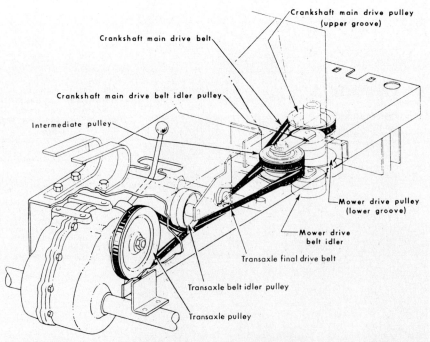

Fig. CC37–Basic drive belt installation diagram for Models 81, 111 and early 182 and 382 tractors. There is no adjustment for drive belt. Drive belt installation on Models 80 and 282 is similar.

must be installed with lip toward bushing or needle bearing.

DRIVE BELTS

Models 80-81-111-182 (Early)-282-382 (Early)

R&R AND DRIVE BELT. There is no adjustment for drive belts. When belt becomes worn or stretched to a point where slippage occurs, belt must be renewed.

To renew drive belt, disconnect spark plug wire and remove mower attachment (if so equipped). Refer to Fig. CC37, and disconnect mower drive belt idler from mower clutch arm. Push up on drive idler to relieve belt tension, then work drive belt off intermediate drive pulley and transmission pulley. After removing transmission belt, crankshaft main drive belt can be removed. Install new belts by reversing removal procedure.

Models (Late) 182-382

R&R DRIVE BELT. A spring loaded belt idler type clutch is used on these tractors. No adjustment is required. If belt slips due to excessive wear or stretching, renew belt.

To remove drive belt, remove engine pulley belt guard (10–Fig. CC38). Unbolt and remove idler pulley (7). Unbolt and remove shift lever (1). Remover retaining screws and move transaxle belt guard (13) out of the way. Remove belt from engine pulley and lift belt up and over transaxle pulley.

Reinstall belt by reversing removal procedure.

Models 482-1100-1204

R&R DRIVE BELT. The drive belt is factory preset and requires no adjust-

ment. When belt becomes worn or stretched to a point where slippage occurs, a new belt should be installed.

To renew drive belt, disconnect battery. Remove drawbar assembly and center frame cover. Depress brake pedal and lock in lowest position. Loosen bolts securing drive belt guides (5–Fig. CC39). Remove idler pulley (4) and two bolts securing right angle drive (3) to crossmember. Rotate right angle drive downward and remove drive belt. When installing new belt, adjust drive belt

guides to gap of ⅛ to 3/16 inch (3-5 mm) between belt and guides.

RIGHT ANGLE DRIVE UNIT

Models 482-1100-1204

R&R AND OVERHAUL. To remove right angle drive unit, remove center frame cover and depress clutch-brake

Fig. CC39 – View of drive belt used on Models 482, 1100 and 1204. Seat and fenders have been removed for ease of viewing. There is no adjustment for drive belt.

1. Mounting bolts
2. Cross support
3. Right angle drive
4. Idler pulley
5. Drive belt guides
6. Input pulley

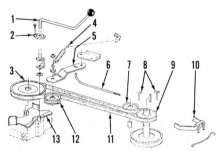

Fig. CC38 – View of drive belt and clutch idler used on late Models 182 and 382 equipped with five-speed transaxles.

1. Shift lever
2. Bushing
3. Transaxle pulley
4. Idler spring
5. Clutch bracket
6. Clutch rod
7. Idler pulley
8. Belt guides
9. Engine pulley
10. Belt guide
11. Drive belt
12. Clutch idler pulley
13. Belt keeper

Fig. CC40 – Exploded view of right angle drive unit used on Models 482 and 1100. Unit used on Model 1204 is similar.

1. Cover
2. Gasket
3. Snap ring
4. Input gear
5. Bearing
6. Input shaft
7. Case
8. Bearing
9. Output gear
10. Output shaft
11. Bearing
12. Gasket
13. Seal retainer
14. Oil seal
15. Bearing
16. Snap ring
17. Oil seal

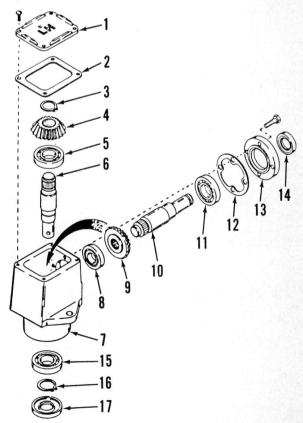

pedal. Drive roll pin from rear half of flexible coupler. Remove mounting bolts and work unit free of drive belt.

To disassemble right angle drive unit, remove cover (1–Fig. CC40), gasket (2) and lubricant. Remove output pulley, seal retainer (13) and bearing (11). Using a brass drift, tap down on output gear (9) while pulling up on output shaft. Continue until shaft is free of inner bearing. Remove oil seal (17) and snap ring (16),

then withdraw input shaft (6) with bearing (5) and gear (4). Bearing (8 and 15) can now be removed. Remove snap ring (3), input gear (4) and bearing (5) from input shaft.

Clean and inspect all parts and renew any showing excessive wear or damage. Reassemble unit by reversing disassembly procedures and fill unit with 4 ounces (118 mL) of "MOLYKOTE" lithium grease or equivalent.

DIFFERENTIAL AND REDUCTION GEAR

R&R AND OVERHAUL

Models 107-109-127-129-147-149-169-1210-1211-1250-1450-1650

With hydrostatic drive and differential assembly removed as outlined in previous paragraphs, remove rear cover (33–Fig. CC41) and drain lubricant. Remove hydrostatic drive unit from differential housing. Support differential drive housing with a jack or blocks. Working through rear cover opening, remove "C" type snap rings from inner end of rear axle shafts. Unbolt axle carriers from differential housing, then remove axle shaft and axle carrier assemblies.

Unbolt and remove differential carrier bearing cages (1) and shim packs (2). Keep shim packs with each cage and identify cages for each side. Turn differential unit as shown in Fig. CC42 and remove unit from housing.

To disassemble differential unit, remove shaft retaining pin (35–Fig. CC41) and drive out shaft (32). Rotate side gears 90 degrees and remove pinion gears (30) and side gears (31). Bearing cones (4) can now be renewed if necessary.

Remove expansion plug (20) and snap ring (21). Then, using a brass drift and hammer, drive bevel pinion shaft (29) rearward out of bearing cone (22) and reduction gear (8). Remove snap ring

(25) and bearing cone (28) from bevel pinion shaft. Remove top cover (6) and gasket (7), then lift out reduction gear (8). Bearing cups (23 and 27) can now be removed from housing. Remove shim pack (26) and identify for aid in reassembly.

Clean and inspect all parts and renew any showing excessive wear or other damage.

Reassemble differential unit by reversing disassembly procedure. Install differential unit and bolt bearing cages (1) with shim packs (2) to housing. Using a cord and spring scale as shown in Fig. CC43, check carrier bearing preload. Add or remove shims (2–Fig. CC41) until a steady pull of 1 to 8 pounds (0.5-3.6 kg) is required to rotate differential unit. Shims are available in thicknesses of 0.004, 0.007, 0.0149 and 0.0299 inch. With preload adjusted, unbolt and remove bearing cages and shim packs, keeping shim packs with cages for later reassembly. Remove differential unit and lay it aside.

If a new bevel pinion shaft (29), differential housing (24) or bearing cup and cone (27 and 28) are installed, select shim pack (26) as follows: Add the number stamped on housing (24), located just left of breather plug (5), to the number stamped on end of bevel pinion shaft (29). The sum of these two numbers plus 0.015 inch will be correct thickness of shim pack (26). Shims are available in various thicknesses. Install shim pack, then press bearing cup (27) in until it bottoms against shims. Install bearing cone (28) and snap ring (25) on bevel pinion shaft (29). Press bearing cup (23) in until it is seated against the shoulder. Then, install bevel pinion shaft assembly and reduction gear (8). Support gear end of bevel pinion shaft with a wood block and press bearing cone (22) on pinion shaft.

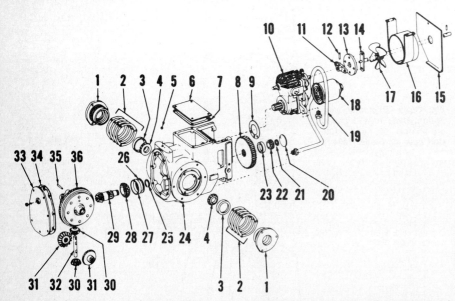

Fig. CC41 – Exploded view of typical IH differential assembly and related parts used on hydrostatic transmission Models 107, 109, 127, 129, 147, 149, 169, 1210, 1211, 1250, 1450 and 1650.

1. Differential bearing cage	10. Hydrostatic unit	19. Suction tube	28. Bearing cone
2. Shims	11. Coupling half	20. Expansion plug	29. Bevel pinion shaft
3. Bearing cup	12. Roll pin	21. Snap ring	30. Differential pinion
4. Bearing cone	13. Coupling disc	22. Bearing cone	31. Differential side gear
5. Breather plug	14. Drive shaft	23. Bearing cup	32. Shaft
6. Top cover	15. Air baffle plate	24. Differential housing	33. Rear cover
7. Gasket	16. Fan shroud	25. Snap ring	34. Gasket
8. Reduction gear	17. Fan	26. Shim pack	35. Pin
9. Gasket	18. Oil filter	27. Bearing cup	36. Ring gear assy.

Fig. CC42 – The differential unit must be turned to position shown to remove unit from housing.

CAUTION: Use extreme care when installing this bearing. Press bearing cone on shaft only to the point where shaft has a zero end play and zero rolling torque. Remove assembly from press and check shaft end play several times during installation of bearing cone to prevent preloading the pinion bearings.

Using a feeler gage, measure distance between bearing cone (22) and front edge of snap ring groove on front end of pinion shaft. This distance minus 0.003 inch (0.076 mm) will determine correct snap ring (21) to be installed. Snap rings are available in various thicknesses. After correct snap ring is installed, tap bevel pinion shaft rearward to seat bearing cone (22) against snap ring. Install a new expansion plug (20).

Reinstall differential unit and carrier bearing cages (1) with shim packs (2). Check backlash between ring gear and bevel drive pinion. The correct backlash is 0.003-0.005 inch (0.076-0.127 mm). Adjust backlash, if necessary, by moving a shim or shims from behind one differential carrier bearing cage to the other bearing cage.

To check ring gear and bevel pinion tooth contact pattern, apply a light coat of Prussian Blue or red lead to bevel pinion teeth. Rotate ring gear and observe contact pattern on pinion teeth. Refer to Fig. CC44. The correct tooth contact pattern is shown at "A." If it is necessary to adjust tooth contact pattern, add or remove shims at shim pack (26 – Fig. CC41) as required. If tooth contact pattern is too low as shown at ("B"– Fig. CC44), add shims to correct the pattern. If pattern is too high as "C", remove shims to correct the pattern.

Reinstall hydrostatic drive unit and axle shaft and axle carrier assemblies.

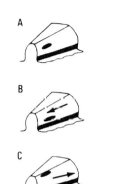

Fig. CC44 – Bevel pinion tooth contact pattern is correct at "A", too low at "B" and too high at "C."

Install assembly on tractor by reversing removal procedure. Fill hydrostatic transmission and differential with 14 pints (6.6 L) of IH Hy-Tran fluid. Adjust brakes and control linkage as necessary.

Models 80-282-382H

To remove reduction gear and differential unit, refer to preceding section and separate hydrostatic transmission from differential. Remove wheel and hub assemblies from axles. Remove park brake disc from brake shaft. Clean axle shafts and remove any burrs from shafts. Unscrew cap screws and drive out dowel pins in cover (29–Fig. CC45). Lift cover off case and axle shaft. Withdraw brake shaft (5), idler gear (4)

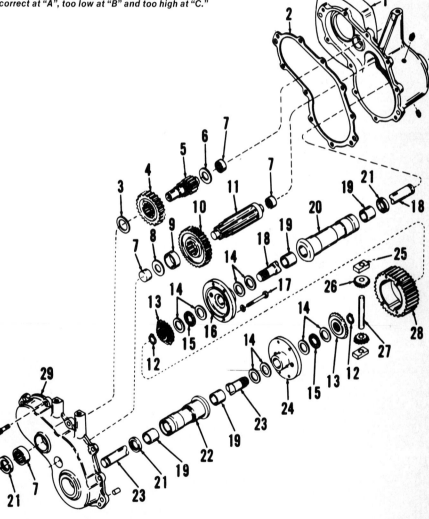

Fig. CC45 – Exploded view of Peerless gear reduction and differential unit used on Models 80, 282 and 382H.

1. Case
2. Gasket
3. Washer
4. Idler gear
5. Brake shaft
6. Washer
7. Bearing
8. Washer
9. Spacer
10. Output gear
11. Output shaft
12. Snap ring
13. Side gears
14. Thrust washers
15. Thrust bearing
16. Differential carrier
17. Bolt
18. Axle shaft (R.H.)
19. Bushing
20. Axle housing
21. Oil seal
22. Axle housing
23. Axle shaft (L.H.)
24. Differential carrier
25. Drive block
26. Drive pinion
27. Drive pin
28. Ring gear
29. Cover

Fig. CC43 – Differential bearing preload is correct when a steady pull of 1 to 8 pounds (0.5-3.6 kg) on a spring scale is required to rotate differential assembly as shown.

and thrust washers (3 and 6) from case. Remove output shaft (11), output gear (10), spacer (9), thrust washer (8) and differential assembly from case. Axle shaft housings (20 and 22) must be pressed from case and cover.

To disassemble differential, unscrew four cap screws (17) and separate axle shaft and carrier assemblies from ring gear (28). Drive blocks (25), bevel pinion gears (26) and drive pin (27) can now be removed from ring gear. Remove snap rings (12) and slide axle shafts (18 and 23) from axle gears (13) and carriers (16 and 24).

Clean and inspect all parts and renew any parts damaged or excessively worn. When installing needle bearings, press bearings in from inside of case or cover until bearings are 0.015-0.020 inch (0.381-0.508 mm) below thrust surfaces. Be sure heads of differential cap screws (17) and right axle shaft (18) are installed in right carrier housing (16). Right axle shaft is installed through case (1). Tighten differential cap screws to 7 ft.-lbs. (9 N·m) and cover cap screws to 10 ft.-lbs. (14 N·m). Differential assembly and output shaft (11) must be installed in case at same time. Remainder of assembly is reverse of disassembly procedure.

Reinstall transaxle assembly and refill unit with approximately 2¾ pints (1.3 L) of SAE 90 EP gear lubricant.

FRONT PTO CLUTCH

ELECTRIC CLUTCH

All Models So Equipped

R&R AND OVERHAUL. To remove clutch, first remove hood side panels and disconnect clutch wire. Remove grille housing and hood as an assembly. Remove brake flange (4–Fig. CC47). Remove retaining bolt, washer and spacer and use a suitable puller to remove clutch rotor assembly (Fig. CC48). Remove stud bolts to take off field coil if necessary. Renewal of field coils, rotor assembly and/or rotor assembly bearing is the only service available on electric clutch.

NOTE: There may be factory installed shims between driving hub and driven disc bearing. Be sure they are in place during reassembly to assure proper braking action.

Before reassembling clutch, check clearance between driven disc and driving hub using a feeler gage (Fig. CC49) at three evenly spaced locations. The gap should be 0.060-0.090 inch (1.524-2.286 mm). Add or subtract shims as required on driving hub.

NOTE: Some late production models do not require shims. The air gap is permanently set. This clutch is unpainted, the early production clutch (shims required) is painted black.

Fig. CC47 – To service clutch, remove grille housing and hood assembly. Remove brake flange (4), retaining bolt (3), washer (2) and spacer (1).

Fig. CC48 – To remove clutch rotor assembly, use a suitable puller.

Fig. CC49 – Check clearance between driven disc and driving hub using feeler gage at three evenly spaced locations. The gap should be 0.060-0.090 inch (1.524-2.286 mm). Refer to text for details.

Fig. CC46 – Cross-sectional view of electric pto clutch. The field coil, rotor assembly and/or rotor assembly bearing are the only renewable parts available for this clutch.

1. Field coil
2. Driving hub
3. Driven disc
4. Rotor assy.

Assemble clutch by reversing disassembly procedure. Adjust clutch as follows: Disengage clutch and check clearance between driven disc and driving hub by placing a feeler gage in the four slots in brake flange (Fig. CC50). The gap should be 0.010 inch (0.254 mm). Tighten or loosen brake flange mounting nuts (1) to obtain correct air gap.

MECHANICAL CLUTCH

All Models So Equipped

R&R AND OVERHAUL. To remove front pto clutch, first remove grille and one some early models, remove grille support. Remove jam set screw and lock set screw from each of the three holes in clutch pulley housing. See Fig. CC51. Withdraw clutch assembly from tractor. Bearing and collar will remain on engine crankshaft as shown in Fig. CC52. Remove three jam nuts (1 – Fig. CC53). Loosen three clutch finger screws (1 – Fig. CC54) evenly and remove pressure plate, friction disc and three compression springs. Fingers (4), thrust button

(2) and pressure springs (3) can now be removed.

Clean and inspect all parts for excessive wear or other damage. A clutch service kit consisting of a friction disc, pressure springs and antichatter springs is available. Reassemble by reversing disassembly procedure and adjust finger screws as follows: Install gage (1 – Fig. CC55) which is furnished in clutch service kit, in position shown. Tighten finger screw (2) (in line with center of gage) until ends of gage contact machined surface of pulley; adjust other two finger screws on same manner. Recheck each of the three positions with gage to make certain all three adjustments are equal. Install jam nuts (1 – Fig. CC53) and tighten to 6-7 ft.-lbs. (8-9 N·m).

If bearing (Fig. CC52) was removed, install bearing flush with end of crankshaft. Align set screw holes in clutch pulley housing with slots in drive pulley cup as shown in Fig. CC56 and slide clutch assembly part way on bearing. Equally space and install three antichatter springs as shown in Fig. CC56. Push clutch assembly the rest of the way

on bearing. Install three cone point (½-inch long) set screws and tighten to 60-72 in.-lbs. (7-8 N·m). Install and tighten flat point (¼ inch long) set screws to 72-84 in.-lbs. (8-9 N·m). Reassemble tractor and with pto clutch hand lever fully forward, adjust turnbuckle to obtain a clearance of 1/64 to 3/64 inch (0.4-1.2 mm) between wear button on linkage arm and thrust button on clutch.

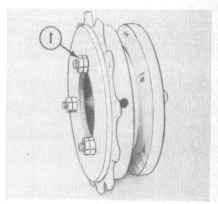

Fig. CC53 — Jam nuts (1) are used to lock clutch finger adjusting screws.

Fig. CC50 — Check clearance between driven disc and driving hub by inserting feeler gage in the four slots in brake flange. Gap should be 0.010 inch (0.254 mm). Tighten or loosen brake flange mounting nuts (1) to obtain clearance.

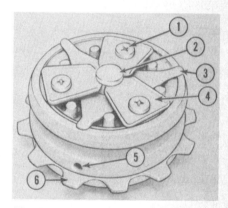

Fig. CC54 — Front pto clutch assembly. Set screw holes (5) must be centered on lugs of clutch disc (6).

1. Finger screws
2. Thrust button
3. Pressure springs
4. Clutch finger
5. Set screw hole
6. Clutch disc

Fig. CC51 — Remove jam set screw and lock set screw from each of the three holes (1), then withdraw front pto clutch.

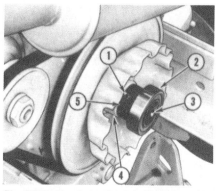

Fig. CC52 — Front pto clutch bearing and collar on engine crankshaft. To lock collar (5) to bearing (2), turn collar in direction of crankshaft rotation.

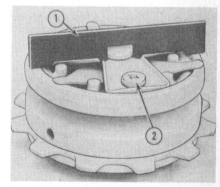

Fig. CC55 — With gage (1) in position shown, adjust finger screw (2) as outlined in text. Adjust other two fingers in same manner.

REAR PTO UNIT

Gear Drive Models So Equipped

A rear pto unit (Fig. CC57) is available on gear drive models equipped with IH transmission and differential. The pto is driven by transmission input shaft. Shift clutch (11) locks splines on pto shaft directly to splines on rear of transmission input shaft. Depress clutch-brake pedal and stop tractor motion before engaging pto. To remove pto unit, remove seven cap screws from retainer (2). Pull shaft and retainer assembly rearward allowing shift clutch (11) to disengage from shift lever shaft (12 or 30). Disassemble removed unit as follows: Loosen set screw in clutch (11) and slide clutch from shaft (6). Remove retaining ring (10) and shield (9), then withdraw shaft and bearing assembly from retainer (2). Remove snap ring (8) and press shaft from bearing (7). Remove oil seal (1) from retainer. If shift lever shaft (12 or 30) is excessively worn, remove exterior linkage and remove shaft from inside differential housing.

Clean and inspect all parts and renew any showing excessive wear or other damage. Reassemble by reversing disassembly procedure. Tighten set screw in clutch (11) only enough to prevent clutch from traveling beyond stops on the cut-a-way spline on shaft. Clutch must slide freely from stop to stop. Oil seal (1) should be installed with lip to inside.

Using new gasket (3), insert pto shaft through hole in differential rear cover (4) and engage pin on shift lever shaft in groove in shift clutch. Move assembly forward and insert pilot end of shaft (11) in rear end of transmission input shaft. Bolt assembly in position.

ELECTRIC LIFT

All Models So Equipped

A self-contained electric lift unit (Fig. CC58) is available on some models. To remove lift unit, first disconnect battery cables. On some models, frame cover and side panel extensions must be removed. On all models, disconnect electrical connector at motor, remove two attaching pins and lift assembly from tractor.

To disassemble unit, remove two screws through motor and pry motor and drive coupling from adapter.

CAUTION: Do not let end plates separate from motor body.

Fig. CC57—Exploded view of rear pto assembly used on gear drive models equipped with IH transmission and differential. Shift linkage (24 through 30) is used on Model 73. Linkage (12 through 23) is used on other gear drive models.

1. Oil seal
2. Retainer
3. Gasket
4. Differential cover
5. Gasket
6. Pto shaft
7. Bearing
8. Snap ring
9. Shield
10. Retaining ring
11. Shift clutch
12. Shift lever shaft
13. Oil seal
14. Spacer
15. Lever
16. Washer
17. Spring
18. Poppet
19. Guide
20. Link
21. Arm
22. Bearing bracket
23. Shift lever
24. Shift lever
25. Guide
26. Spring
27. Collar
28. Spacer
29. Oil seal
30. Shift lever shaft

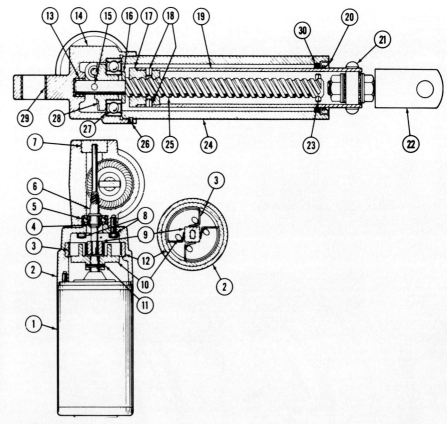

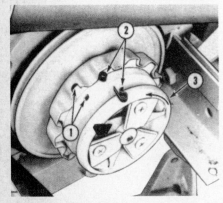

Fig. CC56—View showing front pto clutch installation.

1. Set screw hole aligned with slot
2. Correct installation of antichatter springs
3. Front pto clutch pulley rotation

Fig. CC58—Sectional view of electric lift unit used on some models.

1. Motor
2. Adapter
3. Brake springs
4. Retaining ring
5. Pinion bearing
6. Pinion shaft
7. Pinion bushing
8. "Tap tite" screws
9. Brake cam
10. Drive coupling
11. Spring pin
12. Liner insert
13. Bushing
14. Housing
15. Drive pin
16. Washer
17. Lifting nut
18. Pins
19. Translating tube
20. Oil seal
21. Bushing screws
22. Clevis assy.
23. Stop pin
24. Outer tube
25. Lift screw
26. Set screw
27. Load bearing
28. Spiroid gear
29. Bushing
30. Guide bushing

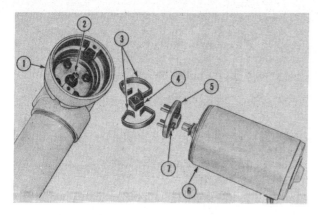

Fig. CC59 — View showing motor, drive coupling and brake assembly removed from lift unit.
1. Adapter
2. Pinion shaft
3. Brake springs
4. Brake cam
5. Drive coupling
6. Motor
7. Spring pin

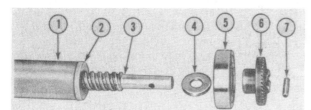

Fig. CC60 — Spiroid gear, load bearing and washer and removed from lift screw after removing drive pin.
1. Translating tube
2. Lifting nut
3. Lift screw
4. Washer
5. Load bearing
6. Spiroid gear
7. Drive pin

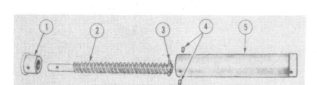

Fig. CC61 — Remove lift screw, drive pins (4) inward and remove lifting nut.
1. Lifting nut
2. Lift screw
3. Stop pin
4. Pins
5. Translating tube

parts with IH 251 HEP grease or equivalent. Install new oil seal (20 – Fig. CC58) with lip towards inside.

Reinstall lift unit on tractor and adjust slip clutch as follows: Attach an implement to tractor hitch, start engine and hold lift switch in raise position. The lift unit should raise implement without slipping, but must rotate freely at the fully raised position. A slight slip on engagement of the load is permissible, but once load is moving slippage should not occur until maximum travel is reached. If slippage is excessive, tighten adjusting nut (3 – Fig. CC63) in increments of 1/8 turn to correct slip clutch setting.

HYDRAULIC LIFT

OPERATION

All Models So Equipped

The hydrostatic drive charge pump furnishes fluid to hydraulic lift system. On models equipped with hydraulic lift, charge pump relief valve is located on right side of transmission center housing under plug (4 – Fig. CC64). The hydraulic relief valve is located on top of center housing under plug (2). Lift pressure is regulated by lift relief valve at 500-625 psi (3448-4309 kPa). The single spool control valve is used to direct pressurized fluid to double action lift cylinder.

PRESSURE CHECK AND ADJUSTMENT

All Models So Equipped

To check hydraulic lift pressure, refer to Fig. CC65 and install a 1000 psi (7000 kPa) test gage in test port (3 – Fig. CC64). Start engine and operate at approximately 2/3 full engine rpm. With lift control valve in neutral, test gage should indicate charge pressure of 70-120 psi (483-827 kPa). With control valve in raise position and lift cylinder at end of its stroke, test gage should indicate maximum lift pressure of 500-625 psi (3448-4309 kPa). Lift pressure can be adjusted by removing plug (2) and installing or removing spring shims as required.

If motor or drive coupling is to be renewed, drive out pin (7 – Fig. CC59) and separate coupling (5) from motor (6). Motor is serviced only as an assembly. Remove brake springs (3) and brake cam (4) from pinion shaft (2). Remove four screws and lift off adapter (1). Pull pinion shaft (6 – Fig. CC58) and bearing (5) from housing, remove retaining ring (4) and press bearing from pinion shaft. Loosen set screw (26) and unscrew housing (14) from outer tube (24). Remove bushing screws (21), pull clevis assembly (22) from translating tube (19) and withdraw lift screw and translating tube assembly from outer tube. Oil seal (20) and guide bushing (30) can now be removed from outer tube. Drive out pin (7 – Fig. CC60) and remove spiroid gear (6), bearing (5) and washer (4) from lift screw (3). Remove lift screw (2 – Fig. CC61), drive both pins (4) inward and remove lifting nut (1) from translating tube (5). Drive stop pin (3) from lift screw. To disassemble clevis and slip clutch assembly, remove self locking nut and slide Belleville washers, thrust washers and bushing from clevis.

Clean and inspect all parts and renew any showing excessive wear or other damage. Reassemble by reversing disassembly procedure, keeping the following points in mind: Belleville washers (1 – Fig. CC62) and thrust washers (2) must

be installed as shown on each side of slip clutch bushing. Tighten self locking nut (1 – Fig. CC63) on slip clutch and clevis to 25-30 in.-lbs. (2.8-3.4 N·m). Stop pin (3 – Fig. CC61) should be installed so equal amount of pin extends from each side of lift screw (2). Lubricate internal

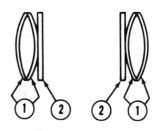

Fig. CC62 — Belleville washers (1) and thrust washers (2) must be installed as shown on each side of slip clutch bushing.

Fig. CC63 — Sectional view showing installation of slip clutch and clevis assembly.
1. Self-locking nut
2. Belleville washer
3. Adjusting nut
4. Thrust washers
5. Bushing

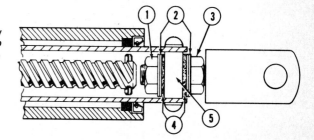

CONTROL VALVE

All Models So Equipped

R&R AND OVERHAUL. To remove control valve, make certain any mounted equipment is in fully lowered position. Shut off fuel, then unbolt and remove fuel tank and side panels as an assembly. Identify and disconnect hydraulic lines from valve. Disconnect control lever link, then unbolt and remove valve assembly.

To disassemble control valve, refer to Fig. CC66 and remove end cap (10). Withdraw spool assembly. Rear "O" ring (12) and bushing (9) will be removed with spool assembly. Unscrew shoulder bolt (7) and separate washers (13), spacer (8) and centering spring (11) from spool (5). Remove front "O" ring from spool bore. Unscrew plug (2) and remove "O" ring (3), spring (4) and lift check valve (1).

Clean and inspect all parts for excessive wear or other damage. If spool (5) or valve body (6) is scored or otherwise

Fig. CC64 — On models equipped with hydraulic lift, charge relief valve is located on right side of transmission center housing and lift relief valve is located on top of center housing.

1. Check valves
2. Hydraulic lift relief valve plug
3. Lift pressure test port
4. Charge relief valve plug

damaged, renew control valve assembly as spool and body are not serviced separately.

When reassembling, use new "O" ring seals and lubricate all parts with clean Hy-Tran fluid. Apply a suitable thread locking solution on threads of shoulder bolt (7), and install washers, spacer and centering spring on spool. Tighten shoulder bolt to 60-90 in.-lbs. (7-10 N·m). Install "O" rings (12), bushing (9) and spool assembly. Tighten end cap (10) to 20-25 ft.-lbs. (27-34 N·m). Install lift check valve (1), spring (4), "O" ring (3) and plug (2).

Reinstall control valve by reversing removal procedure. Start engine and operate at approximately ⅔ full throttle speed. Cycle lift cylinder several times to expel air from system and check for leaks. Check fluid level in differential housing and fill to proper level with IH Hy-Tran fluid.

LIFT CYLINDER

All Models So Equipped

Service on lift cylinder is limited to renewal of hoses, fittings and fitting "O" rings or renewal of complete cylinder assembly. Parts for cylinder are not serviced separately.

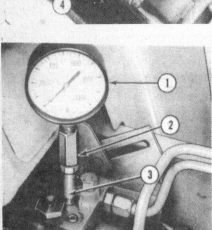

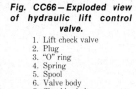

Fig. CC66 — Exploded view of hydraulic lift control valve.

1. Lift check valve
2. Plug
3. "O" ring
4. Spring
5. Spool
6. Valve body
7. Shoulder bolt
8. Spacer
9. Bushing
10. End cap
11. Centering spring
12. "O" rings
13. Washers

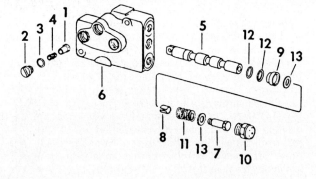

Fig. CC65 — View showing 1000 psi (7000 kPa) test gage installed in lift pressure test port. Refer to text.

1. 1000 psi (6895 kPa) test gage
2. Adapter
3. Pipe nipple (⅛ inch)

JOHN DEERE

CONDENSED SPECIFICATIONS

MODELS

	60	70	100	108	110
Engine Make	Tecumseh	Tecumseh	B&S	B&S	Kohler
Model	VH60	VH70	190707	191707	K161S
Bore	2⅝ in.	2¾ in.	3 in.	3 in.	2⅞ in.
	(66.7 mm)	(69.8 mm)	(76.2 mm)	(76.2 mm)	(73.0 mm)
Stroke	2½ in.	2-17/32 in.	2¾ in.	2¾ in.	2½ in.
	(63.5 mm)	(64.3 mm)	(69.8 mm)	(69.8 mm)	(63.5 mm)
Piston Displacement	13.5 cu. in.	15.0 cu. in.	19.44 cu. in.	19.44 cu. in.	16.22 cu. in.
	(221 cc)	(246 cc)	(319 cc)	(319 cc)	(266 cc)
Horsepower	6	7	8	8	7
Slow Idle Speed – Rpm	1500	1700	1900	1750	1800
High Idle Speed (No Load) – Rpm	3600	3600	3600	3500	3800
Crankcase Oil Capacity	1½ pints	1½ pints	2¼ pints	2¼ pints	2½ pints
	(0.7L)	(0.7L)	(1.0L)	(1.0L)	(1.2L)
Weight –					
Above 32°F (0°C)			SAE 30		
Below 32°F (0°C)			SAE 5W-20		
Transmission Oil Capacity	3 pints	3 pints	3 pints	24 oz.	2 pints
	(1.4L)	(1.4L)	(1.4L)	(710mL)	(0.9L)
Weight	SAE 90	SAE 90	SAE 90	Grease	SAE 90
	(AM30200M)	(AM30200M)	(AM30200M)	(AT30408)	(AM30200M)

MODELS

	110	110	111	112	112
Engine Make	Kohler	Kohler	B&S	Tecumseh	Kohler
Model	K181S	K241AS	252707	HH100	K241AS
Bore	2-15/16 in.	3¼ in.	3-7/16 in.	3-5/16 in.	3¼ in.
	(74.6 mm)	(82.5 mm)	(87.3 mm)	(84.1 mm)	(82.5 mm)
Stroke	2¾ in.	2⅞ in.	2⅝ in.	2¾ in.	2⅞
	(69.8 mm)	(73.0 mm)	(66.7 mm)	(69.8 mm)	(73.0 mm)
Piston Displacement	18.6 cu. in.	23.9 cu. in.	24.4 cu. in.	23.7 cu. in.	23.9 cu. in.
	(305 cc)	(392 cc)	(400 cc)	(388 cc)	(392 cc)
Horsepower	8	10	11	10	10
Slow Idle Speed – Rpm	1800	1200	1750	1700	1200
High Idle Speed (No Load) – Rpm	3800	3800	3500	3800	3800
Crankcase Oil Capacity	2½ pints	3 pints	3 pints	2½ pints	3 pints
	(1.2L)	(1.4L)	(1.4L)	(1.2L)	(1.4L)
Weight –					
Above 32°F (0°C)			SAE 30		
Below 32°F (0°C)			SAE 5W-20		
Transmission Oil Capacity	3 pints	3½ pints	24 oz.	3 pints	3½ pints
	(1.4L)	(1.6L)	(710mL)	(1.4L)	(1.6L)
Weight	SAE 90	SAE 90	Grease	SAE 90	SAE 90
	(AM30200M)	(AM30200M)	(AT30408)	(AM30200M)	(AM30200M)

MODELS

	112	120	140*	200	208
Engine Make	Kohler	Kohler	Kohler	Kohler	Kohler
Model	K301AS	K301AS	K321AS	K181QS	K181S
Bore	3⅜ in.	3⅜ in.	3½ in.	2-15/16 in.	2-15/16 in.
	(85.7 mm)	(85.7 mm)	(88.9 mm)	(74.6 mm)	(74.6 mm)
Stroke	3¼ in.	3¼ in.	3¼ in.	2¾ in.	2¾ in.
	(82.5 mm)	(82.5 mm)	(82.5 mm)	(69.8 mm)	(69.8 mm)
Piston Displacement	29.07 cu. in.	29.07 cu. in.	31.27 cu. in.	18.6 cu. in.	18.6 cu. in.
	(476 cc)	(476 cc)	(512 cc)	(305 cc)	(305 cc)
Horsepower	12	12	14	8	8
Slow Idle Speed – Rpm	1200	1200	1200	1700	1700
High Idle Speed (No Load) – Rpm	3800	3800	3800	3500	3500
Crankcase Oil Capacity	3 pints	3 pints	3 pints	2½ pints	2½ pints
	(1.4L)	(1.4L)	(1.4L)	(1.2L)	(1.2L)
Weight –					
Above 32°F (0°C)			SAE 30		
Below 32°F (0°C)			SAE 5W-20		
Transmission Oil Capacity	3½ pints	10 pints	10 pints	3½ pints	3½ pints
	(1.6L)	(4.7L)	(4.7L)	(1.6L)	(1.6L)
Weight	SAE 90	ATF "F"	ATF "F"	SAE 90	SAE 90
	(AM30200M)			(AM30200M)	(AM30200M)

*Production S.N.10001 and later.

MODELS

	210	212	214	216
Engine Make	Kohler	Kohler	Kohler	Kohler
Model	K241AQS	K301AQS	K321AQS	K341AQS
Bore	3¼ in.	3⅜ in.	3½ in.	3¾ in.
	(82.5 mm)	(85.7 mm)	(88.9 mm)	(95.2 mm)
Stroke	2⅞ in.	3¼ in.	3¼ in.	3¼ in.
	(73.0 mm)	(82.5 mm)	(82.5 mm)	(82.5 mm)
Piston Displacement	23.9 cu. in.	29.1 cu. in.	31.27 cu. in.	35.90 cu. in.
	(392 cc)	(477 cc)	(512 cc)	(588 cc)
Horsepower	10	12	14	16
Slow Idle Speed – Rpm	1700	1700	1700	1700
High Idle Speed (No Load) – Rpm	3500	3500	3500	3500
Crankcase Oil Capacity		3 pints (1.4L)		
Weight –				
Above 32°F (0°C)		SAE 30		
Below 32°F (0°C)		SAE 5W-20		
Transmission Oil Capacity		3½ pints (1.6L)		
Weight		AM30200M Lubricant (SAE 90)		

	300	312	314	316
Engine Make	Kohler	Kohler	Kohler	Kohler
Model	K341AQS	K301AS	K321AQS	K341AQS
Bore	3¾ in.	3⅜ in.	3½ in.	3¾ in.
	(95.2 mm)	(85.7 mm)	(88.9 mm)	(95.2 mm)
Stroke	3¼ in.	3¼ in.	3¼ in.	3¼ in.
	(82.5 mm)	(82.5 mm)	(82.5 mm)	(82.5 mm)
Piston Displacement	35.90 cu. in.	29.07 cu. in.	31.27 cu. in.	35.90 cu. in.
	(588 cc)	(476 cc)	(512 cc)	(588 cc)
Horsepower	16	12	14	16
Slow Idle Speed – Rpm	2000	2400	2000	2000
High Idle Speed (No Load) – Rpm	3500	3500	3500	3500
Crankcase Oil Capacity	3 pints (1.4L)			
Weight–				
Above 32°F (0°C)	SAE 30			
Below 32°F (0°C)	SAE 5W-20			
Transmission Oil Capacity	10 pints (4.7L)			
Weight	ATF Type "F"			

FRONT AXLE SYSTEM

AXLE MAIN MEMBER

All Models

To remove front axle assembly, refer to appropriate Fig. JD1 through JD6, then disconnect tie rod ends and drag link (models so equipped) from steering spindles. Raise front of tractor and remove pivot bolt on all models except Models 108 and 111. On Models 108 and 111, remove hood and muffler assemblies; then, remove four cap screws from pivot anchors and lower axle.

On all models, inspect axle pivot bushing and pivot bolt for wear and renew if necessary. On Models 60, 70 and 100, pivot bolt rides directly in axle.

TIE RODS

All Models

Refer to exploded views showing front axle assemblies and note that front wheel toe-in is adjustable on some models. To adjust toe-in on models with adjustable tie rods, loosen jam nuts and turn tie rod(s) to obtain 3/16-inch (5 mm) toe-in as shown in Fig. JD7. Tighten jam nuts.

STEERING SPINDLES

All Models

To remove steering spindles, raise and support front of tractor and remove front wheels. Refer to appropriate Fig. JD1 through JD6 and disconnect tie rods and drag link from spindles as neces-

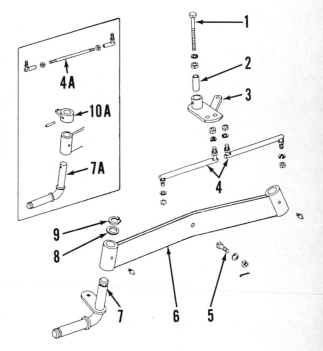

Fig. JD1—Exploded view of front axle assembly used on Models 60, 70 and 100. Adjustable tie rod (4A), spindle (7A) and spindle arm (10A) shown in inset were used on some early tractors.

1. Cap screw
2. Bearing
3. Steering arm
4. Tie rods
5. Pivot bolt
6. Axle main member
7. Steering spindle
8. Washer
9. Snap ring

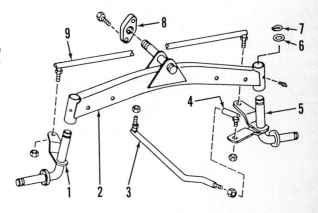

Fig. JD2—Exploded view of front axle assembly used on Models 108 and 111.

1. Steering spindle R.H.
2. Axle main member
3. Drag link
4. Ball joint
5. Steering spindle L.H.
6. Washer
7. Snap ring
8. Pivot pin anchor
9. Tie rod

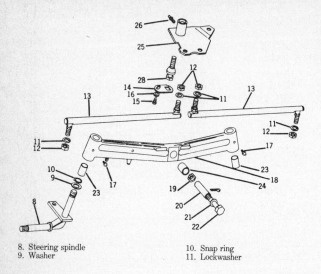

8. Steering spindle
9. Washer

10. Snap ring
11. Lockwasher

Fig. JD3—Exploded view of typical front axle assembly used on Model 110 prior to 1973 and Model 112 prior to 1972. Tie rod is adjustable on some models and steering spindle is retained by a collar on early models.

12. Nut
13. Tie rod
14. Lock plate
15. Self-tapping screw
16. Washer
17. Grease fitting
18. Axle main member
19. Nut
20. Pivot bearing
21. Washer
22. Pivot bolt
23. Spindle bushing
24. Pivot bushing
25. Steering pivot arm
26. Grease fitting
28. Bolt & cone assy.

STEERING CONE ADJUSTMENT

Models 110 (Early)-112 (Early)-120-140-300-312-316

Steering arm (25 – Fig. JD3 or 1 – Fig. JD5) should turn freely through entire steering range. If steering arm turns hard or is too loose, remove bolt and cone assembly (28 or 2). Clean and lubricate cone and arm, then reinstall bolt and cone. With tie rods and drag link disconnected, tighten bolt until slight drag is felt when turning arm by hand and all end play has been removed. Install lock plate (14 or 5) over bolt and reconnect tie rods and drag link.

STEERING GEAR

REMOVE AND REINSTALL

Model 60

To remove steering gear, first remove cap screw (15 – Fig. JD8) and withdraw steering wheel and upper shaft (11). Disconnect drag link (22) from lever arm (19). Unbolt housing (5) from frame and remove steering gear assembly from underside of tractor.

sary. Drive out roll pins or remove snap rings retaining spindles in axle, then lower spindles from axle main member.

On models so equipped, inspect spindle bushings for excessive wear and renew if necessary. New bushings must be reamed to 0.751-0.755 inch (19.075-19.177 mm).

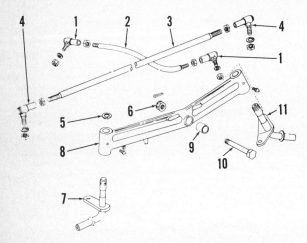

Fig. JD4—Exploded view of front axle assembly used on Model 110 after 1972, Model 112 after 1971 and 200 series tractors.

1. Ball joint
2. Drag link
3. Tie rod
4. Ball joint
5. Snap ring
6. Nut
7. Steering spindle R.H.
8. Axle
9. Bushing
10. Pivot bolt
11. Steering spindle L.H.

Models 70-100

To remove steering gear, remove steering wheel using a suitable puller. Disconnect drag link from lever arm (19 – Fig. JD9). Remove three mounting bolts and remove steering gear assembly from underside of tractor.

Models 108-111

To remove steering gear assembly, remove pin (3 – Fig. JD10) and lift wheel off shaft. Raise hood and remove battery and battery base. Remove support bearing (2) nuts and instrument panel bolts. Disconnect ignition switch and throttle control cable and slide instrument panel off shaft. Remove bolts, spacers (5), washers, clamp plates (6) and steering wheel shaft. Disconnect drag link from sector arm (17). Remove support bracket bolts and gear case mounting bolts and lower gear case assembly from tractor.

All Other Models

To remove steering gear unit, pry emblem out of steering wheel and remove nut. Using a suitable puller, remove steering wheel. Disconnect drag link rear ball joint from lever arm (19 – Fig. JD9). Remove battery, then remove clamp securing steering column to pedestal. Unbolt steering unit from frame, slide steering column down out of dash and remove steering gear assembly from underside of tractor.

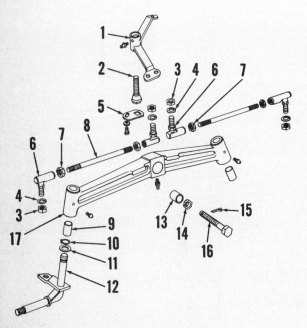

Fig. JD5—Exploded view of front axle assembly used on Models 120 and 140. Axle assembly used on Models 300, 312 and 316 is similar except spindle bushings (9) are not used.

1. Steering arm
2. Bolt & cone assy.
3. Nut
4. Lockwasher
5. Lock plate
6. Ball joint
7. Jam nut
8. Tie rod
9. Bushing
10. Snap ring
11. Washer
12. Steering spindle
13. Bushing
14. Nut
15. Cotter pin
16. Pivot bolt
17. Axle

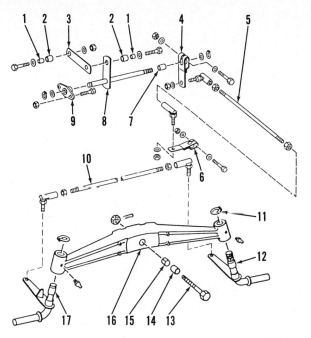

Fig. JD6 — Exploded view of axle assembly used on Model 314.

1. Bushing
2. Bearing
3. Link
4. Steering arm (rear)
5. Drag link
6. Steering arm (front)
7. Bushing
8. Pivot shaft
9. Bearing
10. Tie rod
11. Snap ring
12. Steering spindle L.H.
13. Pivot bolt
14. Bushing
15. Spacer
16. Axle main member
17. Steering spindle R.H.

3/32-inch (1.5-2.5 mm). Tighten jam nut (3) to 22-25 ft.-lbs. (30-34 N·m) torque. Set lever arm in center position (half way between full right and full left turn). Turn tapered stud (20) in to remove all backlash. Tighten jam nut to a torque of 40 ft.-lbs. (54 N·m).

When properly adjusted, a slight drag can be detected as lever arm passes mid-position each time unit is turned through full steering range. Lubricate steering unit with approximately ¼-pound (120mL) multi-purpose grease.

ENGINE

REMOVE AND REINSTALL

Models 60-70

To remove engine, disconnect fuel line, then unbolt and remove hood, grille and fuel tank. Disconnect battery ground cable, starting motor cable, choke-throttle control cable and wires from rectifier panel. Detach spring from primary idler to relieve tension on primary belt. Remove spring locking pin and disconnect pto clutch arm. Slip primary drive belt from engine pulley. Unbolt engine from frame and lift engine from tractor. To reinstall engine, reverse removal procedure.

OVERHAUL

Models 108-111

After removing steering gear case, remove gear case bolts and separate case by tapping lightly with plastic hammer. Remove washers, gears and keys. Slide shafts out of case halves and support bracket. Inspect bearing (16 – Fig. JD10) for wear or looseness. Check leather disc (8) for deterioration. Inspect pinion shaft (9), sector shaft (17), pinion and sector gears for wear, damage or cracks.

Reinstall all parts except steering wheel in reverse order of removal. Apply liberal amounts of multi-purpose type grease on bearings, steering pinion and sector gears. Completely cover gear teeth with grease.

All Other Models

After removing steering gear assembly, remove lever arm and bolt (19 – Figs. JD8 or JD9). Remove adjusting plug (1) and bump worm shaft and bearing out of housing. Check all parts for excessive wear and renew as necessary.

When reassembling, install worm shaft and bearings in housing, then tighten adjusting plug (1) to remove all end play. The worm shaft must still

rotate freely. Install cotter pin to prevent adjusting plug from working loose. Install lever arm and bolt assembly (19), seal (17) and seal retainer (18). Loosen jam nut (21) and turn tapered stud (20) out 2 turns. Tighten adjusting nut (4) on lever arm bolt to remove end play of bolt. At this time, distance between lever arm and housing should be 1/16 to

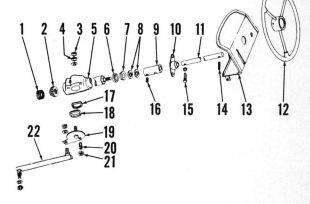

Fig. JD8 — Exploded view of steering gear used on Model 60.

1. Adjusting plug
2. Bearing
3. Jam nut
4. Adjusting nut
5. Housing & shaft assy.
6. Bearing retainer
7. Bearing
8. Felt washers
9. Sleeve coupling
10. Upper shaft bearing
11. Upper steering shaft
12. Steering wheel
13. Dash panel
14. Groove pin
15. Cap screw
16. Set screw
17. Lever arm seal
18. Seal retainer
19. Lever arm
20. Tapered stud
21. Jam nut
22. Drag link

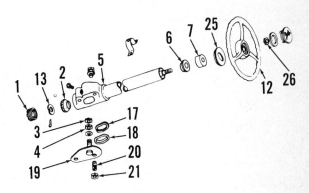

Fig. JD9 — Exploded view of steering gear used on 200 and 300 series tractors and Model 112. Models 70, 100, 110, 120 and 140 are similar.

1. Adjusting plug
2. Bearing
3. Jam nut
4. Adjusting nut
5. Housing & shaft assy.
6. Bearing
7. Seal
12. Steering wheel
13. Spring washer
17. Lever arm seal
18. Seal retainer
19. Lever arm
20. Tapered stud
21. Jam nut
25. Grommet
26. Nut

Fig. JD7 — On models equipped with adjustable tie rods (C), toe-in is correct when distance (A) is 3/16-inch (5 mm) less than distance (B).

Models 100-110-112

To remove engine, first remove grille, hood, grille cowls and engine shields. Disconnect battery ground cable, flexible fuel line at tank connection, ignition wire from coil and wires from starter-generator. Remove fuel tank. Disconnect choke and throttle control cables from engine. Detach pto linkage and wires on electric pto if so equipped. Remove pto unit. Remove drive belts as outlined in DRIVE BELTS section. Unbolt engine from frame and lift engine assembly from tractor. To reinstall engine, reverse removal procedure.

Models 108-111

To remove engine, remove hood assembly. Disconnect battery cables, engine wiring and throttle cable. Remove fuel line at carburetor and drain fuel tank. Mark position of front bumper and remove it. Remove muffler and exhaust pipe. Detach pto linkage and wires on electric pto if so equipped. Remove pto unit. Remove drive belt as outlined in DRIVE BELTS section. Remove crankshaft pulley and key. Unbolt engine and rotate engine to free oil drain while lifting engine out.

Models 120-140

To remove engine, remove hood and grille as a unit. Disconnect fuel line and remove fuel tank. Disconnect battery cables, ignition wires and starter-generator wires and remove battery and base. Disconnect choke and throttle cables. Remove two cap screws to free drive shaft from clutch cone. Remove engine mounting cap screws and lift engine from tractor. To reinstall engine, reverse removal procedure.

Models 200-208-210-212-214-216

To remove engine, remove grille, hood and side panels. Disconnect battery cables, engine wiring harness and starter lead. Shut off fuel at tank and disconnect fuel line at fuel pump. Remove air cleaner assembly and disconnect throttle and choke cables. Disconnect pto linkage and remove clutch. Remove crankshaft pulley bolt, depress clutch and slide pulley and belt off end of crankshaft. Remove engine mounting bolts and lift engine out.

Models 300-312-314-316

To remove engine, remove grille, hood and hood support. Remove air cleaner assembly. Shut off fuel at tank and disconnect fuel line at fuel pump. Disconnect throttle cable and choke cable. Disconnect battery cables, engine wiring harness, starter cable and electric pto clutch wire. Disconnect drive shaft at rear of engine. Remove engine mounting bolts and lift engine from frame using suitable hoist.

OVERHAUL

All Models

Engine make and model are listed at the beginning of this section. To overhaul engine components and accessories, refer to Briggs & Stratton, Kohler and Tecumseh sections of this manual.

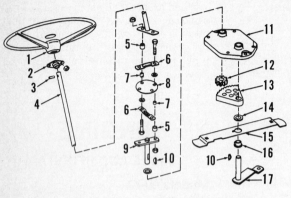

Fig. JD10 — Exploded view of steering gear used on Models 108 and 111.

1. Steering wheel
2. Bearing
3. Pin
4. Steering shaft
5. Spacer (4 used)
6. "U" joint clamp plates
7. Bushing (4 used)
8. Disc
9. Lower shaft
10. Key
11. Case assy.
12. Pinion gear
13. Sector gear
14. Washer
15. Support
16. Bearing
17. Lever arm

Fig. JD11 — Exploded view of clutch assembly used on early Model 60 tractors (prior to S.N. 20001). Countershaft sheave (15) is equipped with renewable bearing (6).

7. Seal
8. Belt guide (front)
9. Clutch rod
10. Clutch idler arm
11. Clutch idler
12. Belt guide
13. Link
14. Idler spring
15. Countershaft sheave
16. Belt guide (rear)
17. Transaxle sheave
18. Belt guide (lower)
19. Countershaft
20. Secondary belt
21. Belt guide (upper)
22. Washer
23. Shield
24. Driven pulley

1. Primary belt
2. Front idler
3. Idler arm
4. Idler spring
5. Countershaft support
6. Bearing assy.

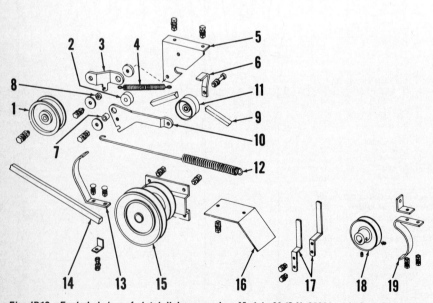

Fig. JD12 — Exploded view of clutch linkage used on Models 60 (S.N. 20001 and after), 70 and 100.

1. Idler pulley
2. Spacer
3. Arm
4. Spring
5. Bracket
6. Belt guide
7. Bearing
8. Bearing
9. Secondary drive belt
10. Clutch idler arm
11. Idler pulley
12. Spring
13. Belt guide
14. Primary drive belt
15. Counter sheave assy.
16. Belt guard
17. Belt guides
18. Transmission drive pulley
19. Belt guide

CLUTCH AND BRAKE

Models 60-70-100

OPERATION. The clutch and brake are operated by a clutch-brake pedal on left side of tractor, except on later models which have separate pedals. When pedal is depressed, clutch idler (11 – Fig. JD11 or JD12) releases tension on secondary drive belt and allows countershaft pulley (15) to turn freely within secondary belt. As belt tension is released, brake band (2 – Fig. JD13 or JD14) is pulled tight on brake drum and tractor motion is stopped. Model 60 tractors with serial numbers prior to 20001 were equipped with step sheaves on countershaft and transaxle which provide a high-low speed range.

ADJUSTMENT. Clutch idler pulley is spring loaded but requires adjustment on models with clutch-brake pedal when secondary belt idler pulley drops low enough to strike lower belt guide as clutch-brake pedal is depressed. To make adjustment, turn adjusting nut on brake linkage (early Model 60) or on brake band (2 – Fig. JD13) until idler does not strike guide. Depress clutch-brake pedal and make certain clutch idler releases secondary belt tension before brake is applied.

CAUTION: Over-tightening brake adjustment can cause simultaneous braking and driving action which can seriously damage transaxle unit.

On later Model 70 and all 100 tractors with separate brake and clutch pedals, brake is adjusted by removing spring pin and turning brake rod (5 – Fig. JD14) into brake strap (4) to tighten brake.

Models 108-111

OPERATION. The clutch and brake are operated by separate pedals. When clutch pedal is depressed, bellcrank assembly (8 – Fig. JD15) pivots and loosens drive belt from drive pulleys stopping forward or reverse movement.

ADJUSTMENT. To adjust clutch, stop engine and put transmission in gear. Loosen center nut on front idler pulley (7 – Fig. JD15). Turn adjusting bolt (20) in or out until there is 3.7 inches (94 mm) between inside of frame and inner surface of flat idler (5). Adjust belt guide (21) to have 3/16-inch (5 mm) clearance between guide and belt.

To adjust brake, be sure parking brake is not engaged and place a feeler gage between brake pad and brake disc. Clearance should be 0.010 inch (0.254 mm). Loosen jam nut and turn inside adjusting nut on brake lever (13 – Fig. JD15A) to obtain clearance.

R&R AND OVERHAUL. Raise and support rear of tractor and remove right rear wheel. Disconnect brake rod (12 – Fig. JD15A) from brake lever (13). Unbolt and remove caliper assembly (14). Withdraw brake disc (17) and inner brake pad from transaxle.

Inspect parts and renew as necessary. Reassemble in reverse of disassembly procedure and adjust as outlined in ADJUSTMENT paragraph.

Model 120

OPERATION. Model 120 is equipped with a cone type clutch and automotive type drum brake. See Figs. JD16 and JD20. The clutch and brake are actuated by clutch-brake pedal on left side of tractor. As pedal is depressed to engage brake, a neutral cam attached to pedal linkage returns hydrostatic transmission to neutral.

ADJUSTMENT. To check clutch adjustment, measure clearance between clutch throw-out arm (7 – Fig. JD16) and throw-out bearing (11) with clutch-brake pedal in engaged (up) position. Clearance should be 1/32 to 1/16-inch (0.8-1.5 mm) as shown in Fig. JD17. To make clutch adjustment, remove battery and base. Loosen nut and move adjusting bolt as shown in Fig. JD18 until correct adjustment is obtained. Retighten nut securely.

To adjust brake, remove clip and pin at end of brake rod and turn clevis. Brake should be adjusted so brake is engaged when clutch-brake pedal is fully depressed but brake should not engage before clutch is disengaged.

R&R AND OVERHAUL CLUTCH. To remove clutch, remove engine as previously outlined and remove clutch

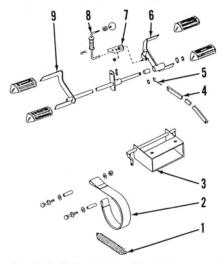

Fig. JD14 – Exploded view of brake linkage used on late Model 70 (after S.N. 50000) and Model 100.

1. Return spring
2. Brake band
3. pedestal & brake rod
4. Brake strap
5. Brake rod
6. Brake pedal
7. Locking pawl
8. Parking brake lever
9. Clutch pedal

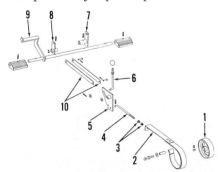

Fig. JD13 – Exploded view of typical brake linkage used on Models 60 and early 70 tractors (prior to S.N. 50001).

1. Brake drum
2. Brake band
3. Adjusting nuts
4. Brake rod
5. Pivot plate
6. Parking brake lever
7. Clutch arm
8. Brake arm
9. Clutch-brake pedal
10. Brake straps

Fig. JD15 – Exploded view of clutch and bellcrank assembly used on Models 108 and 111.

1. Spring
2. Belt guide
3. Support
4. Belt guard
5. Flat idler pulley
6. Bushing
7. "V" idler pulley
8. Bellcrank
9. Bushing
10. Washer
11. Cap
12. Link
13. Spring
14. Mount R.H.
15. Snap ring
16. Washer
17. Clutch shaft
18. Pad
19. Adjusting link
20. Adjusting bolt
21. Belt guard

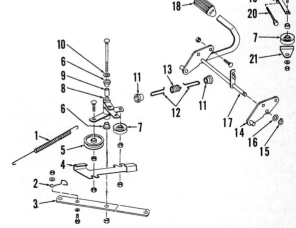

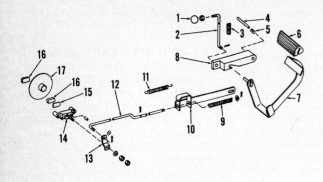

Fig. JD15A — Exploded view of brake linkage used on Models 108 and 111.

1. Knob
2. Parking brake rod
3. Spring
4. Pin
5. Spacer
6. Pad
7. Brake pedal assy.
8. Latch
9. Spring
10. Strap
11. Spring
12. Brake rod
13. Brake lever
14. Caliper
15. Plate
16. Brake pads
17. Rotor

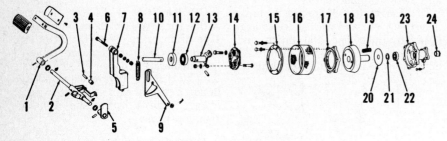

Fig. JD16 — Exploded view of clutch assembly used on Models 120 and 140.

1. Clutch pedal
2. Shaft
3. Spring pin
4. Roller
5. Brake arm
6. Pivot bolt
7. Clutch arm
8. Spring
9. Transmission neutral arm
10. Drive shaft
11. Bearing cap
12. Bearing
13. Drive hub
14. Front hub
15. Screen cap
16. Screen
17. Clutch cup
18. Clutch cone & shaft
19. Spring (4 used)
20. Large washer
21. Small washer
22. Bearing
23. Drive hub
24. Bushing

assembly. Clutch throw-out bearing may also be serviced at this time. Inspect components for excessive wear or damage. Uneven wear of clutch cup lining (17 – Fig. JD16) may indicate excessive clearance between clutch cone shaft and bushing (24). Adequately support drive hub (23) to prevent cracking when pressing against bushing (24). Bronze bushing I.D. is 1.004 inches (25.5 mm) while bushing O.D. is 1.254 inches (31.85 mm). Outside diameter of clutch cone shaft is 0.999 inch (25.374 mm). Clutch springs should test 64-71 pounds (280-316N) when compressed to a length of 1.125 inches (28 mm).

To reassemble clutch, reverse disassembly procedure. When installing bushing (24) in drive hub, refer to Fig. JD19 for bushing location. Tighten drive hub-to-flywheel cap screws to 20 ft.-lbs. (27 N·m). Install 1¾ inch cap screws spaced evenly in clutch cup (17 – Fig. JD16) to pull cup and drive hub together. Install end cap (15) and screen (16) using 1¼ inch cap screws. Tighten all cup cap screws to 20 ft.-lbs. (27 N·m). Adjust clutch as outlined in ADJUSTMENT paragraph.

R&R AND OVERHAUL BRAKES. Model 120 is equipped with an automotive drum type brake. To disassemble brake assembly, support rear of tractor and remove wheel. Remove wheel hub

(17 – Fig. JD20) and using a suitable puller, remove brake drum (16). Remainder of disassembly is self-evident after inspection of assembly. Renew any components showing excessive wear. Be sure wheel hub seal and back plate (11) are properly aligned on axle housing flange before tightening back plate retaining nuts to 15 ft.-lbs. (20 N·m) torque. After assembly, adjust brake as previously outlined.

Model 140

OPERATION. Model 140-H1 tractors with S.N. 10001 through 38000 and Model 140-H3 tractors with S.N. 30001 through 46883 are equipped with a cone type engine disconnect clutch. The

clutch is operated by a foot pedal on left side of tractor. See Fig. JD16.

Model 140 tractors with S.N. 10001 through 3000 are equipped with disc brakes at each rear wheel. Brakes are operated by individual pedals which can be locked together. Model 140-H1 tractors with S.N. 30001 through 38000 and S.N. 46604 and later and Model 140-H3 tractors with S.N. 30001 and later are equipped with automotive type drum and shoe brakes at each rear wheel. Brakes are operated by individual brake pedals which can be locked together. Model 140-H1 tractors with S.N. 38001 through 46603 are equipped with a single automotive drum and shoe brake located at right rear wheel. Brake is operated by brake-neutral return pedal on left side of tractor.

CLUTCH ADJUSTMENT. To check clutch adjustment, measure clearance between clutch release arm (7 – Fig. JD16) and release bearing retainer (11) with clutch pedal in engaged (up) position. Clearance should be 1/32 to 1/16-inch (0.8-1.5 mm). See Fig. JD17. To adjust clearance, remove battery and battery base plate. Loosen nut and move adjusting bolt as shown in Fig. JD18 until correct adjustment is obtained. Tighten nut securely.

BRAKE ADJUSTMENT. To adjust disc brakes on Model 140 with S.N. 10001 through 30000, support rear of tractor so rear wheels are free to turn. Open free-wheeling valve on transmission. Loosen locknuts (12 – Fig. JD21), remove pin (9) from clevis (11) on both brakes. Adjust clevis (11) on right brake rod (14) until a slight drag is felt when rotating wheel (brake rod reconnected). Then, back off clevis just enough to remove all drag. Reconnect brake rod and tighten locknut. Repeat procedure on left brake. Brakes should be adjusted equally so both brakes will be applied simultaneously when pedals are locked together.

To adjust brake on Model 140 with S.N. 38001 through 46603, first discon-

Fig. JD17 — Bottom view showing correct clutch adjustment on Models 120 and 140.

Fig. JD18 — To adjust clutch action on Models 120 and 140, refer to text, loosen nut and move adjusting bolt (6 – Fig. JD16).

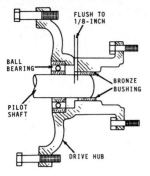

Fig. JD19 — Press bushing (24—Fig. JD16) into drive hub (23) until bushing is seated as shown above.

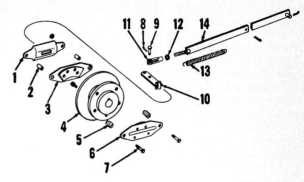

Fig. JD21 — Exploded view of disc brake assembly used on Model 140 tractors with S.N. 10001 through 30000. Disc brakes are used on both rear wheels.

1. Cam plate
2. Spacer
3. Brake pad (inner)
4. Disc & hub
5. Spring
6. Brake pad (outer)
7. Cap screw
8. Clip
9. Pin
10. Actuating cam
11. Clevis
12. Locknut
13. Spring
14. Brake rod

nect clevis (3—Fig. JD20) from brake arm (8). Pull top of brake arm forward. Brake should be applied when brake arm is in vertical position. If not, loosen clamp (9) and readjust position of brake arm on cam (12). Tighten clamp. Adjust clevis (3) on brake rod (7) so brake will be applied immediately after brake-neutral return pedal has moved hydrostatic control to neutral position.

On all other Model 140 tractors equipped with drum and shoe brakes at both rear wheels, adjust brakes as follows: First disconnect clevis (3—Fig. JD20) from brake arm (8) on each brake. Pull top of brake arms forward. Brakes should be applied when brake arms are in vertical position. If not, loosen clamp (9) and readjust position of brake arms on cam (12). Lock brake pedals together. Adjust clevis (3) on each brake rod (7)

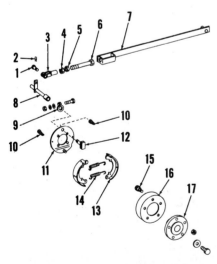

Fig. JD20 — Exploded view of typical drum and shoe brake assembly used on Model 120. Brake assembly used on Model 140 (S.N. 30001 and later) is similar.

1. Pin
2. Clip
3. Clevis
4. Adjusting nut
5. Locknut
6. Bolt
7. Brake rod
8. Brake arm
9. Clamp
10. Spring
11. Back plate
12. Cam
13. Brake shoe
14. Return spring
15. Wheel stud
16. Brake drum
17. Wheel hub

until both brakes are fully applied when pedals are depressed to a point where park lock will engage in second notch.

R&R AND OVERHAUL. To remove clutch, first remove engine and clutch assembly as outlined in ENGINE paragraph. Unbolt and remove ring and screen (15 and 16—Fig. JD16), then remove four cap screws securing drive hub (23) to engine flywheel. Lift clutch assembly from engine. Unbolt clutch cap (17) and separate clutch cone (18), four springs (19), washer (20) and spacer (21) from drive hub (23). To remove clutch release bearing (12), drive out roll pin and remove drive yoke (13) from drive shaft (10). Remove bearing from yoke.

Clean and inspect all parts and renew any showing excessive wear or other damage. Uneven wear of clutch cup lining may indicate excessive clearance between clutch cone shaft and bushing (24). Adequately support drive hub (23) and press ball bearing (22) and bushing (24) from hub. Bushing inside diameter is 1.004 inch (25.5 mm) and outside diameter is 1.254 inches (31.85 mm). Outside diameter of clutch cone shaft is 0.999 inch (25.375 mm). Clutch springs should test 64-71 pounds (280-316N) when compressed to a length of 1⅛ inches (28 mm).

To reassemble clutch, reverse disassembly procedure. When installing bushing (24) in drive hub (23), refer to Fig. JD19 for bushing location. Tighten drive hub to flywheel cap screws to a torque of 20 ft.-lbs. (27 N·m). Install three evenly spaced 1¾ inch long cap screws in clutch cup (17—Fig. JD16) to pull cup and drive hub together. Then, install ring (15) and screen (16) using 1¼ inch long cap screws. Tighten all cup cap screws to 20 ft.-lbs. (27 N·m) torque.

With engine and clutch assembly reinstalled, adjust clutch as required.

OVERHAUL (DISC BRAKE). To disassemble brakes, support rear of tractor and remove rear wheels. Disconnect clevis (11—Fig. JD21) from actuating cam (10). Remove cap screws (7),

then remove cam plate (1), cam (10), brake pads (3 and 6), spacers (2) and springs (5).

Clean and inspect all parts and renew any showing excessive wear or other damage. Thickness of new brake pads is ¼-inch (6.35 mm). Pads should be renewed when worn to a thickness of ⅛-inch (3.2 mm) or less. If disc (4) is damaged, use a suitable puller to remove wheel hub, then unbolt disc from hub.

When reassembling, tighten disc retaining cap screws to a torque of 10 ft.-lbs. (14 N·m) and wheel hub retaining nut to 250 in.-lbs. (28 N·m). Adjust brakes as required.

OVERHAUL (DRUM & SHOE BRAKE). To disassemble brakes, support rear of tractor and remove rear wheels. Remove cap screw securing wheel hub (17—Fig. JD20), then attach a suitable puller and remove wheel hub and brake drum assembly. Remove return springs (14), unhook shoe hold

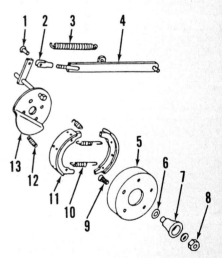

Fig. JD22 — Exploded view of drum and shoe brake assembly used on Models 300, 312, 314 and 316.

1. Pin
2. Yoke
3. Return spring
4. Brake link
5. Brake drum
6. Felt seal
7. Hub
8. Retaining nut
9. Wheel stud
10. Return springs
11. Brake shoes
12. Hold-down springs
13. Back plate

down springs (10) and remove shoes (13).

Clean and inspect all parts and renew any showing excessive wear or other damage. If brake drum (16) is damaged, press out wheel studs (15) and remove drum from hub (17).

Reassemble by reversing disassembly procedure. Renew felt seal on inner side of wheel hub and tighten hub retaining cap screw to 35-40 ft.-lbs. (47-54 N·m). Adjust brakes as required.

Model 208

OPERATION. The clutch and brake are operated by separate pedals. When clutch pedal is depressed, clutch pulley releases tension on secondary belt and allows drive pulley to turn free within the belt. As brake pedal is depressed, brake band is pulled tight on brake drum and tractor motion is stopped.

ADJUSTMENT. Clutch idler pulley is spring loaded and requires no adjustment. To adjust brake, disconnect brake rod (4–Fig. JD30) from brake pedal stud (10). Turn brake rod into clevis (3) two or three turns to tighten brake. Test operation on level surface at slow speed. Brake is properly adjusted when pedal is depressed and strong resistance is encountered approximately one inch (25 mm) from deck.

Models 300-312-314-316

OPERATION. These tractors are equipped with hydrostatic drive and do not use an engine disconnect clutch. Individual drum-type brakes, located at each rear wheel, are used on all models. On Models 300 and 316, separate brake pedals are used for each rear wheel. On Models 312 and 314, a single brake pedal is used to actuate both brakes simultaneously.

ADJUSTMENT. To adjust brakes, remove pin (1–Fig. JD22) and turn yoke (2) to lengthen or shorten brake link (4). Adjust brakes so both rear wheels are locked when brake pedal or pedals are engaged in second notch of parking brake latch.

R&R AND OVERHAUL. Raise and support rear of tractor and remove rear wheels. Remove hub retaining nut (8–Fig. JD22) and pull brake drum (5) using a suitable puller. Disconnect springs (10 and 12) and remove brake shoes (11).

Inspect all parts for excessive wear or other damage and renew as necessary. Reassemble in reverse order of disassembly. Tighten hub retaining nut to 35-40 ft.-lbs. (47-54 N·m) torque. Adjust brakes as previously outlined.

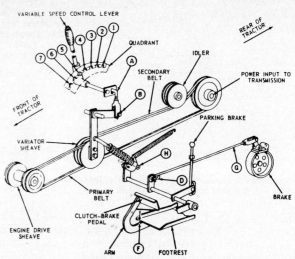

Fig. JD23—View showing clutch, brake and variable drive system used on Model 110 tractors (1966-1972) and Model 112 tractors prior to 1973.

CLUTCH, BRAKE AND VARIABLE DRIVE

Models 110-112-200-210-212-214-216

OPERATION. A variable pulley belt drive system is used on all 110, 112, 200, 210, 212, 214 and 216 models. On early models, clutch and brake are actuated by one pedal while clutch and brake on later models are operated by separate pedals. Depressing clutch pedal will move variator pulleys forward and release tension on primary drive belt thereby allowing engine pulley to turn free in belt. Fully depressing clutch-brake pedal on early models will actuate rear brake.

Models 110 and 112 Prior to S.N. 100,001

ADJUSTMENT. When tractor will not operate with variable speed control lever in notch 1 (rear position on quadrant), refer to Fig. JD23 and adjust linkage as follows:

Remove inspection plate from adjusting hole in pedestal and remove pin (B). Move variable speed lever to notch 5 on quadrant. Remove brake rod pin (D). Disconnect spark plug wire and crank engine several revolutions with starter. Measure distance (F) between footrest and clutch-brake arm. This distance should be ½-inch (13 mm). If not, insert a tapered punch or narrow screwdriver in hole at (H) and turn rod up or down until distance (F) is exactly ½-inch (13 mm). Hold link (A) to top of slot and turn clevis up or down as required until pin

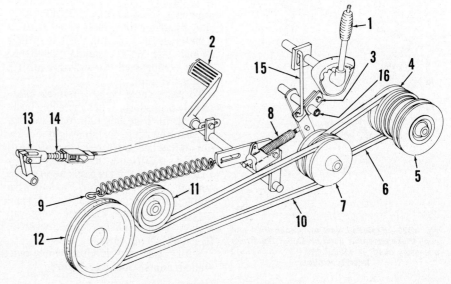

Fig. JD24—View of variable drive used on Models 110 and 112 after S.N. 100,000. Later models have separate clutch and brake pedals.

1. Drive lever	5. Pto pulley	9. Spring	13. Brake yoke
2. Clutch-brake pedal	6. Primary drive belt	10. Secondary drive belt	14. Locknut
3. Adjusting screw	7. Variable pulley	11. Idler pulley	15. Link
4. Engine pulley	8. Clutch override	12. Transaxle pulley	16. Cap screw

(B) can be easily inserted. Secure pin (B) with spring locking pin and install inspection plate. Install pin (D) temporarily and while cranking engine several times with starter, move variable speed control lever to notch 1 (slow position). Depress clutch-brake pedal as far as possible and measure distance between footrest and clutch-brake pedal. This distance should be ¾-inch (19 mm). If clearance is more or less than ¾-inch (19 mm), adjust brake rod (G) until proper clearance is obtained. Secure pin (D) with spring locking pin and connect spark plug wire.

Models 110 and 112 After S.N. 100,000

ADJUSTMENT. Models 110 and 112 after S.N. 100,000 are equipped with variable drive system shown in Fig. JD24. Some models have a clutch-brake pedal while later models have separate clutch and brake pedals.

If tractor will not operate with variable drive lever in slow position (rearmost notch), clutch or clutch-brake pedal must be adjusted. Place variable drive lever in third notch from front. Remove adjusting hole plug from right side of console and loosen adjusting screw (3 – Fig. JD24) as shown in Fig. JD26. Disconnect and ground spark plug wire. Turn engine several revolutions with electric starter until clutch or clutch-brake pedal comes up as high as it will go. Center adjusting screw (3 – Fig. JD24) in adjusting hole and tighten adjusting screw. Check tractor operation. If tractor does not operate at slow speed after clutch adjustment, primary drive belt is stretched and must be renewed.

Brake adjustment is accomplished by disconnecting clevis in brake linkage and turning clevis to effectively lengthen or shorten brake rod. On models with a clutch-brake pedal, distance between pedal and footrest should not be less

than ¾-inch (19 mm) with pedal fully depressed. Parking brake engagement should be possible on all models after brake adjustment.

On models with a clutch-brake pedal, a clutch override unit (8 – Fig. JD24) is provided to insure braking action when pedal is depressed. To adjust clutch override, place variable drive lever in front notch in quadrant and measure distance between end of pedal and footrest as shown in Fig. JD27. If pedal distance is greater than 7 to 8 inches (178-203 mm) with pedal released, clutch override must be adjusted. Turn adjusting screw in clutch override unit as shown in Fig. JD28 by inserting a suitable tool into hole in adjusting screw. Turn screw counter-clockwise to obtain desired pedal height.

Belt guide clearance for primary belt on variator pulley should be 1/16 to ⅛-inch (1.5-3 mm) to prevent primary belt from jumping off pulley when clutch-brake or clutch pedal is depressed.

Models 200-210-212-214-216

ADJUSTMENT. To adjust brake on tractors with S.N. 30001-95000, remove pin from clevis on brake rod and turn clevis as necessary to put brake pedal arm in first notch of parking brake ratchet. See Fig. JD29 or JD30.

To adjust brake on tractors after S.N. 95000, disconnect clutch-brake strap (2 – Fig. JD31) and turn strap into clevis to tighten brake. Brake is properly adjusted when strong resistance is encountered as clutch-brake pedal is depressed to within approximately one inch (25 mm) from deck.

If tractor will not operate in slow speed position, clutch pedal must be adjusted. Place variable drive lever in third notch from front. Remove button plug from adjusting hole in right side of console and loosen cap screw one to two turns. Disconnect spark plug wire and

crank engine with starter until clutch pedal raises as high as it will go. Push down on cap screw to remove slack in linkage and retighten screw. Check tractor operation; if tractor does not operate at slow speed after adjustment, primary drive belt is stretched and must be renewed.

Fig. JD26 – View showing location of adjusting screw (3 – Fig. JD24) to adjust variable drive.

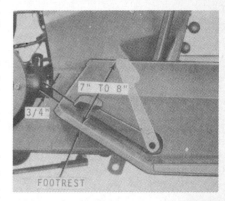

Fig. JD27 – Clutch-brake pedal on later Models 110 and 112 that are so equipped, should have ¾-inch (19 mm) clearance between pedal and footrest when pedal is fully depressed. Pedal height shouldn't be greater than 7-8 inches (178-203 mm). See Fig. JD28.

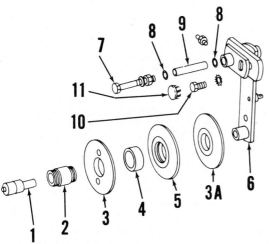

Fig. JD25 – Exploded view of variable drive pulley and control lever.

1. Bearing & shaft
2. Hub
3. Outer flange
3A. Outer flange
4. Bearing
5. Moveable flange
6. Lever
7. Cap screw
8. "O" ring
9. Ferrule
10. Adjusting screw
11. Plug

Fig. JD28 – Adjust clutch override as outlined in text to obtain 7-8 inches (178-203 mm) pedal height shown in Fig. JD27.

Adjust variator spring (13 – Fig. JD31) to obtain desired load sensing characteristics as follows: To increase load sensitivity, loosen spring tension by lengthening eyebolt. Tightening spring tension (shortening eyebolt), will reduce load sensitivity.

All Models

OVERHAUL. To remove variable drive pulley, remove secondary belt from pulley and depress clutch-brake or clutch pedal. Loosen primary belt guide screw so primary belt can be removed from variable drive pulley. Disconnect

variable drive spring. Disconnect clutch override, on models so equipped, from pulley lever. Remove battery and battery base. Disconnect speed control link at lower end. Unscrew pivot cap screw (7 – Fig. JD25) and remove variable drive pulley from bottom of tractor by passing pivot end of assembly through notch in frame.

Variable pulley outer flanges (3 and 3A – Fig. JD25) are threaded on hub (2). Unscrew flange (3) counter-clockwise by inserting a suitable tool in holes in flange. Remove moveable flange (5). Press against outer race of bearing (1) to separate bearing and lever (6) from

pulley assembly. Unscrew outer flange (3A) from hub by using same procedure used to remove flange (3).

Inspect components for excessive wear and damage. Moveable flange bearing (4) and flange (5) are available only as a unit. Bearing (4) is self-lubricating and no attempt should be made to lubricate bearing. Note following dimensions: Moveable flange bearing (4) I.D. – 2.0015-2.0025 inches (50.838-50.863 mm); Hub (2) O.D. – 1.999-2.001 inches (50.775-50.825 mm); Hub (2) I.D. – 1.1790-1.180 inches (29.947-29.972 mm); Bearing (1) O.D. – 1.1806-1.1811 inches (29.987-30.000 mm); Bearing shaft (1) O.D. – 0.6262-0.6267 inch (15.905-15.918 mm); Lever (6) bearing shaft bore I.D. – 0.6240-0.6255 inch (15.850-15.888 mm).

When assembling variable drive pulley assembly, note the following: Press bearing (1 – Fig. JD25) into hub (2) until bearing is flush with outer surface of flange (3A). Press lever (6) on bearing shaft (1) so end of shaft is flush with outer edge of lever. Stake threads in three or four places after outer flanges (3 and 3A) are installed on hub (2). Be sure "O" rings (8) are not dislodged during installation of assembly on tractor.

DRIVE BELTS

REMOVE AND REINSTALL

Models 60-70-100

To remove primary belt, first detach primary idler spring (Fig. JD32). Remove spring locking pin and disconnect pto clutch arm. Slip belt out of sheaves. When installing new primary belt, make certain belt is turned and positioned exactly as shown in Fig. JD32. A reverse twist of belt will result in reverse tractor travel and possible transaxle damage. After primary belt is installed, disconnect spark plug wire and slowly turn engine with recoil starter while checking belt travel direction.

To remove secondary (range) belt on early Model 60, remove thumb screws and pivot tractor seat and fender assembly rearward. Loosen wing nuts on tractor frame (top and bottom) and slide belt guides to rear of slotted holes. Remove thumb screw and belt guide forks between clutch idler and transaxle input pulley. Depress clutch-brake pedal and lock in down position. Remove belt from sheaves.

To remove secondary drive belt on late Model 60 and Models 70 and 100, depress clutch-brake pedal and set parking brake. Remove seat and fender unit. Loosen cap screws and slide rear belt guide out of way. See Fig. JD33. Remove front belt guide, unhook front

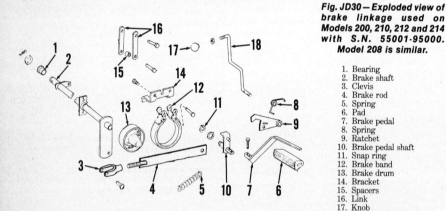

Fig. JD29 — Exploded view of brake mechanism used on Models 200, 210, 212 and 214 with S.N. 30001-55000.

1. Key
2. Set screw
3. Arm
4. Brake shaft
5. Clevis
6. Brake rod
7. Spring
8. Brake pedal assy.
9. Pad
10. Ratchet
11. Snap ring
12. Brake band
13. Brake drum
14. Bracket
15. Pin
16. Link
17. Knob
18. Parking brake rod
19. Spring

Fig. JD30 — Exploded view of brake linkage used on Models 200, 210, 212 and 214 with S.N. 55001-95000. Model 208 is similar.

1. Bearing
2. Brake shaft
3. Clevis
4. Brake rod
5. Spring
6. Pad
7. Brake pedal
8. Spring
9. Ratchet
10. Brake pedal shaft
11. Snap ring
12. Brake band
13. Brake drum
14. Bracket
15. Spacers
16. Link
17. Knob
18. Parking brake rod

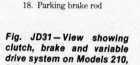

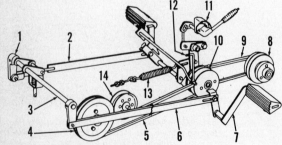

Fig. JD31 — View showing clutch, brake and variable drive system on Models 210, 212, 214 and 216 with S.N. 95001 and up.

1. Brake arm
2. Clutch-brake strap
3. Brake shaft
4. Transaxle pulley
5. Secondary drive belt
6. Brake pedal straps
7. Brake pedal
8. Crankshaft pulley
9. Primary drive belt
10. Variator pulley
11. Variable speed control assy.
12. Parking brake rod
13. Variator spring
14. Idler pulley

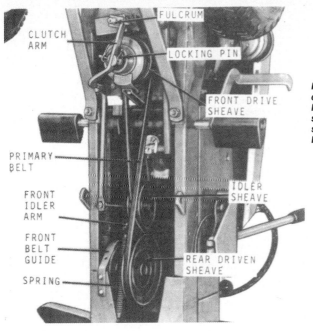

Fig. JD32—Underside view of primary drive belt on Models 60, 70 and 100. Be sure belt is installed as shown. A reverse twist of belt will result in reverse tractor travel.

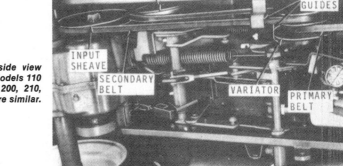

Fig. JD34—Underside view of drive belt on Models 108 and 111. Belt tension is adjusted by turning bolt "A". Refer to text for procedure.

idler arm spring and remove primary belt from rear pulley. Unhook rear idler arm spring, loosen cap screws on rear idler mount and remove secondary belt. When reinstalling belt guides, there should be approximately 1/16-inch (1.5 mm) clearance between guide and belt.

When installing secondary belt, reverse removal procedure. The belt may be installed in either Hi-range or Lo-range set of grooves on early Model 60. (Hi-range grooves are the outside set.) Install belt guides in their original positions. Adjust brake as previously outlined. Lower seat assembly and install thumb screws.

Models 108-111

To remove drive belt, engage pto lever. Loosen idler pulley center bolt and belt tightener bolt, then move pulley and guard away from belt. Disconnect drag link from steering arm. Remove steering support mounting bolts and turn support parallel with belt. Remove clutch idler pulley belt guard. Depress clutch pedal and remove belt.

Reinstall drive belt by reversing re-

moval procedure. Adjust belt tension as follows: With clutch engaged, pedal up, loosen nut ("C"–Fig. JD34) on idler ("B") and turn adjusting bolt ("A") to obtain 3.7 inch (94 mm) clearance between flat idler and inside of frame. Adjust belt guide to 3/16-inch (5 mm) clearance from belt and tighten idler nut.

Models 110-112

If excessive belt stretching allows secondary belt idler to rub on lower belt strand, additional belt tension can be obtained by moving transaxle rearward to

second set of mounting holes in frame. After adjusting linkage as previously outlined and tractor still does not move when variable speed lever is in notch 1, renew primary belt.

To remove primary belt, first remove secondary belt as follows: Block up secondary idler to remove belt tension. See Fig. JD35. Unbolt transaxle input pulley, slide pulley off hub and remove

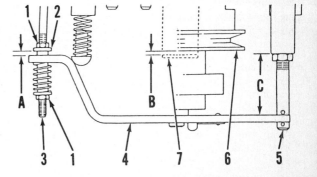

Fig. JD35—Underside view of drive belts on Models 110 and 112. Models 200, 210, 212, 214 and 216 are similar.

Fig. JD33—View of secondary drive belt on late Model 60 and Models 70 and 100.

Fig. JD36—View of manual pto control linkage used on Models 110 and 112 after 1973 equipped with a Kohler engine. Other models so equipped are similar. Refer to text for adjustment.

1. Adjusting nuts
2. Washer
3. Clutch rod
4. Clutch arm
5. Fulcrum bolt
6. Pulley
7. Clutch brake

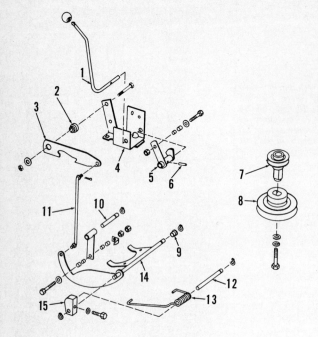

Fig. JD37 – Exploded view of manual pto linkage used on Models 108 and 111.

1. Pto lever
2. Pivot
3. Arm
4. Pivot bracket
5. Follower
6. Pin
7. Crankshaft pulley
8. Pto pulley
9. Bearing
10. Shaft
11. Link
12. Shaft
13. Return spring
14. Actuator
15. Bearing

secondary belt. Remove engine muffler, belt guard, primary belt guide and pto on models so equipped. Depress clutch-brake pedal and lock in down position to hold variator forward. Lift primary belt off variator and engine sheaves.

Reinstall belts by reversing removal procedure. If a new secondary belt is being installed, transaxle must be in front mounting position. After renewing belts, readjust linkage as previously outlined.

Models 200-210-212-214-216

To remove primary belt, remove right hand side panel. Disconnect pto linkage and remove pto clutch pulley. Move variable speed control lever forward. Push up on secondary belt idler and remove secondary belt from variator pulley. See Fig. JD35. Loosen primary belt guide at variator, depress clutch pedal and remove primary belt.

To remove secondary belt, move variable speed control lever forward. Push up on idler pulley and slip belt off variator pulley. Depress clutch pedal to allow belt to pass brake pedal shaft. Loosen transaxle pulley cap screws and slide pulley far enough off hub to remove belt.

Reinstall belts by reversing removal procedure. After renewing belts, readjust variator and brake as previously outlined.

Model 208

To remove secondary belt, push up on secondary idler pulley and slip belt off clutch pulley. Depress clutch pedal to allow belt to pass brake pedal shaft. Loosen transaxle pulley cap screws and slide pulley far enough off hub to remove belt.

To remove primary belt, disconnect pto linkage and remove pto clutch pulley. Push up on secondary belt idler and slip secondary belt off clutch pulley. Loosen belt guide, depress clutch pedal and remove belt. Reinstall new belt by reversing removal procedure.

MANUAL PTO CLUTCH

Models 60, 70, 100, 110, 112, 200, 208, 210, 212, 214 and 216 may be equipped with a cone type manual pto clutch. The pto pulley is supported on engine crankshaft by two roller bearings and is forced against clutch cone on engine pulley by pto clutch linkage. Disengaging pto clutch slides pto pulley from clutch cone and against a brake shoe which stops pto pulley rotation.

ADJUSTMENT

Models 60-70-100

To adjust clutch linkage, first engage clutch. Clutch arm (4 – Fig. JD36) should be parallel to frame. If not, remove locking pin, lower arm and turn fulcrum bolt (5) in or out. Slowly engage and disengage clutch. When clutch cone contacts clutch cup, clutch arm (4) should have raised 1/2-inch (13 mm). Turn adjusting nuts (1) clockwise to increase or counterclockwise to decrease arm movement. With pto engaged, there should be 1/16-inch (1.5 mm) clearance (B) between clutch cone and brake shoe (7). Loosen cap screw retaining brake and adjust position of brake shoe to obtain clearance.

Models 108-111

To adjust clutch linkage, engage pto lever. Loosen cap screw and slide block (15 – Fig. JD37) back and forth to center clutch fork. There should be approximately 1/16-inch (1.5 mm) clearance between fork and cone on each side.

Model 110 Prior to 1973

To adjust pto clutch linkage on these models, refer to Fig. JD38 and turn inner nut (B) until there is 1-5/16 inches (33 mm) between nut and inner beginning of threads. Turn outer nut (A) to provide 5/8-inch (16 mm) between nut and outer end of link (C). There must be gap of at least 3/8 to 3/4-inch (10-19 mm) between end of clutch arm and channel as shown in Fig. JD38 when pto linkage is actuated. On early models it may be necessary to lower fulcrum bolt (Fig. JD40) in tractor frame by slotting mounting holes in frame to obtain desired 3/8 to 3/4-inch (10-19 mm) clearance.

Free travel of pto control lever in instrument panel should be approximately 1/2 total travel of lever. To obtain desired free travel, screw fulcrum bolt shown in Fig. JD40 in or out. There should be approximately 1/16-inch (1.5 mm) clearance between brake shoe and pto pulley when pto is engaged. To adjust brake shoe clearance, loosen brake shoe mounting screw and move brake shoe.

All 1973 110 Models and 1974 Model 110 w/8 hp Engine

To adjust clutch linkage, move pto clutch lever to disengaged position (down). Adjust location of jam nuts (6 – Fig. JD39) to provide 1/8-inch (3 mm) clearance between spring pin (7) and

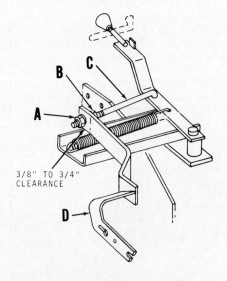

Fig. JD38 – View of manual pto clutch linkage on Models 110 and 112 prior to 1974 equipped with 8 hp Kohler engine. Refer to text for adjustment.

A. Outer nut
B. Inner nut
C. Link
D. Clutch arm

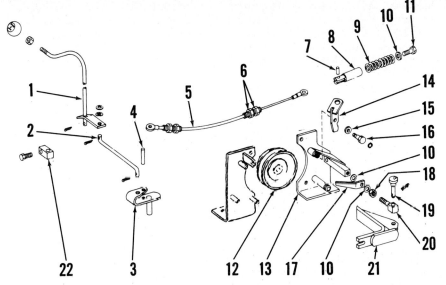

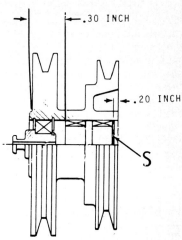

Fig. JD42—Install bearings and seal (S) on models with inset clutch cone as shown above.

Fig. JD39 — Exploded view of pto clutch linkage used on 1973 Models 110 and 112 and 1974 Model 110 with 8 hp engine.

1. Handle	7. Spring pin	12. Pto clutch	17. Spring
2. Link	8. Spring rod	13. Bracket	18. Nut
3. Pivot bracket	9. Spring	14. Cam lever	19. Pin
4. Spring pin	10. Washer	15. Spring washer	20. Pivot bolt
5. Cable	11. Cap screw	16. Shoulder bolt	21. Clutch lever
6. Adjusting nuts			22. Pivot block

cam lever (14) when control lever is in engaged position (up).

There should be approximately 1/16-inch (1.5 mm) clearance between brake shoe and pto pulley when pto is engaged. To adjust brake shoe clearance, loosen brake shoe mounting screw and move brake shoe.

Models 110 and 112 After 1973 Except 8 hp

Refer to Fig. JD36 and adjust fulcrum bolt (5) to 2½ inches (63.5 mm) (C) as shown. Engage pto and adjust position of nuts (1) to obtain 11/64-inch (4 mm) gap (A) between washer (2) and clutch arm (4) as shown. Clutch arm should be close to parallel with pto pulley. If necessary, screw fulcrum bolt in or out to correct angle of clutch arm but be sure to retain 11/64-inch (4 mm) gap between washer and clutch arm. With pto engaged, there should be 1/32-inch (1 mm) clearance (B) between pulley (6) and

brake shoe (7). Loosen cap screw retaining brake and adjust position of brake shoe to obtain desired clearance.

Models 200-208-210-212-214-216

To adjust pto clutch linkage, first adjust length of fulcrum bolt (5—Fig. JD36) to a setting of 2½ inches (63.5 mm) "C" as shown. With clutch engaged, adjust nuts (1) to obtain 11/64-inch (4 mm) gap "A" between clutch arm (4) and washer (2) on models prior to S.N. 80001. On tractors with S.N. 80001 and after, gap "A" should be 3/32-inch (2 mm). On all models, clutch arm (4) should be approximately parallel with pulley. If necessary, readjust fulcrum bolt (5) to obtain correct angle of clutch arm. With pto engaged, there should be 1/32-inch (1 mm) clearance "B" between pulley (6) and brake shoe (7). Loosen retaining screw and reposition brake as necessary.

OVERHAUL

All Models So Equipped

Disassembly and assembly of manual pto clutch unit is evident after inspection of unit and referral to exploded view in

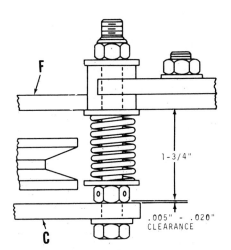

Fig. JD40 — Refer to text to adjust travel of pto control lever on Models 110 and 112. Initial adjustment of fulcrum bolt in frame (F) and clutch arm (C) is shown.

Fig. JD41 — Exploded view of typical manual pto clutch used on Models 110, 112, 200, 208, 210, 212, 214 and 216.

1. Actuator bolt
2. Snap ring
3. Bearing
4. Snap ring
5. Pulley
6. Clutch cup & pulley
7. Snap ring
8. Bearings
9. Oil seal
10. Cap screw
11. Snap ring
12. Washer
13. Bearing inner race
14. Engine pulley & clutch cone
15. Brake

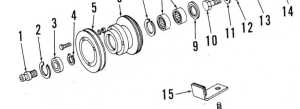

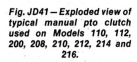

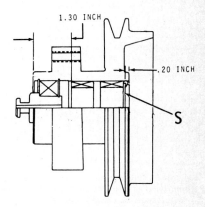

Fig. JD43 — Install bearings and seal (S) on models with clutch cone outboard as shown above.

Fig. JD 41. Refer to Fig. JD42 or JD43 and locate roller bearings and seal (S) as shown. Seal lip should be toward engine. Pack bearings with John Deere High-Temperature Grease or equivalent.

Some 110 and 112 models prior to 1971 were not equipped with pto clutch arm fulcrum bolt shown in Fig. JD40. This bolt assembly is available as a kit and should be installed to dimensions shown in Fig. JD40 on models lacking this bolt.

ELECTRIC PTO CLUTCH

All Models So Equipped

Some later Models 108, 111 and 112 and Models 120, 140, 300, 312, 314 and 316 may be equipped with an electric pto clutch. Refer to Fig. JD44 for a cross-section of typical clutch. Note that armature (2) is keyed to engine crankshaft. When an electric current energizes field windings (4), the resulting magnetic field pulls spring-loaded armature against rotor (3) to transfer power to pto pulley. Pulley and rotor are mounted on a ball bearing as is field assembly. The field assembly remains stationary while the rotor turns. Armature, rotor and bearing are available as a unit as are field coil assembly and bearing.

TESTING. Use the following procedure for locating pto malfunction. Turn ignition switch to "ON" position and actuate pto switch. If clutch does not engage, disconnect wiring connector at field coil and use a 12-volt test lamp to check continuity of wire coming from pto switch. If lamp lights, pto is either defective or wiring connection at clutch field coil is poor. To check field coil, remove it from tractor. Ground field coil frame and energize coil lead wire with known 12-volt source. Hold a suitable piece of metal adjacent to coil and note if metal is attracted. If metal is not attracted, renew field coil assembly.

ADJUSTMENT. Pto clutch used on Models 108, 111, 300, 312, 314 and 316 must be adjusted if clutch has been disassembled or operation becomes erratic. With clutch disengaged, there must be 0.012-0.014 inch (0.305-0.356 mm) clearance between armature (2 – Fig. JD44) and rotor (3). To adjust, insert feeler gage through slots (7 – Fig. JD45) provided in armature housing (8) and adjust nuts (6) to obtain correct clearance.

TRANSAXLE

LUBRICATION

All Models So Equipped

For all models except Models 108 and 111, refer to the CONDENSED SPECIFICATIONS tables at the beginning of this section for approximate transaxle lubricating fluid capacity for the model being serviced. Fluid is added through shift lever opening. Transaxle used on Models 108 and 111 is packed at the factory with 24 ounces (710 mL) of lithium base grease.

REMOVE AND REINSTALL

Models 60-70

To remove transaxle unit, first unbolt and remove seat and fender assembly. Disconnect clutch idler spring and brake rod. Loosen wing nuts on tractor frame (top and bottom) and slide belt guides to rear of slotted holes. Remove secondary belt from transaxle input sheave. Unbolt and remove rear hitch plate. Place a block under front of transaxle unit to prevent it from tilting forward. Remove axle support clamps and cap screws securing transaxle to frame. Using a jack or hoist, raise tractor frame and remove transaxle assembly.

When reinstalling unit, reverse removal procedure and check brake adjustment as previously outlined.

Model 100

To remove transaxle, unbolt and remove fender-deck assembly. Disconnect clutch idler spring. Remove rear belt guide and hitch plate. Depress rear idler and remove drive belt from transaxle pulley. Remove screw, washers and nut to disconnect brake band. Place jackstands under frame and remove shift lever knob. Remove transaxle mounting bolts and roll rearward.

When reinstalling unit, reverse removal procedures and check clutch and brake adjustments as previously outlined.

Models 108-111

To remove transaxle, securely block up rear of tractor and place shift lever in neutral. Disconnect brake rod from brake arm. Depress clutch pedal and remove drive belt from transaxle pulley. Disconnect shift arm from transaxle and neutral-start switch. Place a floor jack under transaxle. Remove support bolts, "U" bolts and lower transaxle. Remove rear wheel and hub assemblies.

Reverse removal procedures when reinstalling unit. Check clutch and brake adjustments as previously outlined.

Models 110-112-200-208-210-212-214-216

To remove transaxle assembly, first disconnect neutral start switch wires, then remove seat and fenders. Remove secondary belt idler spring and brake linkage.

CAUTION: On Models 200, 210, 212, 214 and 216, idler spring tension is severe. Place speed control in "Fast" position, then carefully remove spring.

Unscrew cap screws from transaxle input sheave. Slide sheave off hub and remove secondary belt. Remove shift lever knob and on all 4-speed models remove shift lever quadrant. Place a block under front of transaxle unit to prevent it from tilting forward and block up rear of tractor frame. Remove remaining cap screws securing transaxle

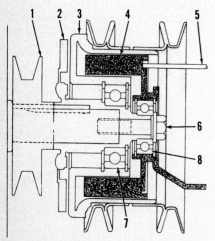

Fig. JD44 – Cross-sectional view of electric pto clutch used on late Model 112 tractors. Other models so equipped are similar.

1. Engine pulley
2. Armature
3. Rotor & pulleys
4. Field windings
5. Field wires
6. Retaining bolt
7. Bearing
8. Bearing

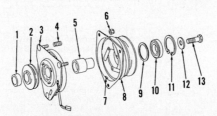

Fig. JD45 – Exploded view of electric pto clutch used on Models 108 and 111. Clutch used on 300 series tractors is similar.

1. Collar
2. Pulley
3. Field coil & rotor assy.
4. Spring (3)
5. Bearing collar
6. Adjusting nut (3)
7. Adjustment slot (3)
8. Armature & pulley assy.
9. Spacer
10. Bearing
11. Snap ring
12. Washer
13. Retaining screw

support and hitch plate to frame. Roll transaxle assembly away from tractor.

When reinstalling unit, reverse removal procedure and adjust variable drive and brake linkage as previously outlined.

OVERHAUL

All Models So Equipped

Models 60, 70 and 100 are equipped with a Peerless 1200 series transaxle. Model 110, prior to serial number 15001, is equipped with a Peerless 2000 series transaxle. Model 110, after serial number 15000, and Models 112, 200, 208, 210, 212, 214 and 216 are equipped with a Peerless 2300 series transaxle. Refer to the appropriate Peerless section in TRANSAXLE SERVICE section for overhaul procedure. Model 112 tractors with hydraulic lift are equipped with a limited-slip differential and use components shown in Fig. JD47.

HYDROSTATIC TRANSMISSION

LUBRICATION

Model 140 S.N. 10001-30000

A free-wheeling valve is located on transmission beneath tractor seat. Opening valve allows transmission oil to recirculate through the motor, by-passing the pump. This allows manual movement of tractor. Free-wheeling valve must be fully closed for full power to be transmitted to rear wheels.

John Deere recommends renewing oil filter after every 100 hours of operation and oil in hydraulic system after every 500 hours of operation. Hydraulic system and differential have a common oil reservoir. To drain fluid, remove drain plug. Recommended lubricant is John Deere All-Weather Hydrostatic Fluid or Type "F" automatic transmission fluid.

Models 120-300-312-314-316-140 S.N. 30001 and Later

A free-wheeling valve knob is located beneath seat. When valve knob is turned clockwise, both check valves are held open and oil is allowed to recirculate through hydraulic motor while by-passing the pump. This allows manual movement of tractor. Free-wheeling valve knob must be turned fully counter-clockwise for full power to be transmitted to rear wheels.

John Deere recommends renewing oil filter after every 100 hours of operation and oil in hydraulic system after every 500 hours of operation. Hydraulic system and differential have a common oil reservoir. To drain fluid, disconnect transmission-to-differential cooling tube at bottom of differential. Oil capacity is approximately 10 pints (4.7 N·m). Recommended lubricant is John Deere All-Weather Hydrostatic Fluid or Type "F" automatic transmission fluid.

LINKAGE ADJUSTMENT

Model 140 S.N. 10001-30000

If tractor creeps with control lever in neutral position, linkage adjustment is necessary. Remove fender-deck assembly and block up under tractor frame so one rear wheel is off ground. Close free-wheeling valve, release parking brake and place control lever in neutral position. Remove ball joint end (11 – Fig. JD49) of control rod from cam (8). Move cam so cam roller (9) is aligned with neutral marks on cam. Holding cam in this position, adjust ball joint of control rod so it will drop into hole of cam and secure with locknut. Start engine and run at idle speed. Being careful not to contact transmission fan, loosen locknut and turn eccentric nut (6) clockwise and counterclockwise to center nut at point where rear wheel will not creep in either direction. Tighten locknut. With engine running and tractor blocked up, check control lever travel from neutral to forward and neutral to reverse at point where rear wheel just begins to creep. Distances should be equal. To adjust control lever neutral position, disconnect control rod ball joint (11) from control cam and turn ball joint. Recheck control lever movement.

Models 120-140 S.N. 30001 and Later

If tractor creeps with control lever in neutral position, linkage adjustment is necessary. Remove fender-deck assembly and block up under tractor frame so one rear wheel is off ground. Be sure free-wheeling valve is closed, release parking brake and place hydrostatic control lever in neutral position. Remove control rod ball joint (9 – Fig. JD50) from control cam (5). Align cam roller (8) with neutral mark

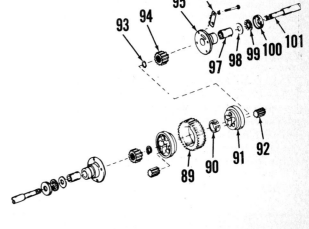

Fig. JD47 — Exploded view of limited-slip differential used in transaxle of Model 112 tractors with hydraulic lift.

89. Ring gear
90. Cylindrical spring
91. Body core
92. Pinion gears
93. Snap ring
94. Side gear
95. Differential carrier
96. Lock plate
97. Spacer
98. Thrust washer
99. Thrust bearing
100. Thrust washer
101. Axle shaft

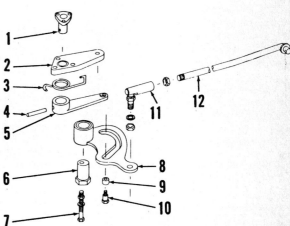

Fig. JD49 — Exploded view of transmission control linkage used on Model 140 tractors with serial number 10001 through 30000.

1. Trunnion shaft
2. Trunnion plate
3. Cam spring
4. Roll pin
5. Swashplate arm
6. Eccentric
7. Cap screw
8. Control cam
9. Cam roller
10. Shoulder bolt
11. Ball joint end
12. Control rod

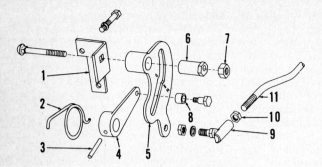

1. Bracket
2. Spring
3. Pin
4. Control arm
5. Control cam
6. Eccentric
7. Nut
8. Cam roller
9. Ball joint end
10. Locknut
11. Control rod

"N" on cam. Note that cam is stepped and when roller is on step, edge of roller will be aligned with neutral mark. Hold cam in neutral position and adjust end of ball joint until it aligns with hole in cam. Install ball joint retaining nut and lockwasher and tighten jam nut. Start engine and run at idle. Being careful not to contact transmission fan, loosen locknut (7) and turn eccentric nut (6) clockwise and counterclockwise to center nut at point where rear wheel will not creep in either direction. Tighten locknut (7). With engine running and tractor blocked up, check control lever travel from neutral to forward and neutral to reverse at point where rear wheel just begins to creep. Distances should be equal. To adjust control lever neutral position, disconnect control rod ball joint (9) from control cam and turn ball joint. Recheck control lever movement.

Models 300-312-314-316

To adjust hydrostatic control linkage, first raise and securely block rear of tractor so one rear wheel is free to turn. With control lever in neutral position, remove pin (6 – Fig. JD51) from clevis and move control arm (7) until roller (8) seats in control arm detent. Start engine

and run at idle speed. Being careful not to contact transmission fan, loosen locknut (2) and turn eccentric (3) until raised wheel stops turning; tighten locknut. Loosen jam nut (1) and turn clevis (4) until pin (6) can be installed, then retighten jam nut.

A slight drag should be felt when moving hydrostatic control lever. To adjust control linkage friction brake, refer to Fig. JD52 and turn adjusting nut (1) to tighten or loosen linkage brake (2) as required.

TESTING

Models 120-140-300-312-314-316

To check implement circuit hydraulic pressure, install a 0-1000 psi (0-7000 kPa) pressure gage at front hydraulic outlet (if so equipped) or tee into hydraulic line going to lift cylinder. Operate hydraulic control level to direct oil flow to pressure gage. With engine at full throttle, pressure should be between 500 and 600 psi (3447 and 4137 kPa). If necessary, shims are available to increase implement relief valve spring pressure.

To check charge circuit pressure, remove pipe plug from top of transmission and install a 0-1000 psi (0-7000 kPa)

pressure gage using 1/8 inch pipe adapter. Refer to Fig. JD53. At half throttle, charge pressure should be 75-110 psi (517-758 kPa).

If pressures are low, check for low transmission oil level, plugged oil filter, defective relief valves, defective charge pump or internal damage to transmission.

Transmission does not have to be removed to service check valves, relief valves or charge pump (except Model 140 serial number 10000-30001). Before removing and disassembling transmission, remove and cut open hydraulic filter and drain transmission oil to check for metal chips or other contamination which might indicate cause of problem. Brass and steel chips in the oil usually indicate transmission internal damage.

REMOVE AND REINSTALL

Models 120-140

To remove hydrostatic transmission, remove fender and deck assembly and disconnect drive shaft at rear flex coupling. Remove transmission fan shield and fan. Disconnect pto shaft extension, if so equipped. Disconnect control rod at control cam and brake rods at brake lever. Disconnect hydraulic oil lines and unscrew hitch plate cap screws. Support rear of tractor. On early Model 140 tractors (serial number 10001-30000), remove hitch plate and unscrew axle housing mounting bolts. On all other models, unscrew transmission bracket cap screws. Roll transmission and differential assembly from rear of tractor. Disconnect oil intake tube to transmission. Transmission may now be removed from differential.

To reinstall transmission, reverse removal procedure.

Fig. JD51 — Underside view of hydrostatic control linkage used on Models 300, 312, 314 and 316.

1. Jam nut
2. Locknut
3. Eccentric
4. Clevis
5. Cotter pin
6. Pin
7. Control arm
8. Roller

Fig. JD52 — On Models 300, 312, 314 and 316, adjust nut (1) to tighten or loosen hydrostatic control linkage brake (2) until a slight drag is felt when moving control lever.

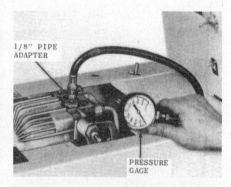

Fig. JD53 — To check hydrostatic transmission charge pressure, install 0-1000 psi (0-7000 kPa) pressure gage using 1/8 inch pipe adapter as shown. Refer to text.

Models 300-312-314-316

To remove hydrostatic transmission remove fender and deck assembly and fuel tank. Drain fluid from gear reduction housing and disconnect hydraulic oil lines. Disconnect drive shaft at rear flex coupling. Disconnect control linkage at control cam, then unbolt and remove cam arm and mounting bracket. Remove six cap screws securing transmission to gear reduction housing and remove transmission through bottom of frame.

OVERHAUL

All Models

Model 140 with serial number 10001 through 30000 is equipped with a right-angle drive Sundstrand hydrostatic transmission. Models 120, 140 (serial number 30001 and later), 300, 312, 314 and 316 are equipped with a "U" type Sundstrand hydrostatic transmission. Refer to the appropriate Sundstrand section in HYDROSTATIC TRANSMISSION SERVICE section for overhaul procedure.

DIFFERENTIAL

Models 120-140-300-312-314-316

REMOVE AND REINSTALL. To remove differential, first raise and support rear of tractor frame. Remove fender and deck assembly and disconnect drive shaft at rear flex coupling. Remove transmission fan shield and fan. Disconnect pto shaft extension, if so equipped. Disconnect control linkage at control cam and brake rods at brake lever. Drain fluid from differential housing and disconnect hydraulic oil lines. On early Model 140 (serial number 10001-30000), remove hitch plate. On all models, support front of transmission with a floor jack, then remove transmission and axle mounting cap screws. Roll transmission and differential assembly rearward away from tractor. Unbolt and remove transmission from differential housing. Cap or plug all hydraulic fittings to prevent entry of dirt.

Reinstall by reversing removal procedure.

Model 140 (S.N. 10001-30000)

OVERHAUL. To disassemble differential, unscrew retaining cap screws and separate axle housing (1 and 21 – Fig. JD55) being careful not to lose rollers of uncaged bearings used in housing of early models. Remove clips securing oil tube in left axle housing (1) and remove tube. Remove countershaft gear

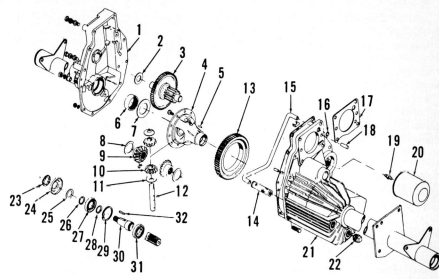

Fig. JD55 — Exploded view of differential assembly used on Model 140 tractors with serial number 10001-30000.

1. Left housing
2. Thrust washer (2)
3. Gear & countershaft
4. Differential case
5. Pinion shaft pin
6. Bearing
7. Thrust washer
8. Thrust washer
9. Side gear
10. Pinion gear
11. Thrust washer
12. Pinion gear shaft
13. Ring gear
14. Oil strainer
15. Oil suction pipe
16. "O" ring
17. Gasket
18. Dowel pin
19. Oil filter fitting
20. Oil filter
21. Right housing
22. Plug
23. Felt seal
24. Bearing retainer
25. Shim
26. Snap ring
27. Bearing
28. Snap ring
29. Snap ring
30. Axle shaft
31. Oil seal
32. Key

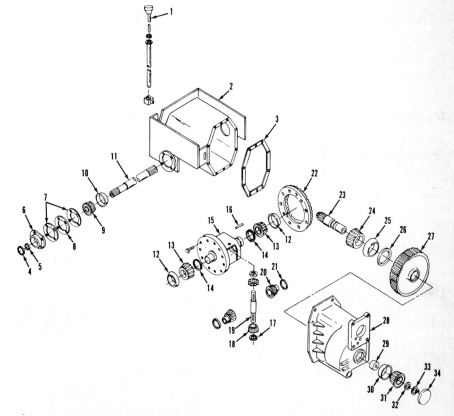

Fig. JD56 — Exploded view of typical differential assembly used on Late Model 140 tractors (S.N. 30001 and later) and all Models 120, 300, 312, 314 and 316.

1. Dipstick
2. Rear housing & mounting bracket
3. Gasket
4. Felt seal
5. "O" ring
6. Seal retainer
7. Gaskets
8. Bearing retainer
9. Bearing cone
10. Bearing cup
11. Axle shaft
12. Bearing cup
13. Bearing cone
14. Shims
15. Case
16. Pin
17. Thrust washer
18. Pinion gear
19. Pinion shaft
20. Side gear
21. Thrust washer
22. Ring gear
23. Drive pinion gear & shaft
24. Bearing cone
25. Bearing cup
26. Shims
27. Spur gear
28. Front housing
29. Spacer
30. Bearing cup
31. Bearing cone
32. Shim
33. Snap ring
34. Expansion plug

(3) and differential assembly. Drive out spring pin (5), then pinion shaft (12). Disassembly of remainder of differential is self-evident with inspection of unit.

Inspect components for damage or excessive wear. Check oil tubes for bends or cracks or the possibility of rubbing against gears. Minimum countershaft (3) journal outside diameter is 0.990 inch (25.146 mm); minimum pinion shaft (12) outside diameter is 0.682 inch (17.323 mm); minimum differential case (4) outer journal outside diameter is 1.874 inch (47.599 mm). When installing ring gear (13) on differential case (4), tighten three opposite screws until gear is pulled up tightly on case, then tighten all screws to 50 ft.-lbs. (68 N·m). On early models with uncaged roller bearings, be sure bearing rollers stay in place during reassembly. Tighten axle housing cap screws to 20 ft.-lbs. (27 N·m). Oil filter should be changed when differential is overhauled to prevent contaminated oil from damaging transmission.

Models 140 (S.N. 30000 and Later)-120-300-312-314-316

OVERHAUL. To disassemble differential assembly, first remove axle shafts as outlined in AXLE SHAFTS section. Unscrew cap screws and separate front housing (28 – Fig. JD56) from rear housing (2). Mark differential case bearing caps to aid in reassembly and remove caps. Remove differential case (15) from housing. It may be necessary to pry case from housing using two wooden handles. Drive pinion pin (16) out of pinion shaft (19) and drive pinion shaft from differential case (15). Remove pinion gears (18) and thrust washers (17). Remove side gears (20) and thrust washers (21). If bearing renewal is required, pull case bearings (13) from case. Unscrew cap screws and drive ring gear (22) off case.

To remove pinion and spur gears, remove expansion plug (34) from front differential housing. Remove snap ring (33) and shim (32). Press pinion gear (23) out of housing. Before applying pressure to pinion shaft, remove side cover of housing and insert ⅛ inch (3 mm) steel spacer or suitable screwdriver blade under edge of spur gear (27) as shown in Fig. JD57. This will prevent spur gear from cocking and possibly cracking differential housing. Catch pinion gear after it is pressed free. Spur gear (27 – Fig. JD56), spacer (29) and outer pinion bearing may now be removed. Press pinion gear out of bearing cone (24). Remove bearing cups (25 and 30) and shim (26) from housing.

Clean and inspect all parts for excessive wear or damage and renew as required.

To reassemble, reverse disassembly procedure. If new pinion gear (23), front housing (28) or bearing cups are installed, select correct shim pack (26) as follows: Install pinion gear with bearing cup and cone in housing without shims. Position tool JDST-10 in bearing cradles as shown in Fig. JD58 and measure distance between tool depth pin and face of pinion gear. Measured distance will be thickness of shim pack (26 – Fig. JD56) to be installed. Shims are available in sizes of 0.003, 0.005, 0.010 and 0.030 inch. Remove pinion gear, bearing cone and cup and install shims. Press outer pinion bearing (31) on pinion gear shaft (23) until there is a slight drag felt when pinion is turned by hand. Install thickest shim (32) which will allow installation of snap ring (33).

If differential case (15) is renewed, install a 0.020 inch shim pack (14) under each differential bearing (13). If differential case is not renewed, reinstall shims which were removed during disassembly. Tighten ring gear cap screws to a torque of 50-55 ft.-lbs. (68-75 N·m). Be sure to install bearing caps in their original marked positions.

Tighten bearing cap retaining screws to 40-45 ft.-lbs. (54-61 N·m).

Gear backlash between ring and pinion gears should be 0.003-0.007 inch (0.076-0.178 N·m). Transfer shims (14) from one side of differential case to the other until correct backlash is obtained. Available shim sizes are 0.003-0.005, 0.010 and 0.030 inch. Paint ring and pinion gears with a suitable gear pattern compound and check mesh position of gears. Adjust size or number of shims (14 or 26) to obtain correct mesh position shown in Fig. JD59.

Reinstall axle and brake assemblies and complete remainder of assembly by reversing disassembly procedure. Fill differential with 10 pints (4.7 L) of John Deere All-Weather Hydrostatic Fluid or automatic transmission fluid Type "F." Adjust clutch, brakes and hydrostatic control linkage as required.

AXLE SHAFTS

Model 140 (S.N. 10001-30000)

Axles, seals, bearings and hubs can be serviced without removing differential assembly. To remove axle, block up under tractor and remove rear wheel, brake and wheel hub. With a suitable size chisel, cut or drive off bearing retainer (24 – Fig. JD55). Note in Figs.

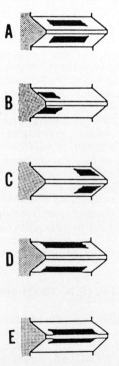

Fig. JD59 – Illustration of typical gear teeth contact patterns encountered when checking ring gear and pinion. "A" pattern desired; "B" too close to toe; "C" too close to heel; "D" contact too low; "E" contact too high.

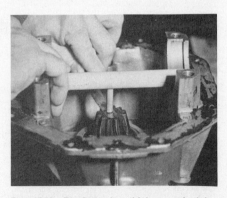

Fig. JD57 – Spur gear (27) should be supported as shown to prevent housing damage when pressing out pinion gear shaft.

Fig. JD58 – To determine thickness of pinion gear shim pack, measure as shown and refer to text.

JD60 and JD61 difference between outer axle assemblies. On Model 140 tractors with serial number 10001 through 14750 shown in Fig. JD60, axle may be withdrawn from axle housing by pulling outward. On Model 140 tractors with serial number 14751 through 30000, remove outer snap ring (5–JD61) before pulling axle assembly from axle housing. Press bearing off axle after removing snap ring (26–Fig. JD55). Remove snap ring from axle tube and remove oil seal.

Inspect components for damage or excessive wear. To reassemble, reverse

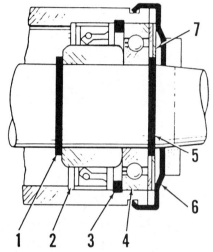

Fig. JD60—Cross-sectional view of rear axle outer bearing, seal and retainer installation on Model 140 with serial number 10001 through 14750.

1. Snap ring
2. Oil seal
3. Snap ring
4. Bearing
5. Snap ring
6. Retainer
7. Metal spacers

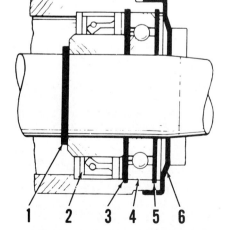

Fig. JD61—Cross-sectional view of rear axle outer bearing, seal and retainer installation on Model 140 with serial number 14751 through 30000.

1. Snap ring
2. Oil seal
3. Snap ring
4. Bearing
5. Snap ring
6. Retainer

disassembly procedure. Early models (serial number 10001-14750) have metal spacers (7–Fig. JD60) between retainer and bearing. Retainer (6) on early models must be crimped into groove around axle tube after installation.

Models 140 (S.N. 30001 and Later)-120-300-312-314-316

Axles, seals, bearings and hubs can be serviced without removing differential assembly. To remove axle, block up tractor under frame and remove rear wheel. Unscrew cap screw and remove washer from center of wheel hub; then, using a suitable puller, remove wheel hub. Remove brake and back plate assembly (Fig. JD62). Remove seal retainer (6–Fig. JD 56), gaskets (7) and bearing retainer (8). Withdraw axle (11) and bearing (9).

NOTE: A ring is epoxied to bearing cup (10) to prevent bearing cone (9) from separating from bearing cup. See Fig. JD63. If ring separates from bearing cup when bearing cone is removed, bearing cup must be removed separately. Press bearing cone off axle shaft.

To reassemble axle, reverse disassembly procedure. Assemble bearing cone, bearing cup and ring on axle before installing axle. Cement ring to bearing cup as shown in Fig. JD63 using an epoxy adhesive. If bearing protrudes slightly, use more than one gasket between end of axle tube and bearing retainer. Make sure hub seal is aligned with axle, then tighten back plate retaining nuts to 15 ft.-lbs. (20 N·m).

HYDRAULIC SYSTEM

All Models So Equipped

OPERATION. Some Model 110, 112, 210, 212, 214 and 216 tractors are equip-

Fig. JD62—Wheel hub and brake drum removed from Model 140 tractor with serial number 30001 and later. Models 120, 300, 312, 314 and 316 are similar. Remove brake and back plate assembly, then withdraw axle shaft and bearing assembly.

ped with a hydraulic lift system. The hydraulic system is pressure fed by a gear type pump driven by tractor engine. Hydraulic fluid is directed by an open center spool control valve to a double-acting cylinder.

Models 120, 140, 300, 312, 314, 316 are equipped with an open center hydraulic system which uses hydraulic pressure supplied by hydrostatic transmission charge pump. A double-acting cylinder rotates a rockshaft to raise and lower implements. Some models are equipped with quick-disconnect auxiliary outlets to allow remote cylinder operation.

NOTE: Hydraulic system components should be cleaned before disconnecting hydraulic lines or disassembling components. Open fittings should be capped to prevent dirt from entering system.

Automatic transmission fluid Type "F" or John Deere All-Weather Hydrostatic Fluid should be used in hydraulic system on all models.

HYDRAULIC PUMP

Models 110-112-210-212-214 215 So Equipped

Two pump configurations have been used. One type has oil reservoir in line with pump drive shaft while other type has oil reservoir at a 90 degree angle to pump drive shaft. Overhaul of these two pumps is similar.

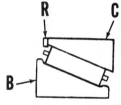

Fig. JD63—Axle bearing cone (B) is retained in cup (C) by ring (R) which is epoxied to edge of cup on Models 120, 140 and 300 series tractors.

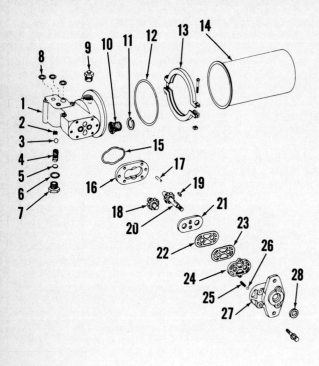

1. Pump body
2. Relief valve seat
3. Ball
4. Valve spring
5. Shim
6. "O" ring
7. Plug
8. "O" ring
9. Vent plug
10. Filter
11. Snap ring
12. "O" ring
13. Clamp
14. Reservoir
15. "O" ring
16. Gear body
17. Dowel pin
18. Driven gear
19. Key
20. Drive gear
21. Diaphragm
22. Heat shield
23. Gasket
24. Seal
25. Spring
26. Check ball
27. Front plate
28. Seal

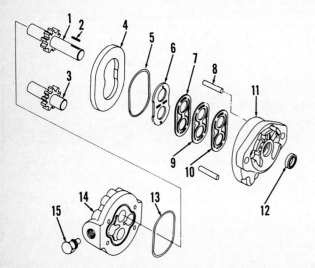

Fig. JD66 — Exploded view of hydraulic pump used on 200 series tractors.

1. Drive gear
2. Key
3. Driven gear
4. Center section
5. "O" ring
6. Wear plate
7. Heat shield
8. Pin
9. Gasket
10. "V" seal
11. Front cover
12. Seal
13. "O" ring
14. Back cover
15. Relief valve

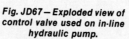

Fig. JD67 — Exploded view of control valve used on in-line hydraulic pump.

1. Cap
2. Bolt
3. Snap ring
4. Washer
5. Spring
6. Spacer
7. Washer
8. "O" ring
9. "O" rings
10. Valve body
11. Spool
12. Lift check plunger
13. Spring
14. "O" ring
15. Plug
16. Cylinder

Remove oil reservoir from pump and scribe a line across pump body (1 – Fig. JD65), gear body (16) and front plate (27). Unscrew four cap screws and tap against front plate (27) to separate front plate, gear body (16) and pump body (1). Remove diaphragm (21), heat shield (22), gasket (23) and seal (24) from front plate (27) being careful not to damage surface of plate. Check depth of relief valve seat (2) in pump body. Renew valve seat if depth is not 1.776-1.786 inches (45.11-45.364 mm) or seat is loose. Loosen valve seat by applying heat to pump body. Use "Loctite" when installing valve seat.

Clean and inspect components for excessive wear and damage. Pump gears should be renewed as a unit. Small scratches and a wear pattern may be present on pump body but should not exceed 0.0015 inch (0.0381 mm). Install a new diaphragm (21) with seal (24), gasket (23) and heat shield (22). Seal (24) must be installed in front plate with "V" groove of seal in front plate. Place diaphragm (21) in front plate with bronze face up. Diaphragm must fit inside raised edge of seal (24). Lubricate gears and shafts with clean oil before assembly and apply a light coat of gasket sealer to machined surfaces of body (16). Complete assembly of pump being sure to align scribed line across front plate (27), body (16) and pump body. Tighten front plate cap screws to 190-210 in.-lbs. (22-23 N·m).

Some models are equipped with a relief valve spring (4) which provides 1500 psi (10342 kPa). Manufacturer recommends relief valve spring H31256H be installed which reduces system pressure to 800 psi (5516kPa) if 1500 psi (10342 kPa) is excessive. Check system pressure after installing spring and add one or more shims (5) to increase pressure if it is below 800 psi (5516 kPa). Pumps used on 200 series tractors have maximum output of 4 gallons (15 L) per minute at 500 to 600 psi (3447-4137 kPa).

Models 120-140-300-312-314-316

The hydrostatic transmission charge pump is the power supply for hydraulic system on these models. For testing and overhaul procedures, refer to HYDROSTATIC TRANSMISSION paragraphs.

CONTROL VALVE

Models 110-112-210-212-214-216 So Equipped

Refer to Figs. JD67, JD68 and JD69 for exploded view of control valves which are used. Hydraulic lines should be marked to aid in reassembly. Drive cross pin out of end of spool being careful not to bend spool. Remove cap (1 – Fig. JD67) and snap ring (3) to remove spool on control valve shown in Fig. JD67. Remove spool on control valve shown in Fig. JD68 and JD69 after unscrewing plug (8 – Fig. JD68 or 3 – Fig. JD69). Note that heat must be applied to bolt end of spool before unscrewing bolt (2 – Fig. JD67 or 4 – Fig. JD69).

Inspect spool, housing and components of control valve. Spool and housing must be renewed as a unit. Renew weak or broken springs. Renew all "O" rings and lubricate "O" rings in housing with oil before installing spool. Be careful not to cut "O" rings when installing spool. Apply "Loctite" on threads of bolt (2 – Fig. JD67 or 4 – Fig. JD69) and tighten bolt to 60-65 in.-lbs. (7 N·m). Tighten control valve to pump body cap screws to 7-10 ft.-lbs. (9-14 N·m).

Model 120

Model 120 is equipped with a single spool control valve. To service control valve, refer to exploded views in Figs. JD70 or JD71. Spool and valve assembly may be removed after removing end cap or plug. If spool or valve bore is damaged, entire valve must be renewed. If spool screw (2) was removed, use Loctite on screw threads when reassembling. Tighten spool end cap or plug so cap or plug is snug but spool will still turn without binding.

Model 140

Three types of control valves have been used. The single spool control valve provides one controllable hydraulic circuit. Using a three spool control valve provides three controllable hydraulic circuits.

To service control valve, refer to exploded views in Figs. JD70, JD71 or JD72. Spool assembly may be removed after removing end cap. Be careful when removing end cap from float detent screw so balls (17 – Fig. JD72) are not lost. Spools should not be interchanged on three spool control valves. If spool or valve bore is damaged, entire valve must be renewed.

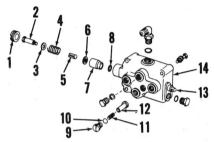

Fig. JD70 — Exploded view of control valve used on early Model 120 tractors and Model 140-H1 tractors (serial number 10001 through 30000).

1. End plug	8. "O" ring
2. Spool screw	9. Plug
3. Washer	10. "O" ring
4. Spring	11. Spring
5. Bushing	12. Check valve
6. Washer	13. Spool
7. Bushing	14. Body

When reassembling control valve, note that on three spool control valves a 1¼ inch (32 mm) spring is used with float detent screw and a 1 inch (25 mm) spring is used with other spool screws. Use Loctite on all spool screw threads. Tighten spool end cap or plug so cap or plug is snug but spool will still turn without binding.

Models 300-316

A two spool control valve is used on these models providing two controllable hydraulic circuits. One spool is equipped with a detent to provide a "float" position.

To service control valve, refer to exploded view in Fig. JD73. Spool assemblies can be removed after removing end caps (1) from valve body.

NOTE: When removing float spool cap (longest cap), place a cloth over cap to catch spring-loaded detent balls (2) as cap is removed.

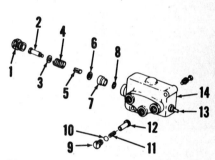

Fig. JD71 — Exploded view of control valve used on late Model 120 tractors. Model 140-H1 tractors (serial number 30001 and later) and Model 312 tractors.

1. End cap	8. "O" ring
2. Spool screw	9. Plug
3. Washer	10. "O" ring
4. Spring	11. Spring
5. Bushing	12. Check valve
6. Washer	13. Spool
7. Bushing	14. Body

Fig. JD68 — Exploded view of control valve used on right angle hydraulic pump.

1. Valve body
2. Washer
3. Spring
4. Spacer
5. Washer
6. Snap ring
7. "O" ring
8. Plug
9. Spool
10. "O" ring
11. Fitting
12. Plug
13. Spring
14. Lift check plunger
15. Fitting

Fig. JD69 — Exploded view of hydraulic lift control valve used on 200 series tractors. Control valve used on Model 314 (serial number 95001 and later) is similar except a retaining ring is used in place of screw (4) to retain centering spring (6).

10. "O" ring
11. Valve body
12. Detent plunger
13. Spring
14. "O" ring
15. Plug

Fig. JD72 — Exploded view of control valve used on Model 140-H3 tractors (serial number 30001 and later).

1. Spools	11. Spring (1 inch)
2. Body	12. Washer
3. Plug	13. Spool screw
4. "O" ring	14. End cap
5. Spring	15. Plug
6. Check valve	16. Float detent screw
7. "O" ring	17. Balls
8. Bushing	18. Spring
9. Washer	19. Spring (1¼ inch)
10. Bushing	

1. "O" ring
2. Spool
3. Cap

4. Screw
5. Washer
6. Spring

7. Spacer
8. Washer
9. Bushing

Spools are select-fitted and should not be interchanged in bores. If spools or valve bores are worn or damaged, complete valve must be renewed.

When reassembling valve, renew all "O" rings (7, 10 and 11) and lubricate with clean oil before installing spools. Note that centering springs (5 and 12) are of different lengths and that a spacer (13) is installed between washers (4) on spool without detent. Apply Loctite to threads of spool screws (3). Tighten end caps until snug making sure spools turn without binding.

Models 312-314

A single spool control valve is used on Models 312 and 314 tractors. Refer to appropriate Fig. JD69 or JD71 for exploded view of valves used. Spool assembly can be removed after removing end cap. If spool or valve bore is worn or damaged, complete valve must be renewed.

When reassembling valve, renew all "O" rings and lubricate all parts with clean oil before assembly. Apply Loctite to spool screw threads and tighten to 5-8 ft.-lbs. (7-11 N·m). Tighten end cap snug but be sure spool turns without binding.

HYDRAULIC CYLINDER

All Models So Equipped

A double-acting hydraulic cylinder is used on all models to raise or lower tractor rockshaft. Hydraulic cylinder is a welded assembly and is not serviceable. Renew cylinder assembly as a unit if malfunction occurs.

To test cylinder for internal leakage, proceed as follows: Fully retract cylinder, then disconnect return hose, going to end of cylinder opposite rod end, at control valve. Place open end of hose in a clean container. With engine running, actuate control lever to retract cylinder. Oil leaking past piston seal ring will be indicated by a continuous flow of oil into container.

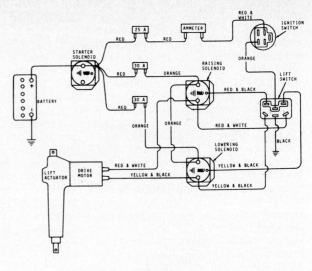

Fig. JD75 — Typical wiring schematic of electric lift system used on some Model 110 and 112 tractors.

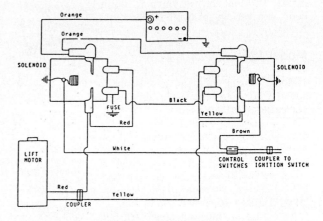

Fig. JD76 — Wiring schematic of electric lift system used on some Model 200, 208, 210, 212, 214 and 216 tractors.

ELECTRIC LIFT

Models 110-112-200-208-210-212-214-216 So Equipped

An electric lift system is available for these models. The lift system consists of lifting linkage, lift actuator, a reversible motor, raising and lowering solenoids and a lift switch. Refer to appropriate wiring diagram in Fig. JD75 or JD76 and exploded view of motor and lift actuator in Fig. JD77.

TESTING. To determine if electric lift malfunction is electrical or mechanical, disconnect wire coupler at electric motor and connect leads from a 12-volt test light or voltmeter into coupler leads from electrical system. Turn ignition switch on and actuate lift switch to "UP" and "DOWN" positions. If voltmeter or test light indicates voltage is present in both lift positions, then malfunction is in motor, lift actuator or mechanical linkage. If voltage is not present, use schematic in Fig. JD75 or JD76 and troubleshoot electrical system.

If previous test indicates a malfunction in electric lift motor, lift actuator or mechanical linkage, inspect linkage for possible binding or obstructions in linkage. To check motor, remove motor and connect leads of motor to battery posts of tractor battery; motor shaft should rotate freely. Reverse motor leads to battery; motor shaft should rotate freely in opposite direction. Renew motor if it fails to operate satisfactorily in both directions. If motor operates satisfactorily, disassemble lift actuator and renew components as necessary.

OVERHAUL. To service lift actuator, remove two through-bolts and

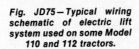

Fig. JD73 — Exploded view of H-2 control valve used on Models 300 and 316.

1. End caps
2. Detent balls & spring
3. Spool screws
4. Washers
5. Spring
6. Bushing
7. "O" ring
8. Spool
9. Lift check valves
10. "O" rings
11. "O" rings
12. Spring
13. Spacer

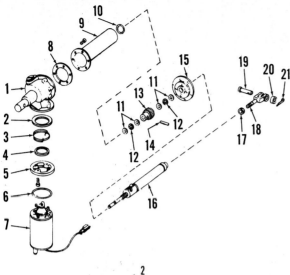

1. Gear housing
2. Gasket
3. Brake spring
4. Spacer
5. Adapter
6. "O" ring
7. Motor
8. Gasket
9. Tube cover
10. "O" ring
11. Thrust washer
12. Thrust bearing
13. Gear
14. Pin
15. Bearing support
16. Actuator rod
17. Locknut
18. Yoke
19. Pin
20. Spacer
21. Cotter pin

with an adjustable cam (3–Fig. JD78), there must be a three inch (76 mm) radius (R) from center of pivot shaft (2) to outer diameter of cam (3). Remove cam and arm assembly from left side of pedestal and install special tool JDM-65 (1) as shown. Loosen cap screws (4) and adjust edges of cam to edges of tool. Tighten cap screws and reinstall cam assembly. On models with one piece cam and arm assembly, cam adjustment is not required; however, cam side play must not exceed 1/16 inch (1.5 mm) (A – Fig. JD79). If side play is excessive, add shim washers (1). There should be two spacers (4) located between switches (3) as shown in Fig. 79; if not, install spacer kit AM36200. On all models, switches must close when on raised surface of cam. If switches do not close properly, loosen retaining nuts and move switches toward cam as required. Both switches should be open at center of cam.

SAFETY INTERLOCK SWITCHES

All Models

All models are equipped with transmission and pto neutral-start interlock switches. Some models are also equipped with a seat interlock switch. All switches must be closed to allow current to flow to starter solenoid.

On models equipped with electric pto clutch, pto switch must be in "OFF" position to activate pto neutral-start switch. Safety switch is not adjustable and must be renewed if testing indicates switch failure.

On models equipped with manual pto clutch, neutral-start switch is closed when control lever is placed in disengaged position. If necessary, loosen switch mounting screws and adjust for proper operation. Be careful not to bottom out switch plunger to prevent damage to switch.

All models are equipped with an adjustable transmission neutral-start switch. To adjust, loosen mounting screws or nuts and move switch until it closes when hydrostatic control lever or transmission shift lever is placed in neutral position. To prevent damage to switch, be sure switch roller is not bottomed out after adjusting switch.

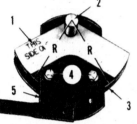

1. JDM-65 tool
2. Pivot shaft
3. Cam
4. Cap screws
5. Arm

remove motor from gear housing. Remove motor adapter (5–Fig. JD77). Pry spacer (4) out of gear housing and withdraw brake spring (3), if so equipped. Do not attempt to remove worm gear from gear housing (1). Gear and housing must be renewed as a complete unit. Remove retaining screws and separate cover tube (9) with actuator assembly from gear housing (1); then, pull cover tube off actuator. Drive out pin (14) and remove thrust washers and bearings, gear and bearing support from actuator (16). If actuator is damaged, complete actuator assembly must be renewed.

When reassembling, lubricate gears and bearings with multipurpose grease. Install brake spring (3) into gear housing with drive shaft arm between prongs of spring, if so equipped. Be sure spring coils are positioned in recess and spring rotates freely. When installing motor, be sure spring ends are located within fork legs of motor shaft bracket.

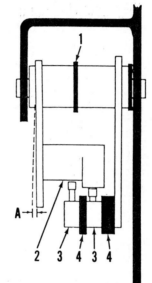

1. Shim washer
2. Cam
3. Switches
4. Spacers

ADJUSTMENT. On Models 110 and 112, it may be necessary to adjust reach of lift actuator rod (16–Fig. JD77) if mower deck contacts drag link. Loosen locknut (17) and turn rod to obtain 1/4 to 3/8 inch (6-10 mm) clearance between mower deck and drag link.

On Models 200, 208, 210, 212, 214 and 216, cam and control switches must be adjusted as follows: On models equipped

DEUTZ-ALLIS
CONDENSED SPECIFICATIONS

	MODELS			
	T-811	912H	914H	916H
Engine Make	B&S	Kohler	Kohler	Kohler
Model	252707	K301S	K321S	K341S
Bore	3-7/16 in.	3⅜ in.	3½ in.	3¾ in.
	(87.3 mm)	(85.7 mm)	(88.9 mm)	(95.2 mm)
Stroke	2⅝ in.	3¼ in.	3¼ in.	3¼ in.
	(66.7 mm)	(82.5 mm)	(82.5 mm)	(82.5 mm)
Piston Displacement	24.36 cu. in.	29.07 cu. in.	31.27 cu. in.	35.89 cu. in.
	(399 cc)	(476 cc)	(512 cc)	(588 cc)
Horsepower	11	12	14	16
Slow Idle Speed – Rpm	1750	1500	1500	1500
High Idle Speed (No Load) – Rpm	3600	3600	3600	3600
Full Load Speed – Rpm	3400	3400	3400	3400
Crankcase Oil Capacity	3 pints	4 pints	4 pints	4 pints
	(1.4 L)	(1.9 L)	(1.9 L)	(1.9 L)
Weight –				
Above 32°F(0°C)		SAE 30		
0°F(−18°C)to 32°F(0°C)		SAE 10W		
Below 0°F(−18°C)		SAE 5W-20		
Transmission Oil Capacity	3½ pints	6 pints	6 pints	6 pints
	(1.6 L)	(2.8 L)	(2.8 L)	(2.8 L)
Weight	SAE 90 EP		Dexron ATF	
Bevel Gear Housing Oil Capacity	.....		1 pint	
			(0.5 L)	
Weight	.....		SAE 90 EP	

FRONT AXLE AND STEERING SYSTEM

AXLE MAIN MEMBER

Model T-811

The axle main member and stabilizer is a welded assembly. The unit pivots on a center mounting bolt and a flange bearing at rear of stabilizer. To remove front axle assembly, raise front of tractor and block securely. Disconnect drag link from steering arm (11 – Fig. DA10). Remove center mounting bolt and pull axle assembly out of flange bearing.

Models 912H-914H-916H

The axle main member and stabilizer is a welded assembly. The unit pivots on a center mounting bolt and rear of stabilizer. To remove front axle assembly, disconnect drag link ball joint end (16 – Fig. DA11) from steering arm (15). Raise front of tractor and remove cap screw (38) and spacer (13) from

center of axle. Lower front of axle and pull forward to slide stabilizer out of frame angle. The frame angle is bolted on main frame and can be renewed if stabilizer pivot hole is excessively worn.

TIE ROD

Model T-811

A single tie rod is used on Model T-811. To adjust toe-in, disconnect tie rod ball joints from steering spindles, loosen locknuts and turn tie rod ball joints in or out as required. Toe-in should be 1/16 to ⅛ inch (1.5-3.0 mm).

Models 912H-914H-916H

The tie rod is nonadjustable and can be removed after disconnecting tie rod from steering spindles.

STEERING SPINDLES

Model T-811

To remove steering spindles, support front of tractor and remove front wheels. Disconnect tie rod ends from spindles. Remove "E" ring (1 – Fig.

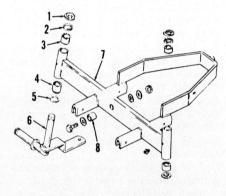
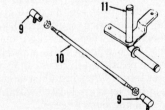

Fig. DA10 – Exploded view of front axle assembly used on Model T-811.

1. Retaining ring
2. Washer
3. Bushing
4. Bushing
5. Washer
6. Steering spindle (R.H.)
7. Axle main member
8. Spacer
9. Tie rod end
10. Tie rod
11. Steering spindle (L.H.)

DA10) from top of steering spindle and lower spindle out of axle main member. Spindle bushings (3 and 4) are renewable. Lubricate with multipurpose lithium base grease.

Models 912H-914H-916H

To remove steering spindles, refer to Fig. DA11, support front of tractor and remove front wheels and tie rod. Remove steering arm and key from left spindle and slide spindle down out of axle main member. Remove retaining pin from right steering spindle and lower spindle from axle. Inspect spindle bushings and renew if necessary. Lubricate with multipurpose lithium base grease.

STEERING GEAR

R&R AND OVERHAUL

Model T-811

To remove steering gear, tilt hood and remove upper dash, fuel tank, lower dash and steering wheel. Disconnect drag link from steering rod. Unbolt and remove steering plate and steering shaft. Remove base plate (11–Fig. DA12), sector gear (10) and steering rod (8) as an assembly. To remove sector gear, remove two set screws and use a suitable puller or press to force steering rod from gear.

When reassembling sector gear and steering rod, install key with rounded end towards bent end of steering rod. Inspect bushings in base plate and steering plate for wear or damage and renew as necessary.

Models 912H-914H-916H

To remove steering gear, remove steering wheel and battery. Disconnect drag link from steering arm (13–Fig. DA13) and turn steering arm to allow access to mounting bolts. Remove mounting bolts and move steering gear assembly forward until casting lug clears edge of frame opening and lower entire assembly.

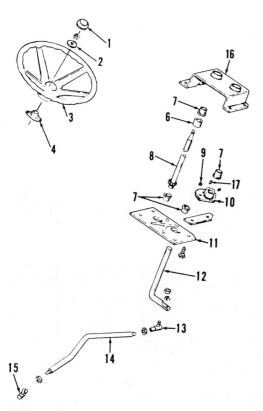

Fig. DA11—Exploded view of front axle assembly used on Models 912H, 914H and 916H.

7. Steering spindle (R.H.)
8. Steering spindle bearings
9. Washers
10. Tie rod spacers
11. Tie rod
12. Axle main member
13. Pivot bolt spacer
14. Steering spindle (L.H.)
15. Steering arm
16. Drag link ends
17. Drag link
32. Set screw
38. Axle pivot pin

Fig. DA12—Exploded view of steering gear used on Model T-811.

1. Cap
2. Compression washer
3. Steering wheel
4. Bearing
6. Spacer
7. Bushing
8. Steering shaft assy.
9. Set screws (2)
10. Sector gear
11. Base plate
12. Steering rod
13. Drag link end
14. Drag link
15. Drag link end
16. Steering plate
17. Key

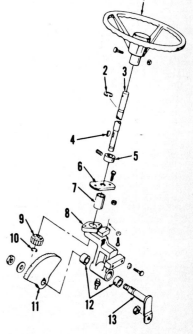

Fig. DA13—Exploded view of steering gear used on Models 912H, 914H and 916H.

1. Steering wheel
2. Retaining ring
3. Steering shaft
4. Key
5. Set collar
6. Steering plate
7. Bushing
8. Casting
9. Pinion
10. "E" ring
11. Bevel gear
12. Needle bearing
13. Steering arm assy

To disassemble steering gear, clamp support casting in a vise and remove locknut (B – Fig. DA14) and washer. Use a plastic mallet to remove steering arm from bevel drive gear and casting. Position steering shaft in a vise. Remove retaining ring (E) and use a piece of hardwood to drive pinion gear off shaft. Remove key from shaft and slide shaft out of bushing. Loosen locknuts and remove adjusting cap screws, adjusting plate and bushing. Use a bearing puller to remove needle bearings from support casting.

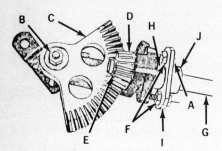

Fig. DA14 – View of steering assembly removed from tractor. Refer to text for disassembly procedure.

A. Adjusting cap screws
B. Locknut & flat washer
C. Bevel gear
D. Pinion
E. "E" ring
F. Locknuts
G. Steering shaft
H. Bushing
I. Steering plate
J. Set collar

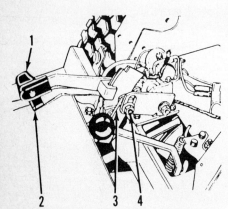

Fig. DA15 – View of variable speed control linkage used on Model T-811.

1. Control lever
2. Handle
3. Bar
4. Shoulder belt

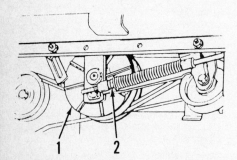

Fig. DA16 – Variable speed pulley (1) and clutch rod used on Model T-811. Adjusting nut (2) is used to adjust clutch. Refer to text.

During reassembly, press needle bearings into each end of bore with end of bearing marked "Torrington" facing outward. The bearing at gear end must be ⅛ inch (3 mm) below surface of casting. The bearing at steering arm end must fit flush with casting. Install bushing (H) and adjusting plate assembly and tighten adjusting plate until about 1/64 inch (0.4 mm) of bushing is above casting surface.

ENGINE

REMOVE AND REINSTALL

Model T-811

To remove engine, set parking brake and block tractor securely. Disconnect battery ground cable from battery. Remove fuel line at carburetor and drain fuel tank. Disconnect throttle cable, choke cable, engine ground wire, charging circuit and starter wires. Remove the four mounting cap screws and lift engine from tractor.

Models 912H-914H-916H

To remove engine, remove hood and front grille assembly. Disconnect fuel line from fuel pump and plug hose or drain fuel tank. Disconnect battery ground cable, all electrical wires, choke cable and throttle cable from engine. Remove flywheel to drive shaft cap screws, washers and spacers. Remove four mounting cap screws and lift engine from tractor.

OVERHAUL

All Models

Engine make and model are listed at the beginning of this section in the CONDENSED SPECIFICATIONS. To

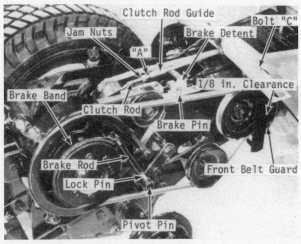

Fig. DA17 – View of clutch rod adjustment similar to procedure on Models 912H, 914H and 916H.

overhaul engine components and accessories, refer to Briggs & Stratton and Kohler engine sections of this manual.

CLUTCH

ADJUSTMENT

Model T-811

Variable speed control and clutch are adjusted together. Place speed control lever up in full speed position, then loosen shoulder bolt (4 – Fig. DA15). With transmission in neutral, start engine, depress clutch pedal, set parking brake and stop engine. Unlatch parking brake and allow pedal to come up slowly, then measure distance from pedal shaft to forward edge of foot rest. Distance should be 5½ inches (140 mm). Adjust nut (2 – Fig. DA16) towards spring to increase measurement or loosen nut to decrease measurement. Place speed control lever down in low speed position, then pull upper handle (1 – Fig. DA15) only upward and hold to lock lever in position. Push bar (3) down and tighten shoulder bolt.

Models 912H-914H-916H

With clutch/brake pedal in engaged position, turn adjusting nuts (Fig. DA17) until clearance ("A") between front nut and clutch rod guide is ¼ inch (6 mm).

BRAKE

ADJUSTMENT

Model T-811

To adjust brake, place transmission in neutral and start engine. Move variable

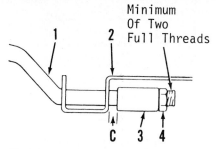

Fig. DA18 — On Model T-811, adjust nut (4) to obtain specified gap at (C) when adjusting brake. Refer to text.

speed control lever to full speed position and shut off engine. Shift transmission into gear without depressing clutch/brake pedal. Pull forward on brake band (2–Fig. DA18) to remove slack and measure gap (C) between spacer (3) and brake band which should be 5/8 to 3/4 inch (16-19 mm). Adjust nut (4) if necessary to obtain correct measurement.

Models 912H-914H-916H

To adjust brake, loosen jam nut on front end of parking brake rod (Fig. DA19) and turn handle and rod end until parking brake is tight when brake handle is against fender in brake lock position. With parking brake engaged and foot pedal released, adjust jam nuts on front of brake rod to obtain 3/4 inch (19 mm) clearance between jam nut and rod guide.

TRANSAXLE

LUBRICATION

Model T-811

Transaxle filler plug is located at the top of the transaxle near the shift lever opening. Transaxle capacity is approximately 3½ pints (1.6 L) of SAE 90 EP gear lubricant.

REMOVE AND REINSTALL

Model T-811

To remove transaxle, remove seat and fender assembly. Disconnect brake rod from brake band and clutch rod from idler bracket. Remove drive belt and transmission pulley. Unbolt and remove shift lever assembly. Remove "U" bolt clamp from right axle and remove frame support and transmission support bolts. Lower transmission and slide it clear of tractor.

OVERHAUL

Model T-811

Model T-811 is equipped with a three-speed transaxle manufactured for Deutz-Allis by Simplicity Manufacturing Company. Refer to Simplicity 3-Speed section in TRANSAXLE SERVICE section for overhaul procedure.

HYDROSTATIC TRANSMISSION

LUBRICATION

Models 912H-914H-916H

Models 912H, 914H and 916H are equipped with Sundstrand 15 series hydrostatic transmissions. Approximate fluid capacity is 6 pints (2.8 L) of Dexron automatic transmission fluid.

ADJUSTMENT

Models 912H-914H-916H

To adjust hydrostatic control linkage, park tractor on level ground, shift control lever to neutral notch and set parking brake. Raise seat deck and check centering mark on hydrostatic control cam (Fig. DA20). If mark is not centered, loosen bolt (A) and move control cam in hydrostatic control strap until mark is centered. Lower seat deck, start engine and release parking brake. If tractor still creeps in neutral, note direction and reset parking brake. Loosen jam nut (B) on cam pivot shaft. If tractor creep was in reverse, turn adjusting nut (C) 1/8 to 1/4-turn clockwise (viewed from R.H. side). If creep was forward, turn adjusting nut 1/8 to 1/4-turn counterclockwise. Tighten jam nut and recheck adjustment.

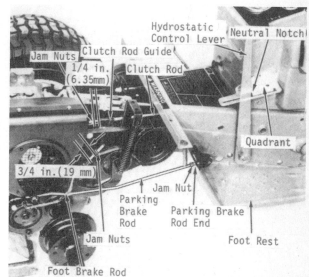

Fig. DA19 — View showing clutch and brake rod adjustments for Models 912H, 914H and 916H.

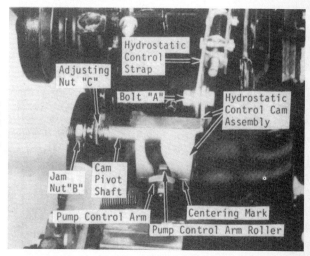

Fig. DA20 — View showing adjustment points for Models 912H, 914H and 916H with hydrostatic transmission. Refer to text for adjusting procedure.

REMOVE AND REINSTALL

Models 912H-914H-916H

To remove hydrostatic transmission, remove seat and fender assembly. Support left rear side of tractor and remove left rear wheel. Remove transmission fan, shroud and deflector. Loosen and remove drive belt, input pulley and fan. Disconnect pump control arm spring. Remove bolt, control arm roller lockwasher and nut. Remove oil filter and drain lubricant from reduction gear housing. Disconnect hydraulic hoses at oil filter assembly. Remove mounting bolts and slide transmission out of gear-case.

To reinstall transmission, reverse removal procedure. Use the following procedure to refill and prive transmission. While holding relief valve up, add recommended oil until oil is visible in filler tube. Remove spark plug wire. Raise rear wheels off the ground, set speed control lever halfway forward and crank engine. When wheels start to move, stop cranking. Reconnect spark plug wire, start and run tractor for 1-2 minutes. Stop engine and hold relief valve in up position. Add oil until oil is within ⅛ inch (3 mm) of top of filler tube. Recheck oil level after 5 hours of operation.

OVERHAUL

Models 912H-914H-916H

Models 912H, 914H and 916H are equipped with Sundstrand Series 15 "U"

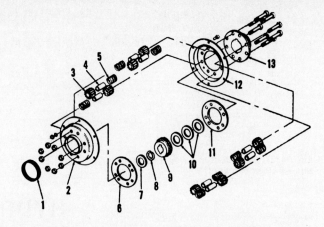

Fig. DA22—Exploded view of differential assembly.

1. Seal
2. Differential cover (R.H.)
3. Pinion
4. Spindle
5. Spring
6. Spacer plate
7. Axle washer
8. Snap ring
9. Differential gear
10. Axle washers
11. Spacer plate
12. Differential cover (L.H.)
13. Carrier

type hydrostatic transmissions. Refer to Sundstrand Series 15 "U" Type section in HYDROSTATIC TRANSMISSION SERVICE section for overhaul procedure.

GEAR REDUCTION UNIT

REMOVE AND REINSTALL

Models 912H-914H-916H

To remove gear reduction unit, support tractor under main frame just ahead of bevel gear housing. Remove seat deck and fender assembly. Drain reduction unit housing. Remove rear wheels, hubs, differential assembly and

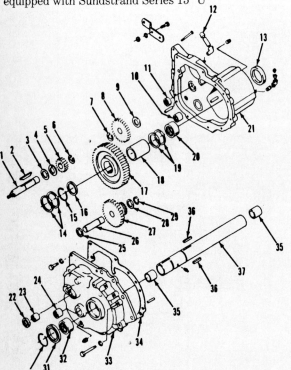

Fig. DA21—Exploded view of gear reduction unit used on Models 912H, 914H and 916H.

1. Brake shaft
2. Key
3. Washer
4. Washer
5. Gear
6. Retaining ring
7. Retaining ring
8. Gear
9. Washer
10. Bearing
11. Bearing
12. Cap
13. Seal
14. Washers
15. Retaining ring
16. Washer
17. Drive gear
18. Spacer
19. Washers
20. Bearing
21. Case
22. Seal
23. Bearing
24. Bearing
25. Washer
26. Intermediate shaft
27. Gear assy.
28. Washer
29. Retaining ring
30. Retaining ring
31. Seal
32. Bearing
33. Cover
34. Gasket
35. Bushings
36. Keys
37. Axle tube

axle shaft. Remove bevel gear pto belt pulley and disconnect pto tension spring. Support gear reduction housing and remove left side plate. Disconnect oil lines and control rod, then unbolt and remove reservoir, oil cooler, shroud and cooler fan. Unbolt and remove hydrostatic transmission and brake band. Remove cap screws securing gear reduction unit to right side plate and lift unit from tractor.

Reinstall by reversing removal procedure. Fill hydrostatic transmission and gear reduction unit as outlined under REMOVE AND REINSTALL in HYDROSTATIC TRANSMISSION section.

OVERHAUL

Models 912H-914H-916H

Remove all paint, rust or burrs from brake drum shaft (1–Fig. DA21) and axle tube (37) to prevent bearing or seal damage during removal or installation. Make certain all grease fittings and keys have been removed from axle tube. Remove cover (33), intermediate shaft (26), gear (27) and washers (25 and 28). Remove drive gear (17), axle tube (37) and thrust washers. Remove all seals from case halves. Continue disassembly as necessary.

Reassembly is reverse order of disassembly procedure. When renewing bearings, always press against end stamped with manufacturers name or number. Press bearings into housing until outside edge of bearing is flush with outside edge of small bore in housing.

DIFFERENTIAL

R&R AND OVERHAUL

Models 912H-916H

To remove differential, block up rear of tractor and remove rear wheels.

Remove set screws from left hub and remove hub and key. Loosen set screws and remove set collar and washers from axle on left side of transmission. Remove right hub, differential and axle assembly. It may be necessary to tap on the edge of differential hub to remove it from axle tube.

To disassemble differential, remove set collar from right end of axle shaft. Remove bolts from outer edge of differential case. Remove nuts from inner row of cap screws and separate case halves, leaving cap screws in position to stabilize pinions, spacers and washers (or springs). Identify all parts to aid in reassembly. The rest of disassembly is evident upon inspection of unit and reference to Fig. DA22.

Coat all parts with multipurpose grease during reassembly. Unit is lubricated with multipurpose grease through lubrication fitting on right rear hub. When reinstalling assembled unit, make sure axle and differential are properly seated so seal between differential and wheel hub is compressed. The axle is held in this position by the set collar on axle shaft at left side of transmission case.

POWER TAKE-OFF

ADJUSTMENT

Model T-811

On models equipped with pto, a spring loaded idler is used to apply tension on pto belt. Correct belt tension is maintained by adjusting idler tension spring length. Tension of idler pulley against drive belt should be sufficient to drive implement without belt slippage. Excessive tension will cause premature failure of belts and pulley bearings.

Fig. DA23—View of pto clutch used on Models 912H, 914H and 916H. Adjust clutch to obtain 1/16 inch (1.5 mm) at dimension "B."

Models 912H-914H-916H

All models use a mechanical, friction-type pto clutch. Belt tension is adjusted by changing position of idler pulley. Pto clutch is properly adjusted when clutch pulley (Fig. DA23) moves away from clutch cone 1/16 inch (1.5 mm) as shown at "B" when clutch is disengaged. Turn adjusting nuts "A" on pto clutch rod clockwise to increase pulley travel or counterclockwise to decrease travel.

R&R AND OVERHAUL

Models 912H-914H-916H

Remove drive belt from pto pulley. Remove retaining nut (15–Fig. DA24) and withdraw clutch plate (14). Protect threads on pto shaft and pry key out of shaft keyway. Pto pulley is spring loaded. Compress pulley with a C-clamp, then remove retaining ring (13). Remove pivot assembly retaining screws. Slowly release C-clamp and remove pto clutch assembly. Remove cotter pin retaining idler pivot to right side plate, then withdraw idler assembly.

Check pto shaft runout at outer retaining ring groove with a dial indicator. If runout exceeds 0.010 inch (0.254 mm), shaft should be renewed or straightened. Refer to following BEVEL GEARS paragraphs. Inspect all parts for excessive wear or other damage and renew as necessary.

Reassembly is reverse order of disassembly procedure. Be sure bearing (11) is installed with locking groove facing outward. If clutch plate retaining nut (15) is ¾ inch, tighten to 70 ft.-lbs.

(95 N·m); if ½ inch nut is used, tighten to 50 ft.-lbs. (68 N·m). Adjust clutch as previously outlined.

BEVEL GEARS

R&R AND OVERHAUL

Models 912H-914H-916H

To remove bevel gear unit, complete drive unit, pulleys and belts must first be removed. Refer to REMOVE AND REINSTALL under HYDROSTATIC TRANSMISSION paragraphs. Refer to POWER TAKE-OFF paragraphs and remove pto clutch assembly and idler pulley assembly. Remove pulley from right side of bevel gear unit. Disconnect drive shaft from bevel gear input shaft. Remove cap screws securing gearbox to side plates. Pull side plates apart and withdraw bevel gear unit.

To disassemble bevel gear unit, remove housing cover (11–Fig. DA25) and drain lubricant. Drive output shaft (16) to the left until key is free of bevel gear (18). Remove key and disengage snap ring (17) from groove in shaft. Remove bevel gear and snap ring as shaft is withdrawn from housing. Remove cap screw and bearing clamp plate (14), then bump input shaft assembly rearward out of housing. Remove cap screw (12) and washers (13) and withdraw bevel gear (10) and bearing (9) from input shaft (7). Bearings (5, 20 and 22) and oil seals (3, 19 and 23) can now be removed from housing (21).

Clean and inspect all parts and renew any showing excessive wear or other

Fig. DA24—Exploded view of pto clutch and idler pulley assembly used on Models 912H, 914H and 916H.

1. Clutch control handle
2. Control rod
3. Interlock switch
4. Brake disc
5. Spring washer (2)
6. Spacer (2)
7. Pivot assy.
8. Retaining ring
9. Spring
10. Spring guides
11. Bearing
12. Pulley
13. Retaining ring
14. Clutch plate
15. Retaining nut
16. Tensioning lever
17. Tension rod
18. Washers (4)
19. Rear idler pulley
20. Spacers
21. Front idler pulley
22. Spacer
23. Pivot arm
24. Tension spring

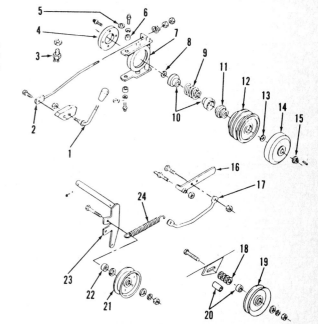

damage. Using new oil seals and gasket, reassemble by reversing disassembly procedure. Be sure to install washers (13) with concave side facing head of cap screw (12); tighten cap screw to 27 ft.-lbs. (37 N·m). Fill unit to level plug or dipstick with recommended oil.

Reinstall bevel gear unit in reverse order of removal.

ELECTRIC LIFT

OVERHAUL

Model T-811

To disassemble, remove cap screws securing electric motor (4 – Fig. DA26)

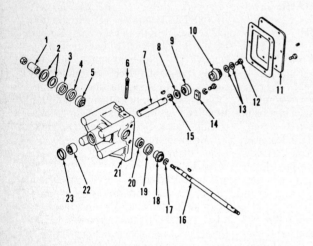

Fig. DA25 — Exploded view of bevel gear drive unit.

1. Spacer
2. Shims
3. Oil seal
4. Spacer
5. Bearing
6. Dipstick
7. Input shaft
8. Washer
9. Bearing
10. Bevel gear (drive)
11. Cover
12. Cap screw
13. Washers
14. Clamp plate
15. Retaining ring
16. Output shaft
17. Retaining ring
18. Bevel gear (driven)
19. Oil seal
20. Bearing
21. Housing
22. Bearing
23. Oil seal

to gearcase and withdraw motor. Motor is serviced as a complete unit. To remove tube assembly, remove cap screw (7) from gearcase and withdraw tube with a rotating motion. Screw and brake assembly (12) and tube (9) are serviced as an assembly.

To disassemble gearcase, unbolt and remove end cover (1) and withdraw intermediate gear assembly (2). Remove outer tube and screw assembly. Use a suitable punch to drive brake pin (6) out of clutch gear shaft (5). Using C-clamps or vise grips, compress Belleville washers and remove snap ring from clutch gear shaft. Disassemble clutch gear assembly and inspect for excessive wear or other damage. Renew complete assembly if service is required.

Reassemble by reversing removal procedure. Lubricate with multipurpose grease.

HYDRAULIC LIFT

Models 912H-914H-916H

Models 912H, 914H and 916H are equipped with hydraulic implement lift. Hydraulic power supply is provided by the hydrostatic transmission charge pump. The hydraulic cylinder is serviced as an assembly. Two different control valves have been used. Refer to Fig. DA27 and DA28. If valve spool (4) or body (3) is excessively worn or damaged, complete valve assembly must be renewed.

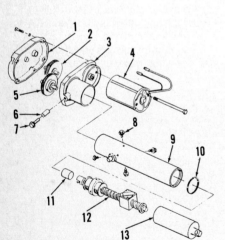

Fig. DA26 — Exploded view of typical electric lift assembly used on Model T-811.

1. Cover
2. Intermediate gear
3. Housing
4. Motor
5. Clutch gear assy.
6. Drive pin
7. Cap screw
8. Cap screw (4)
9. Outer tube
10. Seal ring
11. Sleeve
12. Screw & brake assy.
13. Inner tube

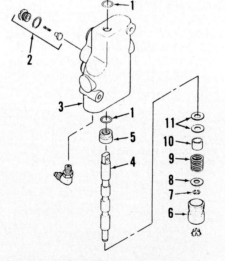

Fig. DA27 — Exploded view of CESSNA lift control valve used on some models equipped with hydraulic lift.

1. "O" rings
2. Check valve assy.
3. Valve body
4. Valve spool
5. Bushing
6. End cap
7. Retaining ring
8. Washer
9. Spring
10. Spool
11. Washers

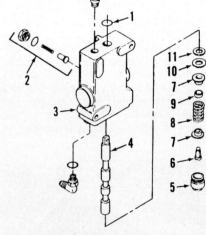

Fig. DA28 — Exploded view of AICO lift control valve used on some models.

1. "O" rings
2. Check valve assy.
3. Valve body
4. Valve spool
5. End cap
6. Spool stem
7. Spring seats
8. Spring
9. Spool stop
10. Washer
11. Quad ring

ENGINEERING PRODUCTS CO.

CONDENSED SPECIFICATIONS

	Jim Dandy			Special
Engine Make	B&S	B&S	Kohler	Kohler
Model	23DFB	243431	K321	K331
Bore	3 in.	3-1/16 in.	3½ in.	3⅝ in.
	(76.2 mm)	(77.8 m)	(88.9 mm)	(92.1 mm)
Stroke	3¼ in.	3¼ in.	3¼ in.	3¼ in.
	(82.5 mm)	(82.5 mm)	(82.5 mm)	(82.5 mm)
Piston Displacement	22.97 cu in.	23.94 cu. in.	31.27 cu. in.	33.6 cu. in.
	(376 cc)	(392 cc)	(512 cc)	(551 cc)
Horsepower	9	10	14	12.5
Slow Idle Speed – Rpm	1200	1200	1000	1000
High Idle Speed (No Load) – Rpm	3600	3600	3600	3600
Full Load Speed – Rpm	3300	3300	3300	3300
Crankcase Oil Capacity	4 pints	4 pints	4 pints	6 pints
	(1.9L)	(1.9L)	(1.9L)	(2.8L)
Weight –				
Above 32°F (0°C)		SAE 30		
0°F (–18°C) to 32°F (0°C)		SAE 10W		
Below 0°F (–18°C)		SAE 5W-20		
Transmission Oil Capacity		½ pint (0.2L)		
Weight		EP 80-90		
Final Drive Oil Capacity	¾ pint	¾ pint	¾ pint	1½ pint
	(0.3L)	(0.3L)	(0.3L)	(0.7L)
Weight		EP 80-90		
Differential Oil Capacity		2 pints (0.9L)		
Weight		EP 80-90		

	Power King			1612
Engine Make	Kohler	Kohler	Kohler	Kohler
Model	K241	K301	K321	K301
Bore	3¼ in.	3⅜ in.	3½ in.	3⅜ in.
	(82.5 mm)	(85.7 mm)	(88.9 mm)	(85.7 mm)
Stroke	2⅞ in.	3¼ in.	3¼ in.	3½ in.
	(73.0 mm)	(82.5 mm)	(82.5 mm)	(88.9 mm)
Piston Displacement	23.9 cu. in.	29.07 cu. in.	31.27 cu. in.	29.07 cu. in.
	(392 cc)	(476 cc)	(512 cc)	(476 cc)
Horsepower	10	12	14	12
Slow Idle Speed – Rpm	1000	1000	1000	1000
High Idle Speed (No Load) – Rpm	3600	3600	3600	3600
Full Load Speed – Rpm	3300	3300	3300	3300
Crankcase Oil Capacity	5 pints	5 pints	4 pints	4 pints
	(2.3L)	(2.3L)	(1.9L)	(1.9L)
Weight –				
Above 32°F (0°C)		SAE 30		
0°F (–18°C) to 32°F (0°C)		SAE 10W		
Below 0°F (–18°C)		SAE 5W-20		
Transmission Oil Capacity		½ pint (0.2L)		
Weight		EP 80-90		
Final Drive Oil Capacity		1½ pints		¾ pint
		(0.7L)		(0.3L)
Weight		EP 80-90		
Differential Oil Capacity		2 pints (0.9L)		
Weight		EP 80-90		

	Power King			
	1614	**1616**	**2414**	**2416**
Engine Make...................	Kohler	B&S	Kohler	B&S
Model...................	K321	326437	K321	326437
Bore...................	3½ in.	3-9/16 in.	3½ in.	3-9/16 in.
	(88.9 mm)	(90.5 mm)	(88.9 mm)	(90.5 mm)
Stroke...................	3¼ in.	3¼ in.	3¼ in.	3¼ in.
	(82.5 mm)	(82.5 mm)	(82.5 mm)	(82.5 mm)
Piston Displacement...................	31.27 cu. in.	32.4 cu. in.	31.27 cu. in.	32.4 cu. in.
	(512 cc)	(531 cc)	(512 cc)	(531 cc)
Horsepower...................	14	16	14	16
Slow Idle Speed – Rpm	1000	1200	1000	1200
High Idle Speed (No Load) – Rpm	3600	3600	3600	3600
Full Load Speed – Rpm...................	3300	3300	3300	3300
Crankcase Oil Capacity	4 pints (1.9L)			
Weight –				
Above 32°F (0°C)	SAE 30			
0°F (–18°C) to 32°F (0°C)	SAE 10W			
Below 0°F (–18°C)	SAE 5W-20			
Transmission Oil Capacity	½ pint (0.2L)			
Weight	EP 80-90			
Final Drive Oil Capacity...................	1½ pints (0.7L)			
Weight	EP 80-90			
Differential Oil Capacity	2 pints (0.9L)			
Weight	EP 80-90			

FRONT AXLE AND STEERING SYSTEM

AXLE MAIN MEMBER

All Models

The axle main member (4 – Fig. E1) is mounted to the main frame and pivots on stud (15). To remove front axle assembly, disconnect drag link from arm on steering spindle. Remove nut from front of pivot stud (15). Block up under front of tractor frame and move axle assembly forward off pivot stud. The two needle bearings (3) can now be removed from axle main member center bore.

TIE ROD

All Models

The tie rod (2 – Fig. E1) is adjustable on all models and front wheel toe-in should be adjusted to ⅛-inch (3 mm). Removal of tie rod is evident after examination of unit and reference to Fig. E1.

STEERING SPINDLES

All Models

To remove steering spindles (8 and 16 – Fig. E1), support axle main member and remove front wheels. Disconnect drag link from left steering spindle. Remove steering arms (5) and keys from top of steering spindles and lower steering spindles down out of axle main member. Bushings (6) and bearings (7)

can now be removed. Axle shaft (9) is removable from steering spindle.

STEERING GEAR

All Models

REMOVE AND REINSTALL. To remove steering gear assembly, first remove steering arm from steering unit. Unbolt steering gear from frame and lift

steering gear assembly from tractor. To reinstall unit, reverse removal procedure.

Early Models

OVERHAUL. To disassemble removed steering gear, remove steering wheel (2 – Fig. E2), clamp (8) and slide jacket assembly from steering shaft. Unbolt and remove side cover (16) and

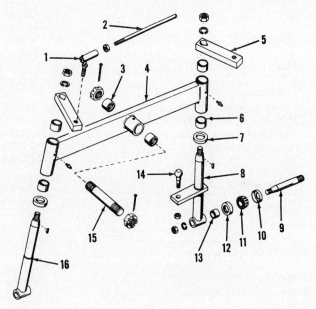

Fig. E1 – Exploded view of typical front axle assembly.

1. Tie rod end
2. Tie rod
3. Pivot bearing
4. Axle main member
5. Steering arm
6. Bushing
7. Load bearing
8. L.H. steering spindle
9. Axle shaft
10. Bearing cup
11. Bearing cone
12. Oil seal
13. Spacer
14. Ball stud
15. Axle pivot stud
16. R.H. steering spindle

withdraw levershaft assembly (18). Remove cap screws securing upper cover (9) to steering gear housing (20) and withdraw steering shaft assembly. The balance of disassembly is evident after examination of unit and reference to Fig. E2.

When reassembling, add or remove shims (10) to adjust steering shaft bearings. Steering shaft (14) should rotate freely with zero end play. Shims are available in 0.002, 0.003 and 0.010 inch thicknesses. Using a new gasket (17), install levershaft assembly and side cover. Loosen locknut and turn adjuster screw (15) to adjust the levershaft to cam backlash. Turn steering shaft from full left to full right turn to make certain unit has zero end play but does not bind when passing mid-position. To complete assembly, install jacket and bearing assembly and steering wheel. Fill steering gear to level plug with EP80-90 gear lubricant.

Late Models

OVERHAUL. To disassemble removed steering gear, first remove steering wheel. Then, unbolt and remove side cover assembly (2–Fig. E3) and withdraw levershaft (4). Remove locknut (18), lock ring (17) and adjuster plug (16). Steering shaft (13) and bearings can now be removed. Upper shaft bearing (7) can be removed from housing tube and renewed if necessary.

When reassembling, install new oil seal (9) with lip to inside. With upper shaft bearing in place, install steering shaft and bearings. Tighten adjuster plug (16) until shaft rotates freely with zero end play. Secure adjuster plug with lock ring and locknut. Install levershaft and side cover with new gasket (3). Locate levershaft in mid-position (half way between full right and full left turn). Turn adjusting screw (1) in until zero backlash is obtained and tighten locknut. Steering shaft should turn from full left to full right turn without binding. Fill steering gear housing to level plug with EP80-90 gear lubricant.

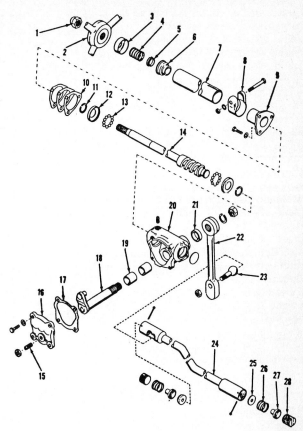

Fig. E2—Exploded view of steering gear used on early model tractors prior to S.N. 12876.

1. Acorn (cap) nut
2. Steering wheel
3. Cup
4. Spring
5. Spring seat
6. Bearing
7. Jacket
8. Clamp
9. Upper cover
10. Shims
11. Snap ring
12. Ball cup
13. Balls
14. Steering shaft
15. Adjuster screw
16. Side cover
17. Gasket
18. Levershaft
19. Bushing
20. Gear housing
21. Oil seal
22. Steering arm
23. Ball stud
24. Drag link
25. Spacer
26. Spring
27. Ball seat
28. Adjuster plug

tion wire, choke and throttle control cables from engine. Working through openings in clutch housing, remove cap screws securing engine to clutch housing; remove all set screws, located at bottom of belt groove, securing flywheel to engine crankshaft. Unbolt engine from mounting bracket, slide engine forward while prying rearward on flywheel until engine shaft is clear of flywheel, then lift engine from tractor.

Reinstall engine by reversing removal procedure.

OVERHAUL. Engine make and model are listed at beginning of section. To overhaul engine components and accessories, refer to Briggs & Stratton or Kohler sections of this manual.

CLUTCH

The clutch used on all models is a 6½ inch (165 mm), dry disc, spring loaded type.

All Models

R&R AND OVERHAUL. To remove clutch assembly, separate flywheel housing from clutch housing as follows: Shut off fuel at fuel tank and disconnect fuel line from engine. Remove hood and grille assembly. On electric start models, disconnect battery cables, starter and generator wires. If equipped with hydraulic lift, disconnect hydraulic hoses from hydraulic pump. On all models, disconnect choke and throttle control

ENGINE

All Models

REMOVE AND REINSTALL. To remove engine, first shut off fuel at fuel tank and disconnect fuel line from engine. Remove hood and grille assembly. On electric start models, disconnect battery cables, starter and generator wires and other electrical wiring as needed. On all models, disconnect igni-

Fig. E3—Exploded view of typical late model steering gear assembly. Locknut (18) differs in later production, and spring (5) and spring seat (6) are not used.

1. Adjuster screw
2. Side cover
3. Gasket
4. Levershaft
5. Spring
6. Spring seat
7. Jacket tube bearing
8. Housing & tube assy.
9. Seal
10. Steering arm
11. Ball cup
12. Balls

13. Steering shaft
14. Balls
15. Ball cup

16. Adjusting plug
17. Lockwasher
18. Locknut

cables and electrical wiring as necessary. Remove cap screws securing flywheel housing to clutch housing. Unbolt engine from mounting bracket; slide engine forward to clear clutch shaft, then lift engine from tractor.

Unbolt and remove clutch assembly from flywheel (2–Fig. E4). If necessary to remove flywheel, be sure to remove all set screws, located at bottom of pulley groove, before pulling flywheel off engine shaft. Renew seal (15) and pilot bearing (16) in flywheel if necessary.

Clutch disc lining consists of 8 segments (4 thick and 4 thin). When relining clutch disc (4), the 4 thick segments (3) must be installed on flywheel side of disc. Ball type clutch release bearing (13) can be inspected and renewed, if necessary, at this time.

Before reinstalling clutch assembly on flywheel, lubricate clutch shaft pilot bearing (16). Align clutch and clutch shaft splines by turning engine front pulley, then complete reassembly by reversing removal procedure.

TRANSMISSION

The automotive type transmission has 3 forward gears and 1 reverse. An optional tandem transmission, mounted behind regular transmission, is availabe on some models to provide 6 forward speeds and 3 reverse speeds. Tandem transmission is an exact duplicate of regular transmission.

All Models

REMOVE AND REINSTALL. To remove transmission, first separate clutch housing from flywheel housing as outlined in CLUTCH paragraph. Unbolt and remove clutch housing from front of transmission case. Remove cap screws securing front of drive shaft tube to rear of transmission case. Slide transmission forward to disconnect drive shaft splines and remove transmission from tractor.

OVERHAUL. Unbolt and remove transmission top cover and shift control assembly. Remove cap screws from input shaft bearing retainer (11–Fig. E5) and withdraw input shaft (17) and bearing assembly.

NOTE: Watch for center bearing (18), consisting of 13 rollers, as they can fall into lower part of transmission case as input shaft is removed.

Remove snap ring retaining main shaft bearing (23) in case and bump shaft out of case. Sliding gears (20 and 21) will be removed as main shaft (19) is withdrawn. Unbolt and remove lock

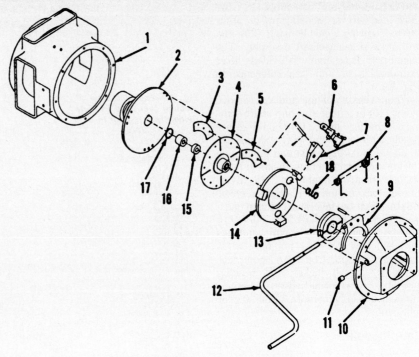

Fig. E4 — Exploded view of clutch assembly.

1. Flywheel housing
2. Flywheel
3. Clutch lining (thick)
4. Clutch disc
5. Clutch lining (thin)
6. Lever bracket
7. Lever
8. Pedal return spring
9. Release fork
10. Clutch housing
11. Pedal shaft bushing
12. Clutch pedal/shaft
13. Release bearing
14. Pressure plate
15. Oil seal
16. Pilot bearing
17. Snap ring
18. Clutch spring

1. Shift lever
2. Spring
3. Expansion plugs
4. Retaining pin
5. Transmission cover
6. Shift rail
7. Retaining pin
8. Shift fork (1st & Rev.)
9. Shift fork (2nd & 3rd)
10. Shift rail
11. Bearing retainer
12. Gasket
13. Retaining ring
14. Snap ring
15. Front bearing
16. Oil slinger
17. Input shaft
18. Center bearing
19. Main shaft
20. Sliding gear (2nd & 3rd)
21. Sliding gear (1st & Rev.)
22. Oil slinger
23. Main shaft bearing
24. Retaining rings
25. Snap ring
26. Lock plate
27. Countershaft
28. Bushings
29. Cluster gear
30. Reverse idler gear
31. Bushing
32. Idler shaft
33. Case
34. Springs
35. Balls
36. Interlock plunger
37. Plug

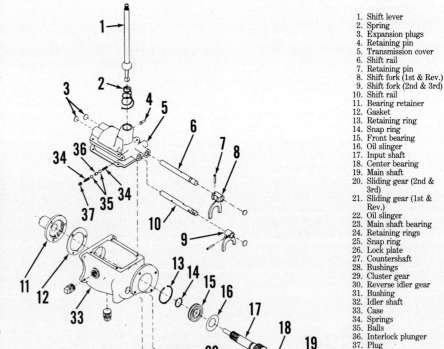

Fig. E5 — Exploded view of transmission. Tandem transmission, when furnished for extra gear reduction, is identical except for shape of shift lever.

SERVICE

plate (26) retaining idler shaft (32) and countershaft (27) in transmission case. Remove idler shaft and reverse idler gear (30) and countershaft and cluster gear (29). Drive pins from shift forks and remove expansion plugs from top cover. Remove second and third shift rail (10) and fork (9) and then, first and reverse shift rail (6) and fork (8). A poppet spring and ball are located outside each rail and an interlock plunger (36) is positioned between rails. Further disassembly procedure is evident after examination of unit.

Reassemble in reverse order of disassembly procedure. Refill transmission with ½-pint (0.2L) EP80-90 gear oil.

BRAKE

The brakes are band on drum type and are individually operated. Four different styles of brakes have been used as shown in Figs. E6, E8, E9 and E11. Early models tractors were equipped with hand brake levers located on left and right sides of tractor. Late production tractors are equipped with two brake pedals on right side of tractor.

Jim Dandy and 1612 Models

REMOVE AND REINSTALL. To remove brakes from Jim Dandy tractors prior to S.N. 16834, block up under rear of main frame and remove rear wheels. Drive pins from brake cams (20–Fig. E6) and slide pins and brake lever from bands. Expand bands (19) and remove from drums (18). The drums are integral with wheel hubs. The drums can be removed after first removing snap rings from axle outer ends. Reinstall by reversing removal procedure. On models equipped with foot pedals, adjust linkage (Fig. E7) to equalize pedal height.

On all Model 1612 and Jim Dandy models beginning with production S.N. 16834, brake drum is no longer integral with wheel hub and is mounted outboard of final drive housing on an extension of pinion shaft (24–Fig. E8). Compare Figs. E6 and E8 to identify changes. Service procedures are not greatly altered.

Power King Models and Special

REMOVE AND REINSTALL. To remove brakes from tractors prior to S.N. 52590, support rear of main frame and remove rear wheels. On models having foot brakes, disconnect pedal linkage at rear axle. Unbolt brake housing (2–Fig. E9) from final drive housing and lift off brake assembly. Drive out pin (3) and remove cap screws securing bands (6) inside housings. Brake drums (7), located on final drive pinion shafts (13), can be

removed after first removing set screws. Reinstall by reversing removal procedure. Equalize pedal height on models with foot brakes by adjusting threaded clevises on brake links (Fig. E10).

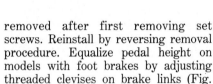

Fig. E6—Exploded view of early style (L.H.) brake assembly used on early Jim Dandy models. See Fig. E8 for newer design.

1. Needle bearing
2. Washer
3. Pinion shaft
4. Needle bearing
5. Oil seal
6. Axle tube
7. Lever knob
8. Hand lever
9. Inner bearing
10. Cover
11. Gasket
12. Snap ring
13. Drive (bull) gear
14. Key
15. Snap ring
16. Axle shaft
17. Snap ring
18. Hub & brake drum
19. Brake band
20. Brake cam
21. Oil seal
22. Outer bearing
23. Housing
24. Brake spring

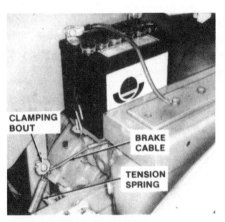

Fig. E7—Adjust brake cable length to equalize pedal height on Model 1612 and late Jim Dandy models equipped with foot pedal operated brakes.

On models beginning with S.N. 52590, brake housing (2–Fig. E9) is no longer used and operating linkage is different. Refer to Figs. E11 and E12. Service procedure is similar to early models as outlined above.

To adjust brake pedal spring tension, turn adjusting nut (5–Fig. E12) to compress or release spring (4). To adjust brake band, loosen jam nut (6) and turn adjusting nut (8) to reposition transfer block (7); turning adjusting nut clockwise tightens brake band around brake drum. Whenever transfer block is moved, stop bolt (10) must be moved an equal distance.

FINAL DRIVE

Jim Dandy-1612

REMOVE AND REINSTALL. After removing brakes as previously outlined, place a jack or blocks under differential housing. Remove cap screws securing final drive to main frame. Pull straight

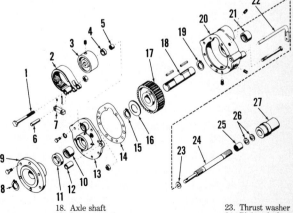

Fig. E8—Exploded view of up-to-date design brake and final drive assembly for Jim Dandy and 1612 models. Note that drum (3) is no longer part of hub (9) and that lever (22) is part of pedal linkage (not hand operated as before).

1. Band anchor bolt
2. Brake band
3. Brake drum
4. Seal
5. Pinion bearing
6. Cam pin
7. Brake cam
8. Snap ring
9. Hub
10. Outer bearing
11. Oil seal
12. Spacer
13. Cover
14. Gasket
15. Outer snap ring
16. Thrust washer
17. Bull gear
18. Axle shaft
19. Inner snap ring
20. Housing
21. Inner bearing
22. Brake lever
23. Thrust washer
24. Pinion shaft
25. Shaft bearing
26. Bearing seals
27. Axle tube

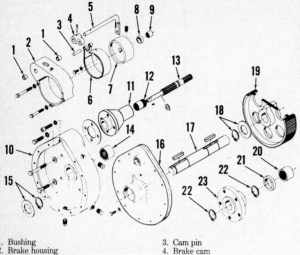

Fig. E9 — Exploded view of brake and final drive for Power King models prior to S.N. 52590. Brake lever (5) connects to pedal linkage. See Fig. E11 for latest design.

5. Brake lever
6. Brake band
7. Brake drum
8. Shaft seal
9. Pinion bearing
10. Final drive housing
11. Pinion tube
12. Bearing & seal
13. Pinion shaft
14. Axle inner bearing
15. Thrust washer & snap ring
16. Final drive cover
17. Axle shaft
18. Thrust washer & snap ring
19. Bull gear
20. Axle outer bearing
21. Oil seal
22. Snap ring (2)
23. Wheel hub

1. Bushing
2. Brake housing
3. Cam pin
4. Brake cam

REMOVE AND REINSTALL. To remove final drives, first remove brakes as covered in preceding text. Remove snap ring, wheel hub and key from axle shaft. Unbolt and remove final drive cover (16 – Fig. E9 or E11) followed by drive (bull) gear (19) and axle shaft (17). Support differential housing using a jack or blocks. Remove cap screws securing final drive housing (10) to tractor main frame and pull final drive housing straight out from differential housing. Final drive pinion shaft (13) can now be removed. Further disassembly procedures are apparent after examination of unit.

Reinstall final drive by reversing removal procedure, and refill each final drive housing with 1½ pints (0.7L) of EP80-90 gear lubricant.

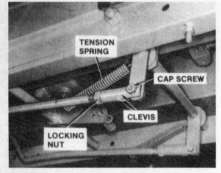

Fig. E10 — Equalize brake pedal height by adjusting threaded clevises on brake links.

out on final drive and remove assembly from tractor. Unbolt and remove final drive cover (10 – Fig. E6) or (13 – Fig. E8) and then remove drive gear (bull gear) and axle shaft. If final drive pinion shaft was not removed with final drive housing, it can be withdrawn from differential at this time.

Reinstall final drive by reversing removal procedure and refill each final drive with ¾-pint (0.3L) of EP80-90 gear lubricant.

DIFFERENTIAL

All Models

REMOVE AND REINSTALL. To remove differential assembly, first remove brakes and final drives as outlined in preceding sections. Then, unbolt and remove seat and bracket assembly. Remove cap screws which secure differential housing to drive shaft tube. Move differential assembly rearward to disconnect drive shaft splines, then lift differential from tractor. To reinstall, reverse sequence of these operations.

OVERHAUL. To disassemble removed differential assembly, unbolt and remove rear cover (22 – Fig. E13). Remove cap screws which hold bearing retainer clamps (21) and lift out ring gear and differential case assembly with side bearings (19 and 20).

IMPORTANT NOTE: Observe number and placement of adjusting shims (18) which will be needed in reassembly. In current production, side bearing adjusting shims are placed between bearing cone and differential case.

Continue disassembly by removal of lock pin and differential pinion shaft (28) followed by thrust block (31). Rotate differential side gears and remove pinion gears (30), side gears (27) and thrust washers (26 and 29). After removing nut (5) from bevel pinion (17), bump pinion rearward out of differential housing. Oil baffle (6), slinger (7), bearing cone (8), shims (10) and spacer (13) will be removed with bevel pinion. Bevel pinion bearing cups (9 and 15) and shim pack (14) can now be removed from differential housing (12).

When reassembling, adjust bevel pin-

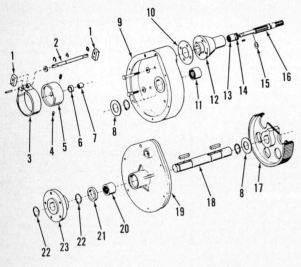

Fig. E11 — Exploded view of latest style brakes and final drive assembly used on Power King models with S.N. 52590 and after.

1. Brake cams
2. Brake shaft
3. Brake band
4. Set screw
5. Brake drum
6. Seal
7. Bearing
8. Thrust washers
9. Final drive housing
10. Gasket
11. Axle inner bearing
12. Bearing housing
13. Bearing
14. Seal
15. Thrust washer
16. Pinion shaft
17. Bull gear
18. Axle
19. Cover
20. Axle outer bearing
21. Seal
22. Snap rings
23. Wheel hub

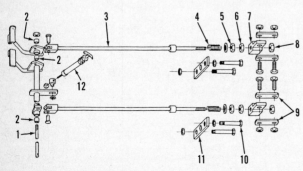

Fig. E12 — Exploded view of brake control linkage used on Power King models with S.N. 52590 and after.

1. Brake pedal shaft
2. Bushings
3. Brake link
4. Return spring
5. Adjusting nut
6. Jam nut
7. Brake transfer block
8. Adjusting nut
9. Transfer straps
10. Stop bolt
11. Support bracket
12. Park brake control

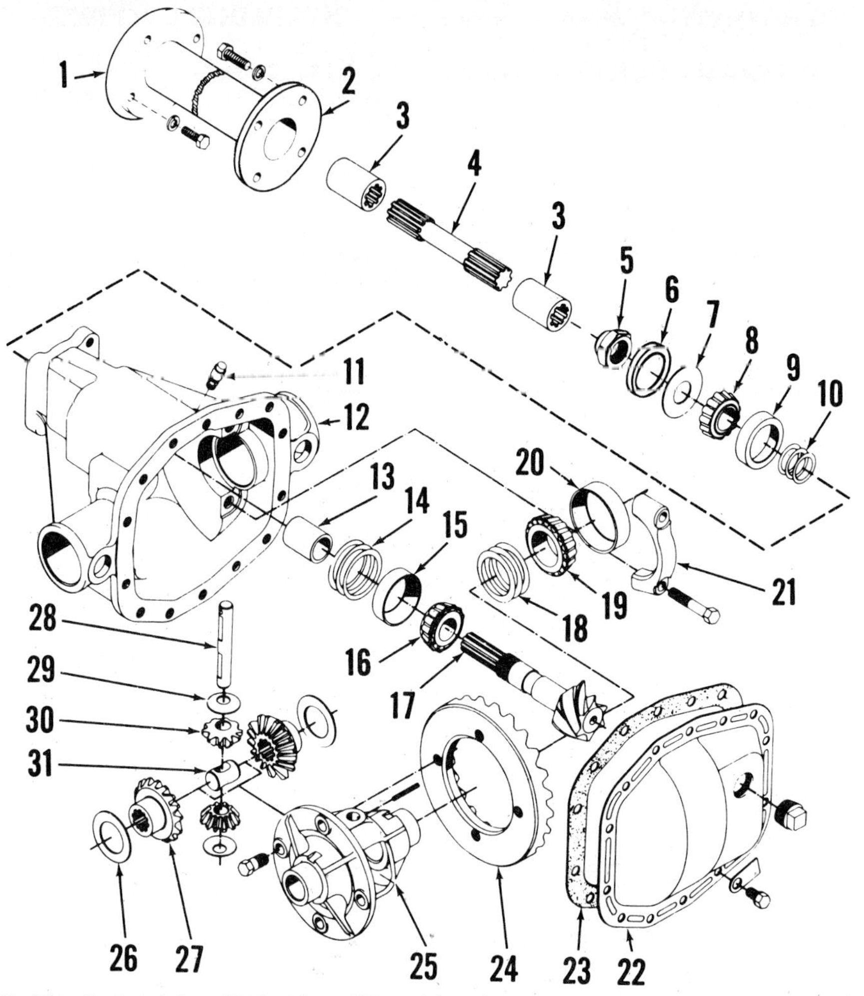

tween ring gear and pinion and adjust to approximately 0.005 inch (0.127 mm) by shifting shims (18) from one side of differential case to the other. After these adjustments are made, apply a thin coat of red lead or Prussian Blue to ring gear teeth. Then rotate gears and check tooth contact pattern by observing how coloring has been rubbed off ring gear teeth. A correct pattern is one which is well centered. If pattern is too high, move shims as necessary from forward pinion bearing position to rear bearing location. If pattern is too low on gear teeth, move shims from rear pinion bearing to forward end of pinion shaft. After pattern is confirmed as correct, it will be necessary to readjust backlash in the gearset. To complete reassembly, reverse disassembly procedure. Refill differential with two pints (0.9L) of EP80-90 gear oil.

HYDRAULIC LIFT

All Models So Equipped

Some models are equipped with a hydraulic lift system. A gear type hydraulic pump is belt driven from a pulley on engine crankshaft. Hydraulic oil or automatic transmission fluid (Dexron) should be used in hydraulic system. Capacity is approximately five quarts (4.7L). Fluid should be 1½ inches (38 mm) below top of reservoir tank with hydraulic cylinder fully retracted.

NOTE: Hydraulic system components should be cleaned before disconnecting hydraulic lines or disassembling components. Open fittings should be capped to prevent dirt from entering system.

HYDRAULIC PUMP AND DRIVE BELT

All Models So Equipped

Service parts are not available for hydraulic pump. If service is necessary, renew pump as a complete unit.

Pump drive belt tension is adjusted by adjusting position of nut (Fig. E14) on tensioning rod. Tension is correct if belt doesn't slip when system is under load;

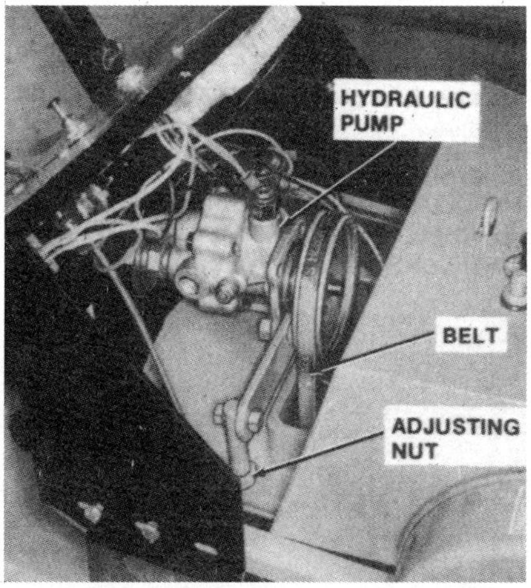

Fig. E13 — Exploded view of typical Dana differential used on all models. Principal change made in recent production is in design of drive shaft (4). Oil baffle (6) is not used on late models.

1. Gasket	11. Breather	22. Rear cover
2. Shaft tube	12. Housing	23. Gasket
3. Coupling	13. Spacer	24. Ring gear
4. Drive shaft	14. Shim pack	25. Differential case
5. Pinion nut	15. Bearing cup	26. Thrust washer
6. Oil baffle	16. Bearing cone	27. Side gear
7. Oil slinger	17. Pinion	28. Pinion shaft
8. Bearing cone	18. Shim pack	29. Thrust washer
9. Bearing cup	19. Bearing cone	30. Differential pinion
10. Shim pack	20. Bearing cup	31. Thrust block
	21. Bearing cap	

ion bearings by adding or removing shims (10) until pinion will revolve freely with zero end play. Install ring gear and differential case assembly with shim packs (18) made up to eliminate differential case side play. Check backlash be-

Fig. E14 — Hydraulic pump, on models so equipped, is mounted on top of flywheel housing. When adjusting drive belt tension, do not overtighten.

Fig. E15 — Typical wiring diagram of tractor equipped with lighting and electromagnetic pto clutch.

1. Battery
2. Solenoid
3. Starter
4. Rectifier
5. Headlights
6. Light switch
7. Magnetic clutch (pto)
8. Clutch switch
9. Seat switch
10. To ignition coil
11. Ignition switch
12. Fuse

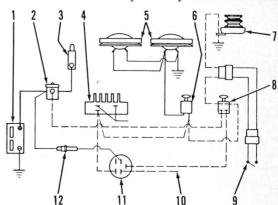

do not overtighten.

To renew drive belt, engine must be pulled forward to disengage crankshaft from flywheel. Unbolt engine from mounting bracket and clutch housing. Remove all set screws, located at bottom of pulley groove, securing flywheel to engine shaft. Pull engine forward while prying rearward on flywheel until shaft is separated from flywheel. Install new belt and recouple engine to flywheel. Ad-just belt tension as previously outlined.

HYDRAULIC CONTROL VALVE

All Models So Equipped

A single spool, four way valve is used with raise, lower, hold and float positions. A relief valve located in valve body limits system pressure to 1000 psi (6895 kPa). Valve spool and body must be renewed as a unit.

HYDRAULIC CYLINDER

All Models So Equipped

A cylinder repair kit is available to renew packing and "O" rings. To disassemble cylinder, remove snap ring from ram end of cylinder and withdraw end cap and ram from cylinder tube. Be sure to clean all parts thoroughly and lubricate packing and "O" rings with clean hydraulic oil when reassembling.

FORD

CONDENSED SPECIFICATIONS

GEAR DRIVE MODELS

	LT75	LT80	LT8
Engine Make	B&S	Kohler	B&S
Model	170702	K181S	190000
Bore	3 in.	2-15/16 in.	3 in.
	(76.2 mm)	(74.6 mm)	(76.2 mm)
Stroke	2⅜ in.	2¾ in.	2¾ in.
	(60.3 mm)	(69.8 mm)	(69.8 mm)
Piston Displacement	16.79 cu. in.	18.6 cu. in.	19.44 cu. in.
	(275 cc)	(305 cc)	(319 cc)
Horsepower	7	8	8
Slow Idle Speed – Rpm	1750	1000	1750
High Idle Speed (No Load) – Rpm	3600	3800	3700
Full Load Speed – Rpm	3250	3600	3400
Crankcase Oil Capacity	2¼ pints	2¼ pints	2¾ pints
	(1 L)	(1 L)	(1.3 L)
Weight –			
Above 32°F (0°C)		SAE 30	
0°F (–18°C) to 32°F (0°C)		SAE 10W	
Below 0°F (–18°C)		SAE 5W-20	
Transmission Oil Capacity	1½ pints	1½ pints	*
	(0.7 L)	(0.7 L)	
Weight	SAE 90 EP	SAE 90 EP	*

*Refer to LUBRICATION under TRANSAXLE paragraphs.

GEAR DRIVE MODELS

	LT100, LT110	LT11	LGT100	LGT120
Engine Make	B&S	B&S	Kohler	Kohler
Model	252707	250000	K241S	K301S
Bore	3-7/16 in.	3-7/16 in.	3¼ in.	3⅜ in.
	(87.3 mm)	(87.3 mm)	(82.5 mm)	(85.7 mm)
Stroke	2⅝ in.	2⅝ in.	2⅞ in.	3¼ in.
	(66.7 mm)	(66.7 mm)	(73.0 mm)	(82.5 mm)
Piston Displacement	24.36 cu. in.	24.36 cu. in.	23.9 cu. in.	29.07 cu. in.
	(399 cc)	(399 cc)	(392 cc)	(476 cc)
Horsepower	11	11	10	12
Slow Idle Speed – Rpm	1750	1750	1000	1000
High Idle Speed (No Load) – Rpm	3600	3600	3800	3800
Full Load Speed – Rpm	3300	3300	3600	3600
Crankcase Oil Capacity	2½ pints	2½ pints	3 pints	3 pints
	(1.2 L)	(1.2 L)	(1.4 L)	(1.4 L)
Weight –				
Above 32°F (0°C)		SAE 30		
0°F (–18°C) to 32°F (0°C)		SAE 10W		
Below 0°F (–18°C)		SAE 5W-20		
Transmission Oil Capacity	1½ pints	*	4 pints	4 pints
	(0.7L)		(1.9L)	(1.9L)
Weight	SAE 90 EP	*	SAE 90 EP	SAE 90 EP

*Refer to LUBRICATION under TRANSAXLE paragraphs.

HYDROSTATIC TRANSMISSION MODELS

	LT85	LT11H	LGT125
Engine Make	B&S	B&S	Kohler
Model	191707	250000	K341AS
Bore	3 in.	3-7/16 in.	3⅜ in.
	(76.2 mm)	(87.3 mm)	(85.7 mm)

HYDROSTATIC TRANSMISSION MODELS (Cont.)

	LT85	LT11H	LGT125
Stroke	2¾ in. (69.8 mm)	2⅝ in. (66.7 mm)	3¼ in. (82.5 mm)
Piston Displacement	19.44 cu. in. (319 cc)	24.36 cu. in. (399 cc)	29.07 cu. in. (476 cc)
Horsepower	8	11	12
Slow Idle Speed – Rpm	1750	1750	1000
High Idle Speed (No Load) – Rpm	4000	3600	3800
Full Load Speed – Rpm	3600	3300	3600
Crankcase Oil Capacity†	2¾ pints (1.3 L)	2½ pints (1.2 L)	3 pints (1.4 L)
Weight –			
Above 32°F (0°C)	SAE 30		
0°F (–18°C) to 32°F (0°C)	SAE 10W		
Below 0°F (–18°C)	SAE 5W-20		
Transmission Oil Capacity	*		
Weight	Ford M-2C41-A Fluid		
Differential Oil Capacity	2¾ pints (1.3L)	....	....
Weight	SAE 90 EP	.....	....

*Refer to LUBRICATION under HYDROSTATIC TRANSMISSION paragraphs.
†Crankcase capacity may vary between early and late models. Always fill to proper level indicated on dipstick.

HYDROSTATIC TRANSMISSION MODELS

	LGT140	LGT145	LGT165
Engine Make	Kohler	Kohler	Kohler
Model	K321S	K321AS	K341AS
Bore	3½ in. (88.9 mm)	3½ in. (88.9 mm)	3¾ in. (95.2 mm)
Stroke	3¼ in. (82.5 mm)	3¼ in. (82.5 mm)	3¼ in. (82.5 mm)
Piston Displacement	31.27 cu. in. (512 cc)	31.27 cu. in. (512 cc)	35.89 cu. in. (588 cc)
Horsepower	14	14	16
Slow Idle Speed – Rpm	1000	1000	1000
High Idle Speed (No Load) – Rpm	3800	3800	3800
Full Load Speed – Rpm	3600	3600	3600
Crankcase Oil Capacity†	4 pints (1.9 L)	3 pints (1.4 L)	3 pints (1.4 L)
Weight –			
Above 32°F (0°C)	SAE 30		
0°F (–18°C) to 32°F (0°C)	SAE 10W		
Below 0°F (–18°C)	SAE 5W-20		
Transmission Oil Capacity	*		
Weight	Ford M-2C41-A Fluid		
Differential Oil Capacity	2 pints (0.9L)	....	....
Weight	SAE 90 EP	....	....

*Refer to LUBRICATION under HYDROSTATIC TRANSMISSION paragraphs.
†Crankcase capacity may vary between early and late models. Always fill to proper level indicated on dipstick.

FRONT AXLE AND STEERING SYSTEM

AXLE MAIN MEMBER

All Models

Axle main member is center mounted to the frame and pivots on a bolt or pin riding in a tube or bushings. Refer to Figs. F1, F2, F3 or F4 for exploded view of front axle assembly. To remove front axle assembly, detach implement lift bars, if so equipped, and disconnect drag link ball joint end from steering arm. Using a suitable jack under main frame, raise front of tractor and remove pivot bolt or pin. Raise front of tractor until axle is clear of frame and roll front axle assembly from tractor.

Inspect axle pivot bushings and pivot bolt or pin for excessive wear and renew as necessary. Lubricate with multipurpose grease.

TIE ROD

All Models

To adjust tie rod for correct front wheel toe-in, disconnect tie rod ball joints from both steering spindles. Loosen locknuts and turn tie rod ends in or out as required to obtain 1/8 to 1/4 inch (3-6 mm) toe-in.

STEERING SPINDLES

All Models

To remove steering spindles, refer to Fig. F1, F2, F3 or F4. Raise and block front axle, then remove front wheels. Disconnect tie rod and drag link ball joints from spindle steering arms. Drive out roll pins, remove steering arm and lower spindles from axle main member.

Lubricate spindles with multipurpose grease. Reinstall by reversing removal procedure.

STEERING GEAR

Models LT75-LT80-LT85-LT100-LT110

R&R AND OVERHAUL To remove steering gear, remove hood, disconnect battery cables and remove battery. Disconnect drag link from steering arm (12–Fig. F5). Remove steering wheel. Drive out pin and remove pinion gear (11). Withdraw steering shaft (4). Remove steering arm and then remove quadrant gear and shaft assembly (9).

To reassemble, reverse disassembly procedure. Adjust thrust spacer (15) to eliminate excessive gear backlash, but be sure gears do not bind when turning. Lubricate steering gears with light coat of multipurpose grease.

Models LT8-LT11

R&R AND OVERHAUL. Raise and secure hood. Disconnect negative and then positive battery cables and remove

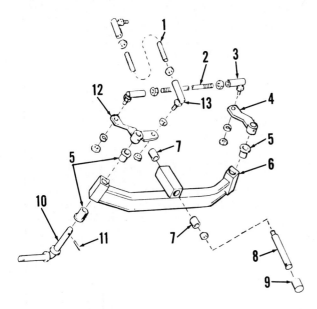

Fig. F1 – Exploded view of front axle assembly used on Models LT75, LT80, LT85, LT100 and LT110.

1. Drag link
2. Tie rod
3. Ball joint
4. Tie rod arm
5. Bushing
6. Axle main member
7. Bushing
8. Pivot bolt
9. Cap
10. Steering spindle
11. Pin
12. Steering arm
13. Ball joint

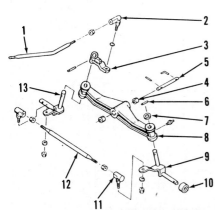

Fig. F2 – Exploded view of front axle assembly used on Models LGT100, LGT120, LGT125, LGT145 and LGT165.

1. Drag link
2. Ball joint
3. Steering arm
4. Bushing (2)
5. Pivot pin
6. Roll pin
7. Washer
8. Axle main member
9. Steering spindle (R.H.)
10. Wheel bearing
11. Ball joint
12. Tie rod
13. Steering spindle (L.H.)

Fig. F3 – Exploded view of front axle assembly used on Model LGT140 tractors.

1. Groove pin
2. Washer
3. Axle main member
4. Pivot tube
5. Pivot bolt
6. Steering arm
7. Drag link
8. Ball joint
9. Steering spindle (L.H.)
10. Tie rod
11. Steering spindle (R.H.)

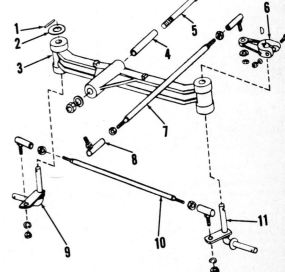

Ford

TRACTOR

battery. Remove cotter pin (12—Fig. F5A) and remove spacer (13). Loosen but do not remove the nuts from the two lower bearing retaining bolts (14). Com-

press bellows (5) to expose bolt (3). Remove bolt (3) and lift steering wheel (2), bellows cap (4) and bellows (5) off steering shaft (11). Disconnect drag link

end (8). Remove spring clip and clevis pin connecting end of speed control rod to speed control bellcrank (gear selector lever at transaxle). Remove parking brake knob, jam nut and washers. Push brake link in and allow to drop down as far as possible. Remove slotted machine screw and remove pto lever "T" handle knobs. Remove the two cap screws retaining pto support bracket at bottom side of steering and pto crossmember and work pto lever assembly out from behind the crossmember. Remove "E" clip (10) and carefully work plastic split bushing and steering sector out of crossmember. Remove bushing from steering sector. Locating tab on bushing should be aligned with slot in crossmember. Remove the four cap screws retaining steering and pto steering support crossmember between frame, rotate crossmember 90 degrees and work crossmember off of steering gear sector arm. Carefully drive top bushing on steering gear sector arm upward until unseated from frame saddle. Remove the throttle control knob. Remove the two screws attaching throttle control to instrument panel and work throttle control out slot in instrument panel. Remove necessary nuts and wire connections and remove ammeter from instrument panel. Remove the eight self-tapping screws along bottom side edges of instrument panel shroud and the two bolts (6) retaining upper bearing. Pivot front of instrument panel upward (note location of any electrical connections which may become disconnected) and lift panel off steering shaft. Pull steering shaft out of lower bearing. Remove lower bearing as required. Carefully remove steering sector assembly up out of frame.

When reinstalling steering assemblies, liberally grease gear teeth with lithium base grease (Ford part 1T-M1C137-B). Steering wheel spokes are centered with the centerline of tractor when front wheels are in the straight forward position. Gear mesh is controlled by lower bearing position and gears should mesh evenly and smoothly. Tighten bearing flange retaining bolts to 10-15 ft.-lbs. (13-20 N·m). Steering wheel play of 1½ inches (38 mm) measured at outside diameter of steering wheel is considered excessive and indicates need to adjust gear mesh or renew worn parts.

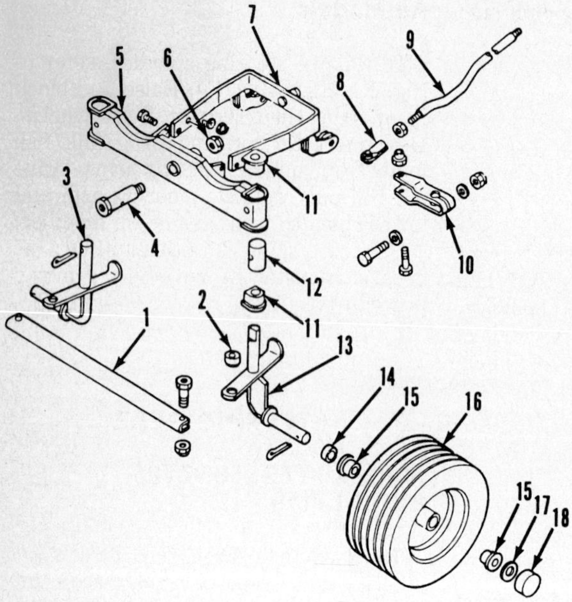

Model LT11H

R&R AND OVERHAUL. Raise and secure hood. Disconnect negative and then positive battery cables and remove battery. Remove cotter pin (12—Fig. F5A) and remove spacer (13). Loosen but do not remove the nuts from the two

Fig. F4—Exploded view of front axle used on Models LT8, LT11 and LT11H.

1. Tie bar
2. Pivot bushing
3. Right spindle
4. Pivot bolt
5. Axle main member
6. Nut
7. Pivot bracket
8. Drag link end
9. Drag link
10. Steering arm
11. Bushing
12. Spacer
13. Left spindle
14. Spacer
15. Bushing
16. Tire & hub
17. Washer
18. Dust cap

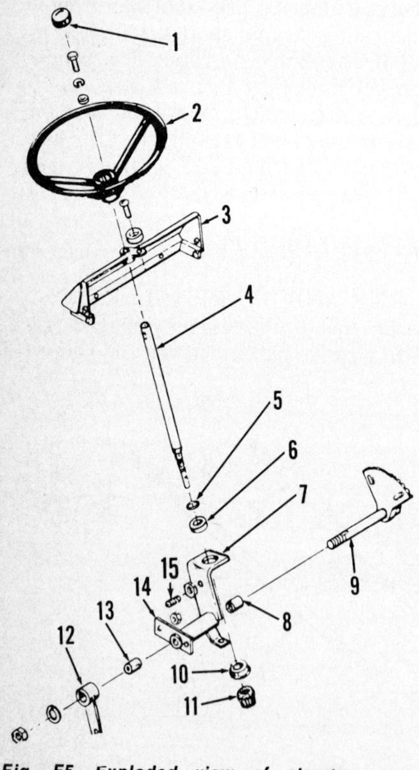

Fig. F5—Exploded view of steering gear assembly used on Models LT75, LT80, LT85, LT100 and LT110.

1. Cap
2. Steering wheel
3. Instrument panel
4. Steering shaft
5. "O" ring
6. Seal
7. Support assy.
8. Pivot bushing
9. Quadrant gear & shaft
10. Bearing
11. Pinion gear
12. Arm
13. Bushing
14. Shaft support
15. Thrust spacer

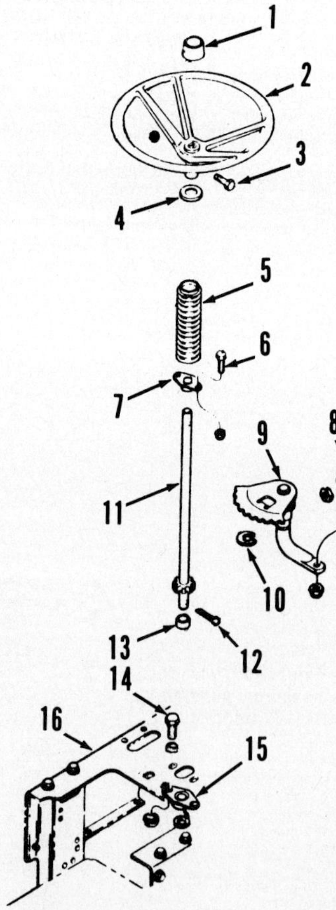

Fig. F5A—Exploded view of steering column used on Models LT8, LT11 and LT11H.

1. Cap
2. Steering wheel
3. Bolt
4. Retaining cap
5. Bellows
6. Bolt
7. Upper bearing
8. Drag link end
9. Steering sector
10. "E" clip
11. Steering shaft & gear
12. Cotter pin
13. Spacer
14. Bolt
15. Lower bearing
16. Frame

148

lower bearing retaining bolts (14). Compress bellows (5) to expose bolt (3). Remove bolt (3) and lift steering wheel (2), bellows cap (4) and bellows (5) off steering shaft (11). Turn steering wheel all the way to the right and disconnect drag link end (8). Remove the cap screw, locknut and washer holding steering arm to steering gear sector shaft and pull steering arm off of shaft. Remove the key and spacer from steering gear sector shaft. Remove the throttle control knob. Remove the two screws attaching throttle control to instrument panel and work throttle control out slot in instrument panel. Remove necessary nuts and wire connections and remove ammeter. Remove the two cap screws retaining upper bearing to instrument panel shroud. Remove the eight self-tapping screws from bottom side edges of instrument panel shroud. Lift front of instrument panel upward and over steering shaft and remove panel. Pull steering shaft out of lower bearing to remove. Push steering gear sector assembly up and out of hole in frame.

When reinstalling steering assemblies, liberally grease gear teeth with lithium base grease (Ford part 1T-M1C137-B). Steering wheel spokes are centered with

the centerline of tractor when front wheels are in the straight forward position. Gear mesh is controlled by lower bearing position and gears should mesh evenly and smoothly. Tighten bearing flange retaining bolts to 10-15 ft.-lbs. (13-20 N·m). Steering wheel play of 1½ inches (38 mm) measured at outside diameter of steering wheel is considered excessive and indicates need to adjust gear mesh or renew worn parts.

Models LGT100-LGT120-LGT125-LGT145-LGT165

REMOVE AND REINSTALL. To remove steering gear, remove hood, drive shaft and implements attached to underside of tractor which block steering gear removal. Drive out retaining pin to remove steering lever (6 – Fig. F6) from steering gear (3) shaft. Unscrew steering wheel retaining nut (1) and remove steering wheel. Unscrew mounting bolts and remove steering gear out bottom of tractor. Refer to following paragraph for steering gear overhaul.

OVERHAUL. Remove lever and shaft assembly (11 – Fig. F7). Remove cam bearing adjuster plug (17) and bump steering cam assembly (15) out of steering column. Remove and inspect bearings and races.

After unit is assembled, tighten cam adjuster plug (17) until end play is removed from steering shaft (15); but, shaft and cam must still rotate freely. Install cotter pin to prevent plug (17) from moving. Tighten inner nut (6) until steering lever (11) is 3/32 inch (2.4 mm) from housing (4). Tighten jam nut (5) against nut (6). To adjust cam follower, locate cam in mid-position (halfway between full right and full left turn) and turn cam follower screw (10) in until zero backlash is obtained. Tighten locknut (12) to hold screw in position. Steering shaft should turn from lock-to-lock without binding. Lubricate gear through

fitting on housing with multipurpose lithium grease.

Model LGT140

R&R AND OVERHAUL. To remove steering gear, first remove steering wheel (1 – Fig. F8). Raise tractor hood and loosen set screw in collar (3). Using a jack or hoist, raise front of tractor. Disconnect drag link ball joint from quadrant arm and remove retaining ring (8) and washer (7) from quadrant shaft. Quadrant shaft can now be withdrawn from bushings (6) located in main frame. Unbolt steering shaft support (10) from tractor frame and rotate support so it can be removed from frame opening. Steering shaft and pinion gear (4) can be lowered through frame opening and removed from underside of tractor. Bushings (2, 6 and 9) can now be renewed if excessive wear is evident.

Reassembly is reverse of disassembly procedure. Steering wheel play can be adjusted as follows: Loosen two bolts securing steering shaft support (10) to frame. Move support towards quadrant gear and tighten bolts. This adjustment moves pinion gear on steering shaft closer to quadrant gear, reducing backlash. Lubricate gear teeth and bushings with light coat of multipurpose grease.

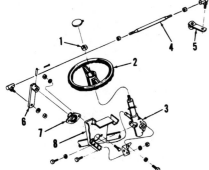

Fig. F6 – Exploded view of typical steering assembly used on Models LGT100, LGT120, LGT125, LGT145 and LGT165. Refer to Fig. F7 for view of steering gear (3).

1. Nut
2. Steering wheel
3. Steering gear
4. Drag link
5. Steering arm
6. Steering lever
7. Bearing
8. Console

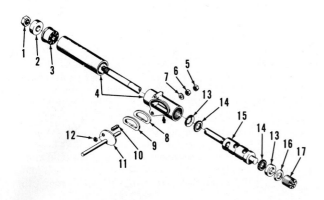

Fig. F7 – Exploded view of steering gear assembly used on Models LGT100, LGT120, LGT125, LGT125 and LGT165.

1. Nut
2. Dust seal
3. Bearing
4. Housing
5. Jam nut
6. Adjusting nut
7. Washer
8. Seal
9. Seal retainer
10. Cam follower screw
11. Lever & shaft
12. Locknut
13. Bearing race
14. Bearing
15. Steering cam & shaft
16. Belleville washer
17. Adjusting plug

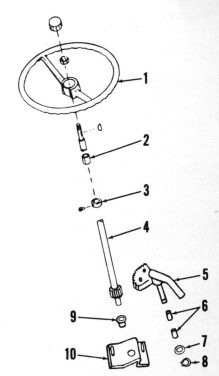

Fig. F8 – Exploded view of steering gear used on Model LGT140 tractors.

1. Steering wheel
2. Shaft upper bushing
3. Collar
4. Steering shaft
5. Quadrant
6. Bushings
7. Washer
8. Retaining rings
9. Shaft lower bushing
10. Shaft support

ENGINE

REMOVE AND REINSTALL

Models LT75-LT85

To remove engine, remove tractor hood and shut off fuel valve under tank. Pull hose from carburetor inlet fitting. Disconnect throttle cable, battery cables, ignition wire and starter solenoid lead between starter and solenoid. Disconnect black wire and yellow wire at rectifier. Disconnect pto clutch actuator rod at front end. Remove pto drive belt. Remove tractor rear cover and rear belt guide and remove main drive belt by depressing clutch pedal so tension is released on belt. Remove pulley from engine crankshaft. Unscrew mounting bolts and nuts and lift engine from tractor.

Reinstall engine by reversing removal procedure.

Model LT80

To remove engine, first remove ground cable from battery. Disconnect fuel line from tank and choke and throttle control cables from engine. Identify and disconnect ignition wires and wires from starter-generator. Unbolt and remove starter-generator. Remove left foot rest and drive belt rear guard. Remove attachment drive clutch control handle and remove thumb screw from attachment clutch housing bracket. Unbolt and remove front belt guard. Depress clutch-brake pedal and lock in down position with park brake. Unbolt engine, remove drive belt from engine pulley and lift engine from tractor.

Reinstall by reversing removal procedure and adjust drive belt as outlined in CLUTCH AND BRAKE section.

Models LT8-LT11

To remove engine, loosen cap screws retaining left and right belt guides and swing belt guides away from pulley. Remove front, upper engine pulley belt guide. Depress clutch/brake pedal and set parking brake. Work drive belt off rear transaxle pulley and front engine pulley. Disconnect the green headlight wire at connector clipped to right side of engine shroud. Remove hood retaining cable and hood. Disconnect all necessary electrical wiring and throttle cable at engine. Turn steering wheel until front wheels are as far right as possible. Remove the four cap screws retaining engine to engine base assembly and lift engine from tractor.

Reinstall engine by reversing removal procedure.

Model LT11H

To remove engine, lift seat pan and loosen traction drive brake adjustment jam nut on top, right side of frame to allow primary traction drive belt to be worked off bottom of inner jackshaft pulley. Remove belt from upper engine pulley. Disconnect green headlight wire at connector clipped to right side of engine shroud. Remove hood retaining cable and hood. Disconnect all necessary electrical wiring and throttle cable at engine. Remove the four cap screws retaining engine to engine base assembly and lift engine from tractor.

Reinstall engine by reversing removal procedure.

Models LT100-LT110-LGT100-LGT120

To remove engine, first remove ground cable from battery. Disconnect fuel line from tank, then unbolt and remove fuel tank assembly. Identify and disconnect ignition wires and wires from starter-generator. Remove starter-generator belt guard and starter-generator assembly. Disconnect choke and throttle control cables. Unbolt and remove left foot rest and drive belt rear guard. Remove attachment drive clutch control handle and remove thumb screw from attachment clutch housing bracket. Rotate housing to separate from bracket. Unbolt and remove front belt guard. Fully depress clutch-brake pedal and lock park brake to hold pedal down. Unbolt engine from tractor frame, remove drive belt from engine pulley and lift engine from tractor.

Reinstall by reversing removal procedure and adjust drive belt as outlined in CLUTCH AND BRAKE section.

Model LGT125-LGT145-LGT165

To remove engine, remove hood and disconnect battery cables, ignition and starter wires. Disconnect pto clutch wires and pto belt on models so equipped. Detach choke and throttle rods and remove drive shaft shield. Disconnect drive shaft. Drain engine oil, unscrew engine mounting bolts on underside of oil pan and lift engine out of tractor.

To install engine, reverse removal procedure. Fill oil pan with recommended oil.

Model LGT140

To remove engine assembly, raise hood and disconnect battery cables. Disconnect fuel line, then unbolt and remove fuel tank assembly. Identify and disconnect ignition wires and wires from starter-generator. Unbolt and remove belt guard and starter-generator assembly. Disconnect choke and throttle control cables. Remove left foot rest and drive belt rear guard. Disconnect pto

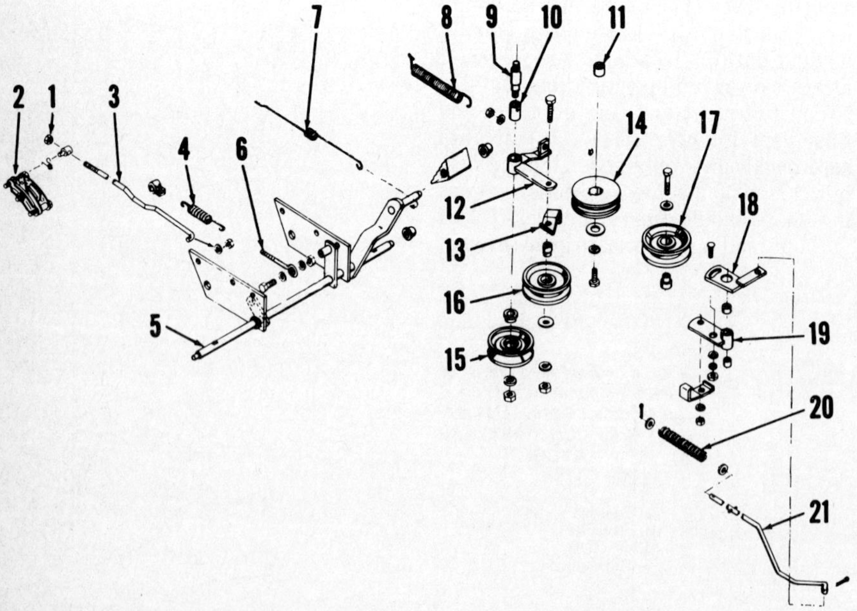

Fig. F9—Exploded view of clutch and brake assembly used on Models LT75 and LT85. Brake adjusting nut is at opposite end of control rod (3) on Model LT85.

1. Adjusting nut	7. Pedal return spring	12. Clutch idler arm	17. Pto idler pulley
2. Brake assy.	8. Spring	13. Belt retainer	18. Pto lever
3. Brake rod	9. Idler shaft	14. Engine pulley	19. Pivot lever
4. Spring	10. Bushing	15. Idler pulley	20. Spring
5. Pedal & shaft	11. Spacer	16. Clutch idler pulley	21. Pto control rod
6. Idler arm link			

clutch wires. Pull clutch cover rod outward, rotate cover and remove assembly from engine. Depress clutch-brake pedal and remove transmission drive belt from engine pulley. Unbolt and lift engine from tractor.

Reinstall by reversing removal procedure. Adjust clutch and brake as required.

OVERHAUL

All Models

Engine make and model are listed at the beginning of this section. To overhaul engine components and accessories, refer to Briggs & Stratton and Kohler sections of this manual.

CLUTCH AND BRAKE

Models LT75-LT85

ADJUSTMENT. The clutch idler pulley is spring loaded and does not require adjustment. Drive belt should be inspected for excessive wear or stretching which may result in clutch slippage. Brake should be adjusted so brake is not engaged until clutch is disengaged. To adjust brake, turn adjusting nut (1 – Fig. F9) until correct brake action is obtained.

Models LT80-LT100-LT110-LGT100-LGT120-LGT140

ADJUSTMENT. To adjust drive belt and brake linkage, first remove left foot rest and drive belt rear guard. With clutch-brake pedal in upper (clutch engaged) position, measure distance between inner sides of drive belt directly over clutch idler pulley as shown in Fig. F10. This distance must be 1⅞ to 2⅛ inches (48-54 mm). If not, loosen engine mounting bolts and move engine forward or rearward as required until proper dimension "A" is obtained.

Depress clutch-brake pedal until band is tight on brake drum and lock park brake. Measure distance (dimension "B" – Fig. F11) between flange of clutch idler pulley to lower edge of frame. This distance must be 1 to 1¼ inches (25-32 mm). If not, release brake lock and on Model LGT140, adjust nut on front of brake rod until dimension "B" is correct. On all other models, disconnect brake rod retainer from brake arm as shown in Fig. F12 and adjust retainer on brake rod to obtain correct dimension "B."

Reinstall belt guard and foot rest.

Models LT8-LT11

ADJUSTMENT. The clutch idler pulley is spring loaded and does not require adjustment. Drive belt should be inspected for excessive wear or stretching which may result in clutch slippage.

Fig. F10 – On Models LT80, LT100, LT110, LGT100, LGT120 and LGT140, clutch adjustment is correct when dimension "A" is 1⅞ to 2⅛ inches (48-54 mm) with clutch engaged.

Fig. F11 – Brake adjustment is correct when dimension "B" is 1 to 1¼ inches (25-32 mm) with clutch-brake pedal fully depressed.

Fig. F12 – View showing location and method of brake adjustment. On Model LGT140, adjustment nut is on front of brake rod. Refer to text.

To adjust brake, fully depress brake pedal. Spring on brake rod (Fig. F13) should be compressed to 2¼ inches (57 mm). Adjust by turning locknut. With pedal depressed and spring correctly adjusted, try to push tractor forward. If brake does not stop rear wheels, loosen

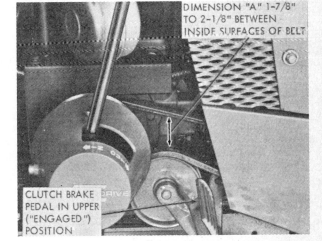

DIMENSION "A" 1-7/8" TO 2-1/8" BETWEEN INSIDE SURFACES OF BELT

CLUTCH BRAKE PEDAL IN UPPER ("ENGAGED") POSITION

PUSH PEDAL DOWN AND SET PARKING BRAKE

DIMENSION "B" 1 TO 1-1/4 INCHES

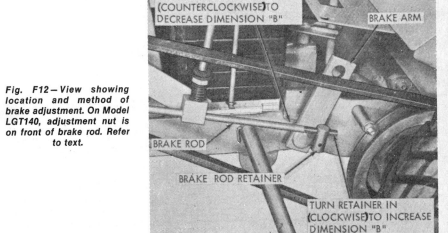

TURN RETAINER TOWARD REAR (COUNTERCLOCKWISE) TO DECREASE DIMENSION "B"

BRAKE ARM

BRAKE ROD

BRAKE ROD RETAINER

TURN RETAINER IN (CLOCKWISE) TO INCREASE DIMENSION "B"

jam nut at brake lever and tighten inner adjustment nut until rear wheels cannot be turned. Tighten jam nut against adjustment nut to 100 in.-lbs. (11 N·m). Release brake pedal. Rear wheels of tractor should be free to turn with pedal in up position. If brake pads drag with pedal in up position, loosen jam nut and adjustment nut slightly. If correct brake adjustment cannot be obtained, renew brake pads.

OVERHAUL. To renew brake pads, raise and support right rear wheel off the ground. Remove "E" ring from axle. Remove washers and right tire and wheel assembly. Disconnect brake adjustment rod from brake lever. Remove the two self-tapping screws retaining brake caliper to transaxle case noting location of spacers. Remove outer caliper half, brake pad, back-up plate and the two brake activating pins. Remove brake disc from transaxle input shaft. Remove inner brake pad from location in transaxle case.

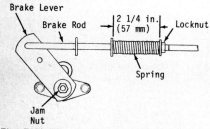

Reassembly is reverse order of disassembly. Lubricate the brake activating pins during reassembly. Tighten the two self-tapping screws to 85-110 in.-lbs. (10-12 N·m). Adjust brake as previously outlined.

Model LT11H

ADJUSTMENT. Clutch/brake pedal is designed to return hydrostatic transmission control lever to neutral position when depressed. If tractor creeps forward or backward after pedal is fully depressed, adjust linkage as outlined under ADJUSTMENT in the following HYDROSTATIC TRANSMISSION paragraphs. To adjust brakes, adjust locknut (Fig. F14) to dimension shown. Lift seat pan and rotate tow valve counterclockwise and pull up to "TOW" position. Depress brake pedal and try to push tractor forward. If tractor can be pushed forward, loosen jam nut and tighten brake adjustment nut. Continue until tractor cannot be pushed forward with brake pedal depressed. Tighten jam nut to 100 in.-lbs. (11 N·m). If correct brake adjustment cannot be obtained, brake pads must be renewed.

OVERHAUL. To renew brake pads, raise and support right rear wheel off the ground. Remove "E" ring from axle. Remove washers and right tire and wheel assembly. Disconnect brake adjustment rod from brake lever. Remove the two self-tapping screws retaining brake caliper to differential case noting location of spacers. Remove outer caliper half, brake pad, back-up plate and the two brake activating pins. Remove brake disc from differential shaft. Remove inner brake pad from location in differential case.

Reassembly is reverse order of disassembly. Lubricate the brake activating pins during reassembly. Tighten the two self-tapping screws to 85-110 in.-lbs. (10-12 N·m). Adjust brake as previously outlined.

Models LGT125-LGT145-LGT165

ADJUSTMENT. These models are not equipped with a clutch. A band type brake operates against a drum attached to a shaft extending from differential unit. Refer to Fig. F15 and turn jam nut (B) and adjusting nut (A) until desired brake adjustment is obtained. Be sure brake does not drag when brake pedal is released.

DRIVE BELT

Model LT75

REMOVE AND REINSTALL. To remove transaxle drive belt, remove cover plate at rear of tractor, depress clutch-brake pedal and set parking brake. Remove pto drive belt from lower groove of engine pulley and transaxle drive belt from upper groove. Work belt free from belt guides and idler pulleys. Remove belt from transmission input pulley. Move belt up through shift lever opening then over end of shift lever and back down through shift lever opening. Remove belt from tractor.

Install belt by reversing removal procedure. Be sure belt is not twisted and not riding on any belt guides with clutch-brake pedal released.

Model LT85

REMOVE AND REINSTALL. To remove primary drive belt, fully depress clutch-brake pedal and set parking brake. Remove belt from right angle drive pulley. Remove pto drive belt from lower groove of engine pulley and primary drive belt from upper groove. Work drive belt free from idler pulleys and belt guides and remove from tractor.

To install primary drive belt, reverse removal procedure. Be sure belt is not

Fig. F13—With brake pedal fully depressed, brake spring should measure 2¼ inches (57 mm) on Models LT8 and LT11. Refer to text.

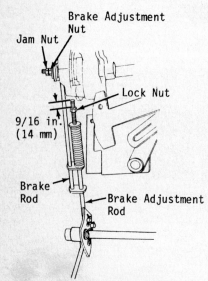

Fig. F14—Locknut on brake adjustment rod must be located 9/16 inch (14 mm) from rod end. Refer to text.

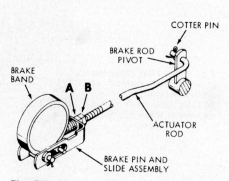

Fig. F15—View of brake assembly used on Models LGT125, LGT145 and LGT165. Adjust brake by turning adjusting nut (A) and jam nut (B).

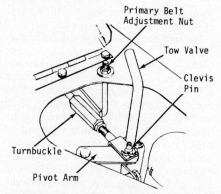

Fig. F16—View showing location of primary drive belt adjustment nuts on Model LT11H.

twisted and not riding on any belt guides when clutch is engaged.

To remove secondary drive belt, remove seat and fender assembly. Release spring tension on idler pulley and remove drive belt between right angle drive and transmission. Reverse removal procedure to reinstall belt.

Models LT8-LT11

REMOVE AND REINSTALL. To remove transaxle drive belt, depress clutch/brake pedal and set parking brake. Note position of belt guides and remove the cap screws retaining flat idler pulley and "V" idler pulley to pivot bracket. Disconnect speed control rod clevis or gear select lever (as equipped) at transaxle. Loosen left and right transaxle belt guides and swing them out of the way. Remove upper engine pulley belt guide and slip traction drive belt down and off both engine pulleys, then through lower belt guide.

When reinstalling new belt, guides must be positioned ⅛ inch (3 mm) from belt and pulley when belt is tight.

Model LT11H

REMOVE AND REINSTALL. To remove primary drive belt, lift fender and seat support up and loosen primary drive belt adjustment nuts (Fig. F16). Work belt off bottom of inner jackshaft pulley, then remove belt from engine pulley and through belt guide.

Install primary drive belt by reversing removal procedure. Belt tension should be adjusted using the primary belts adjustment nuts so light pressure on belt at a point midway between engine pulley and jackshaft pulley deflects belt 1 inch (25 mm).

To remove secondary drive belt, pull spring loaded idler down to loosen belt. Remove belt from outer jackshaft pulley and transmission pulley. Carefully work belt between the flexible fan blades and fan guard to remove.

Install secondary drive belt by reversing removal procedure.

Models LT80-LT100-LT110-LGT100-LGT120-LGT140

REMOVE AND REINSTALL. To remove transaxle drive belt, remove left foot rest and rear belt guard. On later models, remove electric pto clutch as outlined in pto clutch section. On early models, remove attachment drive clutch control handle and remove thumb screw from attachment drive clutch housing bracket. Rotate housing to separate it from bracket. On all models, unbolt and remove front belt guard. Fully depress clutch-brake pedal and lock park brake.

Loosen set screw in transaxle input pulley and slide pulley out on shaft so belt will clear upper and lower belt retainers. Remove drive belt from input pulley first and then from engine drive pulley.

Install new belt by reversing removal procedure and adjust clutch and brake as previously outlined.

DRIVE SHAFT

Models LGT125-LGT145-LGT165

REMOVE AND REINSTALL. To remove drive shaft, unbolt drive shaft front and rear couplings. Loosen set screw in front coupling and slide coupling forward on engine crankshaft. Remove flexible coupling disc, then withdraw drive shaft.

Inspect drive shaft for bending and flexible disc for excessive wear or other damage and renew as necessary. Reassemble by reversing disassembly procedure.

ELECTRIC PTO CLUTCH

All Models So Equipped

Some models are equipped with an electric pto clutch. To remove clutch, disconnect control wires at plug and remove clutch cover control rod. Allow

cover to rotate. Slip pto belt out of pulley. Unbolt and remove clutch from engine. Clutch may be renewed only as a unit.

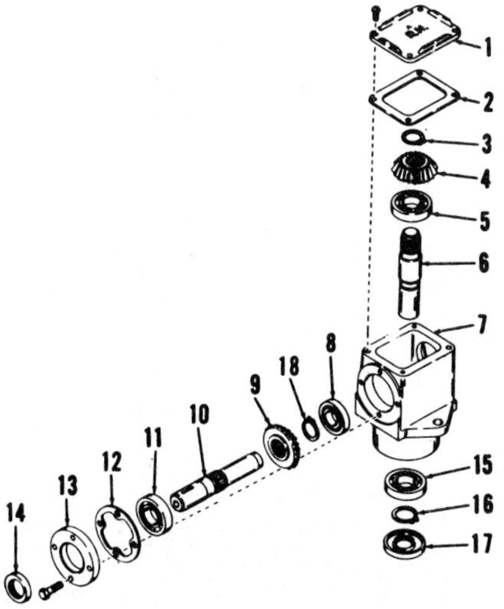

RIGHT ANGLE DRIVE UNIT

Models LT85-LGT100-LGT120

R&R AND OVERHAUL. To remove right angle drive unit, remove seat and fender assembly. Remove drive belts from right angle drive pulleys as previously outlined. Remove lower drive pulley, unscrew drive unit mounting bolts and remove right angle drive unit.

To disassemble right angle drive unit, remove cover (1–Fig. F17), gasket (2) and lubricant. Unbolt and remove seal retainer (13) with oil seal (14) and gasket (12). Withdraw output shaft (10) with bearing (11). Remove snap ring (18) and output gear (9). Remove oil seal (17) and snap ring (16). Drive input shaft (6) with gear (4) and bearing (5) out cover opening of case (7). Bearings (8 and 15) can now be removed from case. Remove snap ring (3) and remove drive gear (4) and bearing (5) from input shaft. Remove bearing (11) from output shaft (10).

Clean and inspect all parts and renew any showing excessive wear or other damage. Reassemble by reversing disassembly procedure and fill unit with 4 ounces (120 mL) of Moly EP lithium base grease.

TRANSAXLE

LUBRICATION

All Models So Equipped

Models LT75, LT80, LT100 and LT110 are equipped with a Peerless 600 series transaxle. Manufacturer recommends filling transaxle with 1½ pints (0.7 L) of SAE 90 EP gear lubricant. Models LT8 and LT11 are equipped with a Peerless 800 series transaxle. Transaxle is filled and sealed at the factory with 30 ounces (0.9 L) of lithium base grease. Models LGT100 and LGT120 are equipped with a Peerless 2300 series transaxle. Manufacturer recommends filling transaxle with 4 pints (1.9 L) of SAE 90 EP gear lubricant.

REMOVE AND REINSTALL

Model LT75

To remove transaxle, remove drive belt and disconnect gearshift lever

Fig. F17 — Exploded view of right angle drive unit used on Models LT85, LGT100 and LGT120.

1. Cover	10. Output shaft
2. Gasket	11. Bearing
3. Snap ring	12. Gasket
4. Input gear	13. Seal retainer
5. Bearing	14. Oil seal
6. Input shaft	15. Bearing
7. Case	16. Snap ring
8. Bearing	17. Oil seal
9. Output gear	18. Snap ring

spring. Place transaxle in neutral and remove shift knob. Remove rear cover at rear of tractor and belt guide. Support rear of tractor using a suitable jack or hoist. Unscrew transaxle retaining bolts and remove transaxle from tractor.

Models LT8-LT11

Remove traction drive belt as outlined under REMOVE AND REINSTALL in the previous DRIVE BELT paragraphs. Disconnect speed control lever or gear selector lever (as equipped) at transaxle. Disconnect brake adjustment rod at brake lever. Raise and support rear of tractor so wheels are off the ground. Remove "E" rings, washers and tires and wheels from each side of axle. Remove axle keys, washers and spacers. Support transaxle under case and remove the cap screws retaining left and right axle mounting brackets to frame. Remove transaxle assembly.

Reverse removal procedure to install transaxle. When reinstalling transaxle assembly, longer wheel spacer is installed on the right axle.

Models LT80-LT100-LT110-LGT100-LGT120

To remove transaxle assembly, first remove both foot rests, drive belt rear guard and brake guard. Unbolt and remove seat and fender assembly. Disconnect brake linkage, loosen set screw in input pulley, depress clutch-brake pedal, slide input pulley out on shaft and remove drive belt. Remove drawbar hitch from rear of main frame. Attach a hoist to main frame in front of transaxle and place a rolling floor jack under transaxle. Unbolt transaxle from main frame, raise tractor with hoist and roll transaxle assembly away from tractor.

Reinstall transaxle assembly by reversing removal procedure and adjust drive belt and brake as outlined in clutch and brake section.

OVERHAUL

All Models So Equipped

Models LT75, LT80, LT100 and LT110 are equipped with a Peerless 600 series transaxle. Models LT8 and LT11 are equipped with a Peerless 800 series transaxle. Models LGT100 and LGT120 are equipped with a Peerless 2300 series transaxle. Refer to the appropriate Peerless section in TRANSAXLE SERVICE section for overhaul procedure.

HYDROSTATIC TRANSMISSION

LUBRICATION

Models LT85-LGT125-LGT145-LGT165

Hydrostatic transmission on Model LT85 is lubricated by oil contained in transmission reservoir. Reservoir should be filled with tractor level, until oil reaches lower lip of reservoir as shown in Fig. F21.

Model LGT125, LGT145 and LGT165 hydrostatic transmission shares a common reservoir with differential unit. Fill differential through fill plug opening (F – Fig. F22) until oil reaches level of plug (L). Recommended transmission oil for all models is Ford M-2C41-A or equivalent.

On Models LGT125, LGT145 and LGT165, transmission oil is routed through an external oil filter (9 – Fig. F23). Manufacturer recommends renewing filter after first 10 hours of operation. Additional filter renewal is not required unless system is contaminated due to servicing or other means.

Model LT11H

Hydrostatic transmission is separate from differential unit on Model LT11H and transmission uses different fluid than the differential unit.

Refer to Fig. F24 to check transmission fluid level when unit is hot or cold. To fill unit, remove filler cap and bleed plug and add SAE 20 detergent oil through filler tube until oil level is at top of air bleed plug opening. Install plug and continue to add oil through filler tube until oil is at the "cold" level line on filler tube.

Differential unit oil level should be at lower edge of oil level plug opening (Fig. F24). Manufacturer recommends SAE

90 EP gear lubricant. Approximate capacity is 2¾ pints (1.3 L).

Model LGT140

Hydrostatic transmission oil level is checked at filler plug located under trac-

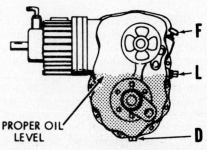

Fig. F22 – Fill rear end unit of Models LGT125, LGT145 and LGT165 through fill hole (F) until oil reaches level of plug hole (L). Drain oil by removing drain plug (D).

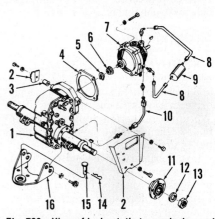

Fig. F23 – View of hydrostatic transmission and gear reduction unit on Models LGT125, LGT145 and LGT165.

1. Gear reduction & differential	8. Hydraulic line
2. Frame	9. Filter
3. Spacer	10. Suction hydraulic line
4. Gasket	11. Axle flange
5. Snap ring	12. Lockwasher
6. Pinion	13. Nut
7. Hydrostatic transmission	14. Hairpin cotter
	15. Clevis pin
	16. Hitch plate

Fig. F21 – Fill hydrostatic transmission reservoir and differential on Model LT85 to levels shown by dotted lines. Refer to text and specifications for type of oil.

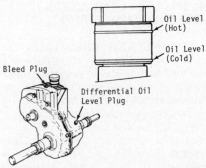

Fig. F24 – On Model LT11H, refer to text for procedures to obtain correct transmission and differential oil level.

tor seat. Oil level should be ½ to 1 inch (13-25 mm) below bottom edge of filler hole. Recommended transmission oil is Ford M-2C41-A or equivalent.

LINKAGE ADJUSTMENT

Model LT85

To adjust hydrostatic transmission linkage, remove cover screen at rear of tractor. Refer to Fig. F25 and turn adjusting nuts on speed control rod where it is attached to speed control arm. Moving adjusting nuts towards front of tractor will increase forward speed while turning nuts in opposite direction will increase reverse speed.

If tractor creeps in neutral, block up tractor so rear wheels do not touch ground. Place speed control lever in neutral position and start engine. Turn adjusting nuts (A and B – Fig. F25) to increase or decrease spring tension against speed control arm until rear wheels remain stationary. Secure adjusting nuts when neutral position is found.

Model LT11H

To check neutral adjustment, start tractor and allow to reach operating temperature. With tractor moving in a forward direction, depress clutch/brake pedal. With tractor moving in a reverse direction, depress clutch/brake pedal. When clutch/brake pedal is depressed, all forward or reverse motion should stop and drive lever should return to neutral position.

To adjust hydrostatic drive lever, position tractor on a level surface. Raise and support left rear wheel off the ground. Disconnect brake adjustment rod at

parking brake ratchet assembly by removing cotter pin. Loosen bolts retaining neutral finger spring bracket (Fig. F26) on left side of differential. Place drive lever in forward position, then fully depress clutch/brake pedal and set parking brake latch. This will set drive lever in neutral position. DO NOT move this lever again during adjustment procedure. Disconnect seat restraint cable and raise fender and seat support. Disconnect clevis attached to turnbuckle from the pivot arm. Lower seat support. Block wheels of tractor to prevent tractor movement. Start engine. Move control arm in conjunction with neutral finger spring and bracket forward or backward until left rear wheel stops turning. Make certain finger is in control arm notch as shown in inset of Fig. F26. Tighten bolts to secure bracket in this position. Stop engine. Loosen jam nut on turnbuckle and turn turnbuckle as required to align hole in clevis with hole in pivot arm. DO NOT move pivot arm to align holes or allow neutral finger spring to slip from notch. With holes aligned, insert pin and secure with cotter pin. Tighten jam nut on turnbuckle. Start engine and recheck neutral lever adjustment.

Model LGT125-LGT145-LGT165

When transmission control lever is in "NEUTRAL" position, tractor should not move either forward or backward. Be sure transmission has been warmed by at least 15 minutes of operation before checking transmission performance. If tractor will not remain stationary with control lever in "NEUTRAL" position, transmission linkage must be adjusted as follows.

Raise rear of tractor so rear wheels may rotate freely. Be sure tractor is blocked to prevent rolling. Refer to Fig.

F27 and loosen nuts (A) and (B). Turn stud (C) towards rear of tractor if tractor creeps forward or towards front of tractor if tractor creeps backward. Tighten nuts (A) and (B) and check transmission operation.

Model LGT140

If tractor creeps in either direction when control lever is in neutral position, adjust control lever linkage as follows: Jack up rear of tractor to allow both rear wheels to rotate freely. Fully depress clutch-brake pedal and apply park brake lock. Loosen set screw on side of drive-no drive control knob and remove knob. Unbolt and remove seat and seat apron. Remove hairpin cotter shown in Fig. F28 from ball joint rod. Slide ball joint rod from control arm and remove bushing. Locate neutral position of transmission speed arm by moving speed arm up and down until a clicking sound is heard as arm locks in neutral notch. Move speed control lever to its neutral lock position. Start tractor engine and make sure rear wheels do not rotate. Loosen locknut on ball joint and turn rod in or out of ball joint until rod end and bushing can be inserted into hole in control arm. Install hairpin cot-

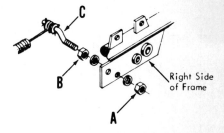

Fig. F27—Loosen nuts (A and B) and turn stud (C) as indicated in text to adjust transmission linkage on Models LGT125, LGT145 and LGT165.

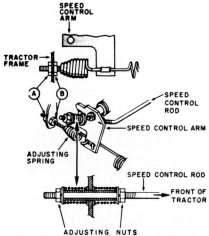

Fig. F25—Views of speed control arm and adjusting nuts on Model LT85 hydrostatic transmission. Refer to text for adjustment.

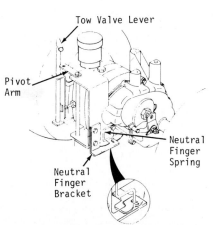

Fig. F26—Neutral finger spring must remain in control arm notch (see inset) during adjustment procedure.

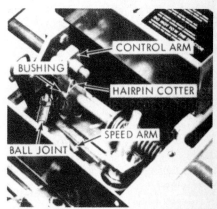

Fig. F28—View showing location of hydrostatic transmission control linkage adjustment on Model LGT140.

ter and tighten locknut on ball joint. Reinstall seat, seat apron and drive-no drive knob.

REMOVE AND REINSTALL

Model LT85

To remove hydrostatic transmission, remove seat and fender assembly and remove transmission drive belt by releasing spring tension against idler pulley. Remove cover at rear of tractor and disconnect speed control rod shown in Fig. F25 from speed control arm. Disconnect springs from speed control arm. Remove brake assembly from brake disc. Support rear of tractor, unscrew axle mounting bolts and remove transmission and differential from tractor. Drain lubricant from differential and separate transmission from differential.

To reinstall transmission, reverse removal procedure. Refill differential with 2¾ pints (1.3 L) of SAE 90 EP gear oil. Adjust speed control linkage and brake as previously outlined.

Model LT11H

To remove transmission and differential assembly, raise and support right wheel of tractor off the ground. Remove right wheel assembly. Remove the three cap screws retaining fan guard, remove fan guard and fan, then reinstall the three cap screws to maintain torque bracket alignment. Temporarily

reinstall right wheel. Disconnect shift lever clevis (Fig. F16) at transmission. Remove rear hitch plate from between main frame. Pull spring loaded idler pulley down and work secondary drive belt off transmission input pulley and idler pulley. Disconnect brake adjustment rod at brake lever. Remove the two locknuts on left and right "U" bolts retaining axle housings to support brackets. Support transmission and remove the three cap screws retaining differential to torque bracket. Raise and support rear main frame and pull differential/transmission assembly out and away from tractor. Remove tire and wheel assemblies. Remove the four cap screws retaining transmission to differential and separate transmission from differential.

Reinstall transmission/differential assembly by reversing removal procedure. Transmission should be filled with approximately 22 ounces (651 mL) of SAE 20 detergent oil. Differential should be filled with approximately 2¾ pints (1.3 L) of SAE 90 EP gear oil.

Model LGT125-LGT145-LGT165

To remove hydrostatic transmission, remove pedals on transmission (16 and 17 – Fig. F29) and brake levers. Detach reverse pedal (19) from transmission lever (15). Unscrew speed range lever (12) and parking brake shaft (7) knobs. Remove rear seat and fender assembly from tractor frame. Disconnect hydrau-

lic hoses to transmission and detach control lever (23) from transmission shaft. Plug openings in transmission and hoses. Remove drive shaft as previously outlined, unscrew mounting bolts and remove transmission.

To reinstall transmission, reverse removal procedure. Refill differential as outlined under LUBRICATION paragraphs.

Model LGT140

To remove hydrostatic drive unit, place a rolling floor jack under reduction-differential housing and raise rear of tractor. Remove rear wheel assemblies. Remove battery cover and battery. Loosen set screw in drive-no drive knob and remove knob. Unbolt and remove seat assembly with seat apron. Remove left foot rest and drive belt rear guard. Depress clutch pedal and remove drive belt. Disconnect and remove brake rear linkage and brake band. Disconnect transmission control linkage at ball joint link. Unbolt and remove hydrostatic drive unit and reduction drive and differential assembly from tractor.

Remove three attaching cap screws and lift hydrostatic unit from reduction and differential assembly.

Reinstall unit by reversing removal procedure. Then, adjust brake and drive as outlined in CLUTCH AND BRAKE section and transmission control linkage as previously outlined.

OVERHAUL

All Models So Equipped

Models LT11H and LT85 are equipped with an Eaton Model 6 hydrostatic transmission. Models LGT125, LGT145 and LGT165 are equipped with an Eaton Model 10 hydrostatic transmission. Model LGT140 is equipped with a Sundstrand "Hydrogear" type hydrostatic transmission. Refer to the appropriate Eaton or Sundstrand section in HYDROSTATIC TRANSMISSION SERVICE section for overhaul procedure.

REDUCTION GEARS AND DIFFERENTIAL

R&R AND OVERHAUL

Model LT85-LT11H

To remove reduction gear and differential unit, refer to transmission section and remove transmission and differen-

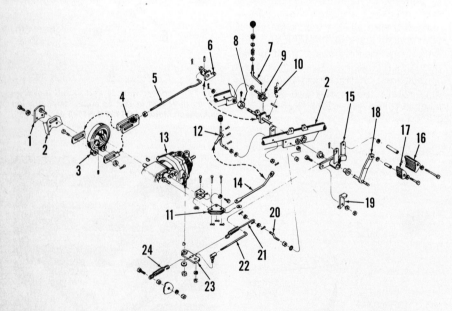

Fig. F29 – View of transmission and brake control linkage on Models LGT125, LGT145 and LGT165.

1. Brake mount	8. Collar	14. Dual range rod	20. Stud
2. Frame	9. Parking brake pawl	15. Transmission control	21. Spring
3. Brake band & drum	10. Spring	levers	22. Transmission control
4. Bracket	11. Bellcrank	16. Forward pedal	rod
5. Brake rod	12. Dual range selector	17. Brake pedal	23. Transmission control
6. Brake arm & sector	13. Transmission & rear	18. Brake lever	arm
7. Parking brake	end	19. Reverse pedal	24. Spring

tial assembly. Remove wheel and hub assemblies from axles. Drain differential lubricant and separate transmission from differential. Remove brake disc from brake shaft. Clean axle shafts and remove any burrs on shafts. Unscrew cap screws and drive out dowel pins in cover (29 – Fig. F38). Lift cover off case and axle shaft. Withdraw brake shaft (5), idler gear (4) and thrust washers (3 and 6) from case. Remove output shaft (11), output gear (10), spacer (9), thrust washer (8) and differential assembly from case. Axle shaft housings (20 and 22) must be pressed from case and cover.

To disassemble differential, unscrew four cap screws (17) and separate axle shaft and carriage assemblies from ring gear (28). Drive blocks (25), bevel pinion gears (26) and drive pin (27) can now be

removed from ring gear. Remove snap rings (12) and slide axle shafts (18 and 23) from axle gears (13) and carriages (16 and 24).

Clean and inspect all parts and renew any parts damaged or excessively worn. When installing needle bearings, press bearings in from inside of case or cover until bearings are 0.015-0.020 inch (0.381-0.508 mm) below thrust surfaces. Be sure heads of differential cap screws (17) and left axle shaft (18) are installed in left carriage housing (16) Left axle shaft is installed through case (1). Tighten differential cap screws to 7 ft.-lbs. (9 N·m) and cover cap screws to 10 ft.-lbs. (14 N·m). Differential assembly and output shaft (11) must be installed in case at same time. Remainder of assembly is reverse of disassembly procedure. After installation, fill reduc-

tion gear and differential assembly with 2¾ pints (1.3 L) of SAE 90 EP gear oil.

Models LGT125-LGT145-LGT165

These tractors are equipped with a dual-range gear reduction assembly which drives through a limited slip differential. To remove gear reduction and differential unit, remove hydrostatic transmission as previously outlined. Drain oil from unit, remove brake assembly and detach dual-range shift linkage. Support rear of tractor and remove bolts securing reduction and differential unit to tractor. Raise rear of tractor and roll unit from tractor. Remove wheels and clean exterior of unit.

To disassemble, remove axle housings (15 – Fig. F39). Position unit with cover up and remove cover (13). Lift out differential assembly and axles (40 through 54). Remove output shaft (36), gear (35) and thrust washers (34 and 37). Unscrew set screw (2) and remove spring (3) and ball (4). Remove brake shaft (32), sliding gear (33) and shift fork (10) and rod (8). Remove input shaft and gear components (18 through 25).

To disassemble differential assembly, remove cap screws (53) and remove differential carriers (41 and 52) and axles from ring gear assembly. Remove snap ring to separate axle gear, carrier and axle. Remove pinions (47) and separate body cores (45 and 48) from ring gear (46).

Inspect components for damage or excessive wear. To reassemble unit, reverse disassembly procedure. Check movement of shift rod when tightening set screw (2). Install gears (22 and 25) so bevels of gears face together as shown in Fig. F40. Install carrier cap screws (53 – Fig. F39) so head of cap screw is on side of shorter carrier (52). Do not rotate axle housings after housing has been pressed tight against seal (11) as seal may be cut.

Fill unit with Ford M-2C41-A oil or equivalent and allow fluid to seep past roller bearings into axle housings. Recheck fluid level and add fluid to correct level at check plug opening in case.

Install unit in tractor by reversing removal procedure. Adjust brake linkage.

Model LGT140

Remove reduction gear and differential assembly as outlined in transmission section.

Drain unit, then loosen set screws and remove brake drum and wheel hubs. If not previously removed, unbolt and remove drawbar hitch and bracket assembly. Remove coupling (8 – Fig. F41) from input shaft. Unbolt and

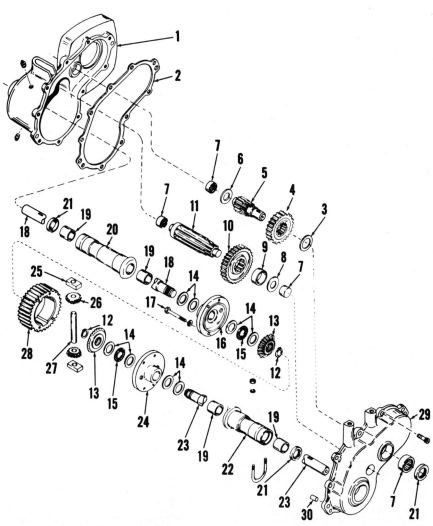

Fig. F38 – Exploded view of gear reduction and differential unit used on Models LT85 and LT11H.

1. Case	9. Spacer	16. Differential carrier	23. Axle shaft (R.H.)
2. Gasket	10. Output gear	17. Bolt	24. Differential carrier
3. Washer	11. Output shaft	18. Axle shaft (L.H.)	25. Drive block
4. Idler gear	12. Snap ring	19. Bushing	26. Drive pinion
5. Brake shaft	13. Side gears	20. Axle housing	27. Drive pin
6. Washer	14. Thrust washers	21. Oil seal	28. Ring gear
7. Bearing	15. Thrust bearing	22. Axle housing	29. Cover
8. Washer			30. Dowel pin

remove axle housings (14 and 37). Remove seal retainers (11) with oil seals (12) and "O" rings (13) by pulling each axle shaft out of case and cover as far as possible. Place unit on the edge of a bench with left axle shaft (40) pointing downward. Remove cap screws securing cover (9) to case (39). Drive aligning dowels out of cover, then lift cover from case. Withdraw differential and axle assembly and lay aside for later disassembly. Remove output gear and shaft (24 and 25) with thrust washers (23 and 26). Remove input shaft (3) with thrust washers (2 and 4), then withdraw idler gear and shaft (17 and 18) with spacer (19) and thrust washers (16 and 20).

To disassemble differential, remove four cap screws and separate axle assemblies from body cores (41). Using suitable snap ring pliers, remove cylindrical spring (43). Pinion gears (28) can now be removed from body cores. Separate body cores from ring gear (42). Remove snap ring (29) at end of axle and disassemble axle assembly.

Clean and inspect all parts and renew any showing excessive wear or other damage. When installing new needle bearings, press carrier bearings (10) in from inside of case and cover until bearings are 0.290 inch (7.366 mm) below face of axle housing mounting surface. All other needle bearings are to be

pressed in from inside of case and cover to a depth of 0.015-0.020 inch (0.381-0.508 mm) below thrust washer surfaces.

To reassemble differential, install body cores (41) in ring gear (42) so gear pockets in one core are out of alignment with gear pockets in other core. Reassemble axle assemblies. Install pinion gears (28) in one body core, then hold pinion gears in core by installing differential carrier and axle assembly and turn differential cover. Be sure pinion gears mesh with side gear. Install pinion gears in other body core being sure gears mesh with previously installed pinion gears. Install cylindrical spring (43) so it bottoms against side gear. Spring should be in contact with most of the ten pinion gears. Install axle assembly and differential retaining bolts. Tighten bolts to 7-10 ft.-lbs. (9-14 N·m).

Reassemble remainder of unit by reversing disassembly procedure. Renew gasket (6), "O" rings (13) and oil seals (12) during reassembly and install new oil seals (7 and 38) after unit is assembled. Tighten cover to case cap screws to 10 ft.-lbs. (14 N·m) and axle housing cap screws to 13 ft.-lbs. (18 N·m).

Fill reduction gear and differential assembly, after unit is installed on tractor, to level plug opening with SAE 90 EP gear oil.

HYDRAULIC LIFT

All Models So Equipped

OPERATION. The hydraulic implement lift receives hydraulic power supply from hydrostatic transmission charge pump. A single spool, open center control valve directs fluid to a double-acting hydraulic cylinder. The control valve is equipped with an adjustable relief valve that limits system pressure at approximately 600 psi (4137 kPa). Seal repair kits are only service parts available for control valve and hydraulic cylinder.

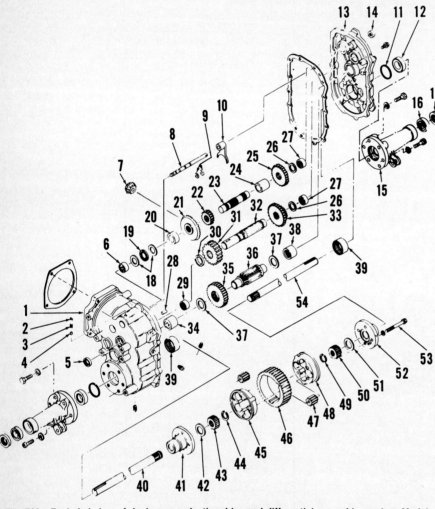

Fig. F39 — Exploded view of dual-range reduction drive and differential assembly used on Models LGT125, LGT145 and LGT165.

1. Case	14. Seal	28. Dowel pin
2. Set screw	15. Axle housing	29. Needle bearing
3. Spring	16. Ball bearing	30. Spacer
4. Ball	17. Seal	31. Gear (17T)
5. Seal	18. Thrust washers	32. Brake shaft
6. Needle bearing	19. Thrust bearing	33. Sliding gears
7. Transmission output gear	20. Spacer	34. Needle bearing
8. Shift rail	21. Bevel gear	35. Gear (33T)
9. Snap rings	22. Gear (low range)	36. Output shaft
10. Shift fork	23. Shaft	37. Thrust washer
11. Quad ring	24. Spacer	38. Needle bearing
12. Tapered roller bearing	25. Gear (high range)	39. Needle bearing
13. Cover	26. Thrust washer	40. Axle shaft (L.H.)
	27. Needle bearing	41. Differential carrier (L.H.)

42. Thrust washer	
43. Axle gear	
44. Snap ring	
45. Body core	
46. Ring gear	
47. Pinion gears (8)	
48. Body core	
49. Snap ring	
50. Axle gear	
51. Thrust washer	
52. Differential carrier (R.H.)	
53. Cap screw	
54. Axle shaft (R.H.)	

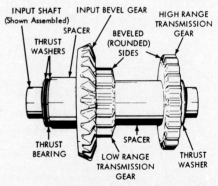

Fig. F40 — View of input shaft and gears. Note position of bevels on gears.

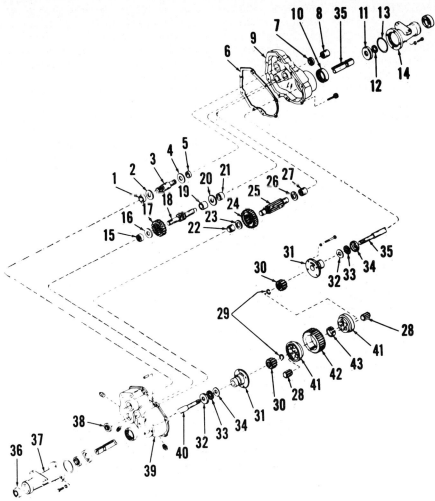

TESTING. When checking relief valve pressure setting, hydraulic fluid must be at normal operating temperature. Shut off engine and relieve hydraulic pressure in system. Using a ¼ inch tee fitting, install a 0-1000 psi (0-7000 kPa) pressure gage in piston end of hydraulic cylinder. With engine speed at high idle, operate hydraulic control lever to move piston to end of its stroke and observe pressure gage reading. Pressure should be approximately 600 psi (4137 kPa). If necessary, adjust system relief valve, located in control valve, to obtain desired system pressure. If 600 psi (4137 kPa) operating pressure can not be attained, check the following: Low hydraulic fluid level, hydraulic filter plugged, defective relief valve, restriction in hydraulic line, charge pump worn.

CONTROL VALVE. A single spool, open center control valve equipped with an integral pressure relief valve is used. Refer to Fig. F42. Seal repair kit is only service part available.

To remove valve, raise hood and remove side panels and battery. Clean exterior of valve, then disconnect and remove valve. Plug all openings to prevent entry of dirt.

To disassemble valve, remove end cap (18–Fig. F42) and withdraw spool assembly from valve body. Remove acorn nut (1), loosen jam nut (3) and remove relief valve assembly.

Clean and inspect all parts for wear or other damage. Complete valve assembly

Fig. F41—Exploded view of reduction drive and differential assembly used on Model LGT140.

1. Needle bearing	22. Needle bearing	33. Thrust bearing
2. Thrust washer	23. Thrust washer	34. Thrust washer
3. Input shaft	24. Output gear	35. Axle shaft (R.H.)
4. Thrust washer	25. Output shaft	36. Axle ball bearing
5. Needle bearing	26. Thrust washer	37. Axle housing (L.H.)
6. Gasket	27. Needle bearing	38. Oil seal
7. Oil seal	28. Pinion gear	39. Case
8. Coupling	29. Snap ring	40. Axle shaft (L.H.)
9. Cover	30. Side gear	41. Body core
10. Carrier bearing	31. Differential carrier	42. Ring gear
11. Seal retainer	32. Thrust washer	43. Cylindrical spring
12. Oil seal		
13. "O" ring		
14. Axle housing (R.H.)		
15. Needle bearing		
16. Thrust washer		
17. Idler gear		
18. Brake shaft		
19. Spacer		
20. Thrust washer		
21. Needle bearing		

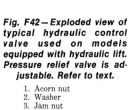

Fig. F42—Exploded view of typical hydraulic control valve used on models equipped with hydraulic lift. Pressure relief valve is adjustable. Refer to text.

1. Acorn nut
2. Washer
3. Jam nut
4. Adjusting screw
5. Washer
6. Spring
7. Ball retainer
8. Ball
9. Seat
10. Valve body
11. Spool
12. "O" rings
13. Washer
14. Centering spring
15. Cup
16. Washer
17. Screw
18. End cap

Fig. F43—Exploded view of typical hydraulic lift cylinder used on models so equipped.

1. Cylinder tube	8. Seal
2. Nut	9. Back-up ring
3. Piston	10. "O" ring
4. "O" ring	11. Rod guide
5. Back-up rings	12. "O" ring
6. "O" ring	13. Rod
7. Snap ring	

must be renewed if service is necessary. Reassemble valve using new "O" ring seals. Coat all parts with clean hydraulic oil prior to assembly. Thread relief valve adjusting screw (4) into body approximately ¼ inch (6 mm) for initial setting. Reinstall valve assembly and adjust pressure setting as outlined in TESTING paragraph.

HYDRAULIC CYLINDER. To remove lift cylinder, retract cylinder then shut off engine and move control lever back and forth to relieve hydraulic pressure. Raise hood and remove side panels. Disconnect hydraulic lines and plug all openings. Remove cotter pins and slide cylinder off mounting pins.

To disasemble cylinder, remove hydraulic fitting and snap ring (7 – Fig. F43) from rod end of cylinder. Pull rod, rod guide and piston out of cylinder tube. Unscrew piston retaining nut and remove piston from rod.

NOTE: Do not clamp rod or piston in a vise. Be careful not to scratch or mar rod.

Seal repair kit is only service part available for cylinder repair. Inspect rod, piston and cylinder bore for wear or other damage and renew as necessary. Coat all parts with clean hydraulic fluid prior to assembly. Do not over stretch "O" rings and back-up rings when installing. Be sure "O" rings are not twisted or cut when reassembling. Align tapped port in rod guide (11) with hole in cylinder tube prior to assembly.

Reinstall cylinder and check hydraulic oil level. Start engine and cycle cylinder several times to purge air from system.

GILSON BROTHERS CO.

CONDENSED SPECIFICATIONS

MODELS

	754, 769	755	768	770, 771	772, 775
Engine Make	B&S	B&S	B&S	B&S	B&S
Model	243434	320424	19070b	300424	170705
Bore	3-1/16 in.	3-9/16 in.	3 in.	3-7/16 in.	3 in.
	(77.8 mm)	(90.5 mm)	(76.2 mm)	(87.3 mm)	(76.2 mm)
Stroke	3¼ in.	3¼ in.	2¾ in.	3¼ in.	2⅜ in.
	(82.5 mm)	(82.5 mm)	(69.8 mm)	(82.5 mm)	(60.3 mm)
Piston Displacement	23.94 cu. in.	32.4 cu. in.	19.44 cu. in.	30.16 cu. in.	16.79 cu. in.
	(392 cc)	(531 cc)	(319 cc)	(494 cc)	(275 cc)
Horsepower	10	14	8	12	7
Slow Idle Speed – Rpm	1000	1000	1750	1000	1750
High Idle Speed (No Load) – Rpm	3600	3600	3600	3600	3600
Full Load Speed – Rpm	3240	3240	3000	3240	3000
Crankcase Oil Capacity	4 pints	4 pints	2¼ pints	4 pints	2¼ pints
	(1.9L)	(1.9L)	(1L)	(1.9L)	(1L)
Weight –					
Above 32°F (0°C)			——— SAE 30 ———		
0°F (–18°C) to 32°F (0°C)			——— SAE 10W ———		
Below 0°F (–18°C)			——— SAE 5W-20 ———		
Transmission Oil Capacity	4 pints	4 pints	1½ pints	4 pints	1½ pints
	(1.9L)	(1.9L)	(0.7L)	(1.9L)	(0.7L)
Weight			——— SAE 90 EP ———		

MODELS

	773, 776	774, 867	780	52072, 52080	52073, 52081
Engine Make	B&S	B&S	Kohler	B&S	B&S
Model	170702	320424	K181S	190707	252707
Bore	3 in.	3-9/16 in.	2-5/16 in.	3 in.	3-7/16 in.
	(76.2 mm)	(90.5 mm)	(58.7 mm)	(76.2 mm)	(87.3 mm)
Stroke	2⅜ in.	3¼ in.	2¾ in.	2¾ in.	2⅝ in.
	(60.3 mm)	(82.5 mm)	(69.8 mm)	(69.8 mm)	(66.7 mm)
Piston Displacement	16.79 cu. in.	32.4 cu. in.	18.6 cu. in.	19.44 cu. in.	24.36 cu. in.
	(275 cc)	(531 cc)	(305 cc)	(319 cc)	(399 cc)
Horsepower	7	14	8	8	11
Slow Idle Speed – Rpm	1750	1000	1200	1000	1000
High Idle Speed (No Load) – Rpm	3600	3600	3600	3600	3600
Full Load Speed – Rpm	3000	3240	3240	3240	3240
Crankcase Oil Capacity	2¼ pints	4 pints	2½ pints	2¼ pints	2½ pints
	(1L)	(1.9L)	(1.2L)	(1L)	(1.2L)
Weight –					
Above 32°F (0°C)			——— SAE 30 ———		
0°F (–18°C) to 32°F (0°C)			——— SAE 10W ———		
Below 0°F (–18°C)			——— SAE 5W-20 ———		
Transmission Oil Capacity	1½ pints	8 pints	3 pints	24 oz.	24 oz.
	(0.7L)	(3.8L)	(1.4L)	(710mL)	(710mL)
Weight	SAE 90 EP	ATF "A"	SAE 90 EP	EP Lithium Grease	EP Lithium Grease

MODELS

	52082, 52083	52112	52113	52117, 52122
Engine Make	B&S	B&S	B&S	B&S
Model	252707	252707	190707	252707
Bore	3-7/16 in.	3-7/16 in.	3 in.	3-7/16 in.
	(87.3 mm)	(87.3 mm)	(76.2 mm)	(87.3 mm)
Stroke	2⅝ in.	2⅝ in.	2¾ in.	2⅝ in.
	(66.7 mm)	(66.7 mm)	(69.8 mm)	(66.7 mm)
Piston Displacement	24.36 cu. in.	24.36 cu. in.	19.44 cu. in.	24.36 cu. in.
	(399 cc)	(399 cc)	(319 cc)	(399 cc)
Horsepower	11	11	8	11
Slow Idle Speed – Rpm	1000	1000	1000	1000
High Idle Speed (No Load) – Rpm	3600	3600	3600	3600
Full Load Speed – Rpm	3240	3240	3240	3240
Crankcase Oil Capacity	2½ pints	2½ pints	2¼ pints	2½ pints
	(1.2 L)	(1.2 L)	(1 L)	(1.2 L)
Weight –				
Above 32°F (0°C)	———————————————— SAE 30 ————————————————
0°F (–18°C) to 32°F (0°C)	———————————————— SAE 10W ————————————————
Below 0°F (–18°C)	———————————————— SAE 5W-20 ————————————————
Transmission Oil Capacity	24 oz.	22 oz.	24 oz.	24 oz.
	(710 mL)	(651 mL)	(710 mL)	(710 mL)
Weight	EP Lithium Grease	EP Lithium Grease	EP Lithium Grease	EP Lithium Grease

MODELS

	53000, 53005	53001, 53006	53002	53003, 53004
Engine Make	B&S	B&S	B&S	B&S
Model	243434	320424	300424	320424
Bore	3-1/16 in.	3-9/16 in.	3-7/16 in.	3-9/16 in.
	(77.8 mm)	(90.5 mm)	(87.3 mm)	(90.5 mm)
Stroke	3¼ in.	3¼ in.	3¼ in.	3¼ in.
	(82.5 mm)	(82.5 mm)	(82.5 mm)	(82.5 mm)
Piston Displacement	23.94 cu. in.	32.4 cu. in.	30.16 cu. in.	32.4 cu. in.
	(392 cc)	(531 cc)	(494 cc)	(531 cc)
Horsepower	10	14	12	14
Slow Idle Speed – Rpm	1000	1000	1000	1000
High Idle Speed (No Load) – Rpm	3600	3600	3600	3600
Full Load Speed – Rpm	3240	3240	3240	3240
Crankcase Oil Capacity	4 pints	4 pints	4 pints	4 pints
	(1.9 L)	(1.9 L)	(1.9 L)	(1.9 L)
Weight –				
Above 32°F (0°C)	———————————————— SAE 30 ————————————————
0°F (–18°C) to 32°F (0°C)	———————————————— SAE 10W ————————————————
Below 0°F (–18°C)	———————————————— SAE 5W-20 ————————————————
Transmission Oil Capacity	4 pints	4 pints	4 pints	8 pints
	(1.9 L)	(1.9 L)	(1.9 L)	(3.8 L)
Weight	SAE 90 EP	SAE 90 EP	SAE 90 EP	AFT "A"

MODELS

	53008, 53009	53010	53019, 53021	53020, 53022	53023
Engine Make	B&S	B&S	B&S	B&S	B&S
Model	325434	325434	326437	326437	243434
Bore	3-9/16 in.	3-9/16 in.	3-9/16 in.	3-9/16 in.	3-1/16 in.
	(90.5 mm)	(90.5 mm)	(90.5 mm)	(90.5 mm)	(77.8 mm)
Stroke	3¼ in.	3¼ in.	3¼ in.	3¼ in.	3¼ in.
	(82.5 mm)	(82.5 mm)	(82.5 mm)	(82.5 mm)	(82.5 mm)
Piston Displacement	32.4 cu. in.	32.4 cu. in.	32.4 cu. in.	32.4 cu. in.	23.94 cu. in.
	(531 cc)	(531 cc)	(531 cc)	(531 cc)	(392 cc)
Horsepower	15	15	16	16	10
Slow Idle Speed – Rpm	1000	1000	1000	1000	1000
High Idle Speed (No Load) – Rpm	3600	3600	3600	3600	3600
Full Load Speed – Rpm	3240	3240	3240	3240	3240

	MODELS (Cont.) 53008, 53009	53010	53019, 53021	53020, 53022	53023
Crankcase Oil Capacity	4 pints (1.9 L)				
Weight –					
Above 32°F (0°C)	SAE 30				
0°F (−18°C) to 32°F (0°C)	SAE 10W				
Below 0°F (−18°C)	SAE 5W-20				
Transmission Oil Capacity	4 pints (1.9 L)	8 pints (3.8 L)	4 pints (1.9 L)	8 pints (3.8 L)	4 pints (1.9 L)
Weight	SAE 90 EP	ATF "A"	SAE 90 EP	ATF "A"	SAE 90 EP

	MODELS 53024, 53025, 53026	53027, 53028	53030, 53031, 53032	53033, 53034	53038, 53039
Engine Make	B&S	B&S	B&S	B&S	B&S
Model	326437	326437	326437	251707	252707
Bore	3-9/16 in. (90.5 mm)	3-9/16 in. (90.5 mm)	3-9/16 in. (90.5 mm)	3-7/16 in. (87.3 mm)	3-7/16 in. (87.3 mm)
Stroke	3¼ in. (82.5 mm)	3¼ in. (82.5 mm)	3¼ in. (82.5 mm)	2⅝ in. (66.7 mm)	2⅝ in. (66.7 mm)
Piston Displacement	32.4 cu. in. (531 cc)	32.4 cu. in. (531 cc)	32.4 cu. in. (531 cc)	24.36 cu. in. (399 cc)	24.36 cu. in. (399 cc)
Horsepower	16	16	16	10	11
Slow Idle Speed – Rpm	1000	1000	1000	1000	1000
High Idle Speed (No Load) – Rpm	3600	3600	3600	3600	3600
Full Load Speed – Rpm	3240	3240	3240	3240	3240
Crankcase Oil Capacity	4 pints (1.9 L)	4 pints (1.9 L)	4 pints (1.9 L)	2½ pints (1.2 L)	2½ pints (1.2 L)
Weight –					
Above 32°F (0°C)	SAE 30				
0°F (−18°C) to 32°F (0°C)	SAE 10W				
Below 0°F (−18°C)	SAE 5W-20				
Transmission Oil Capacity	4 pints (1.9 L)	10 pints (4.7 L)	4 pints (1.9 L)	4 pints (1.9 L)	4 pints (1.9 L)
Weight	SAE 90 EP	*	SAE 90 EP	SAE 90 EP	SAE 90 EP

*Refer to LUBRICATION under HYDROSTATIC TRANSMISSION paragraphs.

FRONT AXLE AND STEERING SYSTEM

AXLE MAIN MEMBER

Models 768-772-773-775-776

To remove axle main member (4 – Fig. G1), disconnect drag link (2) from steering arm (3). Support front of tractor and remove pivot pin (5). Raise front of tractor to clear axle and roll front axle assembly from tractor.

Models 754-755-780-53000-53001-53008

To remove axle main member (2 – Fig. G2), disconnect drag link from steering arm (3). Support front of tractor and remove pivot bolts from axle and stabilizer. Raise front of tractor slightly and roll front axle assembly from tractor. Unbolt stabilizer (1) from axle main member. Renew pivot bushings (4 and 8) as necessary.

Models 769-770-771-774-867-53002-53003-53004-53005-53006-53009-53010

To remove axle main member (7 – Fig. G3), disconnect drag link from steering

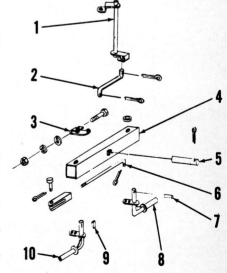

Fig. G1 – Exploded view of front axle assembly used on Models 768, 772, 773, 775 and 776.

1. Steering shaft
2. Drag link
3. Steering arm
4. Axle main member
5. Pivot pin
6. Tie rod
7. Roll pin
8. Steering spindle (L.H.)
9. Key
10. Steering spindle (R.H.)

spindle arm. Support front of tractor, loosen set screw (9) and remove pivot pin (8). Raise front of tractor to clear axle and roll axle assembly from tractor.

Models 52072-52073-52080-52081-52082-52083-52112-52113-52117-52122-53033-53034-53038-53039

To remove axle main member (14 – Fig. G4 or G5), support front of tractor and disconnect mower (if so equipped) from axle pivot bracket. Disconnect drag link (21) from steering arm (22). Remove axle pivot bolt (16) and roll front axle away from tractor.

Inspect pivot bolt and pivot bushings and renew as necessary. Reinstall axle by reversing removal procedure.

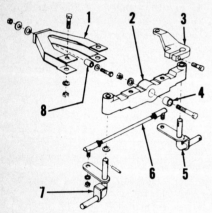

Fig. G2 — Exploded view of front axle assembly used on Models 754, 755, 780, 53000, 53001 and 53008.

1. Axle stabilizer	5. Steering spindle (L.H.)
2. Axle main member	6. Tie rod
3. Steering arm	7. Steering spindle (R.H.)
4. Pivot bushing	8. Spacer bushing

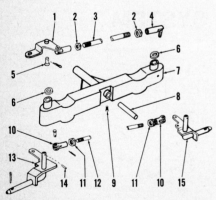

Fig. G3 — Exploded view of front axle assembly used on Models 769, 770, 771, 774, 867, 53002, 53003, 53004, 53005, 53006, 53009 and 53010.

1. Bellcrank	
2. Nut	10. Clevis
3. Drag link	11. Nut
4. Ball joint	12. Tie rod
5. Swivel pin	13. Steering spindle (R.H.)
6. Washer	14. Roll pin
7. Axle main member	15. Steering spindle (L.H.)
8. Pivot pin	
9. Set screw	

Models 53019-53020-53021-53022-53023-53024-53025-53026-53027-53028-53030-53031-53032

To remove axle main member (6 – Fig. G6), first support front of tractor. Disconnect drag link from steering spindle arm. Loosen set screw (10) and remove pivot pin (8), then raise front of tractor to clear axle and roll axle assembly away from tractor.

TIE RODS

All Models

Removal of tie rod is evident after examination of unit and reference to Figs. G1 through G6. To adjust front wheel toe-in on models equipped with adjustable tie rods, disconnect tie rod ends from steering spindle arms, loosen jam nuts and turn ends in or out as required. Toe-in should be 1/8 inch (3 mm) measured as shown in Fig. G7.

STEERING SPINDLES

Models 768-772-773-775-776

To remove steering spindles (8 and 10 – Fig. G1), support front of tractor

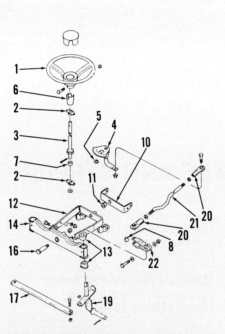

Fig. G4 — Exploded view of front axle and steering gear assembly used on Models 52072, 52073, 52080, 52081, 52082, 52083, 52112, 52113, 52117 and 52122.

1. Steering wheel	12. Axle bracket
2. Bearings	13. Spindle bushing
3. Steering shaft	14. Axle main member
4. Quadrant gear	16. Pivot bolt
5. "E" ring	17. Tie bar
6. Sleeve	19. Steering spindle (L.H.)
7. Spacer	20. Ball joints
8. Spacer	21. Drag link
10. Axle pivot bracket	22. Steering arm
11. Bushing	

and remove front wheels. Disconnect drag link (2) and tie rod (6). Remove steering arm (3), key (9) and right steering spindle (10). Drive out roll pin (7) and remove left steering spindle (8).

Models 754-755-780-53000-53001-53008

To remove steering spindles (5 and 7 – Fig. G2), support front of tractor and remove front wheels. Disconnect drag link and tie rod. Remove steering arm (3), key and left steering spindle (5). Drive out roll pin and remove right steering spindle (7).

Reassemble by reversing removal procedure. Lubricate with multipurpose grease.

Models 769-770-771-774-867-53002-53003-53004-53005-53006-53009-53010

To remove steering spindles (13 and 15 – Fig. G3), support front of tractor and remove front wheels. Disconnect

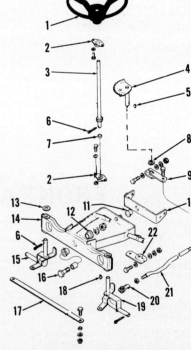

Fig. G5 — Exploded view of front axle and steering gear assemblies used on Models 53033, 53034, 53038 and 53039.

1. Steering wheel	13. Flat washer
2. Bearing	14. Axle assy.
3. Steering shaft	15. Steering spindle (R.H.)
4. Quadrant gear	16. Pivot bolt
5. Key	17. Tie bar
6. Cotter pin	18. Key
7. Spacer	19. Steering spindle (L.H.)
8. Spacer	20. Ball joint
9. Steering arm	21. Drag link
10. Axle pivot bracket	22. Steering arm
11. Bearing	
12. Axle pivot bushing	

drag link and tie rod from spindle arms. Drive out roll pins and remove steering spindles.

Inspect parts for excessive wear or other damage and renew as necessary. Lubricate with multipurpose lithium base grease.

Models 52072-52073-52080-52081-52082-52083-52112-52113-52117-52122-53033-53034-53038-53039

To remove steering spindles (15 and 19 – Fig. G4 or G5), support front of tractor and remove front wheels. Disconnect tie bar (17) and drag link (21) from spindle arms. Loosen clamp bolt and remove steering arm (22) and left steering spindle (19). Remove cotter key and lower right steering spindle from axle.

Inspect all parts for excessive wear or other damage. Some models are equipped with renewable spindle bushings. Lubricate with multipurpose lithium base grease.

Models 53019-53020-53021-53022-53023-53024-53025-53026-53027-53028-53030-53031-53032

To remove steering spindles (7 and 12 – Fig. G6), support front of tractor and remove front wheels. Disconnect drag link and tie rod from spindle arms. Drive out roll pins and lower spindles from axle.

Clean and inspect parts for excessive wear. All models are equipped with renewable spindle bushings (5). Lubricate with multipurpose lithium base grease.

STEERING GEAR

Models 768-772-773-775-776

Remove hood for access to steering gear. Drive out roll pin (3 – Fig. G8) and remove steering wheel. Disconnect drag link (7) from arm on quadrant gear (6). Unbolt and remove quadrant gear. Remove bolt (8) and steering shaft (2), then withdraw pinion gear (5).

Models 754-755-780-53000-53001-53008

To remove steering gear, refer to Fig. G9 and disconnect drag link (7) from

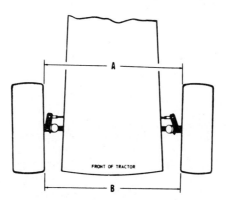

Fig. G7 — Toe-in is correct when distance "B" is 1/8 inch (3 mm) less than distance "A" with both measurements taken at hub height.

quadrant shaft (8). Remove nuts (10 and 11), drive out roll pin (6) and withdraw shaft (8). Remove quadrant gear (5). Drive out roll pins (13) and remove steering wheel (1) and pinion gear (4). Unbolt flange bearing (2) and remove steering shaft (3) and bracket (12). Support (9) can now be unbolted and removed if necessary.

Reassembly is reverse of disassembly procedure. To adjust steering gear play, loosen locknut (11) and turn adjusting nut (10) until steering wheel turns freely with minimum of play. Tighten locknut (11). Lubricate steering mechanism at grease fittings with multipurpose grease and apply light coat of grease to steering gears. Apply SAE 30 oil at oil hole in steering support (9).

Models 52072-52073-52080-52081-52082-52083-52112-52113-52117-52122

To remove steering gear, remove steering wheel. Remove cotter pin from bottom of steering shaft (3 – Fig. G4). Unbolt shaft upper bearing and withdraw steering shaft assembly. Disconnect drag link (21) from quadrant gear (4), remove "E" ring (5) and withdraw gear.

Inspect bearings and gears for wear and renew as necessary. Reassemble by reversing disassembly procedure. Lubricate bearings and gears with multipurpose grease.

To adjust steering gear mesh, loosen lower flange bearing mounting bolts and move steering shaft (3) towards steering gear (4). When gears mesh smoothly and evenly, tighten mounting bolts.

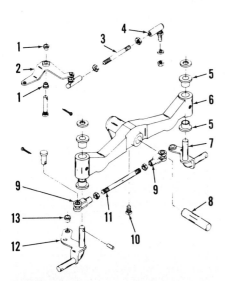

Fig. G6 — Exploded view of front axle assembly used on Models 53019, 53020, 53021 and 53022. Models 53023, 53024, 53025, 53026, 53027, 53028, 53030, 53031 and 53032 are similar.

1. Bushings
2. Bellcrank
3. Drag link
4. Ball joint end
5. Flanged bushings
6. Axle main member
7. Steering spindle (L.H.)
8. Pivot pin
9. Clevis
10. Set screw
11. Tie rod
12. Steering spindle (R.H.)
13. Bushing

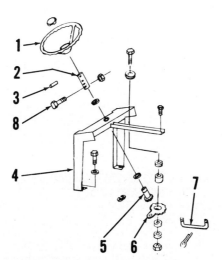

Fig. G8 — Exploded view of steering gear assembly used on Models 768, 772, 773, 775 and 776.

1. Steering wheel
2. Steering shaft
3. Roll pin
4. Frame
5. Pinion
6. Quadrant gear
7. Drag link
8. Bolt

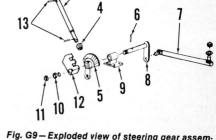

Fig. G9 — Exploded view of steering gear assembly used on Models 754, 755, 780, 53000, 53001 and 53008.

1. Steering wheel
2. Flange bearing
3. Steering shaft
4. Pinion gear
5. Quadrant gear
6. Roll pin
7. Drag link
8. Quadrant shaft & arm
9. Support
10. Adjusting nut
11. Locknut
12. Bracket
13. Roll pins

Gilson Brothers Co.

Models 53033-53034-53038-53039

To remove steering gear, first remove steering wheel. Remove cotter pin from bottom of steering shaft (3 – Fig. G5), unbolt shaft upper bearing flange and withdraw steering shaft. Disconnect steering arm (9) from quadrant gear (4) and withdraw gear.

Inspect bearings and gears for wear and renew as necessary. Reassemble by reversing disassembly procedure. Lubricate bearings and gears with multipurpose grease.

To adjust steering gear mesh, loosen lower flange bearing mounting screws and move steering shaft (3) towards steering gear (4). When gears mesh smoothly and evenly, tighten bearing mounting screws.

All Other Models

Remove steering gear by first disconnecting drag link end (20 – Fig. G10) from quadrant gear (11). Remove nuts (18 and 19) and unbolt supports (14) from frame. Lower the assembly and withdraw shaft (13). Spacer (17), quadrant gear (11) and bushing (12) can be removed as shaft is withdrawn. Drive

out roll pin (10) and remove pinion gear (9) and bracket (16) with bushings (8). Remove cap screw (1) and steering wheel (2), then unbolt bearing (4) and remove shaft (7) and bearing assembly. To reassemble, reverse disassembly procedure.

To adjust steering gear play, loosen set screw (15) and locknut (19). Turn adjusting nut (18) until steering wheel turns freely with a minimum of play. Retighten locknut (19) and set screw (15). Lubricate steering mechanism with light coat of SAE 30 oil.

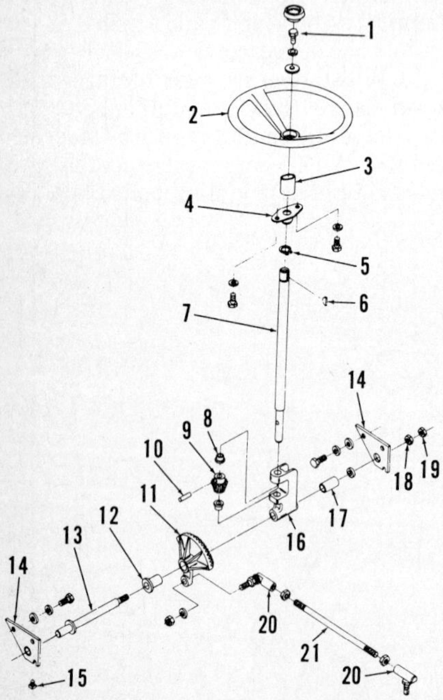

ENGINE

REMOVE AND REINSTALL

Models 754-755-780-53000-53001-53008

To remove engine assembly, loosen hood locks and tilt hood forward. On electric start models, disconnect battery cables and remove battery. Disconnect wires from starter-generator and ignition coil or magneto. On all models, disconnect throttle and choke control cables. Unbolt and remove belt guard from right side of engine. Remove engine draw bolt from front of tractor frame, then remove engine mounting bolts. Remove drive belts from engine and lift engine from tractor.

Reinstall engine by reversing removal procedure. Adjust engine drive belts as follows: Tighten engine drive belts and move engine forward to tighten belts. Make certain engine drive pulley and pulley on jackshaft are aligned, then tighten engine mounting bolts.

Models 768-772-773-775-776

To remove engine assembly, unbolt and remove hood. Disconnect and remove battery on electric start models. Disconnect starter-generator and ignition wires. Detach throttle and choke control cable from engine. Remove drive belts from engine drive pulley on underside of tractor. Remove engine mounting bolts and lift engine from tractor.

Models 52072-52073-52080-52081-52082-52083-52113-52117-52122-53033-53034-53038-53039

To remove engine assembly, remove hood assembly and disconnect battery cables. Lift fender and seat support and turn belt adjusting nut on top of frame counterclockwise 1/2 to 1 1/2 turns. Remove main drive belt and crankshaft

pulley. Disconnect electrical wiring, throttle and choke cables. Shut off fuel valve and disconnect fuel line at carburetor. Remove engine mounting bolts and lift engine from tractor. To reinstall engine, reverse removal procedure. Adjust drive belt as required.

All Other Models

To remove engine assembly, unfasten and tilt hood forward. Disconnect battery cables and remove battery. Disconnect starter-generator and ignition wires. Unbolt drive shaft coupler from rear of engine. Disconnect pto control rod from front pto assembly. Remove pto drive belt. Disconnect throttle and choke cables. Drain engine oil. Unbolt engine from engine base (oil pan) and lift engine from tractor.

NOTE: Engine base is bolted to side and bottom of frame rails and is the front axle support. To remove engine base, support tractor frame, remove front axle pivot pin, then unbolt and remove base.

When reinstalling engine, use new engine base gasket and refill with correct engine oil.

OVERHAUL

All Models

Engine make and model are listed at the beginning of this section. To overhaul engine components and accessories, refer to Briggs & Stratton and Kohler sections of this manual.

CLUTCH AND BRAKE

The clutch used on all gear drive models is belt idler type and is operated by clutch-brake pedal. When pedal is depressed, clutch idler tension is removed from transaxle drive belt. This allows clutch drive pulley to turn free within transaxle drive belt. At this time, brake band is drawn tight on brake-drum, or caliper brake is tightened on brake disc, stopping tractor motion.

Models 774, 867, 52112, 53003, 53004 53010, 53020, 53022, 53027 and 53028 are equipped with a hydrostatic transmission. When pedal on left side of tractor is depressed, drive control linkage is moved to neutral position and hydrostatic transmission dynamically brakes tractor. A mechanical parking brake is also provided.

Fig. G10—Exploded view of typical steering gear assembly used on some models.

1. Cap screw
2. Steering wheel
3. Sleeve
4. Flange bearing
5. Snap ring
6. Key
7. Steering shaft
8. Bushing
9. Pinion gear
10. Roll pin
11. Quadrant gear
12. Bushing
13. Shaft
14. Support
15. Set screw
16. Bracket
17. Spacer
18. Adjusting nut
19. Locknut
20. Ball joint ends
21. Drag link

166

ADJUSTMENT

Models 754-755-780-53000-53001-53008

The clutch idler is spring loaded and requires no adjustment. The clutch-brake pedal (23—Fig. G11) can be adjusted by loosening bolt (21) and moving pedal on adjusting plate (22). When desired pedal position is obtained, tighten bolt (21).

Adjust brake by turning adjusting nut (4) on rear of brake rod (15) Depress clutch-brake pedal and check to see that brake band (5) does not tighten on brake drum (3) until clutch idler tension is removed from transaxle drive belts.

Models 768-772-773-775-776

To adjust clutch, refer to Fig. G12. Remove spring clip and clevis pin from clutch rod clevis. Turn clevis to adjust clutch action. Brake rod should not contact rear of slot in frame when clutch-brake pedal is depressed. Drive belt should be renewed if adjustment will not prevent contact between rod and rear of slot.

To adjust brake, first check clutch adjustment. Turn adjusting nut shown in Fig. G13. Brake should engage when clutch-brake pedal is depressed but should not drag when clutch is engaged.

Models 774-867-52112-53003-53004-53010-53020-53027-53028

These models use a hydrostatic transmission and are not equipped with an engine disconnect clutch. Refer to the following HYDROSTATIC TRANSMISSION section for adjustment of control linkage.

On Models 53027 and 53028, a caliper-disc type brake, located on left side of transaxle, is used. To adjust brake, move speed control lever to "Fast" position. Depress neutral-brake pedal until

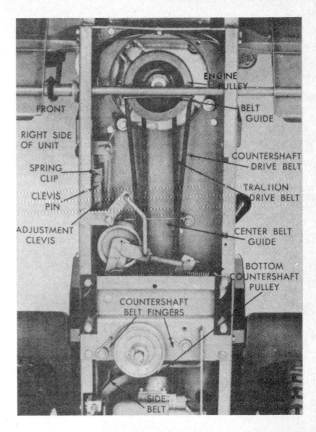

Fig. G12 — Bottom view of Models 768, 772, 773, 775 and 776. For clutch adjustment procedure, refer to text.

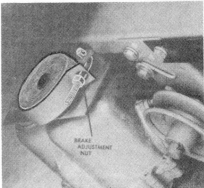

Fig. G13 — View of brake adjusting nut on Models 768, 772, 773, 775 and 776.

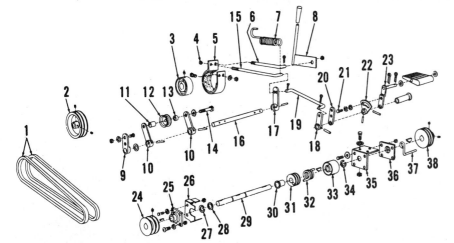

Fig. G11 — Exploded view of clutch-brake system used on Models 754, 755, 780, 53000, 53001 and 53008.

1. Transaxle belts	10. Idler arm	20. Bracket	29. Jackshaft
2. Transaxle input pulley.	11. Bushing	21. Bolt	30. Bearing
3. Brake drum	12. Idler	22. Adjusting plate	31. Clutch drive pulley
4. Adjusting nut	13. Spacer	23. Clutch-brake pedal	32. Torsion spring
5. Brake band	14. Bolt	24. Jackshaft input pulley	33. Spring drive sleeve
6. Park brake rod	15. Brake rod	25. Bearing assy.	34. Snap ring
7. Clutch tension spring	16. Shaft	26. Belt guide	35. Bracket
8. Park brake lever	17. Clutch-brake lever	27. Snap ring	36. Bearing assy.
9. Bracket	18. Arm	28. Washer	37. Belt guide
	19. Clutch-brake rod		38. Pto pulley

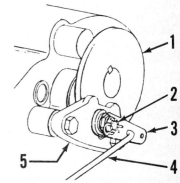

Fig. G14 — On Models 53027 and 53028, turn adjusting nut (2) on brake cam lever (3) to adjust brake.

1. Brake disc	
2. Adjusting nut	4. Brake link
3. Cam lever	5. Caliper assy.

Fig. G15—View of brake linkage adjustment point on Models 774, 867, 53003, 53004, 53010, 53020 and 53022.

speed control lever returns to neutral position, then turn adjusting nut (2—Fig. G14) on disc brake clockwise until brake pads contact brake disc.

A drum type brake, located on left side of transaxle, is used on all other models. To adjust brake, raise seat and loosen front adjustment nut (Fig. G15) and turn rear nut to shorten brake linkage rod. When adjustment is correct, tighten front nut against linkage. If additional adjustment is required, tighten locknut (3—Fig. G16) on brake band rod (2) until brake is locked when park brake handle is ½ inch (13 mm) from end of slot.

Models 769-770-771-53002-53005-53006-53009-53019-53021-53023-53024-53025-53026-53030-53031-53032

The clutch mechansim is spring loaded and does not require adjustment. Drive belt should be inspected for fraying, cracking or excessive wear and renewed as necessary. Check for clutch idler tension against drive belt. There should be no belt slippage when clutch pedal is in up position. If drive belt slips, check for faulty clutch tension spring or for excessive wear or stretching of drive belt.

Brake adjustment is accomplished by turning adjusting nut (Fig. G17) on rod at brake band. Adjust brake so brake band does not contact brake drum until clutch idler tension is removed from transaxle drive belt.

Models 52072-52073-52080-52081-52082-52083-52113-52117-52122

The clutch pivot bracket (1—Fig. G18) is spring loaded and does not require adjustment. There should be no belt slippage when clutch-brake pedal is in up position. If drive belt slips, check for faulty clutch tension spring and be sure pivot bracket is pivoting freely. Check belt for excessive wear or stretching and renew as necessary.

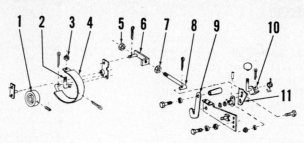

Fig. G16—Exploded view of typical parking brake linkage used on hydrostatic drive models equipped with drum type brake.

1. Brake drum
2. Rod
3. Nut
4. Brake band
5. Adjusting nut
6. Link
7. Adjusting nut
8. Rod
9. Parking brake lever
10. Parking brake latch
11. Ratchet

Disc type brake is located on right side of transaxle. To adjust brake, turn adjusting nuts (Fig. G19) clockwise to tighten brake pads against brake disc. Do not overtighten.

Models 52112-53033-53034-53038-53039

To adjust main drive belt, lift rear fender and seat support assembly. Loosen locknut on underside of frame (Fig. G20). Turn nut on top of frame clockwise to tighten or counterclockwise to loosen. To check belt tension, press downward approximately at mid-point of belt. The belt should move 1 inch (25 mm).

The final drive belt requires no adjustment. The belt is adjusted by a spring loaded idler pulley. Check idler arm to be sure it pivots freely and provides tension.

To adjust brake, remove cotter pin from brake adjusting nut. Turn nut clockwise to tighten brake pad and compensate for wear (Fig. G21). Slight drag is permitted.

DRIVE BELTS

REMOVE AND REINSTALL

Models 754-755-780-53000-53001-53008

To remove transaxle drive belts (1—Fig. G11), first unbolt and remove belt

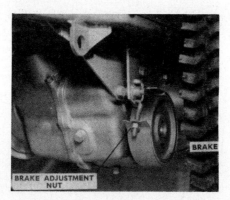

BRAKE ADJUSTMENT NUT
BRAKE

Fig. G17—View of drum type brake, located on side of transaxle, used on some models.

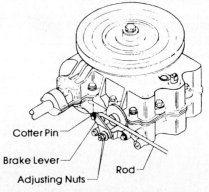

Cotter Pin
Brake Lever
Adjusting Nuts
Rod

Fig. G19—Disc type brake is located on right side of transaxle on Models 52072, 52073, 52080, 52081, 52082, 52083, 52113, 52117 and 52122.

Fig. G18—View of traction drive belt and spring loaded clutch idler used on Models 52072, 52073, 52080, 52081, 52082, 52083, 52113, 52117 and 52122.

1. Pivot bracket
2. Belt finger
3. V-idler pulley
4. Transaxle pulley
5. Belt finger
6. Flat idler pulley
7. Tension spring
8. Traction belt
9. Lower belt retainer
10. Upper belt retainer
11. Engine pulley

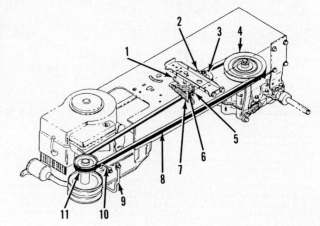

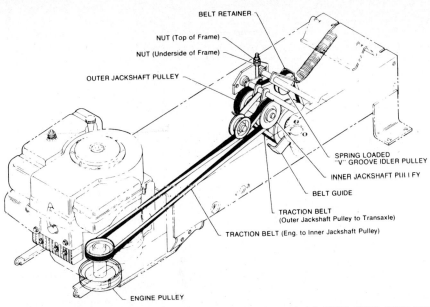

Fig. G20 – View of traction drive belts and adjustment points on Models 52112, 53033, 53034, 53038 and 53039.

guide from around transaxle input pulley (2). Remove cotter pin from left end of shaft (16). Remove bolt (14), then lift out idler (12) with spacer (13) and bushing (11). Slide shaft (16) to the left. Unbolt bracket (35) from tractor frame. Remove belts over end of shaft assemblies.

The transaxle drive belts are serviced only as a matched set and both belts should be renewed at the same time. Install new belts by reversing removal procedure. Adjust clutch-brake pedal position and brake linkage as necessary.

Models 768-772-773-775-776

If tractor must be tipped to reach underside of tractor, remove seat, rear shroud assembly and battery. Remove engine pulley belt guide (Fig. G12) and remove countershaft drive belt from engine pulley. Loosen rear belt guide bolt and side belt guide bolts and slide belt guides away from belt. Remove traction drive belt.

To reinstall drive belt, reverse removal procedure. Position rear and side belt guides so there is 1/16 to 1/8 inch (1.5-3 mm) clearance between belt and guide.

Model 769-770-771-53002-53005-53006-53009-53019-53021-53024-53025-53026-53032 (With Variable Speed)

These models are equipped with an upper pulley which drives the traction drive belt and has a movable flange. Flange position is changed by moving variable speed control lever. As flange

position is changed, radius that traction drive belt follows is altered, thereby changing drive ratio. To remove traction drive belt, remove belt guide around transaxle driven pulley and loosen retaining bolt of upper belt finger and

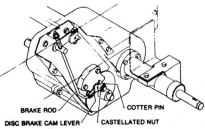

Fig. G21 – View of disc brake adjustment on Models 53033, 53034, 53038 and 53039. Model 52112 is similar.

move belt finger away from belt. Move variable speed control lever rearward to slow position. Spread flanges of drive pulley and remove belt. Push flanges of pulley together so belt can be moved between pulley and control cam as shown in Fig. G22. Remove traction drive belt. When installing traction drive belt, position belt guide and belt finger so there is 1/16 inch (1.5 mm) clearance between guide or finger and belt.

Models 769-770-771-53002-53005-53006-53009-53019-53021-53023-53024-53025-53026-53030-53031-53032 (Without Variable Speed)

To remove traction drive belt, refer to Fig. G23, remove rear belt guide bolt and loosen front guide bolt. Move belt guide away from belt. Loosen belt finger bolt, move finger upward and remove traction drive belt. When installing traction drive belt, position belt guide and belt finger so there is 1/16 inch (1.5 mm) clearance between guide or finger and the belt.

Models 52072-52073-52080-52081-52082-52083-52113-52117-52122

To remove traction drive belt, first remove any attachments mounted under tractor. Set parking brake, then remove flat idler pulley (6 – Fig. G18) and V-idler pulley (3) from pivot bracket (1). Disconnect shift rod from transmission shift lever. Remove upper belt retainer (10), then slip belt off pulleys and remove from tractor.

Install new belt by reversing removal procedure. Belt finger (5) should point directly at left side of frame and belt finger (2) should point directly at right side of frame.

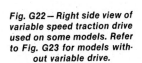

Fig. G22 – Right side view of variable speed traction drive used on some models. Refer to Fig. G23 for models without variable drive.

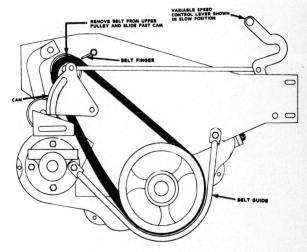

Models 52112-53033-53034-53038-53039

To remove main drive belt, lift rear fender and seat support assembly and refer to Fig. G20. Loosen belt tension adjusting nut. **Do not remove.** Remove engine pulley belt cover. Work belt off inner jackshaft pulley and engine pulley. Install new belt by reversing removal procedure.

To remove final drive belt, depress foot pedal and set parking brake. Loosen "V" groove idler pulley and remove belt. Reassemble by reversing disassembly procedure and adjust belt retainer. With belt engaged, there must be 1/16 to 1/8 inch (1.5-3 mm) clearance between retainer and belt.

CAUTION: All belt guards must be in place before operating tractor.

RIGHT ANGLE DRIVE

Models 769-770-771-53002-53005-53006-53009-53019-53021-53023-53024-53025-53026-53030-53031-53032

R&R AND OVERHAUL. To remove right angle drive unit, raise seat assembly and unbolt drive shaft rear coupling. Remove traction drive belt from pulley, then loosen set screws and remove pulley assembly. Unbolt and remove right angle drive from tractor.

To disassemble unit, remove cover (1 – Fig. G24) and gasket (2). Unbolt and remove retainer (13) with oil seal (14) and gasket (12). Withdraw output shaft (10) and bearing (11), then remove driven gear (9) through cover opening. Remove oil seal (17) and snap ring (16). Push input shaft (6), bearing (5) and drive gear (4) out through cover opening. Gear and bearing can be removed

from input shaft after first removing snap ring (3). To remove bearing (8), either tap outside of housing (7) behind bearing with a mallet or apply heat to housing.

Clean and inspect all parts and renew any showing excessive wear or other damage. Reassemble by reversing disassembly procedure. Use new oil seals and gaskets and fill unit half full with multipurpose lithium base grease.

Reinstall right angle drive unit on tractor by reversing removal procedure.

TRANSAXLE

LUBRICATION

All Models

Model 780 is equipped with a Peerless 1700 series transaxle. Approximate capacity is 3 pints (3.8 L) of SAE 90 EP gear lubricant.

Models 768, 772, 773, 775 and 776 are equipped with a Peerless 600 series transaxle. Approximate capacity is 1½ pints (0.7 L) of SAE 90 EP gear lubricant.

Models 754, 755, 769, 770, 771, 53000, 53001, 53002, 53006, 53008, 53009, 53019, 53021, 53023, 53024, 53025, 53026, 53030, 53031, 53032, 53033, 53034, 53038 and 53039 are equipped with a Peerless 2300 series transaxle. Approximate capacity is 4 pints (1.9 L) of SAE 90 EP gear lubricant. Gear lubricant is added through shift lever opening.

Models 52072, 52073, 52080, 52081, 52082, 52083, 52113, 52117 and 52122 are equipped with a Peerless 800 series transaxle. Transaxle is filled at factory with 1½ pints (0.7 L) of lithium base grease.

REMOVE AND REINSTALL

Models 768-772-773-775-776

To remove transaxle assembly, first remove seat, rear shroud assembly and

battery. Loosen belt guide bolts and slide belt guides away from belt. Remove traction drive belt from transaxle input pulley. Disconnect brake linkage. Remove cap screws retaining transaxle to frame and remove "U" bolts securing axle housings to frame. Raise rear of tractor and remove transaxle assembly from tractor.

Reinstall by reversing removal procedure. Adjust clutch and brake linkage as required.

All Other Models So Equipped

To remove transaxle assembly, first unbolt and remove belt guide from around transaxle input pulley. Depress clutch-brake pedal and remove traction drive belt from transaxle input pulley. Disconnect brake linkage and remove brake band (models so equipped). Place a floor jack under transaxle to prevent unit from tipping forward. Block up under frame, unbolt transaxle from frame, raise rear of frame and roll transaxle rearward from tractor.

To reinstall transaxle, reverse removal procedure.

OVERHAUL

All Models

Model 780 is equipped with a Peerless 1700 series transaxle. Models 768, 772, 773, 775 and 776 are equipped with a Peerless 600 series transaxle. Models

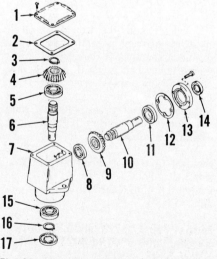

Fig. G24 – Exploded view of right angle drive unit used on models so equipped.

1. Cover	10. Output shaft
2. Gasket	11. Bearing
3. Snap ring	12. Gasket
4. Drive gear	13. Retainer
5. Bearing	14. Oil seal
6. Input shaft	15. Bearing
7. Housing	16. Snap ring
8. Bearing	17. Oil seal
9. Driven gear	

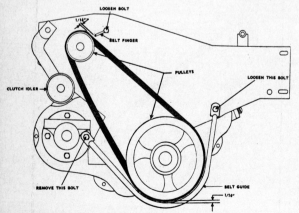

Fig. G23 – Right side view of traction drive belt and pulleys used on models without variable speed.

754, 755, 769, 770, 771, 53000, 53001, 53002, 53006, 53008, 53009, 53019, 53021, 53023, 53024, 53025, 53026, 53030, 53031, 53032, 53033, 53034, 53038 and 53039 are equipped with a Peerless 2300 series transaxle. Models 52072, 52073, 52080, 52081, 52082, 52083, 52113, 52117 and 52122 are equipped with a Peerless 800 series transaxle.

On all models, refer to the appropriate Peerless section in TRANSAXLE SERVICE section for overhaul procedure.

HYDROSTATIC TRANSMISSION

LUBRICATION

Models 774-867-53003-53004-53010-53020-53022

Models 774, 867, 53003, 53004, 53010, 53020 and 53022 are equipped with a Vickers T66 hydrostatic transmission. Recommended oil is Type "A" automatic transmission fluid. The oil should be changed and filter renewed if there is any evidence of oil contamination or if hydrostatic unit is disassembled. Capacity is approximately 8 pints (3 L).

Models 52112

Model 52112 is equipped with an Eaton Model 6 hydrostatic transmission. Hydrostatic transmission is separate from differential unit and transmission uses different fluid than the gear reduction unit. Transmission fluid level should be at the appropriate level line marked on reservoir filler tube when unit is hot or cold.

Models 53027-53028

Models 53027 and 53028 are equipped with Eaton Model 10 hydrostatic transmission. The hydrostatic transmission shares a common reservoir with reduction drive and differential unit. Reservoir may be filled at factory with either Type "A" automatic transmission fluid or SAE 20W SE rated engine oil. If transmission fluid is being renewed, completely drain system and refill with SAE 20W engine oil rated SE. Reservoir capacity is approximately 10 pints (4.7 L).

NOTE: If adding oil to system, do not intermix the two types of fluid.

Transmission oil is routed through an external oil filter. Manufacturer recommends renewing filter after first 50 hours of operation and every 250 hours thereafter.

ADJUSTMENT

Models 774-867-53003-53004-53010-53020-53022

To adjust hydrostatic transmission control linkage, block up under rear of tractor so both rear wheels are free to rotate. Start engine and move transmission control lever to reverse and forward positions, then depress neutral pedal. Wheels should stop turning. If wheels turn when neutral pedal is fully depressed, stop engine. Remove cotter pin (Fig. G34), loosen locknut and rotate turnbuckle one notch at a time as required. If wheels are rotating rearward, rotate turnbuckle to lengthen control rod or if wheels were turning forward, shorten control rod. After each ¼-turn (1 notch) adjustment, start engine and recheck neutral return position. When adjustment is correct, install cotter pin and tighten locknut.

If unable to stop wheels from turning with turnbuckle adjustment, remove spring clip, loosen locknut and remove clevis pin. Rotate clevis ½-turn at a time as required. If wheels turn rearward, lengthen control rod or if wheels turn forward, shorten rod. When adjustment is correct, install spring clip and tighten locknut.

Models 52112-53027-53028

If tractor creeps either forward or backward with neutral-brake pedal depressed, control linkage should be adjusted. Transmission should be at operating temperature before checking or adjusting transmission.

CAUTION: Do not attempt to adjust linkage while engine is running.

Raise and securely block rear of tractor so rear wheels may rotate freely. Refer to Fig. G40 and loosen jam nuts (1). Turn turnbuckle (3) 1/6-turn clockwise (lengthens rod) if tractor creeps backward or counterclockwise if tractor creeps forward. Recheck transmission operation and repeat adjustment procedure as needed. If fine adjustment does not correct creeping, additional adjustment may be obtained as follows: Disconnect clevis (6) from transmission control arm (4) and turn clevis ½-turn counterclockwise (lengthens rod) if tractor creeps backward or clockwise if tractor creeps forward. Check operation and repeat adjustment as required. If tractor begins to creep in opposite direction, make final adjustment with turnbuckle as previously outlined.

If ground speed control lever does not stay in position under load, tighten linkage friction spring to increase tension on control lever. Do not overtighten to the point that depressing neutral-brake pedal will not return control linkage to neutral.

REMOVE AND REINSTALL

Models 774-867-53003-53004-53010-53020-53022

To remove hydrostatic transmission, remove seat pan and shift plate from top of frame. Thoroughly clean transmission and surrounding area to prevent entrance of dirt or other foreign material

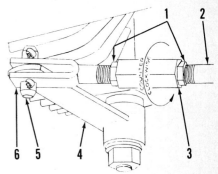

Fig. G40 — View of hydrostatic transmission control linkage. Refer to text for adjustment procedure.

1. Jam nuts
2. Control rod
3. Turnbuckle
4. Control arm
5. Pin
6. Clevis

Fig. G34 — View of hydrostatic control rod adjustment points. Refer to text for procedure.

into system. Disconnect oil lines from transmission and plug or cap openings. Remove control rod clevis pin and loosen set screws in drive shaft rear coupling. Unbolt transmission from reduction drive and differential housing. Move transmission toward right side of tractor, hold unit level and pry input shaft out of drive shaft coupling hub. Tilt front end of transmission downward and lift assembly from tractor.

When reinstalling transmission, renew mounting gasket and reverse removal procedure. Fill reduction drive and differential housing to level plug opening with Type "A" automatic transmission fluid. Start engine and operate at low idle speed for about one minute. Recheck fluid level and add as needed. Start engine and operate at approximately half throttle. Make several short runs forward and rearward at low speed. Stop engine, check for external leakage, then recheck fluid level and add as needed. Check control linkage and adjust as necessary.

Model 52112

To remove transmission and differential assembly, raise and support right wheel of tractor off the ground. Remove right wheel assembly. Remove the three cap screws retaining fan guard. Remove fan guard and fan, then reinstall the three cap screws to maintain torque bracket alignment. Temporarily reinstall right wheel. Disconnect shift lever clevis at transmission. Remove rear hitch plate from between main frame. Pull spring loaded idler pulley down and work secondary drive belt off transmission input pulley and idler pulley. Disconnect brake adjustment rod at brake lever. Remove the two locknuts on left and right "U" bolts retaining axle housings to support brackets. Support transmission, then remove the three cap screws retaining differential assembly to torque bracket. Raise and support rear main frame and pull differential/transmission assembly out and away from tractor. Remove tire and wheel assemblies. Remove the four cap screws retaining transmission to differential and separate assemblies.

Reinstall transmission/differential assembly by reversing removal procedure. Transmission should be filled with approximately 22 ounces (651 mL) of SAE 20 detergent oil. Differential should be filled with approximately 2¾ pints (1.3 L) of SAE 90 EP gear oil.

Models 53027-53028

To remove hydrostatic transmission, first remove seat and fender assembly and shift plate. Disconnect brake return spring and rear brake link at parking brake ratchet. Disconnect transmission control rod clevis from control lever. Loosen set screws and slide fan hub towards transmission and disconnect drive shaft coupling from transmission input shaft. Drain transmission fluid, then identify and disconnect hydraulic hoses to transmission. Plug all openings to prevent entry of dirt. Support transmission to prevent tipping, then remove transaxle mounting bolts. Raise and move rear of frame away from transmission assembly. Remove fan assembly and disconnect intake hose and filter hose from transmission. Unbolt and remove hydrostatic transmission from transaxle.

Reinstall by reversing removal procedure. Renew hydraulic filter and transmission oil. Adjust control linkage as previously outlined.

OVERHAUL

All Models

Models 774, 867, 53003, 53004, 53010, 53020 and 53022 are equipped with a Vickers Model T66 hydrostatic transmission. Model 52112 is equipped with an Eaton Model 6 hydrostatic transmission. Models 53027 and 53028 are equipped with an Eaton Model 10 hydrostatic transmission.

On all models, refer to appropriate Eaton or Vickers section in HYDROSTATIC TRANSMISSION SERVICE section for overhaul procedure.

REDUCTION DRIVE AND DIFFERENTIAL

Models 774-867-53003-53004-53010-53020-53022

R&R AND OVERHAUL. To remove reduction drive and differential unit, first remove hydrostatic transmission as outlined previously. Drain fluid from reduction drive and differential unit. Attach a hoist to rear seat bracket to support tractor. Disconnect brake rod from ratchet. Remove "U" bolts from axle tubes and unbolt unit from frame. Raise rear of tractor frame and roll assembly rearward from tractor.

Remove oil filter, brake drum and rear wheels. Remove nuts (19 – Fig. G44), washers (20) and rear wheel hubs. Slide dust seals (21) from axle shafts, then us-

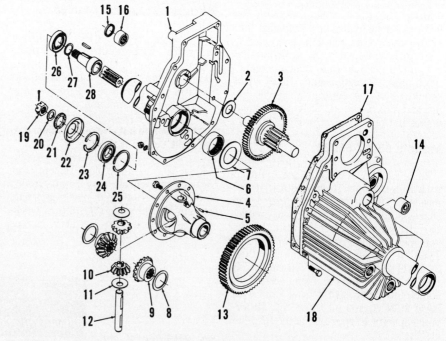

Fig. G44—Exploded view of reduction drive and differential unit used on Models 774, 867, 53003, 53004, 53010, 53020 and 53022.

1. Left housing	15. Oil seal
2. Thrust washer	16. Needle bearing
3. Reduction gear & countershaft	17. Gasket
4. Differential case	18. Right housing
5. Pin	19. Nut
6. Bearing	20. Washer
7. Thrust washer	21. Seal
8. Thrust washer	22. Bearing retainer
9. Side gear	23. Snap ring
10. Bevel pinion	24. Bearing
11. Thrust washer	25. Snap ring
12. Differential pinion shaft	26. Oil seal
13. Ring gear	27. Snap ring
14. Needle bearing	28. Axle shaft

ing a hammer and chisel, remove bearing retainers (22). Remove snap rings (23) and withdraw axle shafts (28) with bearings (24). Oil seals (26) can be removed after removing snap rings (25).

Place reduction drive and differential assembly in a vise with left axle tube pointing downward. Remove housing bolts and drive out two alignment spring pins. Lift off right housing (18). Remove differential and ring gear assembly, then remove reduction gear and countershaft (3). Do not lose the four thrust washers (2 and 7). Drive out pin (5), then drive out differential pinion shaft (12). Rotate side gears (9) until bevel pinions (10) and thrust washers (11) can be removed from case (4), then remove side gears (9) and thrust washers (8). Remove ten retaining cap screws and using a hammer and wooden block, drive ring gear (13) from case (4). Oil seal (15) and needle bearings (6, 14 and 16) can now be removed.

Clean and inspect all parts and renew any showing excessive wear or other damage. Reassemble by reversing disassembly procedure. When installing ring gear (13) on case (4), tighten three opposite cap screws until gear is pulled up tightly on case, then tighten all cap screws to a torque of 50 ft.-lbs. (68 N·m). Renew all seals and gaskets. Install oil seals (2 – Fig. G45) in axle tubes with lip to the inside, then install snap ring (3). Pack axle bearings (4) with high grade multipurpose grease and carefully install axle shaft and bearing assemblies. Install snap ring (5), pack new retainers (6) with multipurpose grease and install retainers.

After unit is installed on tractor and hydrostatic transmission is installed,

renew fluid filter and install new Type "A" automatic transmission fluid. Capacity is approximately 8 pints (3.8 L).

Model 52112

R&R AND OVERHAUL. To remove reduction gear and differential unit, refer to the previous REMOVE AND REINSTALL paragraphs in HYDROSTATIC TRANSMISSION section and remove hydrostatic transmission and differential as a complete assembly. Remove wheel and hub assemblies from axles. Drain differential lubricant and separate transmission from differential. Remove brake disc from brake shaft. Clean axle shafts and remove any burrs on shafts. Unscrew cap screws and drive out dowel pins in cover (29 – Fig. G46). Lift cover off case and axle shaft.

Withdraw brake shaft (5), idler gear (4) and thrust washers (3 and 6) from case. Remove output shaft (11), output gear (10), spacer (9), thrust washer (8) and differential assembly from case. Axle shaft housings (20 and 22) must be pressed from case to cover.

To disassemble differential, unscrew four cap screws (17) and separate axle shaft and carriage assemblies from ring gear (28). Drive blocks (25), bevel pinion gears (26) and drive pin (27) can now be removed from ring gear. Remove snap rings (12) and slide axle shafts (18 and 23) from axle gears (13) and carriages (16 and 24).

Clean and inspect all parts and renew any parts damaged or excessively worn. When installing needle bearings, press bearings in from inside of case or cover until bearings are 0.015-0.020 inch

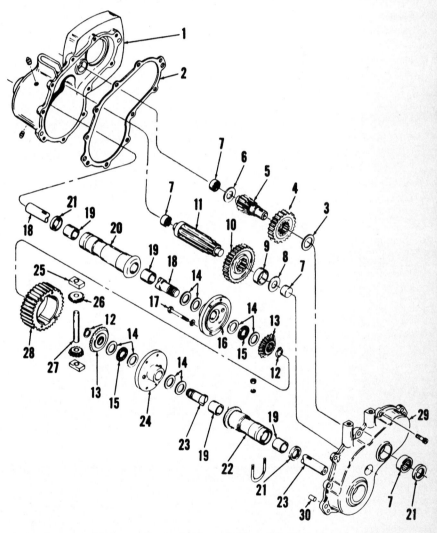

Fig. G46 — Exploded view of gear reduction and differential unit used on Model 52112.

1. Case	9. Spacer	16. Differential carrier	23. Axle shaft (R.H.)
2. Gasket	10. Output gear	17. Bolt	24. Differential carrier
3. Washer	11. Output shaft	18. Axle shaft (L.H.)	25. Drive block
4. Idler gear	12. Snap ring	19. Bushing	26. Drive pinion
5. Brake shaft	13. Side gears	20. Axle housing	27. Drive pin
6. Washer	14. Thrust washers	21. Oil seal	28. Ring gear
7. Bearing	15. Thrust bearing	22. Axle housing	29. Cover
8. Washer			30. Dowel pin

Fig. G45 — Sectional view of axle outer bearing and oil seal installation on Models 774, 867, 53003, 53004, 53010, 53020 and 53022.

1. Snap ring	4. Ball bearing
2. Oil seal	5. Snap ring
3. Snap ring	6. Retainer

(0.381-0.508 mm) below thrust surfaces. Be sure heads of differential cap screws (17) and left axle shaft (18) are installed in left carriage housing (16). Left axle shaft is installed through case (1). Tighten differential cap screws to 7 ft.-lbs. (9 N·m) and cover cap screws to 10 ft.-lbs. (14 N·m). Differential assembly and output shaft (11) must be installed in case at same time. Remainder of assembly is reverse of disassembly procedure. After installation, fill reduction gear and differential assembly with 2¾ pints (1.3 L) of SAE 90 EP gear oil.

Models 53027-53028

R&R AND OVERHAUL. Models 53027 and 53028 are equipped with a dual range gear reduction assembly which drives through a limited slip differential. Remove gear reduction and differential unit and separate hydrostatic transmission from unit as previously outlined in HYDROSTATIC TRANSMISSION section. Remove wheels and clean exterior of unit.

To disassemble, remove axle housings (15–Fig. G47). Position unit with cover up, then remove cover (13). Lift out differential assembly and axles (40 through 54). Remove output shaft (36), gear (35) and thrust washers (34). Unscrew set screw (2) and remove spring (3) and ball (4). Remove brake shaft (32), sliding gear (33) and shift fork (10) and rod (8). Remove input shaft and gear components (18 through 25).

To disassemble differential assembly, remove cap screws (53) and remove differential carriers (41 and 52) and axles from ring gear assembly. Remove snap ring to separate axle gear, carrier and axle. Remove pinions (47) and separate body cores (45 and 48) from ring gear (46).

Inspect components for damage or excessive wear. To reassemble unit, reverse disassembly procedure. Check movement of shift rod when tightening set screw (2). Install gears (22 and 25) so bevels of gears face together as shown in Fig. G48. Install carrier cap screws (53–Fig. G47) so head of cap screw is on side of shorter carrier (52). Do not rotate axle housings after housing has been pressed tight against seal (11) as seal may be cut.

Fill unit with SAE 20W engine oil with API rating SE and allow oil to seep past roller bearings into axle housings. Recheck oil level and add oil to correct level at check plug opening in case.

Install unit in tractor by reversing removal procedure. Adjust brake linkage.

HYDRAULIC SYSTEM

On hydrostatic drive models equipped with hydraulic lift, hydraulic system pressure is provided by charge and auxiliary hydraulic pump located in hydrostatic transmission. Refer to appropriate HYDROSTATIC TRANSMISSION SERVICE section for schematic drawing of hydraulic system and service procedures covering charge pump. Hydraulic control valve directs fluid to lift cylinder.

On gear drive models equipped with hydraulic lift, a self-contained hydraulic unit, consisting of a gear pump, control valve and oil reservoir, is used along with a companion hydraulic cylinder. The hydraulic pump is belt driven.

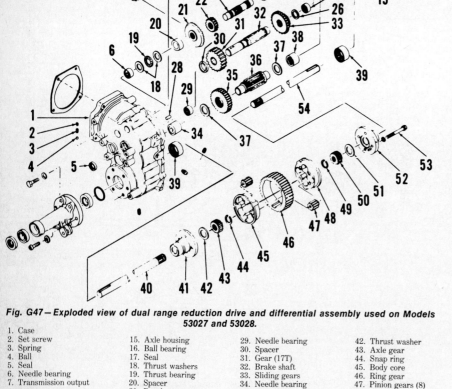

Fig. G47 – Exploded view of dual range reduction drive and differential assembly used on Models 53027 and 53028.

1. Case	15. Axle housing	29. Needle bearing	42. Thrust washer
2. Set screw	16. Ball bearing	30. Spacer	43. Axle gear
3. Spring	17. Seal	31. Gear (17T)	44. Snap ring
4. Ball	18. Thrust washers	32. Brake shaft	45. Body core
5. Seal	19. Thrust bearing	33. Sliding gears	46. Ring gear
6. Needle bearing	20. Spacer	34. Needle bearing	47. Pinion gears (8)
7. Transmission output gear	21. Bevel gear	35. Gear (33T)	48. Body core
8. Shift rail	22. Gear (low range)	36. Output shaft	49. Snap ring
9. Snap rings	23. Shaft	37. Thrust washer	50. Axle gear
10. Shift fork	24. Spacer	38. Needle bearing	51. Thrust washer
11. Quad ring	25. Gear (high range)	39. Needle bearing	52. Differential carrier (R.H.)
12. Tapered roller bearing	26. Thrust washer	40. Axle shaft (L.H.)	53. Cap screw
13. Cover	27. Needle bearing	41. Differential carrier (L.H.)	54. Axle shaft (R.H.)
14. Seal	28. Dowel pin		

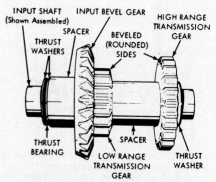

Fig. G48 – View of reduction drive input shaft and gears. Note position of bevels on gears.

NOTE: On some models, hydraulic system may be filled at factory with either Type "A" (red) automatic transmission fluid or SAE 20W (honey color) "SE" rated engine oil. Do not intermix the two type fluids.

TESTING

Hydrostatic Drive Models So Equipped

Hydraulic lift maximum pressure should be 800 psi (5516 kPa) on Models 53027 and 53028. System pressure is regulated by a pressure relief valve located in lift control valve. On all other models, maximum lift pressure should be 500 psi (3447 kPa). Pressure is regulated by auxiliary circuit relief valve located in hydrostatic transmission center section.

To check pressure on all models, proceed as follows: Using a tee fitting, install a 1000 psi (7000 kPa) pressure gage in hydraulic line between control valve and lift cylinder on "lifting" side of cylinder. With oil at operating temperature and engine running at full rpm, actuate control lever until cylinder reaches end of its travel and observe pressure reading. On Models 53027 and 53028, relief valve setting can be adjusted by turning relief valve set screw located in end of control valve – ¼-turn equals approximately 120 psi (827 kPa).

If pressure is low, check the following:
1. System low on oil.
2. Plugged hydraulic filter.
3. Malfunctioning implement relief valve.
4. Hydraulic valve or cylinder leaking internally.
5. Charge pump defective.

Gear Drive Models So Equipped

Hydraulic life system maximum pressure should be 500 psi (3447 kPa). Pressure is regulated by a relief valve (17 – Fig. G49) located in hydraulic unit valve body.

To check lift system pressure, install a 1000 psi (7000 kPa) pressure gage in hydraulic line between hydraulic unit and "lifting" side of cylinder using a tee fitting. With oil at operating temperature and engine running at full rpm, actuate control lever to move cylinder to end of its travel and observe pressure reading. If pressure is low, check the following:
1. System low on oil.
2. Malfunctioning pressure relief valve.
3. Hydraulic cylinder leaking internally.
4. Pump or control valve defective.

HYDRAULIC PUMP

Hydrostatic Drive Models So Equipped

On hydrostatic drive models, hydrostatic transmission charge pump is power source for hydraulic system. Refer to appropriate HYDROSTATIC TRANSMISSION SERVICE section for charge pump service procedures.

Gear Drive Models So Equipped

To disassemble hydraulic unit, first thoroughly clean exterior of unit and refer to Fig. G49. Remove filler plug (19) and drain fluid from reservoir. Unscrew retaining nut (23) and remove reservoir (20). Remove pump cover (12) and withdraw drive gear (15), idler gear (13) and idler shaft (16). Remove pressure relief valve assembly (17). Remove snap ring (1) and withdraw spool valve (6).

Inspect all parts for excessive wear or other damage. If spool or body is worn or damaged, it is recommended that complete hydraulic unit be renewed. Reassemble unit by reversing disassembly procedure. Reinstall unit on tractor and adjust drive belt tension so belt deflects ⅛ to ¼-inch (3-6 mm) midway between pulleys under finger pressure.

CONTROL VALVE

Gear Drive Models So Equipped

On gear drive models, refer to HYDRAULIC PUMP paragraphs for service procedure covering control unit and pump assembly.

Hydrostatic Drive Models So Equipped

Before beginning disassembly of valve, thoroughly clean exterior of valve. Remove screw (1 – Fig. G50) from end of spool (7), then pull spool out con-

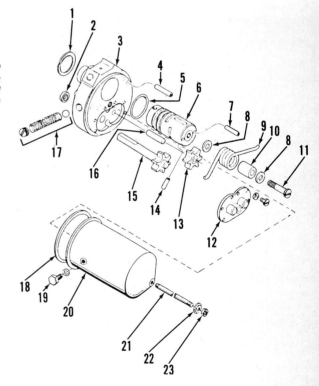

Fig. G49—Exploded view of self-contained hydraulic unit used on gear drive model tractors equipped with hydraulic lift.
1. Snap ring
2. Oil seal
3. Body
4. Roll pin (3/16 x 1-1/2 in.)
5. "O" ring
6. Spool valve
7. Roll pin (5/32 x 1-1/4 in.)
8. Washers
9. Centering spring
10. Sleeve
11. Retaining screw
12. Pump cover
13. Idler gear
14. Roll pin (5/32 x 7/8 in.)
15. Drive gear
16. Idler shaft
17. Relief valve assy.
18. Gasket
19. Plug
20. Reservoir
21. Stud
22. Special washer
23. Nut

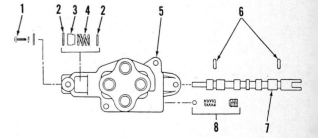

Fig. G50—Exploded view of typical hydraulic lift control valve used on hydrostatic drive model tractors. Open side of lip seals (6) goes towards center of spool.
1. Screw
2. Washers
3. Spacer
4. Centering spring
5. Valve body
6. Lip seals
7. Valve spool
8. Relief valve assy.

trol lever end of valve body. Remove washers (2), spacer (3) and centering spring (4). Unscrew set screw and remove relief valve spring and ball (8).

Inspect parts for wear or other damage. If spool or body is damaged, complete valve assembly must be renewed. Install new seals (6) over each end of spool with open "V" side of seals facing each other. Coat all parts with clean oil and reassemble by reversing disassembly procedure. Be sure end of spool moves through centering spring and washers easily. Reinstall valve assembly and check and adjust relief valve setting as outlined in TESTING paragraph.

HYDRAULIC CYLINDER

All Models So Equipped

To disassemble hydraulic cylinder, first thoroughly clean outside of cylinder and refer to Fig. G51. Note positions of hose fittings, then remove fittings from cylinder body. Remove head (1), guide (8) and piston assembly (6) from tube (3).

Clean and inspect parts and renew as needed. Renew all "O" rings and back-up washers. Coat all parts with clean oil

prior to reassembly. Be sure "O" rings are not cut or twisted when reassembling.

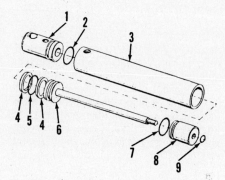

Fig. G51 — Exploded view of typical hydraulic cylinder used on all models equipped with hydraulic lift.

1. Head
2. "O" ring
3. Tube
4. Back-up washers
5. "O" ring
6. Piston assy
7. "O" ring
8. Guide
9. "O" ring

SAFETY INTERLOCK SWITCHES

All Models So Equipped

Some models are equipped with an interlock system which will allow engine to start only if clutch-brake or neutral-brake pedal is fully depressed. On later models, pto lever must also be in disengaged position or held in START position before engine will start.

If engine will not start with controls in correct position, check the following: Check interlock switches to be sure contact is made when controls are moved to starting position. If interlock switches are not being actuated, readjust as necessary. Check for broken or disconnected wires. Use a test light to check continuity and repair as needed.

CAUTION: Being able to start engine without moving pto control to disengaged or start position and/or fully depressing foot pedal is dangerous and should be corrected immediately.

GRAVELY

CONDENSED SPECIFICATIONS

MODELS

	408	424	424	430	430
Engine Make	Kohler	Kohler	Onan	Kohler	Onan
Model	K181	K241	NB	K301	NB
Bore	2-15/16 in.	3¼ in.	3-9/16 in.	3⅜ in.	3-9/16 in.
	(74.6 mm)	(82.5 mm)	(90.5 mm)	(85.7 mm)	(90.5 mm)
Stroke	2¾ in.	2⅞ in.	3 in.	3¼ in.	3 in.
	(69.8 mm)	(73.0 mm)	(76.2 mm)	(82.5 mm)	(76.2 mm)
Piston Displacement	18.6 cu. in.	23.9 cu. in.	30.0 cu. in.	29.07 cu. in.	30.0 cu. in.
	(305 cc)	(392 cc)	(492 cc)	(476 cc)	(492 cc)
Horsepower	8	10	10	12	12
Slow Idle Speed – Rpm	1000	1200	1000	1200	1000
High Idle Speed (No Load) – Rpm	3800	3600	3600	3600	3600
Full Load Speed – Rpm	3600	3240	3000	3240	3000
Crankcase Oil Capacity	2½ pints	5 pints	4 pints	5 pints	4 pints
	(1.2L)	(2.4L)	(1.9L)	(2.4L)	(1.9L)
Weight –					
Above 32°F (0°C)			SAE 30		
0°F (–18°C) to 32°F (0°C)			SAE 10W-30		
Below 0°F (–18°C)			SAE 5W-20		
Transmission Oil Capacity	6 pints	10 pints	10 pints	10 pints	10 pints
	(2.8L)	(4.7L)	(4.7L)	(4.7L)	(4.7L)
Weight			SAE 90 EP		

MODELS

	432	810	812	814	816S
Engine Make	Kohler	Kohler	Kohler	Kohler	B&S
Model	K321	K241	K301	K321	326437
Bore	3½ in.	3¼ in.	3⅜ in.	3½ in.	3-9/16 in.
	(88.9 mm)	(82.5 mm)	(85.7 mm)	(88.9 mm)	(90.5 mm)
Stroke	3¼ in.	2⅞ in.	3¼ in.	3¼ in.	3¼ in.
	(82.5 mm)	(73.0 mm)	(82.5 mm)	(82.5 mm)	(82.5 mm)
Piston Displacement	31.27 cu. in.	23.9 cu. in.	29.07 cu. in.	31.27 cu. in.	32.4 cu. in.
	(512 cc)	(392 cc)	(476 cc)	(512 cc)	(531 cc)
Horsepower	14	10	12	14	16
Slow Idle Speed – Rpm	1200	1200	1200	1200	1200
High Idle Speed (No Load) – Rpm	3600	3600	3600	3600	3600
Full Load Speed – Rpm	3240	3240	3240	3240	3240
Crankcase Oil Capacity	5 pints	5 pints	5 pints	5 pints	4 pints
	(2.4L)	(2.4L)	(2.4L)	(2.4L)	(1.9L)
Weight –					
Above 32°F (0°C)			SAE 30		
0°F (–18°C) to 32°F (0°C)			SAE 10W-30		
Below 0°F (–18°C)			SAE 5W-20		
Transmission Oil Capacity	10 pints	12 pints	12 pints	12 pints	12 pints
	(4.7L)	(5.7L)	(5.7L)	(5.7L)	(5.7L)
Weight	SAE 90 EP		SAE 30		

	MODELS			
	8102	8120, 8121	8122, 8123	8163B
Engine Make	Kohler	Kohler	Kohler	B&S
Model	K241	K301	K301	326437
Bore	3¼ in. (82.5 mm)	3⅜ in. (85.7 mm)	3⅜ in. (85.7 mm)	3-9/16 in. (90.5 mm)
Stroke	2⅞ in. (73.0 mm)	3¼ in. (82.5 mm)	3¼ in. (82.5 mm)	3¼ in. (82.5 mm)
Piston Displacement	23.9 cu. in. (392 cc)	29.07 cu. in. (476 cc)	29.07 cu. in. (476 cc)	32.4 cu. in. (531 cc)
Horsepower	10	12	12	16
Slow Idle Speed – Rpm	1200	1200	1200	1200
High Idle Speed (No Load) – Rpm	3600	3600	3600	3600
Full Load Speed – Rpm	3240	3240	3240	3240
Crankcase Oil Capacity	5 pints (2.4L)	5 pints (2.4L)	5 pints (2.4L)	4 pints (1.9L)
Weight–				
Above 32°F (0°C)	SAE 30			
0°F (−18°C) to 32°F (0°C)	SAE 10W-30			
Below 0°F (−18°C)	SAE 5W-20			
Transmission Oil Capacity	12 pints (5.7L)			
Weight	SAE 30			

FRONT AXLE AND STEERING SYSTEM

AXLE MAIN MEMBER

Model 408

The axle main member (5–Fig. GR1) is mounted directly to front of main frame and pivots on pin (6). To remove front axle main member, disconnect tie rods (4) from steering spindles (1 and 7). Support front of tractor and remove pivot pin (6). Raise front of tractor and roll axle assembly away from tractor.

Reinstall axle by reversing removal procedure. Lubricate with multi-purpose grease.

Models 424-430-432 – Early Models 810-812-814

The axle main member (1–Fig. GR2 or GR3) is mounted directly to front of main frame and pivots on pin (5). To remove front axle main member, disconnect tie rod (2) ends from steering arms (3). Support front of tractor, remove pivot pin (5) and roll axle assembly from tractor.

Inspect parts for wear or other damage and renew as necessary. Reassembly is reverse of removal procedure.

Lubricate pivot pin with multi-purpose grease.

Models 816S-8102-8121-8122-8123-8163B – Late Models 810-812-814

The axle main member (15–Fig. GR7) is mounted directly to main frame and pivots on bolt (17). To remove front axle, disconnect tie rod ends (13) from steering arms (8). Support front of tractor, remove pivot bolt (17) and roll axle assembly from tractor.

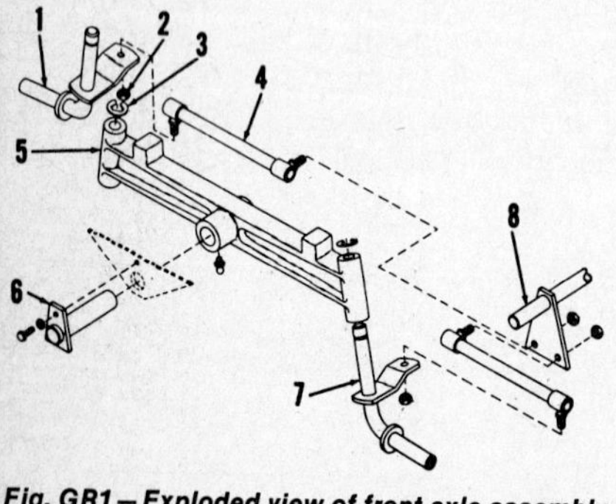

Fig. GR1 – Exploded view of front axle assembly used on Model 408.

1. Steering spindle R.H.
2. Nut
3. "E" ring
4. Tie rod
5. Axle main member
6. Pivot pin
7. Steering spindle L.H.
8. Steering shaft

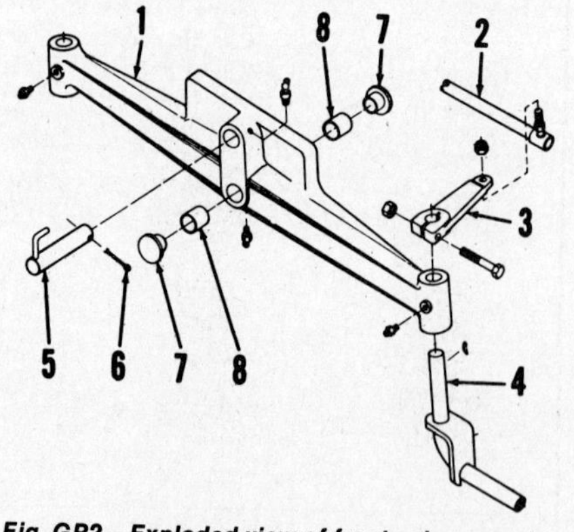

Fig. GR2 – Exploded view of front axle assembly used on Models 424, 430 and 432.

1. Axle main member
2. Tie rod
3. Steering arm
4. Steering spindle
5. Pivot pin
6. Cotter pin
7. Plug
8. Pto shaft bushing

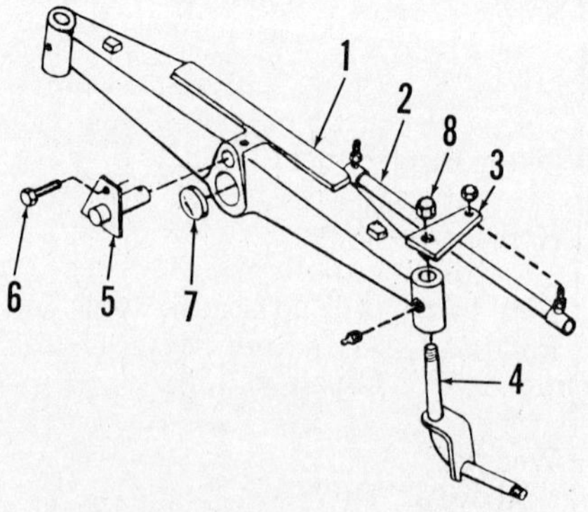

Fig. GR3 – Exploded view of front axle assembly used on early Models 810, 812 and 814.

1. Axle main member
2. Tie rod
3. Steering arm
4. Steering spindle
5. Pivot pin
6. Cap screw
7. Plug
8. Nut

SERVICE

Reinstall axle by reversing removal procedure. Lubricate with multi-purpose grease.

TIE RODS

Models 408-424-430-432 — Early Models 810-812-814

The tie rods are non-adjustable. If ball joints are excessively worn, renew tie rod assemblies.

Models 816S-8102-8120-8121-8122-8123-8163B — Late Models 810-812-814

Toe-in of 0 to ¾-inch (0-19 mm) is recommended. Measure toe-in at wheel hub height at front and back of tires. To adjust toe-in, first check which wheel is excessively toed-in or out. Disconnect tie rod ball joint (13 – Fig. GR7) from steering arm (18) and turn tie rod ends as necessary to obtain desired toe-in. Renew ball joints that are excessively worn.

STEERING SPINDLES

Model 408

To remove steering spindles (1 and 7 – Fig. GR1), support front of tractor and remove wheels. Disconnect tie rods from steering spindles. Remove "E" ring (3) and lower steering spindles out of axle.

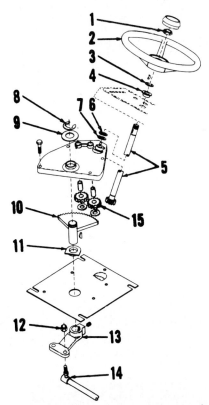

Fig. GR5 — View of exposed steering gear system used on early Models 424, 430 and 432.

Lubricate with multi-purpose grease and reassemble in reverse of removal.

Models 424-430-432 — Early Models 810-812-814

To remove steering spindles (4 – Fig. GR2 or GR3), support front of tractor and remove wheels. Disconnect tie rods from steering arms (3). Unscrew clamp bolt or retaining nut and remove steer-

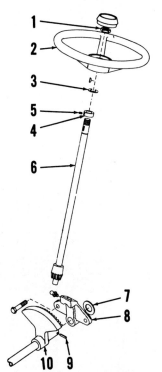

Fig. GR4 — Exploded view of steering gear assembly used on Model 408.

1. Nut	
2. Steering wheel	7. Washer
3. "E" ring	8. Bracket
4. Collar	9. Pin
5. Set screw	10. Quadrant gear &
6. Steering shaft	shaft

Fig. GR6 — Exploded view of enclosed steering gear assembly used on late Models 424, 430 and 432 tractors and early Models 810, 812 and 814 tractors.

1. Nut		8. "E" ring	
2. Steering wheel		9. Washer	
3. "E" ring		10. Quadrant gear	
4. Bushing		11. Bushing	
5. Steering shaft &		12. Nut	
pinion		13. Steering arm	
6. "E" ring		14. Tie rod	
7. Washer		15. Spur gears	

ing arm. Lower steering spindle out of axle.

Inspect for excessive wear or other damage and renew as required. Lubricate with multi-purpose grease.

Models 816S-8102-8120-8121-8122-8123-8163B — Late Models 810-812-814

To remove steering spindles (19 – Fig. GR7), support front of tractor and remove wheels. Disconnect tie rods from spindle arms (18) and remove locknut securing arms to spindles. Slide steering arms off splines and withdraw spindles from axle.

Steering spindles are interchangeable. Lubricate with multi-purpose grease.

STEERING GEAR

Model 408

To remove steering assembly, disconnect tie rods from steering plate. Remove bolts from bracket (8 – Fig. GR4) and lower bracket, gear and shaft from tractor. Remove steering shaft nut (1) and remove steering wheel. Remove key and "E" ring (3). Loosen set screw (5) and lower steering shaft (6) out of tractor.

Reassembly is reverse of disassembly procedure. Adjust mesh of quadrant gear (10) to steering shaft gear by adding or removing washers (7). Lubricate with multi-purpose grease at fitting on bracket (8) and apply thin layer of grease on teeth of steering gears.

Models 424-430-432 — Early Models 810-812-814

EXPOSED STEERING GEAR. Early 424, 430 and 432 models are equipped with an exposed steering gear system as shown in Fig. GR5. To remove quadrant steering gear, disconnect tie rod ends from gear and remove cotter pin holding pivot pin. Remove pivot pin and slide gear out of tractor. To remove steering shaft, remove steering wheel and snap ring. Remove cotter pin holding shaft in frame cross member. Raise shaft up out of frame cross member, then lower shaft out of tractor.

Reassemble steering gear assembly in reverse order of disassembly. Lubricate quadrant gear at grease fitting with multi-purpose grease and apply thin layer of grease on gear teeth.

ENCLOSED STEERING GEAR. Early Models 810, 812 and 814 and later Models 424, 430 and 432 are equipped with an enclosed steering gear system. See Fig. GR6. To remove steering gear assembly, remove hood, fuel tank and battery. Remove steering wheel and "E" ring (3) from steering shaft (5). Disconnect tie rod ends from steering arm (13) and remove bolts securing gear box to frame. Lower gear box and steering shaft down through frame and out of tractor.

To disassemble unit, remove steering arm (13) and mounting plate. Remove "E" ring (8) and withdraw quadrant gear (10). Remove "E" ring (6) and spacer (7) and withdraw steering shaft. On Models 810, 812 and 814, pinion gear may be removed from steering shaft.

Clean and inspect all parts for excessive wear or other damage and renew as necessary. Reassemble in reverse order of disassembly. Pack housing with multi-purpose grease before reinstalling mounting plate.

Models 816S-8102-8120-8121-8122-8123-8163B — Late Models 810-812-814

These tractors are equipped with rack and pinion steering as shown in Fig. GR8. To remove steering shaft (4–Fig. GR7), remove steering wheel, bushing (2) and retainer ring (3). Remove steering shaft nut (12) and withdraw shaft. Disconnect tie rod ends from steering arms (8). Unbolt and remove steering arms, rack (5) and bearing support (10).

Reassembly is reverse of disassembly procedure. Be sure front wheels are positioned straight ahead when installing steering shaft (4). Tighten adjusting nuts (26) to obtain desired gear mesh, then tighten locknuts (27) to secure adjustment. Lubricate with multi-purpose grease.

ENGINE

REMOVE AND REINSTALL

Model 408

To remove engine, remove hood and grille assembly. Remove ground cable from battery and remove belt guard. Disconnect choke and throttle control cables. Disconnect starter cable from starter. Disconnect wiring harness at connector under fuel tank. Slip drive belts off engine drive pulley. Remove engine mounting bolts and lift engine out of tractor.

To reinstall engine, reverse removal procedure.

All Other Models

To remove engine, remove seat and fender assembly and drain transmission oil. Detach ground cable from battery. Disconnect fuel line, choke and throttle cables and starter cable. Disconnect wiring harness connector and remove rear hitch. Use a suitable hoist to support engine. Remove engine bolts and lift engine from tractor.

Refer to Fig. GR9 and remove transmission input gear, thrust bearing and

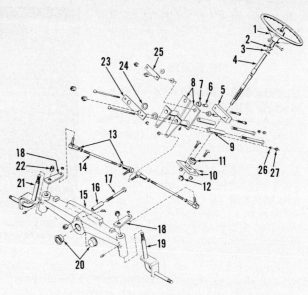

Fig. GR7 — Exploded view of front axle and steering assembly used on late Model 810, 812, 814, 816S and 8000 series tractors.

1. Steering wheel
2. Bushing
3. Retainer ring
4. Steering shaft
5. Rack
6. Rack bushings
7. Flange bearing
8. Steering arm
9. Pivot sleeve
10. Bearing support
11. Bearing
12. Locknut
13. Ball joint
14. Tie rod
15. Axle main member
16. Axle pivot tube
17. Pivot bolt
18. Spindle arms
19. Steering spindle L.H.
20. Caps
21. Steering spindle R.H.
22. Locknut
23. Adjustment plate
24. Thrust washer
25. Strap
26. Adjusting nut
27. Locknut

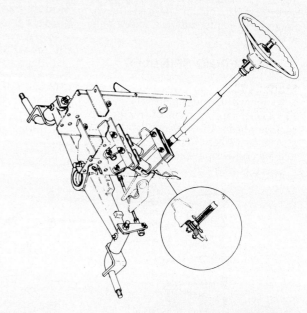

Fig. GR8 — View of front axle and steering assembly used on 8000 series tractors and late Model 810, 812, 814 and 816S tractors.

engine adapter. When reassembling, renew "O" ring seal.

OVERHAUL

All Models

Engine make and model are listed at the beginning of this section. To overhaul engine, refer to appropriate engine section in this manual.

CLUTCH AND BRAKES

Model 408

A belt idler type clutch is used on Model 408 tractor. To adjust clutch, depress clutch pedal and turn adjusting nuts (8 – Fig. GR10) until top of belt idler

Fig. GR9 — View of typical engine adapter plate, transmission input gear, key, "O" ring and thrust bearing used on all models except Model 408. Use suitable gear puller to remove input gear.

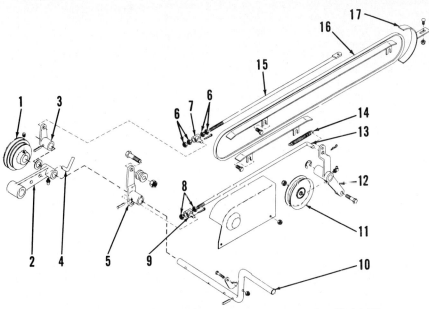

Fig. GR10—Exploded view of clutch-brake system used on Model 408.

1. Engine pulley
2. Pto arm
3. Brake lever
4. Pto rod
5. Clutch arm
6. Adjusting nuts

7. Trunnion
8. Adjusting nuts
9. Trunnion
10. Clutch-brake pedal
11. Clutch pulley

12. Clutch lever
13. Clutch rod
14. Spring
15. Brake rod
16. Drive belt
17. Belt guard

pulley (11) is level with bottom of transmission pulley.

To adjust brake, turn adjusting nuts (6) on brake rod until desired brake action is obtained. Be sure brake does not engage before clutch is disengaged, but there should be sufficient braking action with pedal fully depressed.

Models 424-430-432

Clutch is mounted integrally with transmission; refer to transmission section for servicing. To accomplish clutch adjustment, turn adjusting nuts on Hi-Lo and Forward-Reverse control rods so springs are nearly compressed as control lever is locked into position. Adjust-

ment must be made for each lever position. If clutch slippage still occurs after adjustment is made, refer to transmission section and inspect clutch assembly.

Models 424, 430 and 432 are equipped with band type brakes at each rear wheel and operate independently of each other. Brake action is adjusted by turning nut (N–Fig. GR11) on brake band stud.

Models 810-812-814-816S-8102-8120-8121-8122-8123-8163B

Clutches for forward and reverse speeds are mounted at sides of transmission; forward clutch on right side, reverse clutch on left side. Clutch action is adjusted by placing forward-reverse lever in neutral position and disconnecting clutch rods (4–Fig. GR12). Loosen or tighten nuts (1) until there is 0.020-0.030 inch (0.508-0.762 mm) gap between clutch discs (2). Be sure forward-reverse lever is vertical. Adjust length of clutch rods by turning rods in yoke (5) until rod can be connected to clutch cam (3) without disturbing position of cam or forward-reverse lever.

All models have as standard equipment a band type brake (6) mounted on transmission shaft. Adjust brake by turning brake rod (8) in yoke. Be sure brake linkage cam (7) returns direction control clutches to neutral position before brake begins to apply.

Individual rear wheel drum brakes are available as a kit for some models. Adjust each brake by disconnecting clevis (2–Fig. GR13) from brake arm (1) and turning clevis on brake rod until desired brake action is obtained.

TRANSAXLE

REMOVE AND REINSTALL

Model 408

To remove transaxle, remove belt guard and remove drive belt from transaxle pulley. Disconnect brake rod and re-

Fig. GR12 — View of right side of Model 810 transmission showing forward-reverse clutch and transmission brake. Other models are similar.

1. Adjusting nuts
2. Clutch discs
3. Clutch cam
4. Clutch rod
5. Yoke
6. Transmission brake
7. Brake cam
8. Brake rod

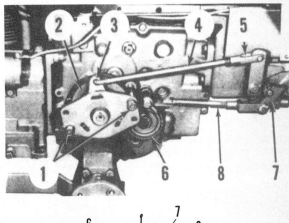

Fig. GR13 — Exploded view of rear wheel band type brake available as a kit for some models. Right side brake is similar.

1. Brake arm
2. Clevis
3. Pin
4. Jam nut
5. Brake rod
6. Spring
7. Brake lever
8. Mounting plate
9. Actuating arm
10. Brake band
11. Drum

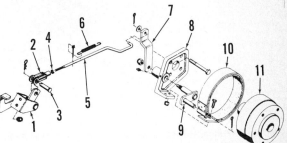

Fig. GR11—Brake action on Models 424, 430 and 432 is adjusted by turning nut (N).

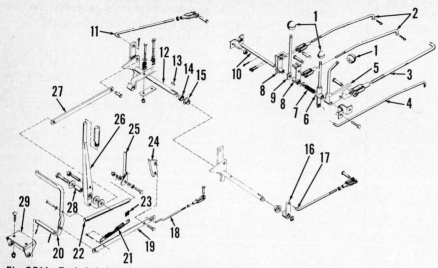

Fig. GR14—Exploded view of clutch and brake linkage used on 8000 series and late Model 810, 812, 814 and 816S tractors.

1. Knob	11. Forward clutch rod	21. Spring
2. Shifting rod	12. Clutch shaft bracket	22. Parking brake rod
3. Pto rod	13. Key	23. Clip
4. 2-speed rod	14. Spacer	24. Brake cam
5. Pto control assy.	15. Bushing	25. Parking brake bracket
6. 2-speed control	16. Reverse clutch arm	26. Forward-Reverse
7. Spring	17. Reverse clutch rod	lever
8. Shifter arm	18. Link	27. Shifter link
9. Shift lever	19. Link	28. Bushing
10. Cross shaft	20. Brake pedal	29. Brake pedal bracket

move brake band assembly. Remove bracket holding transaxle to frame. Remove shift lever knob. Disconnect forward-reverse control rod from shift strap. Remove spring from frame. Remove clamps securing transaxle to tractor frame. Lift rear of tractor frame and roll transaxle away from tractor.

Models 424-430-432

To remove transaxle, remove seat and rear fender assembly. Remove engine as previously outlined. Disconnect brake control rods at brakes. Disconnect lift attachment control rod and transaxle control rods. Disconnect attachment control rod at front end of transaxle. Support rear of tractor frame and remove transaxle retaining bolts and roll transaxle away from tractor.

Models 810-812-814-816S-8102-8120-8121-8122-8123-8163B

To remove transaxle, remove engine as previously outlined. Detach hydraulic lines from pump and drain hydraulic reservoir on models equipped with hydraulic lift. Detach forward and reverse clutch rods from clutch cams (3 – Fig. GR12) and two-speed rod from shifter arm. Remove shift rods from 1-3 and 2-4 shift arms. Remove pto rod from pto lever and lift rod from cross shaft. Detach brake rod from brake band and unscrew bolts securing cross shaft to transmission. Raise cross shaft up to clear transmission. Block rear wheels and support front of transmission. Unscrew transmission to frame bolts and roll frame and forward section of tractor away from transmission.

OVERHAUL

Model 408

To disassemble transaxle, first remove transaxle as previously outlined. Drain lubricant from transaxle and remove brake drum, input pulley, rear hitch, shift lever (77 – Fig. GR16) and rear wheels.

Position transaxle so left axle is down. Unscrew cover screws and lift cover (76) off case (43). Remove sliding gear (62), washer (61), shift fork (74) and shift rod (73). Remove shift rod (69), shift fork (68), sliding gear (63), shaft (64) and gear (66). Remove gear (6), shaft (7) and gear (8). Remove forward-reverse shift shaft (11), shift fork (12), sliding gear (15) and input shaft (16). Remove gears (26, 28 and 30) and shaft (29). Remove gears (48 and 50) and shaft (49). Remove gears (56, 58 and 60), shaft (57) and spacer (59). Remove "E" ring (35) from end of left axle and remove side gear (36) and differential assembly components (37 through 41). Remove washer (52), shaft (53) and gears (54 and 55). Remove axles from case and cover if necessary. Right axle and side gear (34) are retained in cover by "E" ring (35). Disassembly of differential is evident after inspection of unit. Note position of pinion gears (39).

Inspect all components and renew any parts showing damage or excessive wear. To reassemble transaxle, reverse disassembly procedure. When cover assembly is placed on case assembly, there will be approximately one inch gap between case and cover due to case dropping down on axle. Raise case to start bolts. Tighten bolts evenly. Fill transaxle with 6 pints (2.8L) of SAE 90 EP gear oil.

Models 424-430-432

To overhaul transaxle, first remove transaxle from tractor as previously outlined.

To overhaul transaxle sub-assemblies, refer to following paragraphs.

FORWARD-REVERSE SYSTEM. The forward-reverse clutch and gears are housed in front part of transaxle. Remove advance housing (52 – Fig. GR17) and rotate forward-reverse actuating shaft (2) so planetary system is released. Remove clutch and planetary components (45 through 50 and 25 through 36). Note that spacer plate bolts (25) have left hand threads. Inspect components for damage or excessive wear. Inspect clutch cup (48) friction surfaces and renew cup if excessively worn. Inspect surfaces of reverse gear (49) and internal gear (47) and renew if excessively scored to prevent rapid wear of clutch cup.

To reassemble unit, reverse disassem-

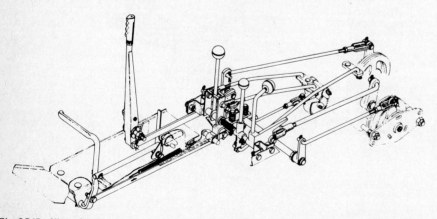

Fig. GR15—View of transmission and brake linkage used on 8000 series and late Model 810, 812, 814 and 816S tractors.

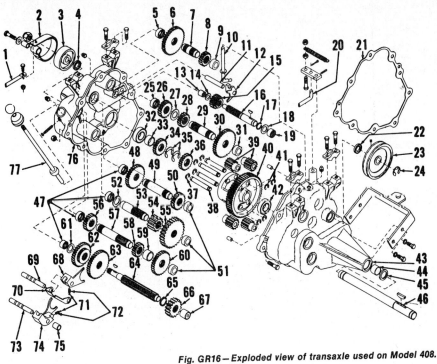

1. Brake rod
2. Brake band
3. Brake drum
4. Oil seal
5. Bearing
6. Gear
7. Shaft
8. Gear
9. Bearing
10. Forward-Reverse shift lever
11. Shift shaft
12. Forward-Reverse shift fork
13. Bearing
14. Thrust washer
15. Sliding gear
16. Input shaft
17. Snap ring
18. Thrust washer
19. Bearing
20. Forward-Reverse shift rod
21. Gasket
22. Oil seal
23. Input pulley
24. "E" ring
25. Bearing
26. Gear
27. Thrust washer
28. Gear
29. Shaft
30. Gear
31. Bearing
32. Bearing
33. Spacer
34. Gear
35. "E" ring
36. Gear
37. "E" ring
38. Pinion pin

39. Pinion gears
40. Ring gear
41. "E" ring
42. Bearing
43. Case
44. Bushing
45. Oil seal
46. Axle shaft
47. Bearings
48. Gear
49. Shaft
50. Gear
51. Bearings
52. Thrust washer
53. Shaft
54. Gear
55. Gear
56. Gear
57. Shaft
58. Gear
59. Spacer
60. Gear
61. Thrust washer
62. Sliding gear (2nd-4th)
63. Sliding gear (1st-3rd)
64. Shaft
65. Snap ring
66. Gear
67. Bearing
68. Shift fork (1st-3rd)
69. Shift shaft
70. Shift stop
71. Shift balls
72. Springs
73. Shift shaft
74. Shift fork (2nd-4th)
75. Spacer
76. Cover
77. Shift lever

Fig. GR16—Exploded view of transaxle used on Model 408.

Fig. GR17—Exploded view of transaxle used on Models 424, 430 and 432.

1. Forward-Reverse lever
2. Forward-Reverse actuating shaft
3. Shift link
4. Hi-Lo actuating shaft
5. Clutch slide rod
6. Clutch slide rod
7. Clutch cup
8. Ring gear
9. Gear cup
10. Gasket
11. Thrust plate
12. Clutch plate
13. Bushing
14. Gear carrier
15. Bushing
16. Orbit gear
17. Bushing
18. Pin
19. Pin spacer
20. Orbit gear
21. Bushing
22. Pin
23. Hi-Lo lever
24. Bolt (L.H. thread)
25. Bolt (L.H. thread)
26. Pin plate
27. Reverse idler gear
28. Bushing
29. Bolt
30. Pin
31. Orbit gear
32. Bearing
33. Quill
34. Sun gear
35. Pin plate
36. Spring
37. Screw
38. Lock plate
39. Bearing adjustment nut
40. Bearing cup
41. Bearing cone
42. Shaft
43. Worm gear
44. Clutch slide rod
45. Clutch slide rod
46. Gear cup
47. Internal gear
48. Clutch cup
49. Reverse gear
50. Thrust bushing
51. Gasket
52. Advance housing
53. Gasket
54. Cover
55. Bearing
56. Thrust washer
57. Pto output shaft
58. Pto clutch dog
59. Pto shaft
60. Pto actuating shaft
61. Bearing cone
62. Bearing cup

183

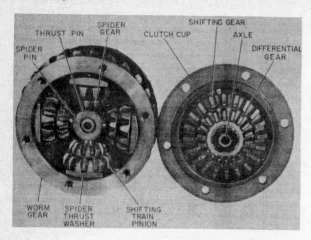

Fig. GR18 — View of differential assembly. All Model 424, 430 and 432 tractors are equipped with spider gear assembly shown in Fig. GR19.

Fig. GR21 — "E" ring (E) must be removed to separate transmission cover from case.

bly procedure. Orbit gears must be timed when installed. When orbit gears are meshed correctly with sun gear (34), small punch marks on orbit gears (31) will form an equilateral triangle.

HIGH-LOW SYSTEM. A high-low planetary gear set and clutch are located in rear of transaxle. To disassemble unit, rotate high-low actuating shaft (4 – Fig. GR17) to release planetary system and remove components (5 through 22).

Inspect components for damage or excessive wear. Inspect clutch cup (7) friction surface and renew cup if excessively worn. Inspect clutch mating surface on clutch plate (12) and ring gear (8) and renew if excessively worn to prevent rapid wear to new clutch cup. To reassemble unit, reverse disassembly procedure.

SWIFTAMATIC DIFFERENTIAL. The Swiftamatic uses a two-speed axle with a differential assembly. To disassemble, unscrew retaining cap screws and remove right axle housing (33 – Fig. GR20). Check to see that stationary clutch (31) does not move in axle housing and that sliding clutch (29) will slide freely on splines of shifter gear (23). To

disassemble differential, remove left axle housing (1) and differential assembly components (5 through 28). Inspect ring gear (20) and worm gear (43 – Fig. GR17). If renewal of worm gear is required, refer to FORWARD-REVERSE section and remove forward-reverse assembly. Unscrew bearing nut (39) and withdraw worm gear and shaft assembly.

To reassemble differential and axle

assemblies, reverse disassembly procedure. Tighten bearing nut (39 – Fig. GR17) until end play is removed from worm gear shaft. Lock nut in place with screw and lock plate (38).

Note difference between early and late differential spider gear assemblies in Figs. GR19 and GR20. On models with ring gear assembly shown in Fig. GR20, some models have only two pinion assemblies (13 through 18) and

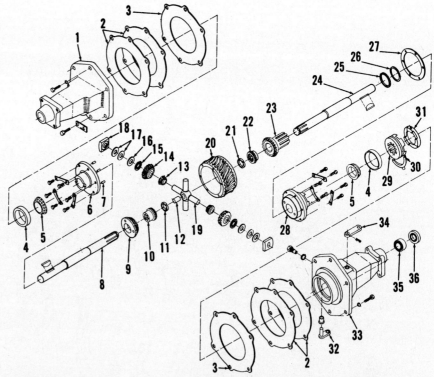

Fig. GR20 — Exploded view of Swiftamatic differential used on Models 424, 430 and 432.

1. Axle housing L.H.	13. Spider gear	25. Thrust bearing
2. Shims	14. Shifting pinion	26. Thrust washer
3. Gasket	15. Thrust bearing	27. Shim
4. Bearing cup	16. Thrust washer	28. Differential carrier
5. Bearing cone	17. Shims	29. Sliding clutch dog
6. Differential carrier	18. Thrust washer	30. Clutch yoke
7. Pin	19. Drive pin	31. Stationary clutch
8. Axle shaft	20. Ring gear	32. Shift lever
9. Shifting gear	21. Snap ring	33. Axle housing R.H.
10. Side gear	22. Side gear	34. Shift arm
11. Snap ring	23. Shifting gear	35. Bearing
12. Thrust pin	24. Axle shaft	36. Oil seal

Fig. GR19 — View of spider gear assembly used on Models 424, 430 and 432.

should be converted by adding two additional pinion assemblies to pins of the cross pin (19) as shown in Fig. GR18. On early type differential assemblies, adjust gear mesh by installing pinion gear assembly components (13 thorough 18 – Fig. GR20) in ring gear (20). Install gears (9 and 10) and carrier (6) on ring gear. Adjust size or number of shims (17) until gears have solid contact without wobble. Shims are available in sizes of 0.005 and 0.020 inch.

On all models, tighten differential carrier cap screws to 20 ft.-lbs. (27 N·m). to determine correct size and number of shims (2) to be installed, install reassembled differential assembly and place equal number and size of shims (2) with

axle housing (1 and 33) and install axle housings. Secure axle housings with two cap screws and measure axle end play. End play should be approximately 0.020 inch (0.508 mm). Change number or size of shims (2) if necessary. Shim pack should be equal on both axle housings. Final tightening of axle housing cap screws should be to 45 ft.-lbs. (61 N·m) except for bottom cap screw on left axle housing which serves as oil drain and should be tightened securely. After assembly, fill transaxle with 10 pints (4.7L) of SAE 90 EP gear oil.

Models 810-812-814-816S-8102-8120-8121-8122-8123-8163B

To overhaul transmission, refer to

previous section and remove transmission from frame. Remove clutch assemblies on each side of transmission and remove keys from shafts. Turn transmission over onto left wheel and remove right wheel and hub. Remove brake assembly from right side and "E" ring (E – Fig. GR21) from pto shaft. Clean dirt or paint from right axle and retainer and remove right axle bearing retainer (2 – Fig. GR22).

Unscrew cover screws and lift transmission cover (1) off case. Gear and bearing (19) should remain in bearing (15). Remove idler gear (6) and bearings. Remove plug (31 – Fig. GR24), spring (32) and ball (33) and remove range shifter fork (23 – Fig. GR22) along

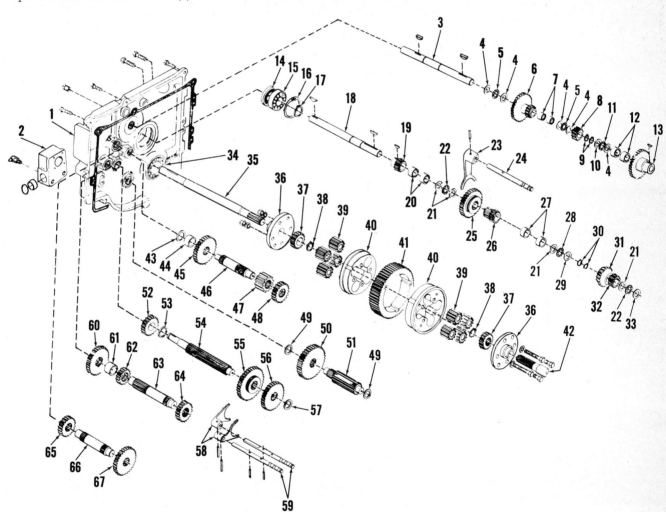

Fig. GR22 — Exploded view of transmission cover and shaft assemblies used on 800 and 8000 series tractors. Differential shown is used on early models. Refer also to Fig. GR23 and GR24.

1. Cover	26. Gear & bearing assy.	40. Body core
2. Right axle bearing retainer	27. Needle bearing	41. Ring gear
3. Shaft	28. Thrust bearing	42. Left axle shaft
4. Bearing race (0.030 in.)	29. Bearing race	43. Thrust washer
5. Thrust bearing	30. Snap ring	44. Spacer
6. Idler gear	31. Bevel gear	45. Gear
7. Needle bearing	32. Gear	46. Shaft
8. Gear	33. Bearing race (0.090 in.)	47. Gear
9. Snap rings	34. Ball bearing	48. Gear
10. Bearing race (0.090 in.)	35. Right axle shaft	49. Thrust washer
11. Thrust bearing	36. End cap	50. Gear
12. Needle bearings	37. Side gear	51. Differential pinion
13. Reverse gear	38. Snap ring	52. Gear
14. Seal	39. Pinion gears	53. Snap ring
15. Ball bearing		54. Shaft
16. Snap ring		55. Sliding gear
17. Snap ring		56. Sliding gear
18. Shaft		57. Thrust washer (0.090 in.)
19. Gear & bearing assy.		58. Shift forks
20. Needle bearing		59. Shift rods
21. Bearing race (0.030 in.)		60. Gear
22. Thrust bearing		61. Spacer
23. Hi-Lo shift fork		62. Gear
24. Shift rod		63. Shaft
25. Hi-Lo gear		64. Gear
		65. Gear
		66. Shaft
		67. Gear

with Hi-Lo gear and shaft assembly (20 through 33). Remove gear (50) and pinion shaft (51) and slide gear (52) and shaft (54) out of sliding gears. Remove gears and shaft (60 through 64) assembly. Remove gear (65) then withdraw gears and shaft (43 through 48). Remove shaft (66) and gear (67). Unscrew plugs (62–Fig. GR24), remove shift detent balls and springs and remove shift forks (58–Fig. GR22) and gears (55 and 56) noting position of forks and gears. Note that interlock pin (66–Fig. GR24) may be dislodged. Remove reverse shaft (3–Fig. GR22), gears (8 and 13) and bearings.

Slide pto yoke shaft (9) through case and remove pto yoke (11). Remove bearing cap (59), snap ring (29) and pto shaft assembly (12 through 28). Disassemble pto assembly using exploded view in Fig. GR24 as a guide. Remove differential assembly from transmission case. Disassemble differential shown in Fig. GR22 or GR23. Bevel gear differential shown in Fig. GR23 is used on tractors after S.N. 18930.

To disassemble clutch assembly, remove snap ring (43–Fig. GR24) and spring (40). Compress Belleville springs (37), remove snap ring (44) and separate clutch components.

To reassemble transmission, reverse disassembly procedure. Tighten differential bolts to 25-30 ft.-lbs. (34-41 N·m). Note location of 0.090 inch (2.286 mm) thick bearing races (10, 22 and 57–

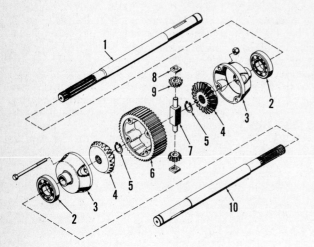

Fig. GR23—Exploded view of differential assembly used on tractors after S.N. 18930. Refer to Fig. GR22 for early model differential.

1. Axle
2. Ball bearing
3. End cap
4. Bevel gear
5. Snap ring
6. Ring gear
7. Pinion shaft
8. Drive block
9. Spider gear
10. Axle

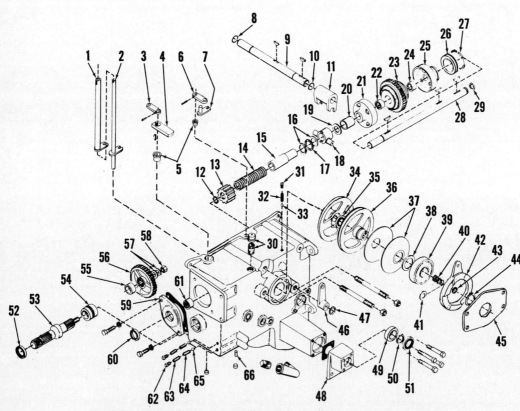

Fig. GR24—Exploded view of transmission case, pto shaft and clutch assemblies.

1. Outer shift tube
2. Inner shift shaft
3. Shift shaft shifter arm
4. Shift tube shifter arm
5. Bushing
6. Hi-Lo shift lever
7. Hi-Lo shift fork arm
8. "O" ring
9. Shaft
10. "O" ring
11. Pto yoke
12. Snap ring
13. Pto gear
14. Spring
15. Pto throwout
16. Bearing races
17. Thrust bearing
18. Pto shift collar
19. Thrust washer
20. Spacer
21. Clutch cup
22. Needle bearing
23. Clutch cone
24. Needle bearing
25. Clutch cup
26. Ball bearing
27. Snap ring
28. Pto shaft
29. Snap ring
30. Fill pipe & cup
31. Plug
32. Spring
33. Hi-Lo detent ball
34. Clutch hub
35. Oil seal
36. Clutch disc
37. Belleville spring
38. Shim
39. Ball bearing
40. Spring
41. Washer
42. Clutch cam
43. Snap ring
44. Snap ring
45. Clutch plate
46. Pto arm
47. Snap ring
48. Left axle bearing retainer
49. Ball bearing
50. Snap ring
51. Seal
52. Seal
53. Pto shaft
54. Bearing
55. Spacer
56. Pto gear
57. Washers
58. Locknut
59. Bearing cap
60. Seal
61. Bearing
62. Plug
63. Plug
64. Spring
65. Detent ball
66. Pin

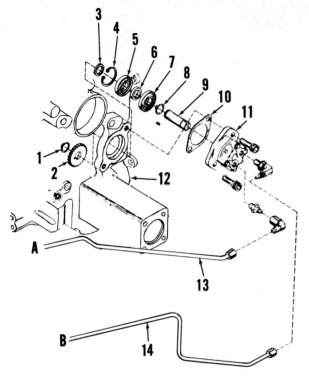

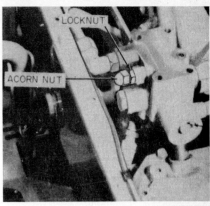

Fig. GR27 — Adjust hydraulic pressure by removing acorn nut, loosening locknut and turning screw covered by acorn nut.

Fig. GR25 — Exploded view of hydraulic pump drive. Also refer to Fig. GR26.

1. Snap ring
2. Pump gear
3. Spacer
4. Snap ring
5. Ball bearing
6. Spacer
7. Ball bearing
8. Snap ring
9. Shaft
10. Gasket
11. Hydraulic pump
12. Transmission case
13. Intake line
14. Exhaust line

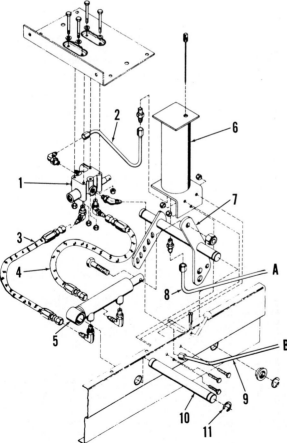

Fig. GR26 — View of hydraulic lift system. Refer to Fig. GR25 for view of hydraulic pump drive.

1. Control valve return
2. Valve-to-reservoir line
3. Hydraulic hose
4. Hydraulic hose
5. Cylinder
6. Reservoir
7. Lift lever
8. Pump intake line
9. Pump exhaust line
10. Shaft
11. "E" ring

Fig. GR22) and 0.030 inch (0.762 mm) thick bearing races (4 and 21). Adjust clutch clearance to 0.030 inch (0.762 mm). Fill transmission with 12 pints (5.7L) of SAE 30 engine oil API classification SE.

HYDRAULIC LIFT

All Models So Equipped

Refer to Fig. GR25 for an exploded view of hydraulic pump drive used on models equipped with hydraulic lift. Remainder of hydraulic system is shown in Fig. GR26. Hydraulic pump is driven by gear (32 – Fig. GR22) in transmission.

Recommended fluid for hydraulic system is Type "A" Suffix "A" automatic transmission fluid such as Shell Donax T-6 or Gulf Dexon ATF. Capacity is 1½ quarts (1.4L) and may be checked with dipstick in reservoir (6 – Fig. GR26). Fluid level should be maintained at "FULL" mark on dipstick.

To check hydraulic system pressure, install a tee fitting in place of 90 degree elbow at "OUT" port of hydraulic pump. Connect hydraulic line to one side of tee and a pressure gage which reads at least 1500 psi (10,000 kPa) to other side of tee. Recheck hydraulic fluid level. Start tractor engine and accelerate to full throttle. Operate hydraulic lift. Pressure should read 950-1050 psi (6550-7240 kPa) when cylinder reaches limit in either direction. If pressure is less than 950 psi (6550 kPa), remove acorn nut (Fig. GR27), loosen locknut and turn screw clockwise ¼-turn and recheck pressure. Do not set pressure higher than 1050 psi (7240 kPa). Pump or control valve is defective if pressure cannot be adjusted to desired pressure.

HONDA
CONDENSED SPECIFICATIONS

	MODEL 3810		MODEL (Cont.) 3810
Engine Make	Honda	Slow Idle Speed	2200
Model	G400	Full Load Speed (Rpm)	3600
Bore	86 mm	Crankcase Oil Capacity	1.2 L
	(3.4 in.)		(1.27 qt.)
Stroke	70 mm	Weight	SAE 10W-40
	(2.8 in.)	Transaxle Oil Capacity	2.4 L
Piston Displacement	406 cc		(2.54 qt.)
	(24.9 cu. in.)	Weight	SAE 10W-40
Horsepower	10		

FRONT AXLE AND STEERING SYSTEM

AXLE MAIN MEMBER

REMOVE AND REINSTALL. To remove axle main member (3–Fig. HN50), raise and support front of tractor. Disconnect outer drag link (8) end. Support main member and remove axle pivot bolt (9). Lower axle main member from main frame pivot point and roll axle out from under tractor.

When reinstalling axle main member, lubricate pivot bolt (9) with lithium base grease prior to installation.

TIE ROD

The tie rod is equipped with threaded ends (4–Fig. HN50) at each end. Recommended toe-in is 3 mm (⅛ inch). Adjust length of tie rod by threading ends in or out as required.

STEERING SPINDLES

REMOVE AND REINSTALL. To remove steering spindles, raise and support front of tractor. Remove left and right hub caps and remove cotter pins, castle nuts and flat washers. Remove tires, wheels and bearings. Disconnect tie rod ends at spindle to be removed.

To remove left spindle, remove clamp bolt (6–Fig. HN50) and spread steering lever (7) open to remove from spindle. Remove washer (5) and slide spindle down out of axle main member. Remove bushings (2) as required. When reinstalling spindle, align punch mark on spindle end with punch mark on steering lever (Fig. HN51).

To remove right steering spindle, remove snap ring (10–Fig. HN50) and slip spindle down out of axle main member. Renew bushings (2) as required.

STEERING GEAR

R&R AND OVERHAUL. To remove steering shaft and gear assembly, remove cover (1–Fig. HN52) and nut (2). Remove steering wheel (3) and flat washer (4). Disconnect drag link end at steering arm (15). Remove cap screws which retain steering plate (8). Remove the three cap screws retaining steering gear holder (17). Remove nut (11) and pull steering shaft (6) out of tractor. Remove gear (9) and washer (10). Remove steering gear (14) and washers (13 and 16). Renew bushings (5, 7 and 12) as required.

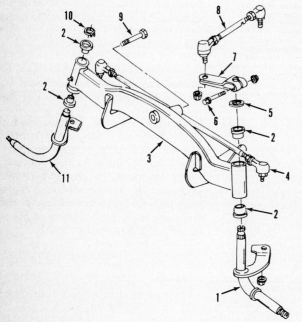

Fig. HN50—Exploded view of front axle assembly.

1. Spindle
2. Bushing
3. Axle main member
4. Tie rod end
5. Washer
6. Bolt
7. Steering lever
8. Drag link
9. Pivot bolt
10. Snap ring
11. Spindle

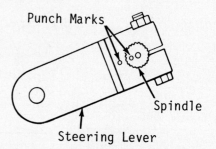

Fig. HN51—When installing steering lever on spindle, align punch marks.

Reverse removal procedure for reassembly. Make certain front wheels are straight ahead, larger opening in steering wheel is toward the top and steering gears are meshed in the center of gear (14) during reassembly. Tighten the three bolts retaining the steering gear holder (17) to 23-30 N·m (17-22 ft.-lbs.) and nuts (2 and 11) to 45-54 N·m (33-40 ft.-lbs.).

ENGINE

REMOVE AND REINSTALL. Disconnect headlight wiring, remove hood restraint cable and hood retaining bolts and remove hood assembly. Disconnect negative and positive bat-

tery cables. Remove the front air shroud assembly. Disconnect the pto clutch cable at the clutch and remove attachment drive belt from pto pulley. Remove exhaust pipe, disconnect throttle cable and fuel line at carburetor. Disconnect all starter, charging coils, ignition wire and ground cables. Remove the four nuts retaining rubber engine mounts. Lift and slide engine from tractor disengaging drive shaft as engine is removed.

Reinstall by reversing removal procedure. Tighten exhaust pipe nuts to 18-24 N·m (13-18 ft.-lbs.). Make certain the lugs on rubber motor mounts are inserted into slots of mounting plates and tighten the four nuts retaining rubber motor mounts to 45-54 N·m (33-40 ft.-lbs.).

OVERHAUL

Model 3810 tractor is equipped with a Honda G400 engine. Refer to the Honda engine service section for overhaul procedure.

DRIVE CLUTCH

ADJUSTMENT. To adjust drive clutch linkage, refer to ADJUSTMENT in BRAKE section. To check condition of drive clutch, place gear shift lever in second speed slot. Raise seat and remove the inspection hole cover. The indicator mark on the clutch lever should be between the two notches on the clutch housing (Fig. HN53). If indicator mark is past the red notch on the clutch housing, clutch disk must be renewed.

R&R AND OVERHAUL (Early Style). Remove drive shaft. Disconnect all clutch linkage. Remove damper hub (23 – Fig. HN54). Remove cap screw (18) and washer (17). Remove the three nuts retaining clutch assembly plate (2) bolted to transaxle input shaft and slide clutch assembly from shaft. Special clutch spring compressor (part 7960-750000A) is required to safely compress clutch spring (19) before nuts (22)

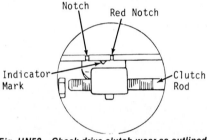

Fig. HN53 — Check drive clutch wear as outlined in text.

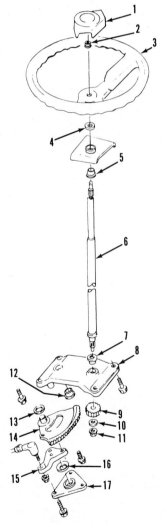

Fig. HN52 — Exploded view of steering shaft and gears.

1. Cover	10. Washer
2. Nut	11. Nut
3. Steering wheel	12. Bushing
4. Flat washer	13. Washer
5. Bushing	14. Gear
6. Steering shaft	15. Steering arm
7. Bushing	16. Washer
8. Steering plate	17. Steering gear holder
9. Gear	

Fig. HN54 — Exploded view of drive clutch assembly used on later models. Dust seal plate (4) and clutch setting springs (20) are not used on early models.

1. Stop bolt
2. Clutch plate
3. Bolt
4. Dust seal plate
5. Clutch rod
6. Bearing lock nut
7. Ramp
8. Ball retainer
9. Rear clutch housing
10. Nut
11. Lifter plate
12. Clutch disc
13. Pressure plate
14. Bearing
15. Bearing
16. Collar
17. Washer
18. Cap screw
19. Spring
20. Clutch setting spring
21. Clutch cover
22. Nut
23. Damper hub
24. Damper
25. Drive shaft

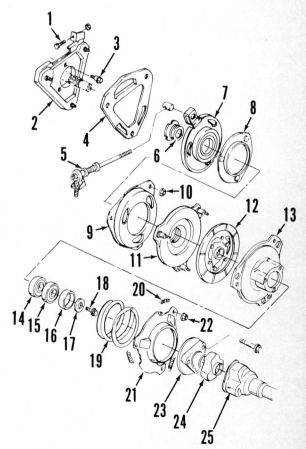

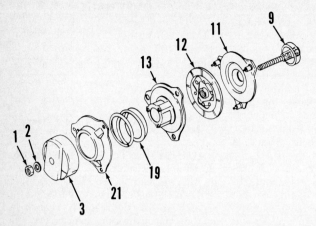

Fig. HN55—Exploded view of spring loaded clutch pack with special spring compressor tool (part 07960-75000A).

1. Nut
2. Washer
3. Special tool part
9. Special tool part
11. Lifter plate
12. Clutch disk
13. Pressure plate
19. Spring
21. Clutch cover

can be removed or installed (Fig. HN55). Old style nut (6 – Fig. HN54) (left-hand thread) with 5 mm slots must be removed with a punch and hammer and renewed with a new nut with 6 mm slots for which tool (part 22583-750-003) is available to aid removal and installation.

Clean and inspect all parts. Thickness of clutch facing on disk (12) should be 5.9-6.1 mm (0.232-0.240 in.). If facing thickness is 3.9 mm (0.154 in.) or less, renew disk. Disk is installed with long side of splined hub toward lifter plate (11). Free length of spring (19) should be 58.2 mm (2.29 in.). If spring free length is 56.2 mm (2.213 in.) or less, renew spring. Nuts (22) retaining clutch spring are tightened to 10-13 N·m (88-115 in.-lbs.).

R&R AND OVERHAUL. (Late Style). Remove drive shaft. Disconnect all clutch linkage. Remove the three cap screws retaining damper hub (23 – Fig. HN54) and remove hub. Remove cap screw (18) and washer (17). Remove the three nuts (10) and slide clutch assembly

off of transaxle input shaft. Use special tool (part 07916-3710100) to remove left-hand thread bearing lock nut (6). Use special spring compressor tool (part 07960-750000A) to compress spring (19) in clutch pack (Fig. HN55). With tool compressing clutch pack, remove the three nuts (22 – Fig. HN54). Slowly unscrew spring compressor tool and disassemble clutch pack.

Clean and inspect all parts. Thickness of clutch facing on disc (12) should be 5.9-6.1 mm (0.232-0.240 in.). If thickness is 3.9 mm (0.154 in.) or less, renew disc. Spring (19) free length should be 58.2 mm (2.29 in.). If free length is 56.2 mm (2.213 in.) or less, renew spring. When reassembling spring loaded clutch pack, refer to Fig. HN55 for assembly sequence. Align spring end with one of the three threaded studs on pressure plate (Fig. HN56). Install side of clutch disc (12 – Fig. HN55) with long side of splined hub toward lifter plate (11). Tighten nuts (22 and 10 – Fig. HN54) to 10-13 N·m (88-115 in.-lbs.). Tighten cap screw (18) to 24-30 N·m (18-22 ft.-lbs.). Make certain dust plate (4) is mounted on clutch plate (2) and that studs on clutch plate are through the holes in the dust plate.

BRAKE

ADJUSTMENT. Depressing brake pedal disengages drive clutch and applies brake. Brake, clutch and shift linkage adjustments must be performed or checked in the following order. Brake

pedal rod must be adjusted so there is no clearance between the end of operating rod and the front end of brake pedal slot when brake pedal is released (Fig. HN58). Loosen jam nut and turn adjusting nut to remove any clearance. Check brake pedal clutch cable free play by placing shift lever in second gear drive slot. Clutch arm link should have 0-0.5 mm (0.02 inch) free play. If adjustment is required, loosen locknuts and push clutch arm outward until shift lever contacts edge of gear plate slot. Reposition cable. Shift lever free play should be checked at this time. With shift lever in second gear slot, measure free movement of shift lever and inner (deepest) edge of slot. There should be 5-10 mm (0.2-0.4 in.) free play. Adjust by varying length of clutch rod (Fig. HN59). Hold the shift lever all the way to the left. Rod end of clutch arm should almost touch the stopper bolt (1 – Fig. HN54). Rod end of clutch arm should be 11-12 mm (0.4-0.5 in.) from the head of stopper bolt when shift lever is allowed to return to the right side position.

REMOVE AND REINSTALL BRAKE SHOES. To check brake shoe wear, depress brake pedal and observe position of brake wear indicator located near brake assembly on transaxle (Fig. HN60). If indicator is near new limit point, renew brake shoes.

To remove brake shoes, remove the rear seat, rear fender and wire protec-

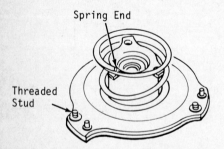

Fig. HN56—Align end of clutch spring with threaded stud prior to assembly.

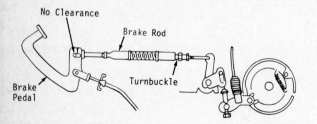

Fig. HN58—Remove clearance by adjusting turnbuckle. Refer to text.

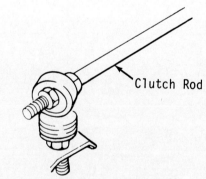

Fig. HN59—Turn clutch rod to adjust length.

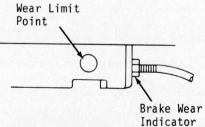

Fig. HN60—Depress brake pedal and look at brake shoe wear indicator to determine if brake shoes should be renewed.

tor. Drain transaxle housing. Remove cap screw (1–Fig. HN61), washer (2) and brake drum (3). Remove brake shoe spring (4) and brake shoes (5).

Clean and inspect all parts. Brake lining thickness should be 4.35-4.65 mm (0.171-0.183 in.). If lining thickness is 2.35 mm (0.093 in.) or less, renew brake shoe. If brake cam (6) is removed, reinstall in brake arm (11) so punch mark on cam is aligned with punch mark on brake arm. Refill transaxle with 2.4 L (2.54 qts.) of SAE 10W-40 oil.

TRANSAXLE

LUBRICATION. Manufacturer recommends checking transaxle fluid level at 100 hour intervals of use. Transaxle fluid capacity is 2.4 L (2.54 qts.). Recommended lubricant is SAE 10W-30 oil.

REMOVE AND REINSTALL. Raise and support rear of tractor. Remove left and right wheel and tire assemblies. Remove drive shaft and drive clutch assembly. Disconnect shift rod at transaxle shift lever. Disconnect all necessary electrical connections. Remove fuel pump assembly. Disconnect brake rod at brake assembly. Support transaxle and remove the transaxle retaining bolts. Lower transaxle assembly out of frame and pull from under tractor.

Reinstall by reversing removal procedure. Refer to LUBRICATION to refill transaxle. Adjust all linkage as outlined under ADJUSTMENT in BRAKE section.

OVERHAUL. No service information available at time of publication.

PTO

PTO LEVER ADJUSTMENT. Pto lever should have 3-5 mm (0.1-0.2 in.) free play. To adjust, loosen the jam nut at cable and bracket and turn the adjuster as required.

DISASSEMBLY. Refer to Fig. HN65 for an exploded view of components. Standard thickness for brake disc is

10.3-10.4 mm (0.406-0.409 in.). If thickness is 8.3 mm (0.327 in.) or less, renew brake disc (17) and friction disc (11). Standard thickness for friction disc (11) is 5.9-6.1 mm (0.232-0.240 in.). If thickness is 3.9 mm (0.154 in.) or less, renew friction disc (11) and brake disc (17). When installing friction disc (11), long side of splined hub is installed toward engine.

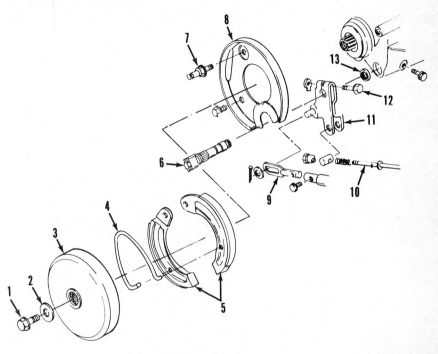

Fig. HN61—Exploded view of brake assembly.

1. Cap screw
2. Washer
3. Brake drum
4. Brake spring
5. Brake shoes
6. Cam
7. Stud
8. Backing plate
9. Parking brake rod
10. Brake rod
11. Brake arm
12. Bolt
13. Seal

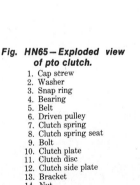

Fig. HN65—Exploded view of pto clutch.

1. Cap screw
2. Washer
3. Snap ring
4. Bearing
5. Belt
6. Driven pulley
7. Clutch spring
8. Clutch spring seat
9. Bolt
10. Clutch plate
11. Clutch disc
12. Clutch side plate
13. Bracket
14. Nut
15. Key
16. Nut
17. Clutch brake disc
18. Ball retainer
19. Pto clutch cable
20. Ramp & bearing
21. Spacer
22. Spring
23. Spring bracket
24. Spring bracket

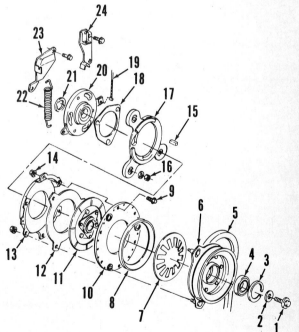

TRANSAXLE SERVICE

FOOTE

Model 4000-5

The Model 4000-5 Foote transaxle is manufactured by the J.B. Foote Foundry Company. The transaxle supplies three forward gears and one reverse gear plus a Hi-Lo torque range.

OVERHAUL. Clear exterior of transaxle. Place shifter lever in neutral and remove drive pulley. Remove shoulder bolt from brake assembly and remove brake jaw (69—Fig. FT10), spring (70), brake pads (71), brake disc (72) and Woodruff key. Unbolt and remove shift lever and cover. Remove the two set screws (12) from case, turn transmission over and catch detent springs (13) and balls.

With transmission upside down, remove case bolts and separate case halves with a mallet. Lift drive shaft

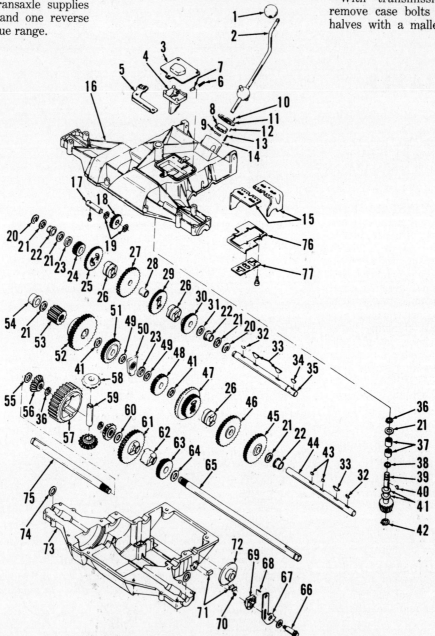

Fig. FT10—Exploded view of Foote Model 4000-5 sliding gear transmission.

1. Knob	15. Shift fork	29. Spacer	41. Shim washer	53. Gear assy. (12T)	65. Axle shaft (R.H.)
2. Shift lever	16. Case half	29. Spur gear (25T)	42. Snap ring	54. Bearing	66. Shoulder bolt
3. Cover plate	17. Idler shaft	30. Spur gear (20T)	43. Woodruff key #3	55. Shim	67. Brake lever
4. Shift fork	18. Reverse idler gear	31. Shim washer	special	56. Bevel gear (15T)	68. Set screw
5. Hi-Lo shift lever	19. Washer	32. Woodruff key #3	44. Drive shaft	splined	69. Brake jaw assy.
6. Detent spring	20. "E" ring	33. Hi-pro key	45. Gear (20T)	57. Spur gear (32T)	70. Spring
7. Pin	21. Shim washer	34. Woodruff key #61	46. Gear (33T)	58. Bevel gears	71. Brake pads
8. Nylon insert	22. Bearing	35. Intermediate shaft	47. Bevel gear assy.	59. Cross shaft	72. Brake disc
9. Wave washer	23. Spacer	36. Snap ring	48. Gear (20T)	60. Shim	73. Case half
10. Set screw	24. Spur gear (13T)	37. Needle bearings	49. Shim washer	61. Spur gear (35T)	74. Felt seal
11. Nylon cover	25. Spur gear (25T)	38. "O" ring	50. Shaft support assy.	62. Gear lock	75. Axle shaft (L.H.)
12. Set screw	26. Clutch collar	39. Input shaft	51. Gear (25T)	63. Spur gear (22T)	76. Support plate
13. Spring	27. Spur gear (30T)	40. Key	52. Gear (37T)	64. Shim	77. Lockout plate
14. Detent ball					

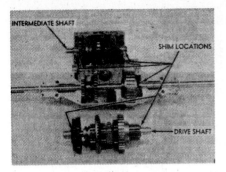

Fig. FT11 — View showing shim locations in Foote Model 4000-5 transmission.

assembly (44) out. All parts on drive shaft are a slip fit. Lift intermediate shaft assembly out and remove "E" ring

(20) from one end. Slide parts off shaft, being careful to keep parts in order. Push axles together as differential assembly is removed. Axle bevel gears are a press fit; all other parts are slip fit. Further disassembly is evident after examination.

Clean and inspect all parts and renew any showing excessive wear or damage. Before installing input shaft, pack needle bearings with grease. Install Hi-Lo shift mechanism and check for free action. Apply a light coating of grease to reverse idler shaft and gear and tighten mounting bolt to 80-90 in.-lbs. (9-10 N·m). Assemble intermediate shaft with light coating of grease and new "E" rings (20). Intermediate and drive shaft

end play should be 0.020-0.030 inch (0.508-0.762 mm). End play is adjusted by changing shim thickness as shown in Fig. FT11. Input shaft end play should be 0.010-0.020 inch (0.254-0.508 mm). End play is adjusted by changing shim washer (21 – Fig. FT10) under snap ring (36). When installing detent balls, springs and set screws, tighten set screws until heads are flush with top of case.

Pack axle cavities in both case halves with 24 ounces (710 mL) of Shell Darina "O" or equivalent grease. Spread grease equally in main part of gearcase. Tighten the 14 case bolts to 80-90 in.-lbs. (9-10 N·m). Tighten center bolt to 100-110 in.-lbs. (11-12 N·m).

INTERNATIONAL HARVESTER

3-Speed

OVERHAUL. Remove rear axles and carriers. Remove shift lever and transmission top cover assembly. Remove shifter fork retaining cap screws and rotate shifter rails to unseat poppet balls. Slide rails forward out of shifter forks and case.

CAUTION: Insert a small punch into poppet bores to prevent poppet balls from flying out when rails are being removed.

Remove cap screws from main shaft bearing retainer (9 – Fig. IH100) and bump main shaft (7 or 32) and bearing forward and out of case. The first and reverse and second and third sliding gears will be removed as shaft is withdrawn from case. Remove cap

screw from reverse idler shaft (3) and remove shaft and reverse idler gear (2). Before removing countershaft (10), differential unit must be removed from housing.

To remove differential unit, remove right and left differential bearing cages. Identify number and thickness of shims removed from each side for aid in reassembly. Turn differential unit as shown in Fig. IH101 and remove unit from housing.

Remove countershaft nut and bump shaft rearward out of transmission as gears and spacers are removed. Note sequence of spacers and gears for reassembly. See Fig. IH102. Remove countershaft front bearing, retainer and shims. Identify shims for reassembly.

To disassemble differential, remove differential lock pin (12 – Fig. IH103)

Fig. IH101 — The differential unit must be turned to position shown to remove unit from housing.

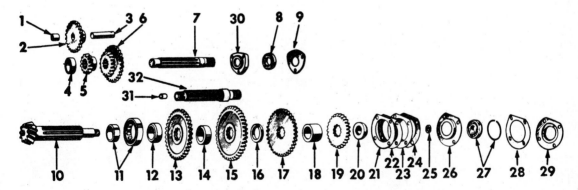

Fig. IH100 — Exploded view of transmission gears and shafts used in International Harvester 3-speed transaxle.

1. Reverse idler gear bushing
2. Reverse idler gear
3. Reverse idler shaft
4. Main shaft rear bearing
5. First & reverse sliding gear
6. Second & third sliding gear
7. Main shaft
8. Main shaft front bearing
9. Bearing retainer
10. Countershaft (bevel pinion)
11. Countershaft rear bearing
12. Spacer
13. Reverse gear
14. Spacer
15. First speed gear
16. Spacer
17. Second speed gear
18. Spacer
19. Third speed gear
20. Spacer
21. Shim
22. Shim
23. Shim
24. Shim
25. Nut
26. Bearing retainer
27. Countershaft front bearing
28. Gasket
29. Bearing retainer
30. Bearing cage
31. Bushing
32. Mainshaft

and drive out pinion shaft (11). Rotate side gears 90 degrees and remove pinion gears and side gears

When reassembling, differential bearings should be adjusted to obtain a pre-load of 1 to 8 pounds (4.4-35.6 N) force on a spring scale measured as shown in Fig. IH104. This is done by adding or removing shims behind differential bearing cages. Check backlash and adjust to 0.003-0.005 inch (0.076-0.127 mm) by moving shim or shims from behind one differential bearing cage to the other bearing cage.

Adjustment of bevel pinion (counter-shaft) for proper tooth contact is done by adding or removing shims behind countershaft front bearing retainer. Pint bevel pinion teeth with Prussian Blue or red lead and rotate ring gear. Observe contact pattern on tooth surfaces. Refer to Fig. IH105. The area of heaviest contact will be indicated by coating being removed at such points. On the actual pinion, areas shown in black on the illustrations will be bright.

The correct tooth contact pattern is shown at "A." If pattern is too low as "B," remove shims as necessary to correct pattern. If pattern is too high as "C," add shims to correct pattern.

Reassembly of remainder of transmission and differential is reverse of disassembly.

Fig. IH104 — Differential bearing preload is correct when a steady pull of 1 to 8 pounds (4.4-35.6 N) on spring scale is necessary to rotate differential as shown.

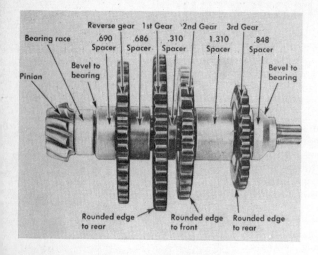

Fig. IH102 — View showing correct installation of gears and spacers on countershaft (bevel pinion).

Fig. IH105 — Bevel pinion tooth contact pattern is correct at "A," to low at "B" and too high at "C."

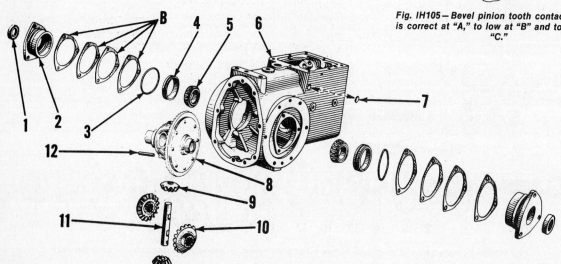

Fig. IH103 — Exploded view of International Harvester differential assembly.

B. Shims
1. Oil seal
2. Differential bearing cage
3. "O" ring
4. Bearing cup
5. Bearing cone
6. Transmission case
7. Expansion plug
8. Ring gear & differential housing
9. Pinion gear
10. Side gear
11. Pinion shaft
12. Pinion shaft lock pin

MTD

Model 717-0750A

OVERHAUL. Thoroughly clean exterior of transaxle case. Remove input pulley and key (1 – Fig. MT100). Remove brake caliper assembly, brake disc (27) and key (26). Remove all cap screws retaining upper case half (5) to lower case half (45). Carefully separate upper case half from lower case half. Remove snap rings (2 and 11), washers (3 and 4), gear (10), thrust washer (9) and square seal (8). Remove input shaft (7) and bearings (6) as required. Remove shifter assembly (14). Lift drive/brake shaft (17) and gear assembly out as an assembly and disassemble as required. Lift axle shafts (28) and differential as required. Lift axle shafts (28) and differential assembly out as an assembly. Remove the cap screws retaining differential housing (39) to differential gear (33). Remove snap rings (42), cross shaft (41) and spider gears (34). Remove nuts (36 and 37) and remove axle gears (35). Pull axles out of housing and gear assembly.

Reassemble by reversing disassembly procedure. Before installing upper case half, pack tranaxle housing with 10 ounces (296 mL) of lithium base grease.

PEERLESS

Series 600

The Peerless 600 series transaxle is a lightweight unit which has a vertical input shaft at the top of the case. There are two basic types of 600 series transaxles. The 600 series is the standard model and the 601 series is a slow speed transaxle. Model number and series number will be located on a metal tag or stamped in case as indicated by (I – Fig. PT19). Variations in model number (603, 603A, 609, etc.) indicate differences in shift lever shape, axle lengths, axle machining for wheel hub attachment, axle housing variations or size of the brake shaft. Overhaul procedure is similar for all 600 series transaxles.

OVERHAUL. To disassemble the transaxle, remove drain plug and drain lubricant. Remove brake assembly, input pulley and rear wheel assemblies. Remove all keys from keyways and

Fig. MT100 – Exploded view of MTD Model 717-0750A transaxle.

1. Key	12. Spring detent	23. Washer	35. Axle gear
2. Snap ring	13. Detent ball	24. Flange bearing	36. Nut
3. Washer (0.040 in)	14. Shifter	26. Key	37. Nut
4. Washer (0.030 in.)	15. Flange bearing	27. Brake disc	38. Flange bearing
5. Upper case half	16. Washer	28. Axle shaft	39. Housing
6. Bearings	17. Drive/brake shaft	29. Seal	40. Thrust bearing
7. Input shaft	18. Washer	30. Sleeve bearing	41. Cross shaft
8. Square seal	19. Bevel gear	31. Sleeve bearing	42. Snap ring
9. Thrust washer	20. Key	32. Washer	43. Washers
10. Gear	21. Clutch collar	33. Differential gear	44. Flange bearing
11. Snap ring	22. Bevel gear	34. Spider gear	45. Lower case half

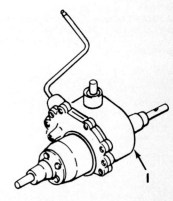

Fig. PT19 – Model and series numbers will be stamped into case or on a metal tag attached to case at location (I).

polish any burrs or rust from exposed shafts. Place shift lever in neutral position, then unbolt and remove shift lever and housing assembly. Unbolt and remove axle housings (16 and 52 – Fig. PT20). Place unit in a vise so heads of socket head cap screws are pointing upward. Drive dowel pins out of case and cover. Unsrew socket head cap screws and lift off cover (55). Install two or three socket head screws into case to hold center plate (76) down while removing the differential assembly. Pull differential assembly straight up out of case. It may be necessary to gently

bump lower axle shaft to loosen differential assembly. Remove center plate (76). Hold shifter rods (19) together and lift out shifter rods, forks (20), shifter stop (23), shaft (27), sliding gears (25 and 26) and spur gear (24) as an assembly. On early model transaxle, remove idler shaft (29) and gear (30) as individual parts. On late model transaxle, remove idler shaft and gear as an one-piece assembly as shown in (29A – Fig. PT21). On all models, remove reverse idler shaft (79 – Fig. PT20), spacer (80) and gear (81). On early model transaxle, with reference to

Fig. PT20, remove cluster gears (35, 36 and 37) on sleeve (41) and thrust washer (42). On late model transaxle, with reference to Fig. PT21, remove cluster gears (35, 36 and 37), spacers (S) on countershaft (C) and thrust washer (42). On all 600 series standard models, remove bevel gear (31 – Fig. PT20), washers (32 and 34) and thrust bearing (33). On 601 series slow speed models, remove bevel gear (31) and the single thrust washer (32). On all models except Model 612, remove input shaft oil seal (9), snap ring (10), input shaft (48) and gear (49). Washers (45 and 47) and thrust bearing (46) are removed with input shaft. Model 612 is equipped with a ball bearing in place of seal (9). To remove Model 612 input shaft, remove snap ring in case, ball bearing, snap ring (10), input shaft (48) and gear (49). Washers (45 and 47) and thrust bearing (46) are removed with input shaft. On all models, remove bearing (11) and bushing (12).

To disassemble cluster gear assembly, press gears and key from sleeve (41). Bushings (38 and 40) are renewable in sleeve (41).

To disassemble the differential, drive roll pin (71) out of drive pin (74). Remove

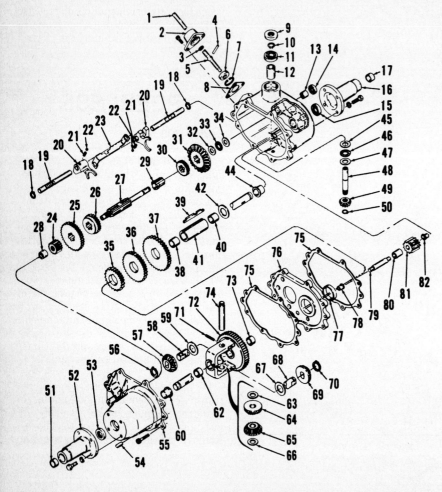

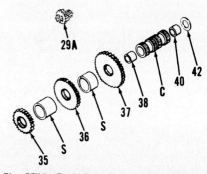

Fig. PT21—Exploded view showing late style countershaft assembly and one-piece idler shaft and gear assembly used on late 600 series transaxles.

C. Countershaft
S. Spacer
29A. Idler shaft & gear assy.
35. Gear
36. Gear
37. Gear
38. Bushing
40. Bushing
42. Thrust washer

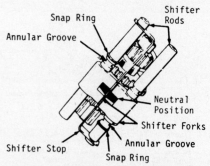

Fig. PT22—To position shifter assembly in neutral for reassembly, align notches in shifter forks with notch in shifter stop.

Fig. PT20—Exploded view of an early Peerless 600 series transaxle. Late model is similar, refer to Fig. PT21 for internal parts differences. On Model 601, slow speed transaxle, bevel gear (31) and input shaft assembly are not interchangeable with the 600 series parts.

1. Shift lever
2. Lever housing
3. Quad ring
4. Roll pin
5. Shift lever
6. Retainer
7. Snap ring
8. Gasket
9. Oil seal
10. Snap ring
11. Ball bearing
12. Bushing
13. Needle bearing
14. Oil seal
15. Oil seal
16. Axle housing
17. Bushing
18. Snap ring
19. Shift rod
20. Shift fork
21. Spring
22. Detent ball
23. Shifter stop
24. Spur gear
25. Sliding gear (1st & reverse)
26. Sliding gear (2nd & 3rd)
27. Shift & brake shaft
28. Needle bearing
29. Idler shaft
30. Gear
31. Bevel gear
32. Washer
33. Thrust bearing
34. Washer
35. Gear
36. Gear
37. Gear
38. Bushing
39. Key
40. Bushing
41. Sleeve
42. Thrust washer
44. Bushing
45. Washer
46. Thrust bearing
47. Washer
48. Input shaft
49. Pinion gear
50. Snap ring
51. Bushing
52. Axle housing
53. Oil seal
54. Dowel pin
55. Cover
56. Snap ring
57. Side gear
58. Axle shaft
59. Thrust washer
60. Bushing
62. Bushing
63. Thrust washer
64. Bevel pinion gear
65. Bevel pinion gear
66. Thrust washer
67. Thrust washer
68. Axle shaft
69. Side gear
70. Snap ring
71. Roll pin
72. Differential carrier & gear
73. Bushing
74. Drive pin
75. Gasket
76. Center plate
77. Bushing
78. Bushing
79. Reverse idler shaft
80. Spacer
81. Reverse idler gear
82. Bushing

drive pin, thrust washers (63 and 66) and bevel pinion gears (64 and 65). Remove snap rings (56 and 70) and withdraw axle shafts from side gears (57 and 69). Remove side gears.

Clean and inspect components for excessive wear or other damage. Renew all seals and gaskets. Check for binding of shift forks on shift rods. When reassembling, position shift forks in neutral position by aligning notches on shift rods with notch in shifter stop. See Fig. PT22. Install input shaft assembly by reversing the removal procedure. Position case so open side is up. Install needle bearing (13–Fig. PT20) and oil seal (14). On early model, install idler shaft (29) and gear (30). On late model transaxle, install one-piece idler shaft and gear (29A–Fig. PT21). On all models, install bevel gear (31–Fig. PT20), washers (32 and 34) and thrust bearing (33). Be sure thrust bearing is positioned between washers. Reverse idler shaft (79) may be used to temporarily hold idler gear assembly in position. On early model transaxle, place cluster gear (35, 36 and 37) on key (39) so bevel on gears (35 and 36) is toward large gear (37) and short section of key

(39) is between middle gear (36) and large gear (37) as shown in Fig. PT23. Press gears and key on sleeve (41–PT20). On late model transaxle, install thrust washer (42–PT21), countershaft (C), cluster gears (35, 36 and 37) and spacers (S). On all models, install shifter assembly (18 through 27–Fig. PT20) in case, making certain that shifter rods are properly seated. Install reverse idler shaft (79), gear (81) and spacer (80). Beveled edge of gear should be up. Install gasket (75) and center plate (76), then second gasket (75) on case. Assemble differential by reversing disassembly procedure. Install differen-

tial assembly in case with longer axle pointing downward. Install locating dowel pins and secure cover (55) to case. Install oil seals (15 and 53), axle housing (16 and 52). Transaxle housing should be filled through shifter opening with SAE 90 EP gear lubricant. Capacity will vary according to specific model numbers (603, 603A, 609, etc.) or mounting position on unit. Refer to CONDENSED SPECIFICATIONS or TRANSAXLE LUBRICATION paragraphs under appropriate TRACTOR SERVICE SECTION for specific model being serviced. Install shift lever assembly (1 through 8).

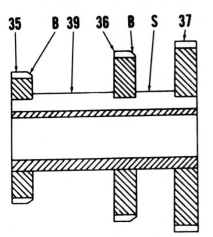

Fig. PT23—On early model transaxle, note positions of bevels (B) on cluster gears and short section (S) of key (39) between gears (36 and 37).

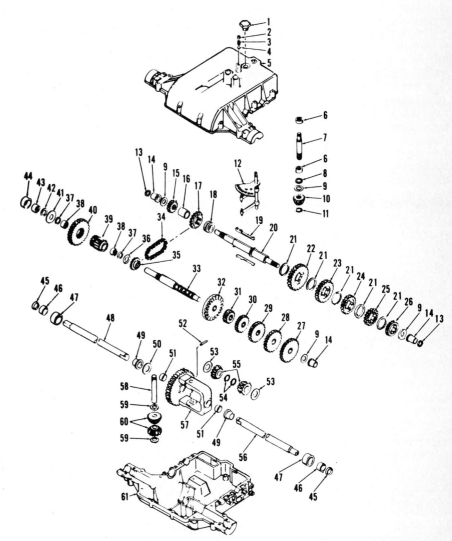

Fig. PT31—Exploded view of Peerless 800 series transaxle.

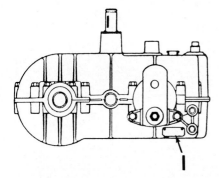

Fig. PT30—Model and series numbers are located on a metal tag attached on transaxle case at location (I).

1. Plug
2. Set screw
3. Spring
4. Ball
5. Cover
6. Needle bearing
7. Input shaft
8. Square cut ring
9. Thrust washer
10. Input pinion
11. Snap ring
12. Shift fork assy.
13. Square cut ring
14. Bushing
15. Spur gear (12 or 15 tooth)
16. Spacer
17. Sprocket (18 tooth)
18. Shift collar
19. Key
20. Brake shaft
21. Thrust washer
22. Spur gear (35 tooth)
23. Spur gear (30 tooth)
24. Spur gear (25 tooth)
25. Spur gear (22 tooth)
26. Spur gear (20 tooth)
27. Gear (30 tooth)
28. Gear (28 tooth)
29. Gear (25 tooth)
30. Gear (20 tooth)
31. Spur gear (12 or 15 tooth)
32. Bevel gear (42 tooth)
33. Countershaft
34. Drive chain
35. Sprocket (9 tooth)
36. Flat washer
37. Square cut ring
38. Needle bearing
39. Output pinion
40. Output gear
41. Flat washer
42. Square cut seal
43. Needle bearing
44. Spacer
45. Oil seal
46. Needle bearing
47. Spacer
48. Axle shaft (short)
49. Bushing
50. Washer
51. Bushing
52. Pin
53. Thrust washer
54. Snap rings
55. Bevel side gears
56. Axle shaft (long)
57. Differential gear assy
58. Drive pin
59. Thrust washer
60. Bevel pinion gears
61. Case

Series 800

The 800 series transaxle may have 4 or 5 forward speeds and a single reverse speed. Bearings are oil impregnated bushings with needle bearings or ball bearings on axles, input and output shaft. The model number will be found on a tag located at (I – Fig. PT30).

OVERHAUL. To disassemble the transaxle, first remove drain plug and drain lubricant. Place shift lever in neutral and remove shift lever. Remove set screw (2 – Fig. PT31), spring (3) and index ball (4). Remove the 17 cap screws retaining cover (5). Push shift fork assembly (12) in while removing cover. Before removing gear shaft assemblies, shift fork (12) should be removed. It will be difficult to keep parts from falling off. Note position of parts before removal. Remove gear and shaft assemblies from case taking care not to disturb drive chain (34). Remove needle bearing (43), flat washer (41), square cut seals (42), output gear (40) and output pinion (39) from the countershaft. Angle the two shafts together (Fig. PT32). Mark the position of chain on sprocket collars and remove chain. Remove sprocket (35 – Fig. PT31), bevel gear (32), gears (27, 28, 29, 30), spur gear (31), thrust

washer (9) and flange bushing (14). All gears are splined to the countershaft. Disassembly of brake shaft is self-evident from observation. Remove snap ring (11), input pinion (10) and pull input shaft (7) through cover.

To disassemble the differential, drive roll pin out of drive pin (58) and remove drive pin. Remove pinion gears (60) by rotating gears in opposite directions.

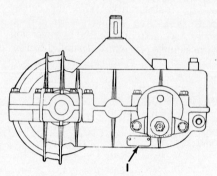

Fig. PT35 – Transaxle identification tag is located at (I).

Remove snap rings (54), side gears (55), thrust washers (53) and slide axles out.

Clean and inspect all parts and renew any showing excessive wear or other damage. When installing new inner input shaft needle bearings, press bearing in to a depth of 0.135-0.150 inches (3.43-3.81 mm) below flush. When installing thrust washers and shifting gears on brake shaft, the 45 degree chamfer on inside diameter of thrust washers must face shoulder on brake shaft (Fig. PT33). The flat side of gears must face shoulder on shaft. Before upper cover (5 – Fig. PT31) is joined with case (61), pack 24 ounces (0.7 L) of EP lithium base grease into case. Complete reassembly and tighten case to cover cap screws to 80-100 in.-lbs. (9-11 N·m).

Series 900

The 900 series transaxle may have 1, 2, 3 or 4 speeds forward and a single reverse speed. Bearings are oil impregnated bushings with needle bearings or ball bearings on axles, input

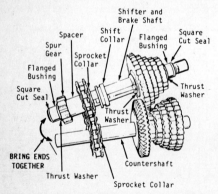

Fig. PT32 – Mark position of chain on sprocket collars, angle shafts together and remove chain.

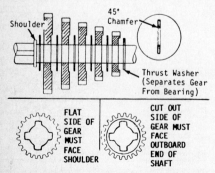

Fig. PT33 – When installing thrust washers and gears on brake shaft, 45 degree chamfer on inside diameter of thrust washers must face shoulder on brake shaft.

Fig. PT36 – Exploded view of Peerless 900 series transaxle.

1. Set screw
2. Spring
3. Detent ball
4. Retaining ring
5. Shifter
6. "O" ring
7. Bushing
8. Thrust washer
9. Gear
10. Collar
11. Key
12. Key
13. Shifter/brake shaft
14. Needle bearing
15. Input shaft
16. Needle bearing
17. Square cut seal
18. Thrust washer
19. Bevel gear
20. Retaining ring
21. Reverse gear (thick collar toward gears)
22. Neutral spacer
23. Gear
24. Washer (chamfered)
25. Gear
26. Washer (chamfered)
27. Gear
28. Thrust washer
29. Bushing
30. "O" ring
31. Large bushing
32. Thrust washer
33. Output gear
34. Output pinion
35. Thrust washer
36. Bushing
37. Thrust washer
38. Reverse gear (thick collar toward gears)
39. Chain
40. Countershaft
41. Bearing block
42. Gear (bevel installed toward sprocket)
43. Thrust washer
44. Spur gear
45. Spur gear
46. Spur gear
47. Thrust washer
48. Bushing
49. Washer
50. Axle shaft
51. Washer
52. Axle gear
53. Bearing block
54. Bearing block
55. Differential gear
56. Spider gear
57. Shaft
58. Spider gear
59. Snap ring
60. Axle gear
61. Washer
62. Axle shaft
63. Washer
64. Wicks (4)
65. Case
66. Inner brake pad
67. Disc
68. Outer brake pad & plate
69. Caliper
70. Spacer
71. Actuating pins
72. Brake lever
73. Cap screw
74. Cap screw
75. Washer
76. Adjustment nut
77. Jam nut

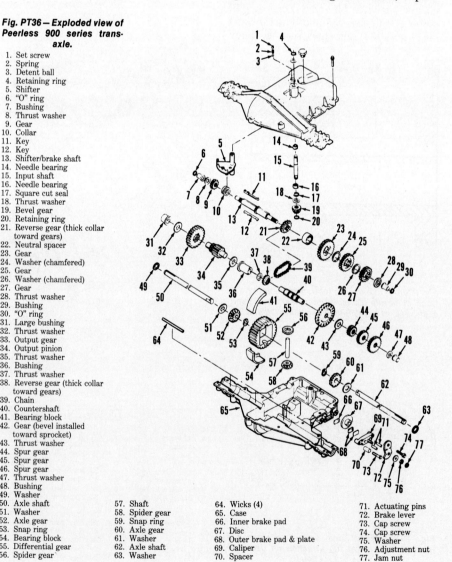

shaft and output shaft. The model number will be found on a tag located at 1 – Fig. PT35.

OVERHAUL. To disassemble the transaxle, first remove drain plug and drain lubricant. Place shift lever in neutral position. Remove set screw (1 – Fig. PT36), spring (2) and detent ball (3). Remove neutral start switch (as equipped). Remove cap screws and separate cover from case. It will be necessary to push shift lever rod in while pulling cover off of case. Remove brake caliper cap screws (73 and 74) and remove brake assembly, brake disc (67) and inner brake pad (66). Remove grease from unit as unit is disassembled. Remove shifter assembly (5). Note how "V" notches on flange bushings fit into recess "V" of case (Fig. PT37), then remove gear and shaft assemblies. Pull countershaft, output pinion and shaft assembly apart. To disassemble countershaft, remove the two thrust washers, sprocket bevel gear, spur gears and flanged bushing. Sprocket and spur gears are splined to the countershaft. To disassemble the output pinion and shaft, remove the large brass bushing, large washer, large output gear, washer and bushing. The shaft is pressed into the output pinion gear and is available as an assembly only. To disassemble the shifter shaft, remove the two square cut "O" rings and the two flanged bushings, the two thrust washers on shaft ends, shift collar with keys, sprocket, spacer, shifter gears and thrust washers.

The differential assembly is held together by its position in the case. Differential assembly is disassembled as unit is removed from case. Remove all flat washers on axle ends.

To disassemble input shaft, remove the retaining ring on bevel gear end of input shaft, remove bevel gear and pull shaft through case. The square cut "O" ring must be renewed if removed.

Clean and inspect all parts. Lubricate all parts during reassembly. Needle bearing (14 – Fig. PT36) is pressed into bearing bore just far enough to allow installation of upper thrust washer and retaining ring (4). Needle bearing (16) is pressed into bearing bore of cover 0.135-0.150 inch (3.4-3.8 mm) below flush. Install input shaft and bevel gear in cover. Slide keys and collar on shifter and brake shaft. Assemble shifter/brake shaft and countershaft at the same time. Install reverse chain on reverse sprockets. Collars of reverse sprockets should be on the same side of the chain. Slide larger sprocket onto shifter/brake shaft with collar away from shifting keys and shoulder on shifter/brake shaft. Slide keys through gear and install the neutral collar over ends of shift-

ing keys and pull back until gears touch shoulder of the shaft. Insert splined countershaft into smaller reverse sprocket. Place the large beveled gear on countershaft with beveled side of gear towards reverse sprocket. If unit is a 1, 2 or 3 speed unit, place a washer over the shaft and next to the backside of the large bevel gear. If the unit is a 4 speed unit, there will not be a washer in this location. Install spur gears onto the countershaft, alternating with mating gear on the shifter/brake shaft. Install largest shifting gears with the flat side of gear next to the neutral collar. On older models, install thrust washer with 45 degree chamfer on inside diameter of washer next to gear. Chamfer must face towards shifting keys. On newer models, thrust washer will have rounded sides and rounded side must face towards shifting keys. Older chamfered thrust washer and newer rounded thrust washer are interchangeable. Install thrust washer on each end of countershaft and a bushing next to the last spur gear on countershaft. Install larger thrust washer next to the smallest shifting gear, then install bronze bushing and "O" ring. Some units will use a stepped thrust washer; install washer onto shaft so the step is facing away from the shifting gears. The end of the shifter/brake shaft (opposite shifting gears) has a spline. Install spur gear that drives output gear onto this spline. Install thrust washer, bushing and "O" ring.

To assemble output shaft, install bronze bushing with collar, flat down, next to pinion. Install output gear over pinion with a washer on the outside of gear. After assembly of both shafts, install correct size flanged bushing on each end.

To assemble differential, assemble unit and hold in position while unit is installed in case. Axles and gears must be on center line of ring gear. Bearing block in case must have flange to the left-hand side. Block in cover must have flange to the right-hand side. Prior to differential installation in case, insert the four felt wicks with bosses and tabs

to hold bearing blocks in position. Apply Bentonite grease to these bearing areas after wicks have been installed.

Install shifter assembly and pack 24 ounces (710 mL) of Bentonite grease around bearings and gears. Install cover on case and tighten cap screws to 90-100 in.-lbs. (10-11 N·m). Install detent ball, spring and set screw. Tighten set screw one turn below flush. Install neutral safety switch and brake unit.

Series 1200 And Series 1400

The 1200 series and 1400 series transaxle has three forward speeds and one reverse speed. The 1200 series and 1400 series transaxle are equipped with axle support housings which are pressed from the inside of the case to the outside. Entire transaxle must be disassembled before axle housings can be removed. Variations in model numbers, within the series, indicate shift lever shape, axle lengths, axle machining for wheel hub attachment, axle housing variations, size of the brake shaft or the placement of the input shaft on the left-hand or right-hand side of the transaxle. Series and model numbers may be stamped into case or on a metal tag attached to case at locations indicated at (I – Fig. PT50).

OVERHAUL. Remove brake components and input pulley. Remove all keys from keyways and polish any burrs or rust from exposed shafts. Place shift lever in neutral position, unscrew shift housing cap screws and withdraw shift assembly from case. Place transaxle in a vise with longer axle pointing downward. Unscrew case cap screws and drive out dowel pins. Separate cover from case and lift cover upward off axle shaft. Brake shaft (30 – Fig. PT51) and idler gear (29) will be removed with cover. Remove output shaft (41) with output gear (40), spacer (39) and washer (38). Withdraw differential and axle shaft assembly and lay aside for later disassembly. Hold upper ends of shifter rods together and lift out shifter rods, forks, shifter stop, shifter shaft (20) and

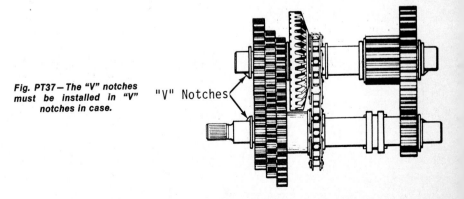

Fig. PT37 – The "V" notches must be installed in "V" notches in case.

"V" Notches

sliding gears (22 and 23) as an assembly. Remove reverse idler gear (27), idler shaft (28) and spacer (26), then remove idler shaft (32) along with idler gears (33, 35 and 37) and spacers (34 and 36). Withdraw input shaft (24) and gear (25) from case. To remove brake shaft (30) and idler gear (29) from cover, block up under idler gear (29) and press brake shaft (30) out of gear while being careful pressure is not applied on cover during

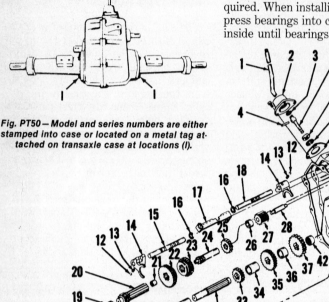

Fig. PT50—Model and series numbers are either stamped into case or located on a metal tag attached on transaxle case at locations (I).

operation. Renew seals and bushings in axle housing (51 and 60) as required.

To disassemble differential, unscrew four cap screws and separate axle shaft and carriage assemblies from ring gear (68). Drive blocks (65), bevel pinion gears (66) and drive pin (67) can now be removed from ring gear. Remove snap rings (43) and slide axle shafts (45 and 57) from bevel gears (44) and carriers (48 and 62).

Clean and inspect all parts for damage or excessive wear and renew as required. When installing needle bearings, press bearings into case and cover from inside until bearings are 0.015-0.020 in-

ches (0.381-0.508 mm) below thrust surfaces. Renew all seals and gaskets and reassemble transaxle assembly by reversing disassembly procedure. Install reverse idler gear (27) into case so rounded edge of gear teeth and spacer (26) will be towards cover. When installing idler shaft (32), place short spacer (36) between gears (35 and 37) and long spacer (34) between gears (33 and 35). Bevels on gear teeth of gears (33 and 35) must be on side of gear nearest large gear (37). Before installing shifter assembly, fill transaxle housing with SAE 90 EP gear lubricant. Capacity for Models 1203, 1204, 1204-A and 1205 through 1208 is 3 pints (1.4 L). Capacity for all other models is 2 pints (0.9 L). When installing shifter assembly, position shifter rods in neutral position as shown in Fig. PT52. Differential cap screws are tightened to 7 ft.-lbs. (9 N·m). Tighten case-to-cover and shift lever housing cap screws to 10 ft.-lbs. (14 N·m) and axle housing cap screws to 13 ft.-lbs. (18 N·m).

Series 1700 And Series 2000

The Peerless 1700 series and 2000 series transaxle are similar to the 1200 series transaxle except that the axle housings bolt to the outside of the transaxle case disassembly. Model and series numbers are at the same locations as those for 1200 series transaxles (Fig. PT50).

OVERHAUL. Clean exterior of unit. Remove drain plug and drain lubricant. Remove brake band, brake drum and input pulley. Loosen set screws and remove rear wheel and hub assemblies. Place shift lever in neutral position, remove the three cap screws from shift lever housing, then withdraw shift lever assembly. Remove cap screws securing transaxle cover (59—Fig. PT61) to case (14). Place unit on the edge of a bench or in a vise with right axle pointing downward. Drive dowel pins out of cover. Remove all rust, paint or burrs from outer ends of axle shafts. Separate cover from case and lift cover upward

Fig. PT51—Exploded view of Peerless 1200 series and 1400 series transaxle.

1. Shift lever	19. Bearing	34. Spacer
2. Shift housing	20. Shifter shaft	35. Gear
3. Quad ring	21. Bearing	36. Spacer
4. Roll pin	22. Sliding gear	37. Gear
5. Shift lever	(1st & reverse)	38. Washer
6. Keeper	23. Sliding gear	39. Spacer
7. Snap ring	(2nd & 3rd)	40. Output gear
8. Gasket	24. Input shaft	41. Output shaft
9. Bearing	25. Gear	42. Bearing
10. Oil seal	26. Spacer	43. Snap ring
11. Case	27. Reverse idler gear	44. Bevel gear
12. Steel ball	28. Reverse idler shaft	45. Axle shaft
13. Spring	29. Idler gear	46. Thrust bearings
14. Shifter fork	30. Brake shaft	47. Thrust bearing
15. Shifter rod	31. Spacer	48. Differential carrier
16. Snap ring	32. Idler shaft	49. Thrust washers
17. Shifter stop	33. Gear	50. Bushing
18. Shifter rod		

51. Axle housing	
52. Oil seal	
53. Oil seal	
54. Bearing	
55. Cover	
56. Dowel pin	
57. Axle shaft	
58. Oil seal	
59. Bushing	
60. Axle housing	
61. Thrust washers	
62. Differential carrier	
63. Thrust washers	
64. Thrust bearing	
65. Drive blocks	
66. Bevel pinion gear	
67. Drive pin	
68. Ring gear	

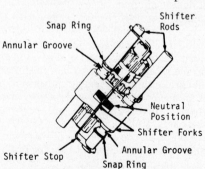

Fig. PT52—To position shifter assembly in neutral for reassembly, align notches in shifter forks with notch in shifter stop.

off axle shaft. Brake shaft (33) and idler gear (32) will be removed with cover. Remove output shaft (45) with output gear (44), spacer (43) and washer (42). Withdraw differential and axle shaft assembly and lay aside for later disassembly. Hold upper ends of shifter rods together and lift out shifter rods, forks, shifter stop, shifter shaft (26) and sliding gears (28 and 29) as an assembly. Remove reverse idler gear (17), shaft (15) and spacer (18), then remove idler shaft (34) with idler gears (35, 37 and 39) and spacers (36 and 38). Input shaft (30) and input gear (31) can now be removed from case. To remove brake shaft (33) and idler gear (32) from cover, block up under idler gear (32) and press brake shaft (33) out of gear while being careful pressure is not applied on cover during operation.

To disassemble differential, unbolt and separate axle shaft and carriage assemblies from ring gear (49). Drive blocks (52), bevel pinion gears (51) and drive pin (50) can now be removed from ring gear. Remove snap rings (53) and slide axle shafts (47 and 55) from axle gears (54) and carriages (48 and 58).

Unbolt axle housings (12 and 64) and renew bushings (13 and 65) and seals (11 and 63) as required.

Clean and inspect all parts and renew any showing excessive wear or other damage. When installing needle bearings, press bearings in from inside of case and cover until bearings are 0.015-0.020 inch (0.381-0.508 mm) below thrust surfaces. Renew all seals and gaskets and reassemble by reversing removal procedure. Install reverse idler gear (17) into case so the rounded edge of the gear teeth and spacer (18) will be to the top. When installing idler shaft (34) and idler gears, position gears and spacers as follows: idler gear (39) with raised hub up, short spacer (38), idler gear (37) with rounded teeth edge down, long spacer (36) and idler gear (35) with rounded teeth edge down. Tighten differential cap screws to 7 ft.-lbs. (9 N·m). Tighten case-to-cover and shift lever housing cap screws to 10 ft.-lbs. (14 N·m) and axle housing cap screws to 13 ft.-lbs. (18 N·m). Fill transaxle housing to level plug opening with SAE 90 EP gear lubricant. Approximate capacity is 2 pints (0.9 L).

Series 2300

The Peerless 2300 series transaxle is a heavy-duty transaxle with four forward speeds and one reverse speed. The 2300 series transaxle is designed for small tractors which can be equipped with ground engaging attachments. The transaxle case is cast iron. The series and model numbers are stamped into the

case or on a metal tag attached on the case in either location shown at (I – Fig. PT80).

OVERHAUL. Clean exterior of unit. Remove drain plug and drain lubricant. Loosen set screws, remove snap rings, then remove rear wheel and hub assemblies. Remove brake assembly and input pulley. Place shift lever (1 – Fig. PT81) in neutral position, then unbolt and remove shift lever assembly. Remove axle housings (14 and 64) and remove seal retainers (11) with oil seals (12) and "O" rings (13) by pulling each axle shaft

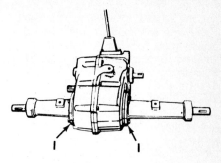

Fig. PT80 – On 2300 series transaxle, model and series numbers are stamped into the transaxle case or are on a metal tag attached on the case in either location (I).

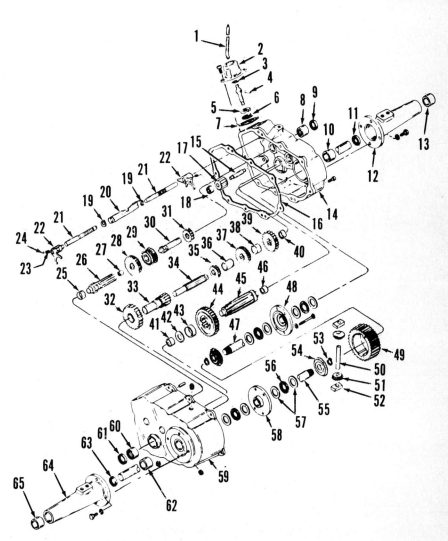

Fig. PT61 – Exploded view of Peerless 1700 series transaxle. Series 2000 is similar except sealed ball bearings are used in place of bushings (13 and 65).

1. Shift lever	18. Spacer	34. Idler shaft	50. Drive pin
2. Shift lever housing	19. Snap ring	35. Idler gear	51. Bevel pinion gear
3. Seal ring	20. Shifter stop	36. Long spacer	52. Drive block
4. Roll pin	21. Shifter rod	37. Idler gear	53. Snap ring
5. Retainer	22. Shifter fork	38. Short spacer	54. Bevel axle gear
6. Snap ring	23. Spring	39. Idler gear	55. Axle shaft
7. Gasket	24. Detent ball	40. Needle bearing	56. Thrust bearing
8. Needle bearing	25. Needle bearing	41. Needle bearing	57. Thrust washers
9. Oil seal	26. Shifter shaft	42. Washer	58. Axle carriage (tapped holes)
10. Bushing	27. Center bearing	43. Spacer	59. Transaxle cover
11. Oil seal	28. Gear (1st & reverse)	44. Output gear	60. Needle bearing
12. Axle housing	29. Gear (2nd & 3rd)	45. Output shaft	61. Oil seal
13. Bushing	30. Input shaft	46. Needle bearing	62. Bushing
14. Transaxle case	31. Input gear	47. Axle shaft	63. Oil seal
15. Reverse idler shaft	32. Idler gear	48. Axle carriage (plain holes)	64. Axle housing
16. Gasket	33. Brake shaft	49. Ring gear	65. Bushing
17. Reverse idler gear			

out of case and cover as far as possible. Place transaxle unit on the edge of a bench with left axle shaft pointing downward. Remove cap screws securing case (16) to cover (66) and drive aligning dowel pins out of case. Lift case (16) up 1½ to 2 inches (40-50 mm), tilt case about 45 degrees, rotate case clockwise and remove from assembly. Input shaft (32) and input gear (33) will be removed with case. Withdraw differential and axle shaft assembly and lay aside for later disassembly. Remove 3-cluster gear (44) with its thrust washer (46) and spacer (42). Lift out reverse idler gear (25), spacer (24) and reverse idler shaft (23). Hold upper ends of shifter rods together and lift out shifter rods, forks, shifter stop (21), sliding gears (30 and 31) and shifter shaft (28) as an assembly. Remove low reduction gear (57), low reduction shaft (56) and thrust washer (55), then remove 2-cluster gear (40) from brake shaft. Lift out the output gear (50), output shaft (51) and thrust washers (49 and 52). To remove brake and cluster shaft (39) and idler gear (38) from cover (66), block up under idler gear and press shaft (39) out of gear. Do not allow cover or low reduction gear bearing boss to support any part of the pressure required to press brake and cluster shaft (39) from idler gear (38). Remove input shaft (32) with input gear (33) and thrust washer (34) from case (16).

To disassemble standard differential, remove four cap screws and separate axle shaft and carriage assemblies from ring gear (79). Drive blocks (78), bevel pinion gears (77) and drive pin (76) can now be removed from ring gear. Remove snap rings (59) and withdraw axle shafts (63 and 67) from axle gears (61) and carriages (62 and 72).

To disassemble limited-slip differential, remove the four cap screws (5 – Fig. PT82) and separate axle assemblies from body cores (10 and 13). Remove snap rings (8 and 15) and remove side gears (7 and 16), carriers (6 and 17) and all thrust washers and bearings. Remove spring (11) on older models so equipped. On all models, remove pinion gears (9 and 14). To reassemble limited-slip differential, install body cores in ring gear so gear pockets in one core are out of alignment with gear pockets in the other core. Reassemble axle assemblies making certain flanged side of thrust washers (2 and 20) are installed toward carriers. Install pinion gears in one body core, then hold pinion gears in core by installing differential carrier and axle assembly. Turn differential over. Be sure pinion gears mesh with side gear. Install pinion gears in remaining body core being sure gears mesh with previously installed pinion gears. Install cylindrical spring (as equipped) so spring bottoms against side gear. Spring (if so equipped) should be in contact with most of the ten pinion gears. Install remaining axle assembly and differential retaining bolts and tighten bolts to 7-10 ft.-lbs. (9-14 N·m).

Clean and inspect all transaxle parts and renew any showing excessive wear or other damage. When installing new needle bearings, press bearing (29 – Fig. PT81) into shifter shaft (28) to a depth of 0.010 inch (0.254 mm) below end of shaft and low reduction shaft bearings (54 and 58) 0.010 inch (0.254 mm) below thrust surfaces of bearing bases. Carrier bearings (10) should be pressed in from inside of case and cover until bearings are

Fig. PT81 – Exploded view of Peerless 2300 series transaxle.

1. Shift lever	22. Shifter fork	41. Bushing
2. Shift lever housing	23. Reverse idler shaft	42. Spacer
3. Seal ring	24. Spacer	43. Bushing
4. Roll pin	25. Reverse idler gear	44. 3-cluster gear
5. Retainer	26. Needle bearing	45. Bushing
6. Snap ring	27. Thrust washer	46. Thrust washer
7. Gasket	28. Shifter shaft	47. Needle bearing
8. Ball bearing	29. Needle bearing	48. Needle bearing
9. Oil seal	30. Gear	49. Thrust washer
10. Carrier bearing	(1st, 2nd & reverse)	50. Output gear
11. Seal retainer	31. Gear (3rd & 4th)	51. Output shaft
12. Oil seal	32. Input shaft	52. Thrust washer
13. "O" ring	33. Input gear	53. Needle bearing
14. Axle housing	34. Thrust washer	54. Needle bearing
15. Axle outer bearing	35. Needle bearing	55. Thrust washer
16. Transaxle case	36. Needle bearing	56. Low reduction shaft
17. Gasket	37. Thrust washer	57. Low reduction gear
18. Detent ball	38. Idler gear	58. Needle bearing
19. Spring	39. Brake & cluster shaft	59. Snap ring
20. Shifter rod	40. 2-cluster gear	60. Thrust washer
21. Shifter stop		

61. Axle gear	
62. Axle carriage	
(plain holes)	
63. Axle shaft	
64. Axle housing	
65. Oil seal	
66. Transaxle cover	
67. Axle shaft	
68. Thrust washer	
69. Thrust bearing	
70. Thrust washer	
71. Bushing	
72. Axle carriage	
(tapped holes)	
73. Thrust washer	
74. Thrust bearing	
75. Thrust washer	
76. Drive pin	
77. Bevel pinion gear	
78. Drive block	
79. Ring gear	

0.290 inch (7.37 mm) below face of axle housing mounting surface. All other needle bearings are to be pressed in from inside of case and cover to a depth of 0.015-0.020 inch (0.381-0.508 mm) below thrust surfaces.

Renew all seals and gaskets and reassemble by reversing disassembly procedure. Install brake and cluster shaft (39) and idler gear (38) with beveled edge of gear teeth up away from cover. Install reverse idler shaft (23), spacer (24) and reverse idler gear (25) with rounded end of gear teeth facing spacer. Install input gear (33) and shaft (32) so chamfered side of input gear is facing case (16). Before installing shifter, fill transaxle housing through shifter opening with 4 pints (1.9 L) of SAE 90 EP gear lubricant. Tighten differential cap screws to 7 ft.-lbs. (9 N·m). Tighten case-to-cover and shift lever housing cap screws to 10 ft.-lbs. (14 N·m) and axle housing cap screws to 13 ft.-lbs. (14 N·m).

SIMPLICITY

2-Speed And 3-Speed

OVERHAUL. To overhaul transaxle, remove pins and slide off rear wheel and hub assemblies. Loosen set screws and slide brake drum off brake shaft (35 – Fig. S50). Drive alignment roll pins out of cover, remove cap screws from cover and pry cover off. Left axle shaft (38) will be removed with cover (10). Align spider gear teeth and withdraw right axle shaft (39). Lift out drive gear and differential assembly. Remove brake shaft (35), cluster gear (36) and low reduction gear and shaft. Remove nuts from shift rails (17 and 20) and reverse pinion shaft (23). Remove shift fork (21), shift rail (20), sliding gear (30) and pulley shaft (31). Shift fork (13), shift rail (17), reverse gear (24) and shaft (23) can now be removed. The balance of disassembly is evident after examination of unit.

When reassembling transaxle, tighten differential bolts to 20 ft.-lbs. (27 N·m) and nuts securing reverse shaft and shift rails to the case to 50 ft.-lbs. (68 N·m). Refill transmission with SAE 90 EP gear oil.

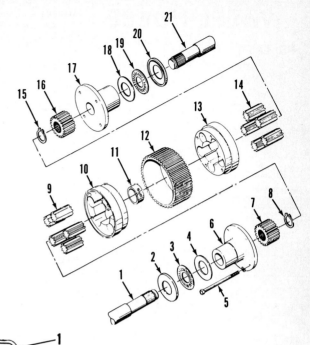

Fig. PT82 — *Exploded view of limited-slip differential assembly available as a transaxle option.*

1. Axle
2. Thrust washer
3. Thrust bearing
4. Thrust washer
5. Cap screw
6. Carrier
7. Side gear
8. Snap ring
9. Pinion gears
10. Body core
11. Spring (early models only)
12. Ring gear
13. Body core
14. Pinion gears
15. Snap ring
16. Side gear
17. Carrier
18. Thrust washer
19. Thrust bearing
20. Flanged thrust washer
21. Axle

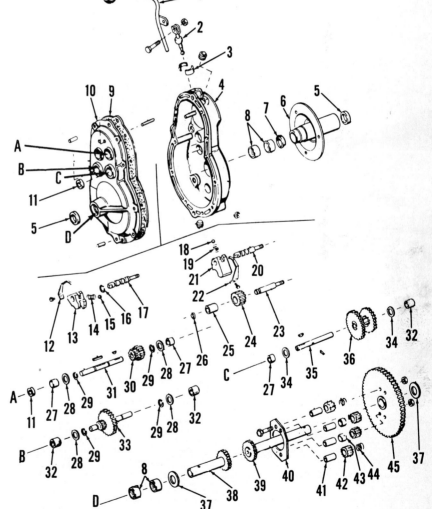

Fig. S50 — Exploded view of Simplicity 3-speed transaxle. Gear and shaft assembly (33) is not used on 2-speed model.

1. Shift lever assy.	15. Shift lock ball
2. Shift rod	16. Retaining ring
3. Bushing	17. Shift rail
4. Gearcase	18. Ball
5. Seal	19. Shift lock spring
6. Axle housing	20. Shift rail
7. Seal	21. Shift fork
8. Roller bearings	22. Spring
9. Gasket	23. Pinion shaft
10. Gearcase cover	24. Reverse pinion gear
11. Seal	25. Roller bearing
12. Spring	26. "O" ring
13. Shift fork	27. Roller bearing
14. Shift lock spring	28. Washer

29. Retaining ring	34. Washer	38. Axle shaft	42. Differential pinion
30. Hi & Lo gear pinion	35. Brake shaft	39. Axle shaft	43. Spacer
31. Pto pulley shaft	36. Cluster gear	40. Differential plate	44. Spring
32. Bearing	37. Washer	41. Spindle	45. Drive gear assy.
33. Gear & shaft assy.			

WHEEL HORSE

4-Speed

OVERHAUL. To overhaul transaxle, first remove and thoroughly clean unit. Loosen retaining set screw and remove shift lever. Remove input pulley and brake assembly. Remove keys from input shaft and brake shaft. Remove wheel assemblies.

Position transaxle so bottom cover (72–Fig. WH125) is up and remove

cover and gasket. Remove thrust bearing (36), washers (35 and 37) and pinion drive gear (34). Remove idler gear (54) with thrust washers (52 and 55). Withdraw reverse idler gear shaft (43) with gear (40). Place shift forks in neutral position as shown in Fig. WH126 and withdraw splined shaft (60–Fig. WH125) and gear (64). Remove first and reverse sliding gear (62) from shift fork. Remove and disassemble cluster gear assembly (45 through 51). Remove second and high speed sliding gear (61) from shift fork.

To remove shift forks, remove plug (29) and carefully pull second and high speed shift fork and shaft (70) out of case. Be careful not to lose detent ball (26) which will be released when shift fork shaft is withdrawn. Remove shift ball assembly (26 through 28). Remove low and reverse shift fork and shaft (69). Stand transmission on end and tap on end of input shaft (58) and remove shaft. Unscrew end cap (17) retaining cap screws and remove end cap with pinion gear shaft (33). Reposition transaxle case with bottom down. Remove left axle assembly from case and disassemble if necessary. Remove differential assembly (23) and thrust bearing (22) and washers (21) from case. Remove

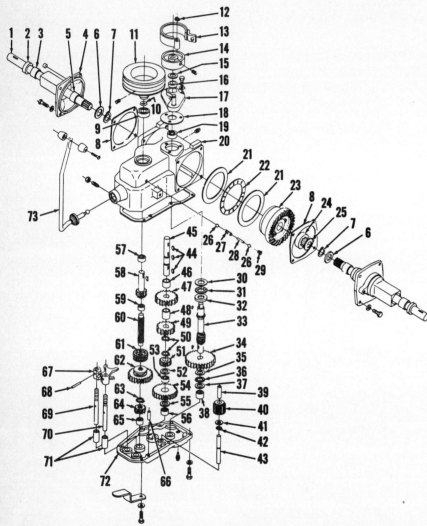

Fig. WH125—Exploded view of Wheel Horse 4-speed transaxle.

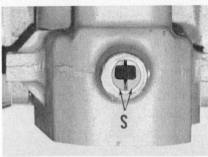

Fig. WH126—Align shift fork notches (S) as shown to set transmission gears in neutral.

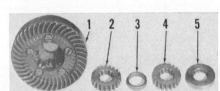

Fig. WH127—View of differential assembly (23–Fig. WH125). Unit (1) must be renewed as an assembly.

1. Differential unit
2. Axle gear (R.H.)
3. Spacer
4. Axle gear (L.H.)
5. Thrust washer

Fig. WH128—Oil slots in end cap (17–Fig. WH125) must align as shown with relief (R) in case.

1. Axle shaft	21. Thrust washer	40. Reverse idler gear	59. Bearing
2. Oil seal	22. Thrust bearing	41. Washer	60. Splined shaft
3. Bearing	23. Differential assy.	42. Snap ring	61. Sliding gear (2nd & 3rd)
4. Axle housing	24. Axle bearing	43. Shaft	62. Sliding gear (1st & reverse)
5. Bearing	25. Spring washer	44. Key	63. Snap ring
6. Thrust washer	26. Ball	45. Cluster gear shaft	64. Gear
7. Snap ring	27. Spring	46. Bearing	65. Bearing
8. Gasket	28. Shift stop pin	47. Gear	66. Dowel pin
9. Bearing	29. Plug	48. Spacer	67. Shift forks
10. "O" ring	30. Thrust washer	49. Second speed gear	68. Pin
11. Input pulley	31. Thrust bearing	50. Snap ring	69. Shift shaft (1st & reverse)
12. Snap ring	32. Thrust washer	51. First speed gear	70. Shift shaft (2nd & third)
13. Brake band	33. Pinion shaft	52. Thrust washer	71. Bushing
14. Brake drum	34. Drive gear	53. Bearing	72. Cover
15. Thrust washer	35. Thrust washer	54. Idler gear	73. Shift lever/seal boot
16. Oil seal	36. Thrust bearing	55. Thrust washer	
17. End cap	37. Thrust washer	56. Bearing	
18. Gasket	38. Bearing	57. Bearing	
19. Bearing	39. Bushing	58. Input shaft & gear	
20. Case			

right axle assembly and disassemble if necessary.

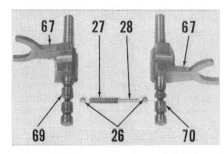

Fig. WH129 — Note difference in detents of shift shaft for first and reverse (69) from those of second and third shift shaft (70). Do not interchange. Identify parts by reference to Fig. WH125.

Inspect all components for damage or excessive wear. Axle gears and differential assembly shown in Fig. WH127 are available only as a unit assembly. To reassemble transaxle, reverse disassembly

Fig. WH130 — Install reverse idler gear on shaft so gear hub (H) is opposite washer (W) and snap ring (S).

procedure and observe the following points: Install right axle assembly so breather plug is towards top of transaxle. Sharp edge of snap rings (7 – Fig. WH125) should be towards axle splines. Splines of left axle thrust washer (5 – Fig. WH127) must be adjacent to differential axle gear (4). Concave surface of washer (25 – Fig. WH125) must be next to axle bearing (24). Note position of thin washer (30) and thick washer (32). When installing end cap (17) and pinion gear shaft assembly in transaxle case, oil slot in end cap must align with relief in case (Fig. WH128). Identify shift forks as shown in Fig. WH129. Do not interchange shift shafts as detents will be incorrectly positioned.

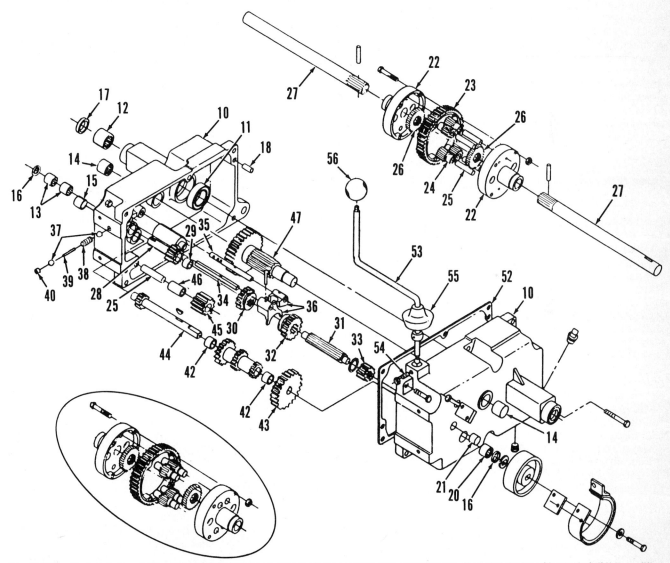

Fig. WH150 — Exploded view of Wheel Horse three (four) speed transmission used in current production. Note that design of input shaft (28) is modified from earlier models. Brake drum, formerly mounted on output shaft (47), is now fitted to cluster gear shaft (44) as shown. Differential pinions are now integral with pinion shafts as shown in inset view. Also see Fig. WH151.

10. Case half				44. Brake/cluster shaft
11. Ball bearing	20. Needle bearing	28. Input gear/shaft	36. Shift fork	45. Reverse idler
12. Needle bearing	21. Needle bearing	29. Needle bearing	37. Shift stop ball	46. Bronze bushing
13. Needle bearing	22. Differential case	30. Second high gear	38. Stop spring	47. Drive gear set
14. Needle bearing	23. Bull gear	31. Spline shaft	39. Pin	52. Gasket
15. Needle bearing	24. Pinion gear	32. Low reverse gear	40. Plug	53. Shift lever
16. Oil seal	25. Pinion shaft	33. Pinion	41. Cluster gear	54. Set screw
17. Oil seal	26. Axle gear	34. Shift rail	42. Bronze bushing	55. Boot
18. Dowel pin	27. Axle shaft	35. Shift rail	43. Reduction gear	56. Knob

To install shift mechanism, install low and reverse shift shaft (69 – Fig. WH125) with shift fork in case. Install shift balls, spring and pin in passage of case and hold in position with a punch. Move shift shaft up or down until shift ball moves into detent on shift shaft. Carefully install second and high shift shaft into case while removing punch. Allow shift shaft to move down only until first detent is engaged by ball. This is second gear position and second and high sliding gear can now be installed. Grooves of sliding gears will be next to each other if gears are properly installed.

Snap rings (63) should be installed on splined shaft so sharp edge of snap ring is nearest short end of shaft. Hub end of reverse idler gear (40) must be opposite washer (41) as shown in Fig. WH130. Position shift forks in neutral position as shown in Fig. WH126 before installing transaxle cover and shift lever. To install shift lever, tighten retaining set screw until snug, then back out set screw 1/8 turn and tighten locknut. After assembly is completed, fill transaxle to level of fill plug with SAE 90 EP gear oil.

Three (Four) Speed

To overhaul transaxle, first remove and thoroughly clean unit.

OVERHAUL. To disassemble transaxle, drain lubricant and remove wheel and hub assemblies. Set transaxle up in a vise or holding fixture so right hand axle shaft points downward. Back out set screw (54 – Fig. WH150) and lift out shift lever assembly (53). Remove lockbolt from extension of brake/cluster shaft (44) and pull brake drum from shaft. On older production models, brake drum was mounted on shaft (47) and retained on shaft end by a snap ring. At this point, transmission case half (10) can be unbolted and lifted off. Be sure axle shafts are cleaned and burrs are removed, especially near keyways. Now lift out differential assembly with axles for later attention. Pull out spline shaft (31) from hubs of sliding gears (30 and

32) and remove sliding gears and reverse idler gear (45). Cluster gear shaft (44) with cluster and reduction gear (43) can now be lifted out. Output drive gear set (47) is next in order for removal. Front shift fork and rail (34) should now be removed, taking care shift stop balls (37) are not dropped and lost when released from detents in shift rail during removal. Cover opening in case with free hand and watch for spring (38) and pin (39) as well. Remove second and high gear fork and rail (35) next. Remove input pulley from shaft end and lift out input/shaft (28).

Disassembly of differential unit requires through-bolts be removed so differential case halves (22) can be separated from bull gear (23) giving access to pinions (24). In later production, pinions and pinion shafts are integral as shown in inset. Finish disassembly by driving out roll pins and removing axle gears (26) from splined ends of axle shafts (27).

All parts should be thoroughly cleaned and inspected. Renew any parts which are severely worn or damaged beyond service limits. Pay particular attention to condition of needle bearings fitted into bosses in case halves. Upon completion, reassemble transaxle by reversing disassembly sequence. Refill unit with approximately 4 pints (1.9 L) of SAE 140 gear oil meeting GL-5 specifications.

Six (Eight) Speed

OVERHAUL. After transaxle and axle assembly is removed from tractor, drain lubricant and remove rear wheels and hub assemblies. Thoroughly clean exterior of unit. For easier and more convenient disassembly, set transaxle up in a holding jig or large shop vise so right hand axle is pointed down. Back out set screw (80 – WH152) so gear shift lever (79) can be removed. Remove anchor bolts (66) if removal of brake band (65) is desired, then remove lockbolt (63) at outer end of cluster/brake shaft (55) so brake drum can be pulled. Watch for special double "D" washer (61). Be sure exposed ends of axles are clean and

burrs are removed, especially near edges of keyways.

Older models of this transaxle have brake drums fitted on shaft end of gear drive set (60) over a Woodruff key and retained at outer shaft end by a snap ring.

Interior of transaxle will be exposed when left-hand case half is unbolted and lifted off over left axle. Differential assembly and both axles can now be lifted out to set aside for later disassembly or repair. Pull out spline shaft (33) and then low-reverse gear (45) and second-high gear (44). Lift out cluster/brake shaft (55) with cluster gear (52) and reduction gear (54). For an easy grip on shaft (55), insert bolt (63) by a few threads to serve as a handle. Now, remove reverse idler gear (57) and idler shaft (59). First and reverse gear shift rail (46) and its shift fork should be removed using caution so stop balls (39) are not dropped and lost when out of engagement with shift rail detents. Balls, as well as spring (40) and guide pin (50) may be caught by holding free hand over case opening. Remove second and third gear (rear) shift rail (47) and fork. Remove output gear drive set (60).

NOTE: When servicing transaxles of late model tractors, refer to Fig. WH153 for design change in output gear and shaft which applies to these models.

Transaxle input pulley should next be removed from outer end of input shaft (29 – Fig. WH152). Now, back out detent bolt (42) and withdraw input shaft (29) which carries input gear and spline (31) and range sliding gear (34). When moving these gears, watch for stop spring (40) and detent ball (39) when range shifter fork (38) is dislodged. Remove range cluster gear (35) and its shaft.

Disassemble limited slip differential assembly by unbolting through-bolts (23) so end caps (14 and 15) can be separated from ring gear (16). Next, remove differential pinions (18), cylindrical spring (22) and drive bodies (20) from each side of ring gear. After snap rings (28) have been removed, axle shafts (26 and 27) can be pulled from internal splines of axle gears (17) and out of end caps. Note that some models are furnished with spur gear differential as shown in upper right inset of Fig. WH152.

Perform detailed clean-up of all disassembled parts and carefully inspect each for damage or undue wear. Renew individual parts as needed and reassemble transaxle by reversal of disassembly procedure. Refill unit to check plug (70) opening with approximately 4 pints (1.9 L) of SAE 140 gear oil of specification GL-5.

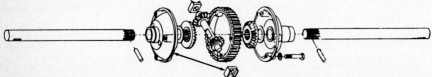

Fig. WH151 – Exploded view of bevel gear differential used on older 3-speed models. Note how drive blocks fit recesses in differential case halves.

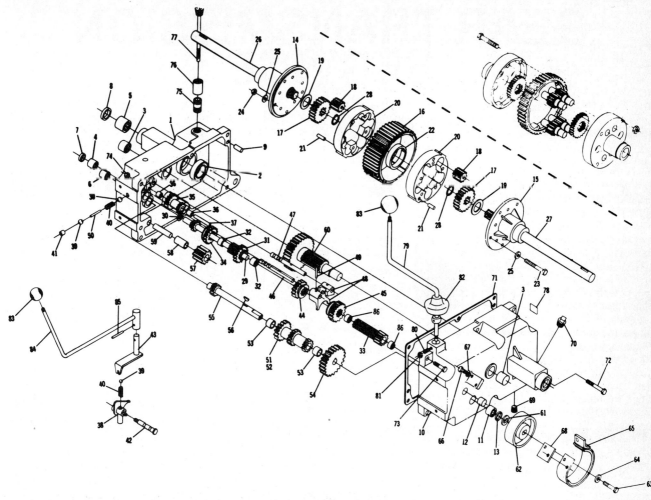

Fig. WH152—Exploded view of Wheel Horse six (eight) speed transaxle used in current production tractors. See Fig. WH153 for recent change in drive gear (60). Differential spur gear pinion set shown in upper right inset is used on late models while limited slip design shown is used on some earlier models. Brake drum was mounted on shaft (60) in earlier models.

1. Case (R.H.)	18. Pinion gear	35. Reduction gear	53. Bronze bearing	70. Check plug
2. Ball bearing	19. Thrust washer	36. Needle bearing	54. Reduction gear	71. Case gasket
3. Needle bearing	20. Differential body	37. Reduction gear shaft	55. Cluster/brake shaft	72. Assembly bolt
4. Needle bearing	21. Roll pin	38. Shift fork	56. Woodruff key	73. Assembly bolt
5. Needle bearing	22. Cylindrical spring	39. Stop ball	57. Reverse idler	74. Locking nut
6. Needle bearing	23. Through-bolt	40. Stop spring	58. Bronze bushing	75. Nipple ½ inch pipe
7. Oil seal	24. Self-locking nut	41. Plug	59. Idler shaft	76. Coupling
8. Oil seal	25. Washer	42. Detent bolt	60. Drive gear set	77. Dipstick
9. Dowel pin	26. Axle (R.H.)	43. Shift lever	61. Double "D" washer	78. Decal
10. Case (L.H.)	27. Axle (L.H.)	44. Second high gear	62. Brake drum	79. Gear selector
11. Needle bearing	28. Snap ring	45. Low reverse gear	63. Lockbolt	80. Set screw
12. Needle bearing	29. Input shaft	46. Shift rail	64. Washer (special)	81. Locknut
13. Brake shaft seal	30. Thrust washer	47. Shift rail	65. Brake band	82. Boot
14. End cap (R.H.)	31. Input gear/spline	48. Shift fork	66. Anchor bolt	83. Knob
15. End cap (L.H.)	32. Needle bearing	49. Roll pin	67. Lockwasher	84. Range selector
16. Ring gear	33. Input pinion/spline	50. Shift stop pin	68. Stop plate	85. Roll pin
17. Axle gear	34. Sliding gear	51. Gear/bearing assy.	69. Drain plug	86. Bronze bushings
		52. Cluster gear		

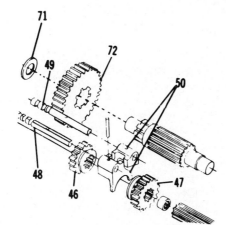

Fig. WH153—Supplemental view showing change made in drive gear (60—Fig. WH152) on late model transaxles. Note that gear (72) is separated from splined shaft.

46. Second high gear	
47. Low reverse gear	50. Shift forks
48. Front shift rail	71. Thrust washer
49. Rear shift rail	72. Gear (44T)

GEAR TRANSMISSION SERVICE

FOOTE

Model 35-3500

OVERHAUL. To disassemble transmission, first unbolt and remove shift lever. Place unit in a vise so sprocket end of output shaft (15–Fig. FT100) is pointing upward. Remove snap ring (12), output sprocket (13) and key (14). Unbolt and remove cover (11) from case (5). Slide forward drive gear (9) from output shaft (15). Lift input and drive pinion assembly (17 through 22) from case (5). Carefully withdraw clutch collar (8) and shift fork (7) from shaft and case, taking care not to lose detent ball (4) and spring (3). Remove key (16), reverse drive gear (19), snap ring (1) and flat washer (2) from output shaft (15), then withdraw shaft from case. Remove snap ring (17), bevel pinion (18) and flange bushings (6 and 10) can be removed from case (5) and cover (11) if necessary.

Clean all parts and renew any showing excessive wear or other damage. Reassemble by reversing disassembly procedure and fill case with 5 ounces (148 mL) of EP lithium base grease.

PEERLESS

Series 350

OVERHAUL. To overhaul transmission, first clean exterior of transmission. Shift transmissin into neutral, unscrew shift lever housing screws and remove shift components (36 through 41–Fig. PT100). Remove snap ring (44) and output sprocket (43). Drive dowel pins out

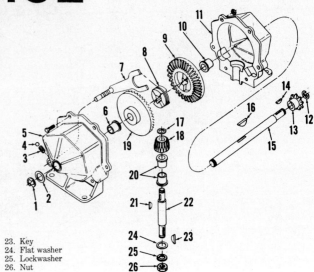

Fig. FT100—Exploded view of Foote Model 35-3500 single speed, forward-reverse gear transmission.

1. Snap ring
2. Flat washer
3. Spring
4. Detent ball
5. Transmission case
6. Flange bushing
7. Shift fork
8. Clutch collar
9. Forward drive gear
10. Flange bushing
11. Transmission cover
12. Snap ring
13. Output sprocket
14. Key
15. Output shaft
16. Key
17. Snap ring
18. Bevel pinion
19. Reverse drive gear
20. Flange bushings
21. Key
22. Input shaft
23. Key
24. Flat washer
25. Lockwasher
26. Nut

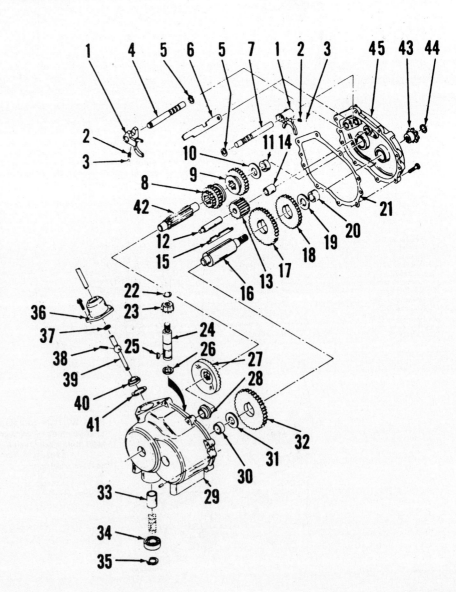

Fig. PT100—Exploded view of Peerless Series 350 gear transmission.

1. Shifter fork
2. Spring
3. Ball
4. Shifter rod
5. Snap ring
6. Shifter stop
7. Shifter rod
8. First & second gear
9. Third & reverse gear
10. Washer
11. Bushing
12. Reverse idler shaft
13. Reverse idler gear
14. Spacer
15. Key
16. Output shaft
17. Medium idler gear
18. Small idler gear
19. Washer
20. Bushing
21. Gasket
22. Snap ring
23. Pinion gear
24. Input shaft
25. Key
26. Thrust bearing
27. Bevel gear
28. Bushing
29. Case
30. Bushing
31. Washer
32. Large idler gear
33. Bushing
34. Bearing
35. Snap ring
36. Shift housing
37. Quad ring
38. Pin
39. Shift lever
40. Shift lever keeper
41. Snap ring
42. Shaft
43. Sprocket
44. Snap ring
45. Cover

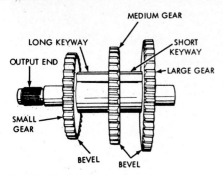

Fig. PT101 — When assembling transmission, be sure idler gears are installed on shaft as shown above.

Fig. PT105 — Exploded view of Peerless Series 500 4-speed gear transmission.

1. Washer
2. Plug
3. Set screw
4. Detent spring
5. Detent ball
6. Transmission cover
7. Snap ring
8. Output sprocket
9. Flange bushing
10. Thrust washer
11. Fourth speed gear
12. Third speed gear
13. Second speed gear
14. First speed gear
15. Output shaft
16. Shifter keys
17. Shift collar
18. Reverse sprocket
19. Thrust washer
20. Flange bushing
21. Reverse chain
22. Flange bushing
23. Thrust washer
24. Reverse drive sprocket
25. Shift rod & fork assy.
26. Countershaft
27. Bevel & first drive gear
28. Second drive gear
29. Third drive gear
30. Fourth drive gear
31. Thrust washer
32. Flange bushing
33. Snap ring
34. Bevel pinion
35. Thrust washer
36. Transmission case
37. Needle bearings
38. Input shaft
39. Thrust washer
40. Snap ring

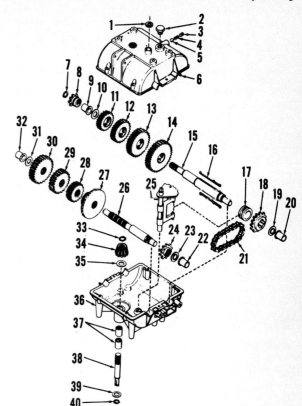

of case, unscrew cover screws and lift cover (45) from case (29). Lift out reverse idler shaft (12), idler gear (13) and spacer (14). Lift shifter assembly (1 through 10) and shaft (42) out of case. Remove output shaft (16) and attached gears (32, 17 and 18) and thrust washers (19 and 31). Remove bevel gear (27) from case. Remove snap ring (22), pinion gear (23) and pull input shaft (24) out bottom of case. Remove snap ring (35) and bearing (34) from shaft. Bushing (33) may now be removed from case.

Inspect components for excessive wear or damage. To reassemble, reverse disassembly procedure. Install gears (32, 17 and 18) on output shaft as shown in Fig. PT101. Note that bevel on small and middle sized gears face toward case, while bevel of large gear faces towards cover. Install reverse idler gear (13 – Fig. PT100) so bevel of gear faces towards case. Pack housing with 12 ounces (355 mL) of EP lithium base grease. Tighen case-to-cover cap screws to 90-110 in.-lbs. (10-12 N·m). Do not force cover to close on case. If cover will not fit correctly, use needlenose pliers to reposition shifter components.

Series 500

OVERHAUL. Clean outside of removed transmission, place shift lever in neutral position, then unbolt and remove

shift lever assembly. Refer to Fig. PT105 and remove set screw (3), detent spring (4) and detent ball (5). Remove six cap screws and lift off cover (6). Remove shift rod and fork assembly (25). Lift output shaft and countershaft as an assembly from case (36) and place assembly on a bench. Remove flange bushings and thrust washers from ends of both shafts. Note collar side of reverse sprockets (18 and 24), then remove sprockets with chain (21) from shafts. Note position of bevel gear and spur gears (27 through 30) and remove gears from countershaft (26). Remove gears (11 through 14) from output shaft (15), then slide shift collar (17) and shifter keys (16) from shaft. Remove snap ring (33), bevel pinion (34) and thrust washer (35) and withdraw input

shaft (38) with snap ring (40) and thrust washer (39). Needle bearings (37) can now be pressed out of case if necessary.

Clean and inspect all parts and renew any showing excessive wear or other damage. Input shaft needle bearings (37) should be installed flush to 0.005 inch (0.127 mm) below case inner and outer thrust surfaces at bearing bore. Using Fig. PT105 as a guide, reassemble transmission by reversing disassembly procedure. Make certain drive lug side of gears (11 through 14) are facing away from shift collar. Fill transmission case with 12 ounces (355 mL) of EP lithium base grease. Tighten cover-to-case cap screws to 90-100 in.-lbs. (10-11 N·m). Install detent ball (5), spring (4) and set screw (3). Tighten set screw two full turns below flush.

SIMPLICITY

3-Speed And 4-Speed With Shuttle Drive

The gear transmission used on tractors equipped with forward-reverse shuttle drive, is equipped with four forward gears. Reverse gear is not required in this transmission since reverse drive, in any gear, is provided by forward-reverse shuttle drive unit. Transmission used on other models has

three forward gears and one reverse. The differential is located at right rear wheel hub on all models.

OVERHAUL. To disassemble transmission, first drain gear oil from unit, then remove brake drum. remove cap screws from transmission cover and drive locating dowel pins into transmission case holes. Using a screwdriver, pry

cover loose and remove from case. Remove gear (41 – Fig. S51), then withdraw axle tube and output gear assembly (65 through 71). Remove second intermediate shaft and gears (44 through 51) and third intermediate shaft and gears (54 through 59). Place shift fork (6) in neutral position and pull shift fork (6A) out of case until input shaft (23) and sliding gears (24 and 75 – Fig.

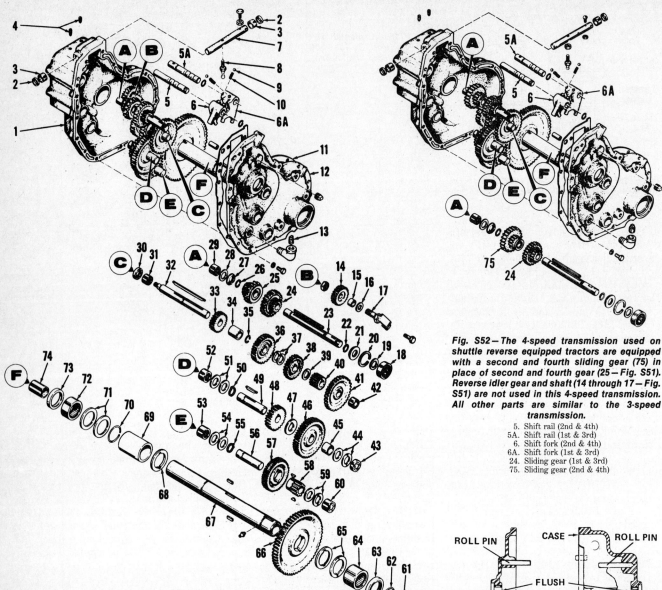

Fig. S51—Exploded view of Simplicity 3-speed gear transmission. The 4-speed gear transmission used on shuttle reverse tractors is similar (refer to Fig. S52).

1. Transmission case
2. Oil seal
3. Spacer
4. Set screws
5. Shift rail (2nd & reverse)
5A. Shift rail (1st & 3rd)
6. Shift fork (2nd & reverse)
6A. Shift fork (1st & 3rd)
7. Shift rod
8. Shifter stem
9. Ball
10. Poppet string
11. Gasket
12. Transmission cover
13. Oil level plug
14. Reverse idler gear
15. Spacer
16. Washer
17. Reverse idler shaft
18. Ball bearing
19. Washer
20. Retaining ring
21. Special washer
22. Snap ring
23. Input shaft
24. Sliding gear (1st & 3rd)
25. Sliding gear (2nd & reverse)
26. Snap ring
27. Special washer
28. Washer
29. Needle bearing
30. Oil seal
31. Needle bearing
32. Brake shaft
33. Reverse gear
34. Spacer
35. Snap ring
36. Second gear
37. Washers
38. Third gear
39. Washer
40. First intermediate pinion
41. First gear
42. Needle bearing
43. Needle bearing
44. Washers
45. Spacer
46. Second intermediate gear
47. Washer
48. Second intermediate pinion
49. Second intermediate shaft
50. Snap ring
51. Washers
52. Needle bearing
53. Needle bearing
54. Washers
55. Snap ring
56. Third intermediate shaft
57. Third intermediate gear
58. Third intermediate pinion
59. Washers
60. Needle bearing
61. Bushing
62. Snap ring
63. Oil seal
64. Needle bearing
65. Washers
66. Output gear
67. Axle tube
68. Washer
69. Spacer
70. Snap ring
71. Washers
72. Needle bearing
73. Oil seal
74. Bushing

Fig. S52—The 4-speed transmission used on shuttle reverse equipped tractors are equipped with a second and fourth sliding gear (75) in place of second and fourth gear (25—Fig. S51). Reverse idler gear and shaft (14 through 17—Fig. S51) are not used in this 4-speed transmission. All other parts are similar to the 3-speed transmission.

5. Shift rail (2nd & 4th)
5A. Shift rail (1st & 3rd)
6. Shift fork (2nd & 4th)
6A. Shift fork (1st & 3rd)
24. Sliding gear (1st & 3rd)
75. Sliding gear (2nd & 4th)

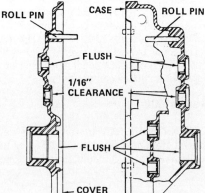

Fig. S53—When renewing bearings, press into transmission case or cover to dimensions shown.

S52) on 4-speed models or (24 and 25–Fig. S51) on 3-speed models, can be removed. Brake shaft (32) with gears (33, 36, 38 and 40) can now be withdrawn. On models so equipped, remove reverse idler gear (14) and shaft (17). Loosen set screws (4) and slide out shift fork and rail assemblies. Remove shifter stem (8) and withdraw shift rod (7) from case. Bearings and oil seals can now be removed from case and cover as required.

Clean and inspect all parts and renew any showing excessive wear or other damage. Using Figs. S51 and S52 as a guide, reassemble transmission by reversing disassembly procedure. When

SERVICE

Simplicity

renewing bearings, press new bearings into case or cover until positioned as shown in Fig. S53. The shifter stem used on some models is adjustable and must be adjusted to ⅝ inch (16 mm) dimension shown in Fig. S54. The two roll pins ("A" and "B"–Fig. S55) which limit shifter stem movement, must be installed to proper height as shown. Check pins even if renewal was not necessary. After unit is reinstalled, fill transmission to level plug opening with recommended lubricant as listed in the CONDENSED SPECIFICATIONS table under appropriate TRACTOR SERVICE SECTION for model being serviced.

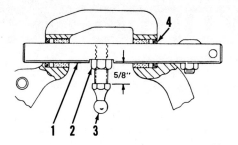

Fig. S54—On models so oquipped, adjust shifter stem (3) to ⅝ inch (16 mm) distance as shown. New style shift stem is nonadjustable. Lubricate seals (4) and shaft (1) prior to installation.

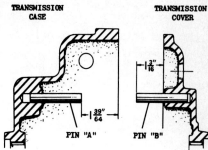

Fig. S55—Roll pins (A & B) limit shifter stem movement and must be set to proper height as shown.

HYDROSTATIC TRANSMISSION SERVICE

EATON

Model 6

OPERATION. The Eaton Model 6 hydrostatic transmission is composed of three major parts: A variable displacement, reversible flow, radial ball piston pump; a fixed displacement, ball piston motor; and a system of valves located between pump and motor. Tractor ground speed is regulated by changing amount of oil delivered by the variable displacement pump. Moving speed control lever in forward direction will control forward ground speed range of 0-4.16 mph at full engine rpm. When speed control lever is moved rearward from neutral position, a reverse range of 0-2.6 mph is achieved.

The pressurized oil from pump (high pressure oil in Fig. EA10) forces directional check valve (A) closed and directs flow to motor. The return oil flow from motor completes the closed loop circuit. Any oil lost due to internal leakage in the motor reduces the volume of oil in return line. This reduced volume (resulting in low pressure) allows directional check valve (B) to open and oil from

reservoir will replace oil lost from circuit. When control lever is moved for opposite direction, hydraulic circuits are reversed.

TROUBLE-SHOOTING. Some problems which might occur during operation of hydrostatic transmission and their possible causes are as follows:
A. No output power in either direction. Could be caused by:
　1. Broken control shaft dowel pin.
　2. Low oil level.
B. Loss of output power under continuous load. Could be caused by:
　1. Internal leakage due to excessive wear.
　2. Water in transmission fluid.
C. No output power in one direction. Could be caused by:
　1. One of the directional valves is stuck.
　2. Loose control shaft dowel pin.
D. External oil leakage. Could be caused by:
　1. Fluid level too high.
　2. Defective input or control shaft seal.
　3. Reservoir loose or defective.
　4. Loose venting plug in body.

E. Excessive noise and violent action at control shaft. Could be caused by:
　1. Directional check ball stuck.
　2. Loose control linkage.
　3. Excessive motor rotor to pintle clearance.
　4. Water in fluid.
　5. Air in system.

OVERHAUL. Before disassembling transmission, thoroughly clean exterior of unit. Remove venting plug (31–Fig. EA11), invert assembly and drain fluid from unit. Remove reservoir (3) or adapter by rotating clockwise (L.H. threads). Remove two cap screws (29) and place transmission (output shaft downward) in a holding fixture similar to one shown in Fig. EA12. Remove aluminum housing (5–Fig. EA11) with control shaft and input shaft assemblies.

CAUTION: Do not allow pump and cam ring assemblies (16 through 20) to lift with housing. If pump rotor is raised with housing, ball pistons may fall out of rotor.

The ball pistons (17) are selective fitted to rotor bores to a clearance of 0.0002-0.0006 inch (0.0051-0.0152 mm) and are not interchangeable. A wide rubber band can be used to prevent ball pistons from falling out. Remove cam ring (20) and pump race (19), then carefully remove pump assembly. Hold downward on motor rotor (49) and remove pintle assembly (46). Place a wide rubber band around motor rotor (49) to prevent balls (41) and springs (40) from falling out of rotor. Remove motor assembly and motor race (33).

Remove snap ring (22), gear (23), spacer (24), retainer (25), snap ring (26) and key (35). Support body (30) and press output shaft (34) out of bearing (27) and oil seal (28) can now be removed from body (30).

Remove retainer (9) and withdraw ball bearing (7) and input shaft (14). Bearing can be pressed from input shaft after removal of snap ring (8). Oil seal (6) can be removed from outside of housing. To remove control shaft (38), drill a 11/32 inch hole through aluminum housing (5) directly in line with center line of dowel pin (10). Press dowel pin from control shaft, remove snap ring (12) and washer (11) and withdraw control shaft. Remove oil seal (39). Thread drilled hole with a ⅛ inch pipe tap.

FLOW DIAGRAM MODEL 6

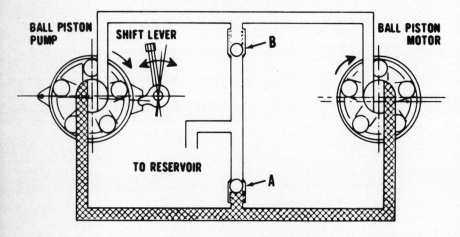

HIGH PRESSURE OIL

LOW PRESSURE OIL

Fig. EA10 – Flow diagram of an Eaton Model 6 hydrostatic transmission. "A" and "B" are directional check valves.

SERVICE

Eaton

To remove directional check valves from pintle (46), drill through pintle with a drill bit that will pass freely through roll pins (47). Redrill holes from opposite side with a ¼ inch drill bit. Press roll pins from pintle. Using a 5/16-18 tap, thread inside of check valve bodies (43) and remove valve bodies using a draw bolt or a slide hammer puller. Remove check valve balls (44) and snap rings (45). Do not remove plugs (48).

Number piston bores (1 through 5) on pump rotor and on motor rotor. Use a plastic ice cube tray or equivalent and mark cavities 1P through 5P for pump and 1M through 5M for motor. Remove ball pistons (17) one at a time from pump rotor and place each ball in correct cavity in tray. Remove ball pistons (41) and springs (40) from motor rotor in same manner.

Clean and inspect all parts and renew any showing excessive wear or other damage. Ball pistons are selective fitted to 0.0002-0.0006 inch (0.0051-0.0152 mm) clearance and must be reinstalled in their original bores. If rotor bushings (18 and 37) are scored or badly worn 0.002 inch (0.051 mm) or more clearance on pintle journals) renew pump rotor or motor rotor assemblies. Install ball pistons (17) in pump rotor (16) and ball pistons (41) and springs (40) in motor rotor (49) and use wide rubber bands to hold pistons in their bores. Install snap rings (45), check valve balls (44) and valve bodies (43) in pintle (46) and secure with new roll pins (47). If plugs (48) are loose, install new plugs. Use "Loctite" grade 35 and tighten plugs to a torque of 12 in.-lbs. (1.4 N·m). Renew oil seals (6 and 39) and reinstall control shaft and input shaft in housing (5) by reversing removal procedure. When installing oil seals (6, 39 or 28), apply a thin coat of "Loctite" grade 35 to seal outer diameter. Press dowel pin (10) into control shaft until end of dowel pin extends 1⅛ inches (28.6 mm) from control shaft. Apply "Loctite" grade 35 to a ⅛ inch pipe plug and install plug in drilled and tapped disassembly hole. Tighten plug until snug. Do not overtighten. Renew oil seal (28) and reinstall output shaft (34), bearing (27), snap rings, retainer, spacer and gear in body (30).

All components must be clean and dry before assembly. Place aluminum housing assembly in holding fixture with input shaft (14) pointing downward. Install pump cam ring (20) and race (19) on pivot pin (13) and dowel pin (10). Insert (21) must be installed in cam ring with hole to outside. If insert is installed upside down, it will contact housing and interfere with assembly. Cam ring must move freely from stop to stop. Install pump rotor assembly and remove rubber band used to retain pistons. Install pintle assembly (46) over cam pivot pin and into pump rotor. Place new "O" ring (15) in position on housing. Lay housing assembly on its side on a clean surface. Place body assembly in holding fixture with output shaft pointing downward. Install motor race (33) in body, then install motor rotor assembly aligning rotor slot with drive pin (36) on output shaft. Remove rubber band used to retain pistons in rotor. Place body and motor assembly on its side on bench so motor rotor is facing pintle in housing assembly. Slide assemblies together and align the two assembly bolt holes. Install two assembly cap screws (29) and tighten them to a torque of 15 ft.-lbs. (20 N·m). Rotate input shaft and output shaft. Both shafts should rotate freely. If not, disassemble unit and correct problem.

Place unit in a holding fixture with reservoir opening and venting plug opening facing upward. Install reservoir or reservoir adapter. Fill unit with Type "A" automatic transmission fluid until fluid overflows out of venting plug hole.

Rotate input shaft and output shaft to purge any trapped air from unit. Install venting plugs (31) and gasket (32). Torque plug to 2-5 ft.-lbs. (3-7 N·m).

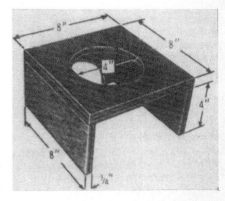

Fig. EA12—View showing dimensions of wooden stand used when disassembling and reassembling Eaton Model 6 hydrostatic transmission.

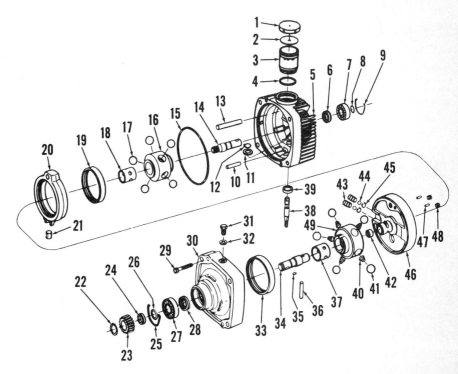

Fig. EA11—Exploded view of a typical Eaton Model 6 hydrostatic transmission. Oil expansion reservoir (3) may be mounted separately.

1. Cover
2. Gasket
3. Reservoir
4. Gasket
5. Housing
6. Oil seal
7. Ball bearing
8. Snap ring
9. Retainer
10. Dowel pin
11. Washer
12. Snap ring
13. Cam pivot pin
14. Input shaft
15. "O" ring
16. Pump rotor
17. Pump ball pistons
18. Rotor bushing
19. Pump race
20. Pump cam ring
21. Insert
22. Snap ring
23. Output gear
24. Spacer
25. Retainer
26. Snap ring
27. Ball bearing
28. Oil seal
29. Cap screw
30. Body
31. Venting plug
32. Gasket
33. Motor race
34. Output shaft
35. Key
36. Drive pin
37. Rotor bushing
38. Control shaft
39. Oil seal
40. Springs
41. Motor ball pistons
42. Needle bearing
43. Directional check valve body
44. Check valve ball
45. Snap ring
46. Pintle
47. Roll pin
48. Plug
49. Motor rotor

213

Model 7

OVERHAUL. Place transmission in a holding fixture with input shaft pointing up. Remove dust shield (1–Fig. EA15) and snap ring (3). Remove cap screws from charge pump body (7). One cap screw is ½ inch (12.7 mm) longer than the others and must be installed in original position. Remove charge pump body (7) with ball bearing (4). Ball bearing and oil seal (6) can be removed after removing retaining ring (2). Remove snap rings (5 and 8) and charge pump rotor assembly. Remove "O" rings (10) and pump plate (11). Turn hydrostatic unit over in fixture and remove output gear. Unscrew the two cap screws until two threads are engaged. Raise body (42) until it contacts cap screw heads. Insert a special fork tool (Fig. EA16) between motor rotor (39–Fig. EA15) and pintle (28). Remove cap screws, lift off body and motor assembly with fork tool and place assembly on a bench or in a holding fixture with output shaft

pointing down. Remove fork and place a wider rubber band around motor rotor to hold ball pistons (38) in their bores. Carefully remove motor rotor assembly and lay aside for later disassembly. Remove motor race (41) and output shaft (40). Remove retainer (45), bearing (44) and oil seal (43). With housing assembly (12) resting in holding fixture, remove pintle assembly (28).

CAUTION: Do not allow pump to raise with pintle as ball pistons (22) may fall out of rotor (21). Hold pump in position by inserting a finger through hole in pintle.

Remove plug (37), spring (36) and charge relief ball (35). To remove directional check valves, it may be necessary to drill through pintle with a drill bit that will pass freely through roll pins. Redrill holes from opposite side with a ¼ inch drill bit. Press roll pin from pintle. Newer units are drilled at factory. Using a 5/16-18 tap, thread inside of valve bodies (34) then remove valve bodies us-

ing a draw bolt or slide hammer puller. Remove check valve balls (33) and retaining ring (32). To remove acceleration valves, remove retaining pin, insert a 3/16 inch (5 mm) rod 8 inches (203 mm) long through passage in pintle and carefully drive out spring (29), body (30) and ball (31). To remove dampening pistons (26), carefully tap outside edge of pintle on work bench to jar pistons free.

NOTE: If pintle journal is damaged, pintle must be renewed.

Remove pump cam ring (24) and pump race (23). Place a wide rubber band around pump rotor to prevent ball pistons (22) from falling out. Carefully remove pump assembly and input shaft (15).

To remove control shaft (19), drill a 11/32 inch hole through aluminum housing (12) directly in line with center line of dowel pin. Press dowel pin from control shaft, then withdraw control shaft. Remove oil seal (18). Thread drilled hole in housing with a ⅛ inch pipe tap. Apply a light coat of "Loctite" grade 35 to a ⅛ inch pipe plug, install plug and tighten until snug. Do not overtighten.

Number piston bores (1 through 5) on pump rotor and on motor rotor. Use a plastic ice cube tray or equivalent and mark cavities 1P through 5P for pump ball pistons and 1M through 5M for motor ball pistons. Remove ball pistons (22) one at a time, from pump rotor and place each ball in the correct cavity in tray. Remove ball pistons (38) and springs from motor rotor in the same manner.

Clean and inspect all parts and renew any showing excessive wear or other damage. Renew all gaskets, seals and "O" rings. Ball pistons are a select fit to 0.0002-0.0006 inch (0.0050-0.0152 mm) clearance in rotor bores and must be reinstalled in their original bores. If rotor bushing to pintle journal clearance is 0.002 inch (0.051 mm) or more, bushing wear or scoring is excessive and pump rotor or motor rotor must be renewed. Check clearance between input shaft (15) and housing bushing. Normal clearance is 0.0013-0.0033 inch

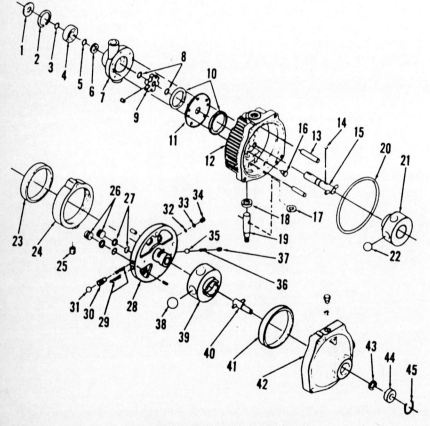

Fig. EA15—Exploded view of Eaton Model 7 hydrostatic transmission.

1. Dust shield	12. Housing	24. Pump cam ring	34. Check valve body
2. Retaining ring	13. Cam pivot pin	25. Cam ring insert	35. Charge relief ball
3. Snap ring	14. Key	26. Dampening pistons	36. Spring
4. Ball bearing	15. Input shaft	27. "O" ring	37. Relief valve plug
5. Snap ring	16. Neutral spring cap	28. Pintle	38. Motor ball piston
6. Oil seal	17. Washer	29. Spring	39. Motor rotor
7. Charge pump body	18. Oil seal	30. Acceleration valve	40. Output shaft
8. Snap ring	19. Control shaft	body	41. Motor race
9. Charge pump rotor	20. "O" ring	31. Acceleration valve	42. Body
assy.	21. Pump rotor	ball	43. Oil seal
10. Square cut seals	22. Pump ball pistons	32. Retaining ring	44. Ball bearing
11. Pump plate	23. Pump race	33. Check valve ball	45. Retainer

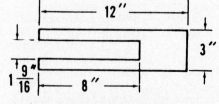

Fig. EA16—Special fork tool fabricated from a piece of ⅛ inch (3 mm) flat stock, used in disassembly and reassembly of hydrostatic transmission.

(0.033-0.0838 mm). If clearance is excessive, renew input shaft and/or housing assembly.

Install ball pistons (22) in pump rotor (21) and ball pistons (38) and springs in motor rotor (39), then use wide rubber bands to hold pistons in their bores.

Install charge relief valve ball (35) and spring (36) in pintle. Screw plug (37) into pintle until just below outer surface of pintle. Install acceleration valve springs (29) and bodies (30) making sure valves move freely. Tap balls (31) into pintle until roll pins will go into place. Install snap rings (32), check valve balls (33) and valve bodies (34) in pintle and secure with new roll pins.

NOTE: When installing oil seals (6, 18 or 43), apply a light coat of "Loctite" grade 35 to seal outer diameter.

Renew oil seal (18) and install control shaft (19) in housing. Install special washer (17), then press dowel pin through control shaft until 1¼ inches (32 mm) of pin extends from control shaft. Renew oil seal (43) and reinstall output shaft (40), bearing (44), retainer (45), output gear and snap ring.

Insert input shaft (15) in housing (12). Install snap ring (8) in its groove on input shaft. Place "O" ring (10), pump plate (11) and "O" ring in housing, then install charge pump drive key (14). Apply light grease or "Vaseline" to pump rollers and place rollers in rotor slots. Install oil seal (6) and pump race in charge pump body (7), then install body assembly. Secure with the five cap screws, making certain long cap screw is installed in its original location (in heavy section of pump body). Tighten cap screws to 28-30 ft.-lbs. (38-41 N·m). Install snap ring (5), bearing (4), retaining ring (2), snap ring (3) and dust shield (1).

Place charge pump and housing assembly in a holding fixture with input shaft pointing downward. Install pump race (23) and insert (25) in cam ring (24), then install cam ring assembly over cam pivot pin (13) and control shaft dowel pin. Turn control shaft (19) back and forth and check movement of cam ring. Cam ring must move freely from stop to stop. If not, check installation of insert (25) in cam ring.

Install pump rotor assembly and remove rubber band used to retain pistons. Install pintle assembly (28) over cam pivot pin (13) and into pump rotor. Place "O" ring (20) in position on housing.

Place body assembly (42) in a holding fixture with output gear down. Install motor race (41) in body, then install motor rotor assembly and remove rubber band used to retain pistons in rotor.

Using special fork tool (Fig. EA16) to retain motor assembly in body, carefully install body and motor assembly over pintle journal. Remove fork tool, align bolt holes and install the two cap screws. Tighten cap screws to 15 ft.-lbs. (20 N·m).

Place hydrostatic unit on holding fixture with reservoir adapter opening and venting plug opening facing upward. Fill unit with recommended fluid until fluid flows from fitting hole in body. Plug all openings to prevent dirt or other foreign material from entering hydrostatic unit.

Model 10 And Model 11

OPERATION. The Eaton Model 10 and Model 11 hydrostatic transmissions are composed of four major parts: A reversible flow, variable displacement, ball piston pump; a fixed displacement, ball piston motor; a system of valves located between pump and motor and a charge and auxiliary hydraulic supply pump. Tractor ground speed is regulated by changing amount of oil delivered by variable displacement pump. Moving speed control pedal in a forward direction will control forward ground speed range of 0-8 mph at full engine rpm. When speed control pedal is moved in reverse direction (depressed with heel), a reverse range of 0-4 mph is achieved.

The system operates as a closed loop type and any internal loss of oil from loop is replaced by oil from the charge pump. See Fig. EA20. This oil is forced into loop circuit through one of the directional check valves, depending on direction of travel. As more oil is pumped by charge pump than is needed to make up losses, all excess oil must pass through charge pressure relief valve and back into reservoir.

OVERHAUL. Before disassembling hydrostatic transmission, thoroughly clean exterior of unit. If so equipped, remove venting plug (59 – Fig. EA21) and reservoir adapter (18 through 21), invert assembly and drain fluid from unit. Place unit in a holding fixture similar to one shown in Fig. EA22 so input shaft is pointing upward.

To disassemble, remove dust shield (1 – Fig. EA21) and snap ring (3). Place an identifying mark across joining edges of each section to aid in correct placement and alignment during reassembly. Remove five cap screws from charge pump body (7). One cap screw is ½ inch longer than the others and must be reinstalled in original location (heavy section of pump body). Remove charge pump body (7) with ball bearing (4). Ball bearing and oil seal (6) can be removed from body (7) after first removing retaining ring (2). Remove six charge pump rollers (12), snap rings (5, 9 and 11) and charge pump rotor (10). Remove "O" rings (14 and 16) and pump plate (15). Invert drive unit in holding fixture so output shaft is pointing upward. Remove snap ring (65) and output gear (64). Unscrew two cap screws (60), then turn them in until two threads are engaged. Raise body (57) until it contacts heads of cap screws (60). Insert a fork tool between motor rotor (53) and pintle (48) until tool extends beyond opposite side. The

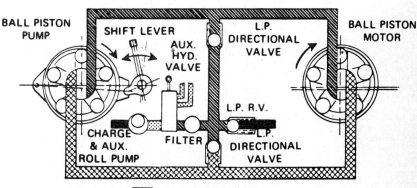

MODEL 10
HYDROSTATIC FLOW DIAGRAM

BALL PISTON PUMP

SHIFT LEVER

AUX. HYD. VALVE

L.P. DIRECTIONAL VALVE

BALL PISTON MOTOR

CHARGE & AUX. ROLL PUMP

FILTER

L.P. R.V.

L.P. DIRECTIONAL VALVE

▨ HIGH PRESSURE OIL
▨ LOW PRESSURE OIL
▨ AUXILIARY PRESSURE OIL
■ RESERVOIR OIL

Fig. EA20 — Flow diagram for Eaton Model 10 hydrostatic transmission. Eaton Model 11 hydrostatic transmission is similar.

special fork tool can be fabricated from a piece of ⅛ inch (3 mm) flat stock approximately 3 inches (76.2 mm) wide and 12 inches (304.8 mm) long. Cut a slot 1-9/16 inches (39.4 mm) wide and 8 inches (203.2 mm) long as shown in Fig. EA23. Taper ends of the prongs. Remove cap screws (60 – Fig. EA21) and by raising ends of forked tool, lift off body and motor assembly. Place removed assembly on a bench or in a holding fixture with output shaft pointing downward. Remove special fork tool and place a wide rubber band around motor rotor to hold ball pistons (51) and springs (52) in their bores. Carefully remove motor rotor assembly and lay aside for later disassembly. Remove motor race (56) and output shaft (55). Remove retainer (63), bearing (62) and oil seal (61).

With housing assembly (22) resting in holding fixture (input shaft pointing downward), remove pintle assembly (48).

CAUTION: Do not allow pump to raise with pintle as ball pistons (35) may fall out of rotor (36).

Hold pump in position by inserting a finger through hole in pintle. Remove plug (45), spring (46) and charge pump relief ball (47). To remove directional check valves from pintle (48), drill through pintle with a drill bit that will pass freely through roll pins (41). Redrill holes from opposite side with a ¼ inch drill bit. Drive or press roll pins from pintle. Using a 5/16-18 tap, thread inside of valve bodies (44), then remove valve bodies using a draw bolt or a slide hammer puller. Remove check valve balls (43) and snap rings (42). Do not remove plugs (40).

Remove pump cam ring (39) and pump race (38). Place a wide rubber band around pump rotor to prevent ball pistons (35) from falling out. Carefully remove pump assembly and input shaft (33).

To remove control shaft (25), drill a 11/32 inch hole through aluminum housing (22) directly in line with center line of dowel pin (27). Press dowel pin from control shaft, then withdraw control shaft. Remove oil seal (24). Thread drilled hole in housing with a ⅛ inch pipe tap. Apply a light coat of "Loctite" grade 35 to a ⅛ inch pipe plug, install plug and tighten it until snug.

Number piston bores (1 through 5) on pump rotor and on motor rotor. Use a plastic ice cube tray or equivalent and mark cavities 1P through 5P for pump ball pistons and 1M through 5M for motor ball pistons. Remove ball pistons (35) one at a time, from pump rotor and place each ball in correct cavity in tray. Remove ball pistons (51) and springs (52) from motor rotor in same manner.

Clean and inspect all parts and renew any showing excessive wear or other damage. Ball pistons are selective fitted to 0.0002-0.0006 inch (0.0051-0.0152 mm) clearance in rotor bores and must be reinstalled in their original bores. If rotor bushings (37 or 50) are scored or badly worn (0.002 inch [0.051 mm] or more clearance on pintle journals), renew pump rotor or motor rotor assemblies. Check clearance between input shaft (33) and housing bushing (17). Normal clearance is 0.0013-0.0033 inch

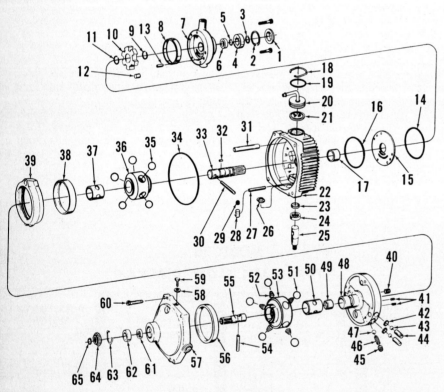

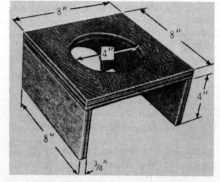

Fig. EA22 – View showing dimensions of wooden stand used when disassembling and reassembling Eaton Model 10 or Model 11 hydrostatic transmission.

Fig. EA21 – Exploded view of Eaton Model 10 hydrostatic transmission. Eaton Model 11 hydrostatic transmission is similar.

1. Dust shield	18. Retainer	34. "O" ring	49. Needle bearing
2. Retaining ring	19. "O" ring	35. Pump ball pistons	50. Rotor bushing
3. Snap ring	20. Reservoir adapter	36. Pump rotor	51. Motor ball pistons
4. Ball bearing	21. Screen	37. Rotor housing	52. Springs
5. Snap ring	22. Housing	38. Pump race	53. Motor rotor
6. Oil seal	23. Bushing	39. Pump cam ring	54. Drive pin
7. Charge pump body	24. Oil seal	40. Plug (2 used)	55. Output shaft
8. Charge pump race	25. Control shaft	41. Roll pins	56. Motor race
9. Snap ring	26. Washer	42. Snap ring (2 used)	57. Body
10. Charge pump rotor	27. Dowel pin	43. Check valve ball	58. Gasket
11. Snap ring	28. Insert	(2 used)	59. Venting plug
12. Pump roller (6 used)	29. Insert cap	44. Directional check	60. Cap screw
13. Dowel pin	30. Drive pin	valve body (2 used)	61. Oil seal
14. "O" ring	31. Cam pivot pin	45. Plug	62. Ball bearing
15. Pump plate	32. Charge pump drive	46. Relief spring	63. Retainer
16. "O" ring	key	47. Charge relief ball	64. Output gear
17. Bushing	33. Input shaft	48. Pintle	65. Snap ring

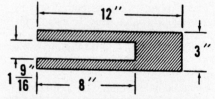

Fig. EA23 – A special fork tool for disassembly and reassembly of Eaton Model 10 or Model 11 hydrostatic transmission can be made from a piece of ⅛ inch (3 mm) flat bar stock using dimensions shown.

(0.0330-0.0838 mm). If clearance is excessive, renew input shaft and/or housing assembly.

Install ball pistons (35) in pump rotor (36) and ball pistons (51) and springs (52) in motor rotor (53), then use wide rubber bands to hold pistons in their bores. Install snap rings (42), check valve balls (43) and valve bodies (44) in pintle (48) and secure with new roll pins (41). Install charge pump relief valve ball (47), spring (46) and plug (45). When installing oil seals (6, 24 or 61), apply a light coat of "Loctite" grade 35 to seal outer diameter. Renew oil seal (24) and install control shaft (25) in housing. Install special washer (26), then press dowel pin (27) into control shaft until end of dowel pin extends 1¼ inches (28.5 mm) from control shaft. Renew oil seal (61) and reinstall output shaft (55) with drive pin (54), bearing (62), retainer (63), output gear (64) and snap ring (65) in body (57).

Insert input shaft (33) with drive pin (30) through bushing (17) in housing. Install snap ring (11) in its groove on input shaft. Place "O" ring (16), pump plate (15) and "O" ring (14) in housing, then install charge pump drive key (32), charge pump rotor (10) and snap ring (9). Apply light grease or Vaseline to pump rollers (12) and place rollers in rotor slots. Install oil seal (6) and pump race (8) in charge pump body (7), then install body assembly. Secure with five cap screws, making certain long cap screw is installed in its original location (in heavy section of pump body). Tighten cap screws to a torque of 28-30 ft.-lbs. (38-41 N·m). Install snap ring (5), bearing (4), retaining ring (2), snap ring (3) and dust shield (1).

Place charge pump and housing assembly in a holding fixture with input shaft pointing downward. Install pump race (38), insert cap (29) and insert (28) in cam ring (39), then install cam ring assembly over cam pivot pin (31) and control shaft dowel pin (27). Turn control shaft (25) back and forth and check movement of cam ring. Cam ring must move freely from stop to stop. If not, check installation of insert (28) and insert cap (29) in cam ring.

Install pump rotor assembly and remove rubber band used to retain pistons. Install pintle assembly (48) over cam pivot pin (31) and into pump rotor. Place "O" ring (34) in piston on housing.

Place body assembly (57) in a holding fixture with gear (64) downward. Install motor race (56) in body, then install motor rotor assembly and remove rubber band used to retain pistons in rotor.

Using special fork tool (Fig. EA23) to retain motor assembly in body, carefully install body and motor assembly over pintle journal. Remove fork tool, align bolt holes and install two cap screws (60 – Fig. EA21). Tighten cap screws to 15 ft.-lbs. (20 N·m).

Place hydrostatic unit on holding fixture with reservoir adapter opening and venting plug opening facing upward. Fill unit with hydraulic oil or Type "A" automatic transmission fluid until fluid flows from fitting hole in body. Install venting plug (59) with gasket (58), then install reservoir adapter (20), screen (21), "O" ring (19) and retainer (18). Plug all openings to prevent dirt or other foreign material from entering hydrostatic unit.

Model 12

OPERATION. The Eaton Model 12 hydrostatic transmission has four major parts: A reversible flow, variable displacement, radial piston pump; a fixed displacement, gear motor; and a charge and auxiliary hydraulic supply pump. Tractor ground speed is regulated by changing oil delivery of variable displacement pump. Moving speed control pedal in a forward direction will control forward ground speed range of 0-8 mph at full engine rpm. When speed control pedal is moved in reverse direction (depressed with heel), a reverse range of 0-4 mph is achieved.

The system operated as a closed loop type and any internal loss of oil from loop is replaced by oil from the charge pump. See Fig. EA25. This oil is forced into loop circuit through one of the directional check valves, depending on direction of travel. As more oil is pumped by the charge pump than is needed to make up losses, all excess oil must pass through charge pressure relief valve and back into reservoir.

The system is protected by a high pressure relief valve located in the circuit after high pressure directional valve. Since a pressure operated directional valve is used, high pressure relief valve will protect circuit whether it is operating in forward or reverse direction.

An unloading valve actuated by a selector lever is used to achieve a neutral or free-wheeling position and oil from gear motor is dumped back into reservoir. This makes it possible to move the tractor when in NEUTRAL while engine is not operating. With selector valve in PARK, unloading valve is also open. However, tractor cannot be moved in this position as parking pawl is engaged. When selector lever is in DRIVE, unloading valve is closed completing closed loop circuit.

OVERHAUL. The Eaton Model 12 hydrostatic transmission was serviced as a direct exchange package only. No detailed service procedures have been released for publication. Operation of this hydrostatic transmission and its flow diagram (Fig. EA25) are covered in preceding OPERATION section. Any attempt to overhaul this model hydrostatic transmission is discouraged, mainly due to limited parts service, even to such basic items as gaskets and seals.

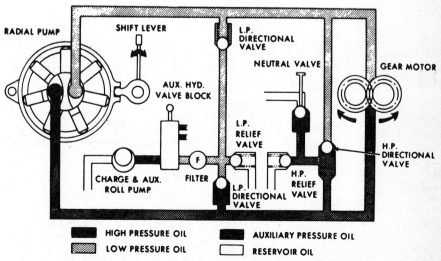

Fig. EA25—Flow diagram of Eaton Model 12 hydrostatic transmission.

SUNDSTRAND

Hydrogear Model

OPERATION. The hydrostatic transmission consists of three main components: A variable displacement, reversible swashplate, axial piston type pump; a fixed displacement, gear motor; a center section which houses a charge pump and a valve system.

When control handle is in neutral position, pump pistons are all in the same plane, no oil is being pumped and tractor does not move. When control handle is moved forward, pump swashplate is tilted and piston stroke is set for controlled volume of oil and flow direction. Refer to Fig. SU10. Oil is pumped through high pressure circuit (A) to gear motor. As oil passes through gear motor, tractor moves forward. The oil then becomes low pressure circuit (B) and flows directly back to the variable pump. When control handle is moved from forward towards neutral, swashplate tilt is reduced. This reduces piston stroke which in turn lowers volume of oil pumped into circuit (A). Since gear motor has a fixed displacement per revolution, lower volume of oil results in a slower forward ground speed.

When control handle is moved in reverse position, swashplate tilt is reversed and oil is pumped into circuit (B). Circuit (B) is now high pressure circuit and (A) becomes low pressure circuit. This rotates gear motor in reverse and tractor moves backward.

The circuits (A and B) are referred to as a closed loop circuit. However, any oil lost internally from loop circuit is replaced by low pressure charge pump through circuit (C). This oil is drawn from reservoir through circuit (S) by charge pump. The oil is then pumpd into circuit (C) and portion needed for make up oil is forced into loop circuit through check valve in low pressure side of circuit. The oil pressure in circuit (C) is maintained at 75-110 psi (517-758 kPa) by charge relief valve. All excess oil in circuit (C) passes through charge relief valve into circuit (R). Circuit (R) circulates oil through variable pump housing, cooling and lubricating pump, and then delivers the oil through a renewable filter to reservoir.

The acceleration control and relief valves, located between circuits (A and B), protect circuits from excessive pressure when control handle is moved quickly to any position. They also prevent all jerking motion or lurch, when control handle is shifted, by diverting part of high pressure oil into low pressure circuit for one or two seconds. Then, as new ground speed is established, valve closes and directs all oil to gear motor. At this time, valve operates as a high pressure relief valve for high pressure circuit.

The drive-no drive valve is a manually operated bypass valve located between circuits (A and B). When valve is in no drive (open) position, oil is allowed to recirculate through gear motor without passing through variable pump. Tractor can be pushed manually in this position. The valve must be in drive (closed) position for normal tractor operation.

OVERHAUL. "Hydrogear" type hydrostatic transmissions were manufactured in an inline and a right-angle configuration. Service procedures are similar.

To disassemble hydrostatic drive unit, first thoroughly clean exterior of unit, then remove control arm, input pulley and cooling fan. Drain unit, then unbolt and remove cover (1–Fig. SU11), spring (2) and filter (3). Remove three Allen head screws securing reservoir (4) to pump housing (11) and lift off reservoir and suction tube (6). Position transmission on a bench so pump input shaft is in horizontal position. Unbolt pump housing from center section. If necessary, tap sides of finned housing with a plastic hammer to break gasket seal loose. As pump is being removed, insert fingers between housing and valve plate to prevent block and piston assembly from falling out. The block (20) and valve plate (22) mating faces are lapped surfaces and extreme caution should be exercised to prevent damage to these parts. Carefully remove block and piston assembly and thrust plate (17). Remove pistons (18) from block by lifting upward on slipper retainer (19).

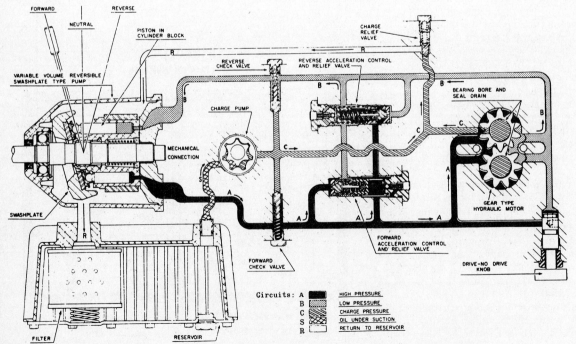

Fig. SU10—Circuit diagram of Sundstrand "Hydrogear" type hydrostatic transmission.

NOTE: Pistons are interchangeable; however, on units with long service, it is advisable to mark and return each piston to its respective bore.

Support housing (11) and drive roll pins down into swashplate (16) until pins bottom on pump housing. Unbolt and remove control detent plate (13), taking care not to lose neutral detent ball and spring. Withdraw control shaft (14), drive hollow stub shaft (10) to inside and lift out swashplate. Remove retaining ring and remove input shaft (5) with bearing (7). Front oil seal (12) can now be removed.

Remove four cap screws securing valve plate (22) to center section (35) and carefully remove valve plate with charge pump gerotor set.

Place a scribe mark across gear motor sections to aid in reassembly. Unbolt end cap (31) and tap firmly with a plastic hammer to separate motor sections. Remove motor gears and shafts and lay removed motor parts aside for later inspection.

Remove acceleration valves (36 through 46), charge relief valve (27), check valves (28) and drive-no drive valve (26). After first removing retaining ring, remove motor output shaft

pilot ring, oil seal, "O" ring and retainer. Remove all port plugs to facilitate cleaning of all internal passages in center section.

Thoroughly clean and inspect all parts and reassemble as follows: When renewing bearing (30), press bearings into location 0.095-0.140 inch (2.413-3.556 mm) below lapped face of end cap or center section. The mating surfaces between all motor sections are lapped surfaces flat within 0.0001 inch (0.0025 mm). Motor gears are lapped 0.0012-0.0014 inch (0.0305-0.0356 mm) thinner than spacer plate (34) to allow clearance for gear lubrication. If ex-

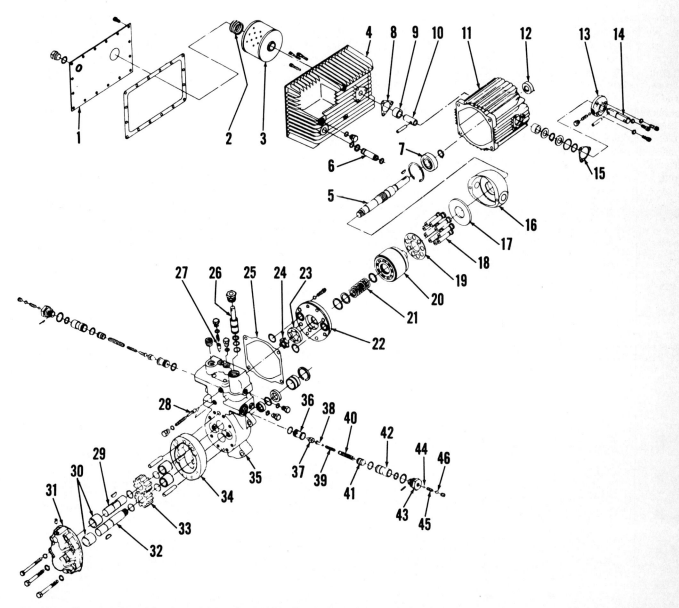

Fig. SU11 — Exploded view of Sundstrand "Hydrogear" in-line type hydrostatic transmission. Gear pump components are positioned perpendicular to pump housing on right-angle type hydrostatic transmissions.

1. Cover	9. Needle bearing	17. Thrust plate	24. Driving rotor	31. End cap	39. Spring (inner)
2. Filter spring	10. Stub shaft	18. Pistons (9)	25. Shim gasket	32. Motor output shaft	40. Spring (outer)
3. Filter	11. Pump housing	19. Slipper retainer	26. Drive-no drive valve	33. Gear set	41. Piston
4. Reservoir	12. Oil seal	20. Pump cylinder block	27. Charge relief valve	34. Spacer plate	42. Sleeve
5. Pump shaft	13. Neutral detent plate	21. Spring	28. Check valve (2)	35. Center section	43. Metering plug
6. Suction tube	14. Control shaft	22. Valve plate	29. Motor idler shaft	36. Seat	44. Ball
7. Ball bearing	15. Shim	23. Driven rotor	30. Bearing	37. Cone	45. Spring
8. Gasket	16. Swashplate			38. Spring guide	46. Spring seat

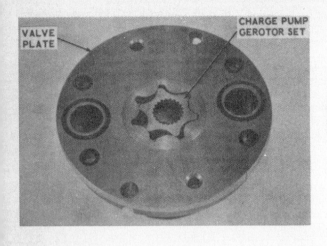

Fig. SU12 — View showing valve plate and charge pump gerotor set used on Sundstrand "Hydrogear" type hydrostatic transmission.

cessive gear wear or severe scoring is evident on end cap or center section motor surface, renew end cap and spacer plate with matched gear set. Center section should be machine lapped to clean up surface if necessary. The maximum amount of stock which may be removed from center section face is 0.010 inch (0.254 mm). Install new output shaft seal and install gear and shaft assemblies. Lightly coat spacer plate with a mixture of shellac and alcohol, ap-

proximately ¼ inch (6 mm) wide at outer edge of mating surfaces. Do not allow mixture to enter drain grooves in faces. Align scribe mark and install spacer plate. Lubricate gears and install end cap. Secure end cap by first tightening two tie bolts in center of end cap to a torque of 13-17 ft.-lbs. (18-23 N·m). Tighten remaining cap screws to a torque of 28-32 ft.-lbs. (38-43 N·m) using a cross tightening sequence. A rolling torque test of output shaft at this time should produce a reading of no more than 3 ft.-lbs. (4 N·m). A higher reading would indicate lack of proper clearance or excess shellac mixture extruded into the gears. The motor must be disassembled and difficulty corrected before proceeding with center section assembly.

Install charge relief valve assembly (27) in its bore and tighten plug to a torque of 22-26 ft.-lbs. (30-35 N·m).

NOTE: Use all new "O" rings when reassembling unit.

Install two check valves (28) and torque both plugs to 22-26 ft.-lbs. (30-35 N·m). Insert drive-no drive valve (26) and tighten shoulder nut securely. When installing acceleration valves, pay particular attention to metering plug portion. Any blocking of metering plug orifice formed by small orifice ball will cause loss of power and slow response. Tighten 1-3/16 inch metering plugs (43) to a torque of 65-70 ft.-lbs. (88-95 N·m). Install all other plugs previously removed for cleaning.

Inspect valve plate (22) and charge pump gerotor set for excessive wear or scratches and renew if necessary. Superficial scratches on charge pump side of valve plate (Fig. SU12) may be removed by hand lapping. On kidney side of valve plate, machine lapping or valve plate renewal is indicated if 0.005 inch (0.127 mm) or more stock must be removed to clean up surface.

NOTE: Do not install valve plate assembly at this time. The valve plate must be used to determine pump mounting shim gasket thickness.

Inspect pump cylinder block (20 – Fig. SU11), pistons (18) and thrust plate (17) for wear or damage and renew or rework as follows: The thrust plate may be lapped to remove scratches or light wear pattern. However, a maximum of 0.010 inch (0.254 mm) stock removal may be allowed for rework. The slippers are the bronze bonnets crimped to pistons. All slippers should be touch lapped by hand to remove superficial scratches. Piston assemblies should be renewed if slipper surface damage is deeper than 0.005 inch (0.127 mm). A lapping plate with

Fig. SU13 — Slipper thickness should not vary more than 0.002 inch (0.051) for all nine pistons. Slipper should be free on piston with a maximum of 0.004 inch (0.102 mm) end play.

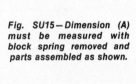

Fig. SU14 — View showing pistons in slipper retainer being installed in pump cylinder block.

Fig. SU15 — Dimension (A) must be measured with block spring removed and parts assembled as shown.

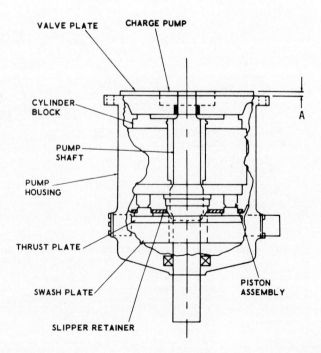

Fig. SU20—View of "piston-to-piston" pump end cap to show location of pressure test ports. Charge pressure and hydraulic lift pressure can be checked at either port.

spring, washers and retaining ring. Lubricate pistons and reinstall them in cylinder block. Reinstall block and piston assembly in pump housing and set pump assembly aside.

Install valve plate and charge pump assembly on center section. Make certain new "O" rings are in proper location on valve plate. Install four cap screws with new copper washers and tighten cap screws to a torque of 36-38 ft.-lbs. (49-52 N·m).

Place previously determined shim gasket on center section. Lubricate mating surfaces of valve plate and cylinder block with clean transmission oil. Lay center section on its side and slide pump housing into position, making sure drive shaft enters bushing in valve plate. Rotate pump shaft until spline enters charge pump rotor. When properly positioned, gap between housing and center section will be 1/8 to 1/4 inch (3-6 mm) and housing will be spring loaded with respect to center section. Install and tighten pump mounting cap screws to a torque of 20-22 ft.-lbs. (27-30 N·m). Check turning torque of pump shaft. A torque reading greater than 3 ft.-lbs. (4 N·m) is excessive and unit should be rechecked for proper shimming.

Install reservoir and suction tube, using new gasket and "O" rings. Tighten Allen head screws to 10 ft.-lbs. (14 N·m)

1500 grit compound or 4/0 grit emery paper should be used for lapping slippers. After lapping, slipper thickness should not vary over 0.002 inch (0.051 mm) for all nine pistons. See Fig. SU13. Slipper should be free on piston with a maximum of 0.004 inch (0.102 mm) end play. When slippers are properly lapped, they should have equal chamfer between slipper face and edges. The block should be renewed if bores show excessive wear or scratches (0.002 inch [0.051 mm] or deeper). The block face (balance land end) is a lapped surface. Light scratches can be removed by hand lapping. Blocks which indicate removal of 0.005 inch (0.127 mm) or more stock to remove severe scratches should be renewed or machine lapped. In no case should more than 0.015 inch (0.381 mm) be removed from block face.

After all parts have been reworked, install new pump shaft seal, pump shaft with bearing, swashplate and shafts in pump housing by reversing disassembly procedure. Install "O" rings, shim and neutral detent plate, making certain detent ball and spring are in position. Compress spring inside of block, remove retaining ring and withdraw spring and washers from block. Install pistons in slipper retainer and insert pistons in block. See Sig. SU14. Make certain lip on slipper retainer and angle of ball hub of block match. Install thrust plate in swashplate and cylinder block assembly on pump drive shaft. Place valve plate on pump as shown in Fig. SU15. Measure dimension (A) as shown (distance surface of valve plate is above housing). Dimension (A) plus 0.003 divided by 0.6 will give nominal shim gasket thickness to be used when installing pump. Shim gaskets are available in 0.010, 0.015, 0.021 and 0.031 inch thickness. If nominal shim thickness is between shim thickness listed, use next larger size. If surface of valve plate is flush to 0.009 inch below pump housing, use one 0.010 inch shim gasket. If valve plate surface

is more than 0.009 inch below face of pump housing, valve plate and/or block must be renewed.

After shim gasket thickness is determined, remove valve plate and block assembly from pump housing. Remove pistons from block and reinstall tension

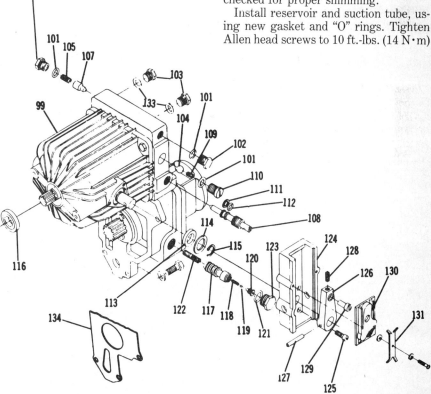

Fig. SU21—Exploded view of typical Sundstrand "piston-to-piston" center section and control cam parts. On models equipped with hydraulic lift, charge relief valve (107) is opposite side of center section and lift relief valve is located in its place.

99. Pump housing	108. Bypass valve	117. Sleeve
101. "O" ring	109. Check valve spring	118. Spring
102. Plug	110. Check valve plug	119. Ball
103. Plug	111. "O" ring	120. Valve
104. Check valve ball	112. Back-up ring	121. "O" ring
105. Charge relief spring	113. Control shaft seal	122. Acceleration valve spring
106. Charge relief plug	114. Trunnion washer	123. Plug
107. Charge relief cone	115. Retainer ring	124. Cam block support
	116. Input shaft seal	125. Socket head screw (3)
		126. Cam follower arm
		127. Roll pin
		128. Set screw
		129. Cam follower pin
		130. Cam
		131. Tension plate (2)
		133. "O" ring
		134. Gasket

torque. Install new filter and gasket, then install filter spring and cover. Cover retaining cap screws should be tightened to a torque of 10 ft.-lbs. (14 N·m).

Piston-To-Piston Model

PRESSURE TEST. If tractor appears to lose power during operation with no deterioration of engine performance, hydrostatic transmission can be checked for hydraulic pressure loss. Such check can help to determine if transmission has internal deterioration due to long term use or simply has a malfunctioning control valve or faulty adjustment. Proceed as follows:

Raise and block up tractor drive axle clear of surface. Connect pressure test gage (0 to 1000 psi [0-7000 kPa] range) after removing ¼ inch pipe plug at either point shown in Fig. SU20. Start engine and run at near full throttle; engage transmission in either forward or reverse. Alternate between forward and reverse for comparison. Note gage reading when transmission is cold, then again after normal operating temperature has been reached. A large drop in pressure as warm-up proceeds indicates internal leakage due to worn parts.

Charge pressure reading should range from 70 to 150 psi (482-1034 kPa). It should never drop below 50 psi (345 kPa).

OVERHAUL. Prior to disassembling hydrostatic unit, thoroughly clean outside of housing. If not previously removed, remove cooling fan and input pulley. Refer to Fig. SU21 and remove control arm asssembly. Separate pump and motor by removing four Allen head screws.

To disassemble pump, unbolt pump housing (1 – Fig. SU22) from pump end cap (26). If necessary, tap sides of housing with a plastic hammer to break gasket loose. Make sure as pump housing and end cap separate that cylinder block assembly (21) stays with input shaft. Carefully slide cylinder block assembly off shaft and place on a lint free towel to prevent damage.

NOTE: If any of the pistons (23) slip out, return them to their original bores.

To remove variable swashplate (12), and input shaft, remove thrust plate (13). Use a sharp awl and remove pump shaft seal and retainer. Remove snap ring from shaft and tap lightly on input end. Use a 3/16 inch punch to drive trunnion shaft roll pins out (Fig. SU23). One roll pin is used in short stub shaft and two pins are used in control shaft. Remove trunnion shaft retaining rings (7 – Fig. SU22) and drive stub shaft (2) inward. Drive control shaft out from inside. Remove swashplate (12) and trunnion seals (5). Press needle bearing out of housing from inside.

Remove valve plate (17) from charge pump housing. Remove charge pump housing mounting bolts and carefully remove pump assembly. If needle bearing (16) in charge pump housing is damaged, remove gerotor assembly (14) and press bearing out. Install new bearing with identification number showing from valve plate side. Press bearing until 0.100 inch (2.54 mm) is left out of the bore.

To disassemble motor, remove cover plate (48) and snap ring (9). Mark motor housing (45) and end cap (35) to aid in reassembly. Remove cap screws and separate housing and end cap. Remove thrust plate and ball bearing (46). Remove centering ring (43) and place motor end cap on press with cylinder

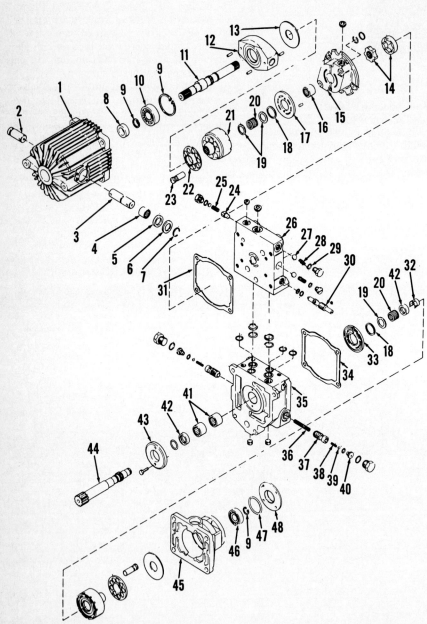

Fig. SU22 — Exploded view of late type "piston-to-piston" hydrostatic transmission.

1. Pump housing		
2. Stub shaft	14. Gerotor assy.	37. Acceleration valve body
3. Control shaft	15. Charge pump housing	38. Spring
4. Needle bearing	16. Needle bearing	39. Ball
5. Seal	17. Valve plate	40. Metering plug
6. Washer	18. Retainer ring	41. Needle bearings
7. Retainer ring	19. Washer	42. Retainer
8. Pump shaft seal	20. Spring	43. Centering ring
9. Snap ring	21. Cylinder block	44. Motor shaft
10. Bearing	22. Slipper retainer	45. Motor housing
11. Pump shaft	23. Piston	46. Ball bearing
12. Variable swashplate	24. Implement relief valve	47. "O" ring
13. Thrust plate	25. Spring	48. Cover plate
	26. Pump end cap	
	27. Charge relief valve	
	28. Spring	
	29. "O" ring	
	30. Free-wheeling valve	
	31. Gasket	
	32. Retainer clip	
	33. Valve plate	
	34. Gasket	
	35. Motor end cap	
	36. Spring	

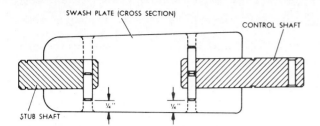

SWASH PLATE (CROSS SECTION)

CONTROL SHAFT

STUB SHAFT

¼"   ¼"

Fig. SU23 — Cross-sectional view of variable swashplate, stub shaft and control shaft. Two roll pins are used to retain control shaft.

block assembly up. Press motor shaft until retaining spring clip (32) pops loose.

CAUTION: Operation requires moving shaft only a short distance. DO NOT press shaft through cylinder block.

Slide cylinder block assembly and retaining clip from motor shaft. Remove valve plate (33) and withdraw shaft. If motor end cap bearings are rough or damaged, press seal retainer and both needle bearings out the cylinder block side. When reinstalling bearings, press output side bearing in first with lettered end out. Press seal retainer insert (42) in with bearing until flush with end cap. Install second bearing from cylinder block side and press bearing (lettered end outward) until 0.100 inch (2.54 mm) is protruding from face of end cap.

Remove acceleration valves (36 through 40) from opposite sides of motor end cap (35), implement relief valve (24), charge relief valve (27) and free-wheeling valve (30). Remove all port plugs to facilitate cleaning of all internal passages.

Clean and inspect all components for damage or excessive wear and reassemble as follows: Install relief valve assembly (24) in its bore and tighten plug to a torque of 22-26 ft.-lbs. (30-35 N·m). Use all new "O" rings when reassembling unit. Install charge relief valve (27) and check valve assembly, then torque plugs to 22-26 ft.-lbs. (30-35 N·m). Insert free-wheeling valve. When installing acceler-

ation valves, pay close attention to metering plug. Any blockage of metering plug orifice formed by the small orifice ball will cause loss of power and slow response. Tighten metering plug to a torque of 65-70 ft.-lbs. (88-95 N·m) and install other plugs.

Inspect pump housing end cap (26) and charge pump gerotor set for excessive wear or deep scratches and renew as necessary. See Fig. SU24. Superficial scratches on pump end cap may be removed by hand lapping. Check bronze side of valve plate (Fig. SU25) for scratches and wear. This surface must be smooth and free of scratches. If wear can be felt with fingernail, renew plate. Pump and motor valve plates are not interchangeable. Bronze side of valve plates must face pump or motor cylinder block.

Inspect cylinder blocks (21 – Fig. SU22), pistons (23) and thrust plates (13) for wear or damage. Thrust plates must be checked for flatness, scoring and imbedded material and renewed as required. The slippers are bronze bonnets crimped to the pistons. Piston assemblies should be renewed if slipper surface damage is deeper than 0.005 inch (0.127 mm). A lapping plate with 1500 grit compound or 4/0 grit emery paper should be used for lapping slippers. After lapping, slipper thickness should not vary over 0.002 inch (0.051 mm) for all pistons. See Fig. SU26. Slipper should be free on piston with a maximum end play of 0.004 inch (0.102 mm). Cylinder block should be renewed if

bores show excessive wear or severe scratches. Block face (balance land end) is a lapped surface. Light scratches can be removed by hand lapping. Renew blocks that require removal of 0.005 inch (0.127 mm) or more stock to remove scratches.

After all parts have been reworked, install new seals and "O" rings applying a light coat of SAE 10W-30 oil to each one. Lubricate mating surfaces of valve plate, cylinder block and bearing surfaces with SAE 10W-30 oil. Reassemble unit by reversing disassembly procedures. Reinstall control cam, input pulley and cooling fan, then install unit on differential assembly.

Series 15 "In-Line" Type

OPERATION. Sundstrand Series 15 "In-Line" hydrostatic transmission consist of three main working components: A variable displacement, reversible swashplate, axial piston type pump

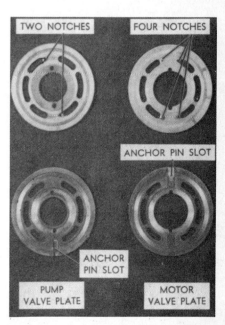

TWO NOTCHES   FOUR NOTCHES

ANCHOR PIN SLOT

ANCHOR PIN SLOT

PUMP VALVE PLATE   MOTOR VALVE PLATE

Fig. SU25 — Views of pump and motor valve plates to show differences. Plates are not interchangeable.

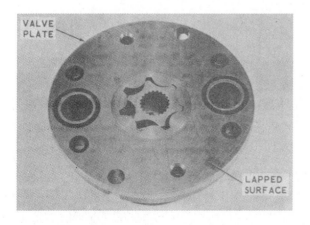

VALVE PLATE

LAPPED SURFACE

Fig. SU24 — View of gerotor charge pump and valve plate assembly.

.004 INCH END PLAY.

SLIPPER THICKNESS

Fig. SU26 — Thickness of slipper should not vary by more than 0.002 inch (0.051 mm) for all nine pistons. Slipper must move freely on piston with maximum end play of 0.004 inch (0.102 mm).

which develops hydraulic pressure needed for motive power. A center or control section which contains a gear-type charge (or make-up) pump and a calibrated, functional set of automatic valves to control and direct oil flow and ensure smooth, shock-free operation. A hydraulic motor, which in "piston-to-piston" design is a fixed displacement, stationary swashplate motor very similar to the pump. Besides necessary external controls, system is complete with a hydraulic fluid reservoir, filter and a reduction gear to differential final drive.

Hydraulic pump is shaft-driven by tractor engine and entire hydrostatic unit is mounted on final drive housing at rear of tractor. Hydrostatic flow diagram of piston-to-piston unit is shown in Fig. SU30.

In operation, with control pedal set in neutral position, movable swashplate of pump is held vertical and all pistons revolve in a plane which is at a right angle to axis of rotating pump shaft. There is no piston stroke, thus no pumping action and no flow of oil. When control shaft is moved, swashplate is tilted, and pistons move in and out in their cylinder bores to develop oil flow and pressure from the pump. Variable tilt angle of pump swashplate controls oil volume and direction of its flow. In Fig. SU30, control is set in forward. Note that oil is pumped at high pressure to piston motor to force motor and its output shaft to turn, imparting forward motion to tractor drive. Oil is returned to pump through opposite side of circuit at

lowered pressure as shown in flow diagram.

When control shaft is tilted only slightly from neutral, so swashplate is tilted very little, stroke of pump pistons will be short and a limited volume of oil will be set in motion toward hydraulic motor. Since piston motor has a fixed displacement for each revolution, a lesser volume of oil being delivered by pump will result in a slower ground speed than if a larger flow is being passed. Speed of tractor is thus controlled by degree of tilt given to swashplate of pump as control shaft is moved by pedal pressure.

When control shaft is shifted from forward to reverse, high pressure will be switched to opposite side of pump to motor circuit and motor will reverse direction of rotation so tractor will back up. A study of flow diagram will show that forward high pressure line will become a return line when swashplate angle is so shifted.

Pump to motor flow pattern is referred to as a closed loop circuit. Any losses of oil due to leakage in pressure circuit are replenished from fluid reservoir by operation of continuous-running charge pump. The amount of oil needed to replenish such loss is forced into the loop circuit through whichever of the two check valves is functioning in low pressure side, determined by flow direction from reversible primary pump. Oil pressure in charge pump (make-up) line is maintained at 70-150 (483-1034 kPa) by charge relief (make-up) valve. Excess oil released is passed to hydraulic

system for implement control, when tractor is so equipped, then is circulated through swashplate pump housing and motor housing to cool and lubricate and finally, to unit reservoir.

Acceleration control and relief valves shown located in high and low pressure circuits serve to protect system from damaging surges of excess pressure due to sudden application of control pedal. They prevent jerking motion and lurch when control is shifted by diverting high pressure oil momentarily into low pressure side of system—a matter of a second or two. As ground speed changes and pressure normalizes, this automatic valve closes and all oil flow is directed to hydraulic motor. In effect, it serves as a pressure relief valve for whichever side of loop circuit is working under high pressure.

Hydrostatic unit is furnished with a "free-wheeling" valve to serve as a bypass valve between circuits; when manually opened, oil will circulate through motor only and tractor can be pushed by hand. This valve must be closed for normal operation.

TESTING. Refer to Fig. SU31 for proper installation of pressure test gages in hydrostatic unit. Gage used must be equipped with a male 1/8 inch pipe thread adapter to fit test ports. A 0-5000 psi (0-35000 kPa) range is recommended for gage used to check system pressure (A) and a 0-1000 psi (0-7000 kPa) range capacity gage for testing charge pressure (B). It is advised that a snubber or needle valve be set into

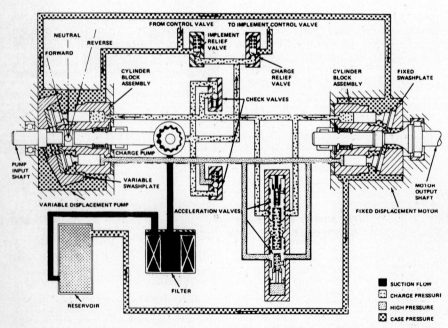

Fig. SU30 — Hydraulic flow diagram of Sundstrand Series 15 "In-Line" type hydrostatic transmission.

- ■ SUCTION FLOW
- ▨ CHARGE PRESSURE
- ▧ HIGH PRESSURE
- ▦ CASE PRESSURE

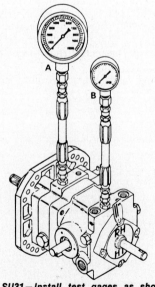

Fig. SU31 — Install test gages as shown for pressure tests. Install in center section (A) for system pressure check or at (B) for testing charge pressure. Gages must fit 1/8 inch female pipe thread in test ports.

gage line hose to dampen fluid pulsation for protection of gages.

Test procedure is as follows:

Remove ⅛ inch socket-head pipe plug from either charge pressure testing port. If no fluid flows (port is dry), turn input shaft slowly (hand crank), until fluid appears, then install gage (B). Start engine and operate at low speed. Observe gage. Normal charge pressure should develop to a steady reading between 70-150 psi (483-1034 kPa). As unit warms up, increase engine speed to full operating rpm and note if charge pressure is maintained. **Charge pressure may increase, but not decrease.** If pressure falls off, shut down system and determine cause. If charge pressure falls below 50 psi (345 kPa), complete overhaul is indicated. If unit is equipped with hydraulic implement circuit, operate implement control valve slowly through a cycle or two and note if pressure is held between 550 and 700 psi (3792 and 4826 kPa), which is normal. Comparison of charge pump pressure reading with implement pressure reading may help in locating a problem. For example, if charge pump pressure holds above 70 psi (483 kPa) and implement pressure falls to 500 psi (3448 kPa), there may be a leak in hydraulic lift system. If this is the case, repair before proceeding. If no leak appears, it is likely implement relief valve is defective. Remove plug (12 – Fig. SU32) followed by implement relief valve components (8, 9 and 10) for inspection and cleaning. If valve condition is satisfactory, pressure may be increased in steps of 50 psi (345 kPa) by adding 0.012 inch shims (10) as needed.

Install gage (A – Fig. SU31) in center section of hydrostatic unit for checking system pressure. Maximum acceptable reading is 300 psi (2070 kPa). Actual working pressure may vary widely, dependent upon throttle setting, tractor load and control position; however, a consistent low reading, especially if supported by other evidence such as marginal or sluggish performance calls for a check of acceleration valves (22 – Fig. SU32).

NOTE: Check valves in center section are not accessible unless hydrostatic unit is removed and disassembled.

Keep in mind that whenever it is planned to remove valves from housing, exterior of unit should be thoroughly cleaned to eliminate chance of dirt entry into system. Removal of valves for cleaning and inspection may often be a solution for erratic or unsatisfactory operation especially if a particular valve or valves appear to be a cause for malfunction based on test procedures.

OVERHAUL. Before disassembling hydrostatic drive unit, thoroughly clean outside of housing; then scribe a mark at joining edges of each section for aid in reassembly. To overhaul unit, proceed in following sequence.

CHARGE PUMP. Place unit, output gear (motor) side down, in an appropriate holding fixture. Inspect exposed position of input shaft (26 – Fig. SU33) for burrs or sharp keyway edges which might damage lips of seal (52). Remove four cap screws (54) and lift off housing (51) noting that left hand marking is upward. Charge pump "O" ring (47), drive pin (48), gerotor assembly (49), bearing (50) and seal (52) should now be inspected carefully to determine if renewal is needed. Scoring, imbedded foreign material or excessive wear in machined and lapped friction surfaces, especially those of gerotor are a reason for new parts.

NOTE: Though there may be no apparent damage or defect, pump may be worn to such extent that minimum 70 psi (483 kPa) required working pressure cannot be maintained. Refer to TESTING.

PUMP SECTION. With pump end placed downward on a smooth, clean surface with a center hole to accommodate protruding input shaft, separate pump, motor and center sections by removal of four long cap screws (1 – Fig. SU33) which hold unit assembled.

NOTE: Sections are lightly spring-loaded; separate with care.

With pump section set aside on clean butcher paper or lint-free shop cloths, disassemble as follows:

Remove cylinder block assembly (6) from pump housing (32) followed by thrust plate (4). To remove variable tilt swashplate (28) from housing (32), place housing with input shaft down through hole in a holding fixture so three roll pins (27) can be lightly tapped from bores in control shaft (33) and trunnion shaft (38). Push shafts out of swashplate and remove swashplate from housing. Inspect needle bearings (34) and side seals (35). If condition is defective, or even doubtful, press from housing for renewal. To remove input shaft (26), remove snap rings (29 and 31) and shaft with bearing (30) can be lightly tapped from housing bore. If bearing is worn, rough or noisy, press off shaft in a shop press for renewal.

CYLINDER BLOCK ASSEMBLIES. Pump and motor cylinders, pistons and slipper retainers are identical, however,

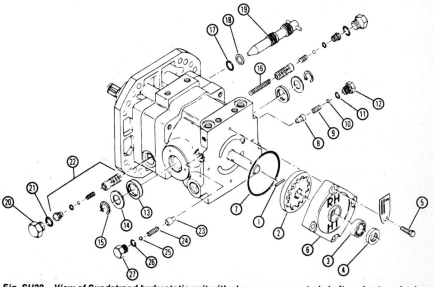

Fig. SU32 — View of Sundstrand hydrostatic unit with charge pump, control shaft, and external valves removed to show their location in housing. These items may be serviced without removing or disassembling unit. Transmission must be disassembled to renew lip seals (4 and 13).

1. Drive pin	8. Relief valve cone (implement)	15. Retainer ring
2. Pump (gerotor set)	9. Implement relief spring	16. Acceleration valve spring
3. Needle bearing	10. Shim pack	17. "O" ring
4. Lip seal	11. "O" ring	18. Back-up ring
5. Cap screw (4)	12. Plug	19. Free-wheeling valve
6. Charge pump housing	13. Lip seal (2)	20. Acceleration valve plug (2)
7. "O" ring	14. Washer (2)	21. "O" ring (2)
		22. Acceleration valve (2)
		23. Charge relief cone
		24. Charge relief spring
		25. Shims
		26. "O" ring
		27. Charge relief plug

due to extremely tight manufacturing tolerances, components are not interchangeable. Individual pistons must always be returned to same cylinder

bores when removed for inspection or cleaning. Before removing pistons from cylinder block bores by lifting slipper retainer, it is advisable to index pistons to their correct bores by use of match marks. A felt-tipped pen will mark

suitably when surfaces are clean and dry.

All parts must be thoroughly cleaned for inspection and to eliminate any chance of scoring from dirt or particles of foreign material. Be sure lube hole in center of slipper face is completely clear. If slight scratches are noted on slipper face, remove them by careful lapping; not to exceed 0.005 inch (0.127 mm). Polish with crocus cloth, nothing coarser.

Entire cylinder block assembly must be renewed under these conditions:

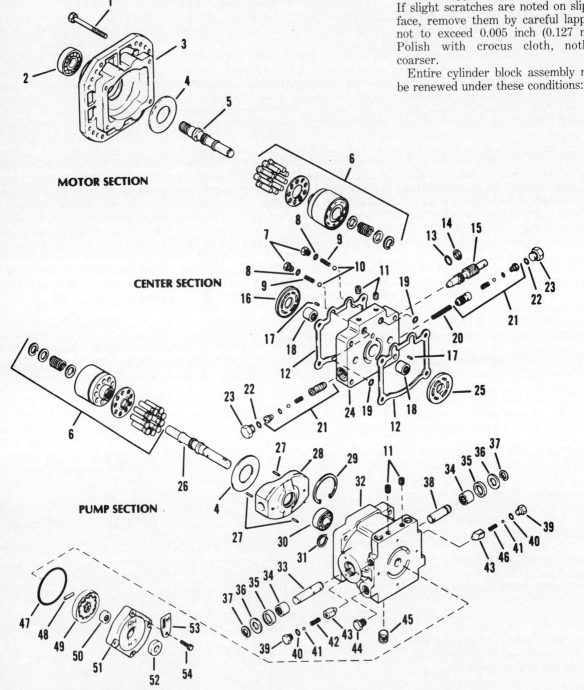

MOTOR SECTION

CENTER SECTION

PUMP SECTION

CHARGE PUMP SECTION

Fig. SU33 — Exploded view of Sundstrand Series 15 "In-Line" type hydrostatic transmission.

1. Assembly cap screw (4)
2. Ball bearing
3. Motor housing
4. Motor thrust plate
5. Motor (output) shaft
6. Cylinder block assy. (2)
7. Check valve cap (2)
8. "O" ring (2)
9. Valve spring (2)
10. Ball (2)
11. Pipe plugs (⅛ inch)
12. Gaskets (2)
13. "O" ring
14. Back-up ring
15. Free-wheeling valve
16. Motor valve plate
17. Locator pin (2)
18. Needle bearing (2)
19. "O" ring
20. Acceleration valve spring
21. Acceleration valves
22. "O" ring
23. Plug (2)
24. Center section
25. Pump valve plate
26. Pump (output) shaft
27. Roll pins (3)
28. Pump swashplate
29. Snap ring
30. Ball bearing
31. Snap ring
32. Pump housing
33. Control shaft
34. Needle bearing
35. Lip seal
36. Washer
37. Retaining ring
38. Trunnion shaft
39. Plug (2)
40. "O" ring (2)
41. Shim pack (2)
42. Charge relief valve spring
43. Relief valve (2)
44. Plug
45. Filter stud tube
46. Implement relief valve spring
47. "O" ring
48. Drive pin
49. Gerotor set (pump)
50. Needle bearing
51. Charge pump body
52. Lip seal
53. Tag
54. Cap screw (4)

Cylinder bores scored or out-of-round.

Valve plate face of cylinder worn, scratched or scored.

Piston barrels scratched or scored.

Slipper edges (contact with thrust plate) worn round in excess of 1/32 inch (0.8 mm).

Thickness of slippers (measure each with micrometer) varies by more than 0.002 inch (0.051 mm).

Slipper retainer must be perfectly flat.

Be sure to remove snap ring retainer from valve plate end of cylinder block; see parts group (6 – Fig. SU33), and also remove internal spring and washers for cleaning. Swab out center bore carefully and blow dry. Reassemble.

Cylinder block assemblies should be set aside after inspection and cleaning in readiness for reinstallation in pump and motor during reassembly of hydrostatic unit.

MOTOR SECTION. Disassemble separated motor section by first removing cylinder block assembly (6 – Fig. SU33), then lift out motor thrust plate (4). To remove output shaft (5) and its bearing (2) from motor housing (3), tap lightly on inner end of shaft, and when bearing (2) is separated from its bore in rear of motor housing, set up shaft and bearing in a shop press for removal of bearing from shaft if renewal is needed. Thoroughly clean all parts in solvent and be sure to inspect motor thrust plate (4) for condition. Renew thrust plate if scratched or scored or if there is a

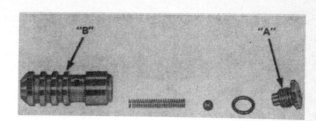

Fig. SU35 – Remove cap "A" from body "B" of acceleration valve for thorough cleaning and inspection. Do not intermix parts.

distinct wear track from contact with motor piston slippers. After thorough cleaning and evaluation, reassemble motor section and set aside for final installation in overhauled drive unit.

CENTER SECTION. When center section is isolated by removal of pump and motor sections, detailed disassembly for inspection and thorough cleaning should be performed in this order:

Remove pump valve plate (19 – Fig. SU34) and motor valve plate (10) with their locator pins (11). Carefully, so as not to gouge or scratch joining surfaces, remove gaskets (6) from each side of center section housing (18). Remove check valve "O" rings (13) from pump side of housing and both check valves (complete) from motor side – items 1, 2, 3 and 4.

IMPORTANT: Lay out all small parts of valve assemblies in proper sequence and maintain order without intermixing during inspection and cleaning process.

Remove ⅞ inch hex plugs (17) and their "O" rings (16) to withdraw and push out forward and reverse acceleration valve assemblies (15) and their common centering spring (14). Take care not to drop valve bodies during removal and do not intermix parts. Clean inside of each valve body very carefully after its metering plug, spring and ball are removed. See Fig. SU35. Since these valves are a key to smooth, trouble free operation of tractor, care and attention at this point will ensure success of overhaul. Keep the following points in mind when servicing acceleration valves:

Be sure all small orifices are open and clear. Use compressed air to clean.

Renew **all** "O" rings.

Set valve ball carefully in its recess in metering plug; assemble against spring making sure it stays in place when plug is screwed back into valve body.

Reassembled valve bodies, coated with clean ATF, are returned to their bores when housing is ready with spring (14 – Fig. SU34) centered between them. Four or five internal threads should show at each open end when valve bodies are inserted so installer will know spring (14) is properly fitted into spring cavity of each valve body. Reinstall plugs (17) with new "O" rings (16) and tighten to 18-20 ft.-lbs. (24-30 N·m).

Press bearings (12) from housing and remove socket-head type ⅛ inch pipe plugs (5) from top. Back out free-wheeling valve (9) with "O" rings (7) and back-up rings (8).

When center section housing (18) has been cleaned with solvent and blown dry with particular attention to threaded portions and all internal passages, reinstall all removed parts with defective items renewed. Note that new bearings (12) are pressed in at each side (printed end of bearing cage outward) so 0.100 inch (2.54 mm) protrudes above polished surface to serve as a center pilot for valve plates. A convenient procedure is to use a number 39 drill (0.0995 inch) as a stop gage for press arbor when pressing these bearings into bores.

When check valves are reinstalled on motor side of housing, be sure to torque check valve caps (1) to 10 ft.-lbs. (14 N·m).

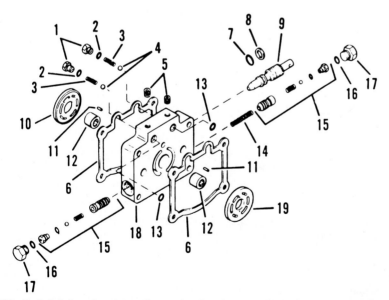

Fig. SU34 – Exploded view of center section used on Sundstrand Series 15 "In-Line" type hydrostatic transmission. Center section is isolated for convenience of identification when overhauling.

1. Check valve cap (2)
2. "O" ring (2)
3. Valve spring (2)
4. Ball (2)
5. Test plugs (⅛ inch pipe thread)
6. Gaskets (2)
7. "O" ring
8. Back-up ring
9. Free-wheeling valve
10. Motor valve plate
11. Locator pin (2)
12. Needle bearing (2)
13. "O" ring (2)
14. Acceleration valve spring
15. Acceleration valve assy. (2)
16. "O" ring (2)
17. Plug (2)
18. Center section body
19. Pump valve plate

Condition of pump and motor valve plates (Fig. SU36) is critical. Sides of plates with anchor pin slots are steel-faced. Friction side, toward pump or motor cylinder, is bronze-finished. Check pin slots for wear as well as condition of pins. If valve plates are pitted or scored or if a wear track can be detected on bronze (friction) surface by contact with a finger nail, then valve plate must be renewed.

Service technician must be especially careful to properly identify valve plates

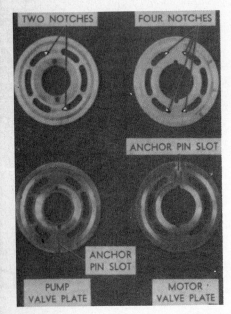

Fig. SU36—View of both sides of pump and motor valve plates. Note four lead-in chamfers (notches) of motor valve plate for rotation in either direction. Refer to text.

during disassembly for overhaul. Note in Fig. SU36 that pump valve plate shown is for left hand rotation. The two notches (lead-ins) must be matched exactly on a renewal valve plate. If placement of these chamfers is opposite to that shown, then plate is for right hand rotation. Because motor rotates either way (changes direction), four chamfers are used at ends of fluid slots in motor plate. These parts must be correct and must be properly installed for normal operation of tractor.

Renew gaskets (6 – Fig. SU34) at each side of center section in preparation for final reassembly of hydrostatic unit.

With all sections reassembled individually and with all friction surfaces and bearings lubricated by a coating of ATF, pump and motor sections should be assembled on center section by alignment on four long cap screws (1 – Fig. SU33) which are fitted through motor section, center section and into pump housing. Draw screws up evenly in alternating sequence to pull sections together gradually overcoming spring pressure as pump and motor cylinder block assemblies are compressed. Tighten cap screw heads at motor section end to 35 ft.-lbs. (47 N·m).

Carefully reinstall charge pump with a new input shaft seal (52) and new housing "O" ring (47) and such other new parts as may be called for. Tighten cap screws (54) to 20 ft.-lbs. (27 N·m).

At this point, test all three exposed shaft ends, input, output and control, by fitting a torque wrench or spring scale to determine that rolling torque of each shaft does not require effort of more than 25 in.-lbs. (2.8 N·m). If this value is exceeded, disassemble unit to locate and

eliminate binding condition. Reinstall bevel output gear on motor shaft end, using a new snap ring if necessary, then complete installation of hydrostatic unit on reduction drive housing as outlined at beginning of this section.

Series 15 "U" Type

OPERATION. The hydrostatic transmission consists of a variable volume, reversible swashplate, axial piston pump; a fixed displacement, axial piston motor; a gerotor charge pump; two check valves; a charge pressure regulator valve and an oil filter. The system operates as a closed loop type. See Fig. SU40. However, any oil lost internally from closed loop circuit is replaced by oil from the charge pump. This make up oil is drawn from the reservoir (differential case) through the oil filter and is pumped into the loop through the check valve on low pressure side at 70-120 psi (483-827 kPa). All excess charge oil passes through charge pressure regulator valve and is dumped on pump and motor; cooling and lubricating the units.

Motor speed is controlled by pump rpm and swashplate angle. Motor direction of rotation is reversed by reversing pump swashplate angle. During normal operation of tractor, operating pressure range is 750-1500 psi (5171-10342 kPa). When control lever is in neutral position, there is no pump swashplate tilt and no pump piston stroke. With no oil flowing through pump, a dynamic braking action takes place and tractor motion is halted. Although braking is normally accomplished by use of the control lever, a foot brake is also provided.

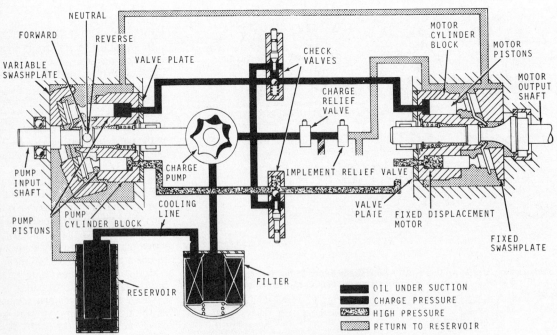

Fig. SU40—Circuit diagram of Sundstrand Series 15 "U" type hydrostatic transmission.

A free-wheeling valve knob is located beneath seat. When valve knob is turned clockwise, both check valves are held open and oil is allowed to recirculate

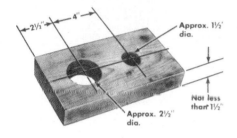

Fig. SU41—View showing dimensions of holding fixture used in disassembly and reassembly of Sundstrand Series 15 "U" type hydrostatic transmission.

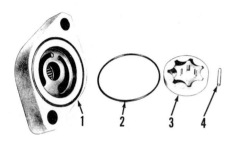

Fig. SU42—Exploded view of charge pump used on Sundstrand Series 15 "U" type hydrostatic transmission.

1. Pump housing
2. "O" ring
3. Rotor assy.
4. Drive pin

through hydraulic motor while bypassing the pump. This allows manual movement of tractor. Free-wheeling valve knob must be turned fully counterclockwise for full power to be transmitted to rear wheels.

OVERHAUL. To disassemble hydrostatic unit, is it suggested that a wooden holding fixture be made from a piece of lumber 2 inches (50.8 mm) thick, 6 inches (152.4 mm) wide and 12 inches (304.8 mm) long as shown in Fig SU41. Thoroughly clean exterior of unit, then place unit in holding fixture with charge pump facing upward. Scribe a mark on charge pump housing and center section to ensure correct reassembly.

Unbolt and remove charge pump assembly. See Fig. SU42. Pry oil seal (29—Fig. SU43) from housing (28), then press needle bearing (30) out front of housing. Remove check valves (20) and relief valves (24 and 34). Unbolt and lift off center section (33).

CAUTION: Valve plates (18 and 36) may stick to center housing. Be careful not to drop them. Remove and indentify valve plates. Pump valve plate has two relief notches and motor valve plate has four notches. See Fig. SU44.

Tilt housing (7—Fig. SU43) on its side, identify and remove cylinder block and piston assemblies from pump and motor shafts. Lay cylinder block assemblies aside for later assembly.

To remove pump swashplate (12), tilt and hold swashplate in full forward position while driving pins (13) out of shafts (2 and 8). Be careful not to damage housing when driving out pins. When pins are free of shafts, withdraw shafts and swashplate. Withdraw pump shaft (11) and bearing (10). Remove cap screws securing motor swashplate (40) to housing, then lift out swashplate and motor shaft (41). Bearings (5 and 6) and oil seals (4 and 9) can now be removed from housing. Remove needle bearings (35) from center section (33).

NOTE: Pump cylinder block and pistons are identical to motor cylinder block and pistons and complete assemblies are interchangeable. However, since pistons or cylinder blocks are not serviced separately, it is advisable to keep each piston set with its original cylinder block.

Carefully remove slipper retainer (16) with pistons (15) from pump cylinder block (17) as shown in Fig. SU45. Check cylinder block valve face and piston bores for scratches or other damage. Inspect pistons for excessive wear or scoring. Check piston slippers for excessive wear, scratches or embedded material. Make certain center oil passage is open in pistons. If excessive wear or other damage is noted on cylinder block or pistons, install a new cylinder block kit which includes pistons, slipper retainer and new cylinder block assembly. If original parts are serviceable, thoroughly clean parts, reassemble and wrap cylinder block assembly in clean paper. Repeat operation on motor cylinder block assembly (37 through 39—Fig.

1. Retaining ring (2)
2. Control shaft
3. Washer (2)
4. Seal (2)
5. Bearing (2)
6. Bearing
7. Housing
8. Trunnion shaft
9. Seal
10. Bearing
11. Pump shaft
12. Swashplate (pump)
13. Spring pins
14. Thrust plate
15. Pump pistons
16. Slipper retainer
17. Cylinder block (pump)
18. Valve plate
19. Dowel pin (2)
20. Check valves
21. Back-up washer
22. "O" ring
23. "O" ring
24. Implement lift relief valve
25. "O" ring
26. Rotor assy.
27. Drive pin
28. Charge pump housing
29. Seal
30. Bearing
31. Oil filter
32. Filter fitting
33. Center section
34. Charge relief valve
35. Bearing (2)
36. Valve plate
37. Cylinder block (motor)
38. Slipper retainer
39. Motor pistons
40. Swashplate (motor)
41. Motor shaft
42. Gasket

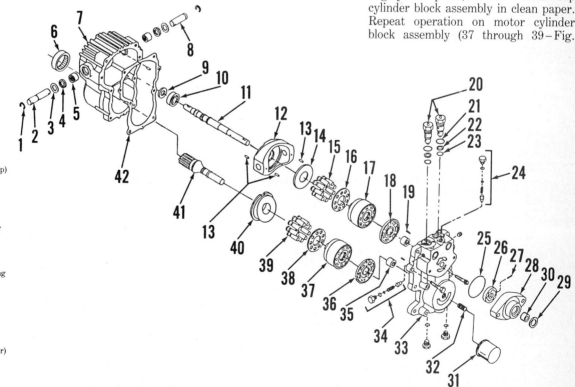

Fig. SU43—Exploded view of Sundstrand Series 15 "U" type hydrostatic transmission.

CHECK FOR WEAR
IN THESE AREAS

PUMP VALVE PLATE
(TWO NOTCHES)

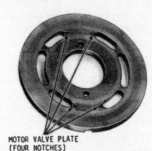

MOTOR VALVE PLATE
(FOUR NOTCHES)

Fig. SU44—View of valve plates used in Sundstrand Series 15 "U" type hydrostatic transmission. Note that pump valve plate has two notches and motor valve plate has four notches.

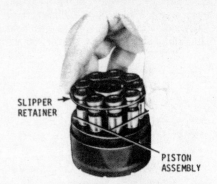

SLIPPER RETAINER

PISTON ASSEMBLY

Fig. SU45—Withdraw slipper retainer with pistons from cylinder block. Pump and motor piston and cylinder block assemblies are identical and must be renewed as complete units.

SU43) using same checks as used on pump cylinder block assembly.

Check pump valve plate (18) and motor valve plate (36) for excessive wear or other damage and renew as necessary. Inspect motor swashplate (40) and pump swashplate thrust plate (14) for wear, embedded material or scoring and renew as required.

Check charge pump housing (28) and rotor assembly (26) for excessive wear, scoring or other damage and renew as necessary. Charge pump relief valve cone should be free of nicks and scratches.

The check valves (20) are interchangeable and are serviced only as assemblies. Wash check valves in clean solvent and

air dry. Thoroughly lubricate check valve assemblies with clean oil before installation.

Renew all "O" rings, gaskets and seals and reassemble by reversing removal procedure, keeping the following points in mind: Lubricate all parts with clean oil. When installing new bearings (35), press bearings in until they are 0.100 inch (2.54 mm) above machined surface of the center housing. Pump swashplate (12) must be installed with thin stop pad towards top of transmission. Be sure control shaft (2) is installed on correct side. Drive new pins (13) into pump swashplate and shafts, using two pins on control shaft (2). Pins should be driven in until ¼ inch (6 mm) below surface of

swashplate. Tighten motor swashplate cap screws to 67 in.-lbs. (7.5 N·m) torque. Be sure pump and motor valve plates (18 and 36) are installed correctly and located on needle bearing (35) and pin (19). Tighten center section to housing cap screws to 30 ft.-lbs. (41 N·m) torque. Rotate pump and motor shafts while tightening these screws to check for proper internal assembly.

Reinstall unit and prime with oil as previously outlined.

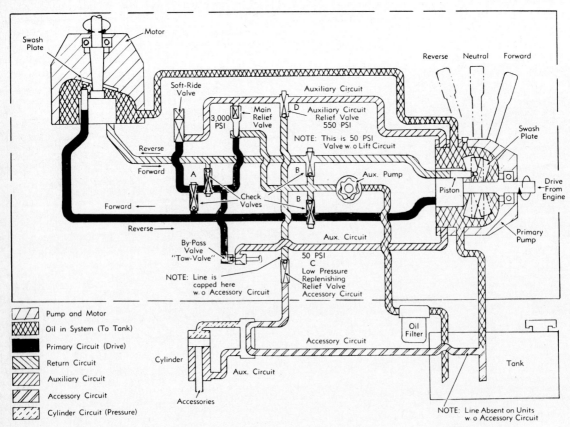

Fig. V10—Hydraulic circuit diagram of Vickers T66 hydrostatic transmission and auxiliary hydraulic system.

VICKERS

Model T66

OPERATION. The Vickers T66 hydrostatic transmission consists of a variable displacement, reversible swashplate, axial piston pump; a fixed displacement, axial piston motor; a gerotor charge pump; two charge pressure check valves and a charge pump relief valve. The system is a closed loop type and reduction drive and differential housing is used as a common reservoir. Oil is directed through an oil filter installed between gear reduction unit and hydrostatic transmission pump. Refer to Fig. V10 for a schematic circuit diagram

of hydrostatic transmission and auxiliary hydraulic system.

Motor speed is controlled by pump swashplate angle and by pump rpm. Reversing pump swashplate angle will reverse motor rotation. Moving control lever varies ground speed from 0-5.5 mph forward or 0-3 mph in reverse. Dynamic braking of tractor is accomplished by moving hydrostatic control lever to neutral position. In neutral, pump swashplate is not tilted resulting in no pump piston stroke. Since there is no oil flow to transmission motor, the motor ceases to turn and rear wheel rotation is stopped. The transmission is

equipped with a release valve which will (when in release position) allow oil to circulate within the motor. This allows motor to turn and tractor can be moved manually. During normal operation, release valve must be in down position.

OVERHAUL. To overhaul removed hydrostatic transmission, first thoroughly clean outside of unit, then refer to Fig V11 and proceed as follows: Drain fluid from transmission. Remove cap screws and separate motor valve plate (101) and motor assembly (73 through 90) from transfer block (100). Remove valve plate cap screws and

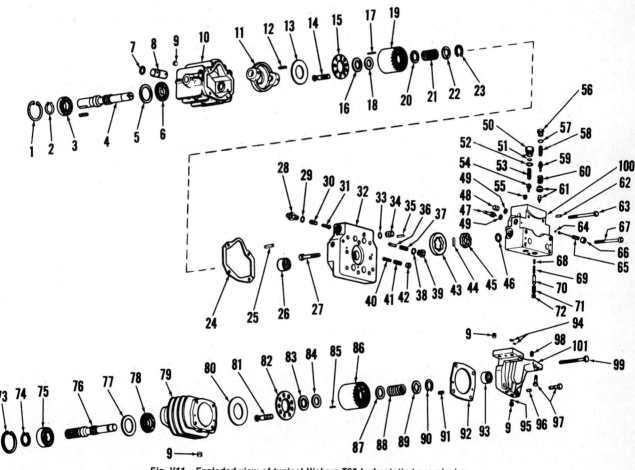

Fig. V11 — Exploded view of typical Vickers T66 hydrostatic transmission.

1. Snap ring	20. Thrust washer	37. Spring	53. Spring	68. Pin (2)	84. Washer
2. Snap ring	21. Spring	38. "O" ring	54. High pressure	69. Spring (2)	85. Pin (3 used)
3. Bearing	22. Spring retainer	39. Plug	relief valve	70. High pressure	86. Cylinder block
4. Pump shaft	23. Snap ring	40. Check valve	55. Plug	check valve	87. Thrust washer
5. Spacer	24. Gasket	(2 used)	56. Cap	(2 used)	88. Spring
6. Oil seal	25. Pin (2 used)	41. Spring (2)	57. "O" ring	71. Guide (2)	89. Spring retainer
7. "O" ring	26. Needle bearing	42. Plug (2)	58. Spring	72. Plug (2)	90. Snap ring
8. Pintle (2 used)	27. Screw (2)	43. Outer rotor	59. Pin	73. Snap ring	91. Pin (2)
9. Plug	28. Connector	44. Drive pin	60. Spring	74. Snap ring	92. Gasket
10. Pump housing	29. "O" ring	45. Inner rotor	61. Soft-ride valve and	75. Bearing	93. Needle bearing
11. Swashplate	30. Spring	46. "O" ring	seat	76. Motor shaft	94. "O" ring
12. Roll pin (2 used)	31. Charge pump relief	47. Release valve	62. Pin	77. Spacer	95. "O" ring
13. Thrust plate	valve	plunger	63. Cap screws (2)	78. Oil seal	96. Pin (2)
14. Piston (9 used)	32. Valve plate	48. Plug	64. Ball	79. Motor housing	97. Cap screw (2)
15. Shoe plate	33. "O" ring	49. "O" rings	65. Spring	80. Thrust plate	98. Pin (2)
16. Spherical washer	34. Plug	50. Plug	66. Plug	81. Piston (9 used)	99. Cap screw (2)
17. Pin (3 used)	35. Pin (2)	51. "O" ring	67. Allen head	82. Shoe plate	100. Transfer block
18. Washer	36. Lift relief valve	52. Shim	cap screw (2)	83. Spherical washer	101. Motor valve plate
19. Cylinder block					

separate valve plate and motor housing. It may be necessary to tap on valve plate with a leather or plastic mallet to separate valve plate from motor. Remove motor piston and cylinder block assembly with thrust plate (80 through 90) from motor housing. Remove thrust plate (80) and lift piston assembly (81 through 84) out of cylinder block (86). Pistons can now be removed for inspection and renewal if required. To remove cylinder block spring (88), insert a ⅜ inch bolt that is 2½ inches long with a 1 inch OD flat washer through bore of cylinder block as shown in Fig. V12. Place a 1 inch flat washer and a nut on bolt and tighten nut until spring tension is relieved from snap ring (90 – Fig. V11). Remove snap ring and loosen nut. Remove spring retainer (89), spring (88) and washer (87). Remove snap ring (73) and tap on inner end of motor shaft (76) to remove shaft, bearing (75) and spacer (77) from housing. Remove snap ring (74) and press bearing from motor shaft. Oil seal (78) can now be removed from housing.

To disassemble hydrostatic drive pump, remove Allen head cap screws (67) recessed in transfer block and hex head cap screws (63), then separate pump valve plate (32) and transfer block (100) from pump housing (10). Remove piston and cylinder block assembly (14 through 23) from pump housing. Remove shoe plate (15), pistons (14) and washers (16 and 18) from pump cylinder block. To remove spring (21), refer to preceding motor disassembly procedure as units are identical. Remove thrust plate (13) from swashplate (11). Remove snap ring (1) and tap on inner end of pump shaft (4) and remove pump shaft, bearing (3) and spacer (5). Remove snap ring (2) and press pump shaft from bearing. Drive roll pins (12) out of swashplate (11), remove pintles (8), then remove swashplate. Oil seal (6) can now be removed from pump housing.

To separate valve plate (32) from transfer block (100), remove Allen head cap screws (27) and tap valve plate with a leather or plastic mallet. Remove gerotor charge pump (43, 44 and 45) from valve plate. Remove and inspect valves from pump valve plate (32) and transfer block (100). Do not interchange valve components. Needle bearings (26 and 93) can be pulled from their respective valve plates.

Clean and inspect all parts for excessive wear or other damage. Inspect cylinder block bores and pistons for scoring and valve plate end of cylinder blocks for scratches or imbedded material. If minor defects in valve plate end of cylinder blocks cannot be removed by light tapping, renew block assembly. Piston shoe thickness

(T – Fig. V13) must not vary more than 0.001 inch (0.025 mm) for all nine pistons in each cylinder block. New pistons should not have more than 0.003 inch (0.076 mm) end play; end play on used pistons must not exceed 0.008 inch (0.203 mm). Pistons and cylinder block should be renewed as a complete assembly. Remove minor scratches from face of thrust plates (13 and 80 – Fig. V11) and valve plates (32 and 101) by light lapping, but renew parts if extensive wear or deep scratches are noted. Inspect faces of inner and outer rotors of gerotor charge pump and remove minor defects by light lapping.

Renew all seals, "O" rings and gaskets and reassemble by reversing disassembly procedure, keeping the following points in mind: Lubricate all parts with new Type "A" automatic transmission fluid. Apply a sealant such as P&OB Sealing Compound Grade No. 4 approximately ⅜ inch (10 mm) wide around outside of valve plate and transfer block. Install gerotor charge pump rotors so dots are located as shown in Fig. V14. When charge pump is installed in valve plate, dots are not visible. When installing high pressure check valves, be sure valve guides (17 – Fig. V11) are installed with open end outward. Tighten plugs (72) to a torque of 30-35 ft.-lbs. (41-47 N·m). Install pintles (8) with pintle end closest to "O" ring groove positioned in swashplate (11). Install roll pins (12) until they are 0.100 inch (2.54 mm) from surface of swashplate. Tighten valve plate to transfer block cap screws (27) to 30 ft.-lbs. (41 N·m) torque. Install thrust plates (13 and 80) so beveled edge is away from pistons as shown in Fig. V15. Tighten transfer block to pump housing Allen head cap screws to a torque of 25-30 ft.-lbs. (34-41 N·m). Tighten all other cap screws to a torque of 17-21 ft.-lbs. (23-28 N·m).

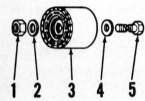

Fig. V12 — To disassemble pump and motor cylinder block, insert a bolt (5) through cylinder block and compress spring to relieve tension against snap ring.

1. Nut
2. Washer
3. Cylinder assy.
4. Washer
5. Bolt (⅜ x 3½ in.)

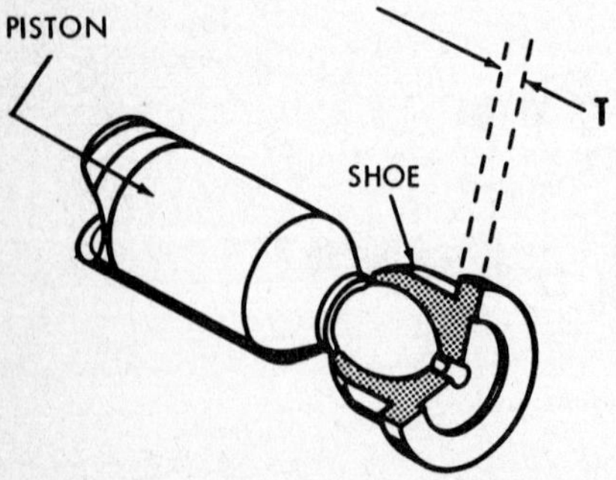

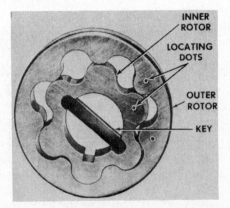

Fig. V14 — Assemble inner rotor of gerotor charge pump in outer rotor with locating dots positioned as shown.

Fig. V15 — Install thrust plates so beveled edge is away from pistons as shown.

Fig. V13 — Shoe thickness (T) of all pistons in a cylinder must be within 0.001 inch (0.025 mm) of each other.

BRIGGS & STRATTON

Model	No. Cyls.	Bore	Stroke	Displacement	Horsepower
19 & 19D	1	3 in.	2-5/8 in.	18.56 cu. in.	7.25
		(76.2 mm)	(66.7 mm)	(304 cc)	(5.4 kW)
23 & 23D	1	3 in.	3-1/4 in.	22.97 cu. in.	9
		(76.2 mm)	(82.5 mm)	(376 cc)	.7 kW)

Engines covered in this Briggs & Stratton section have cast iron cylinder blocks.

MAINTENANCE

SPARK PLUG. Recommended spark plug is Champion J-8, Autolite A-71, AC-GC46 or equivalent. Electrode gap is 0.030 inch (0.762 mm).

CARBURETOR. Float type carburetors are equipped with adjusting needles for both idle and power fuel mixtures. Counter-clockwise rotation of adjusting needles, as shown in Fig. B&S1, richens fuel mixtures. Initial adjustment is ¾ turn open on idle needle valve and 1½ turns open on power needle valve. This will allow engine to start and run, but final adjustment should be made with engine running and hot. Run engine under full load at operating speed and turn power needle valve counter-clockwise until engine begins to run unevenly. Then, turn power needle valve clockwise

slowly until engine runs smoothly. Return engine to idle and adjust idle speed regulating screw so engine is running at 1200 rpm. Adjust idle needle valve until engine runs smoothly. Readjust idle speed regulating screw if necessary.

After making above adjustments, engine should accelerate from idle speed to full speed without sputtering or hesitation. If it does not accelerate properly, turn power needle slightly counter-clockwise to provide a richer fuel mixture.

Correct float setting is shown in Fig. B&S2. Bend tang on float that contacts float valve to bring float setting within specification shown.

Throttle shaft and bushings should be checked for wear and if a diametral clearance of 0.010 inch (0.254 mm) or more can be found, installation of a new

shaft and/or bushings is required. Check upper body for being warped with a 0.002 inch (0.051 mm) feeler gage. If gage can be inserted between upper and lower bodies as shown in Fig. B&S3, a new upper body should be installed. Install new inlet float valve and seat if any wear is visible.

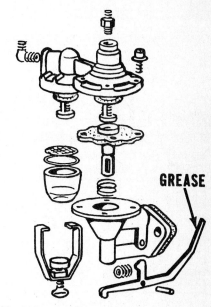

Fig. B&S5 — Exploded view of fuel pump used on some engines.

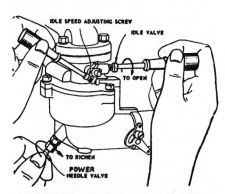

Fig. B&S1 — View showing fuel mixture adjustments and idle speed regulating screw.

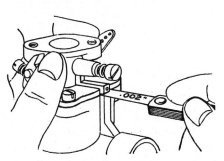

Fig. B&S3 — Checking upper body for warpage with a 0.002 inch (0.051 mm) feeler gage.

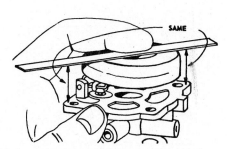

Fig. B&S2 — View showing correct float adjustment.

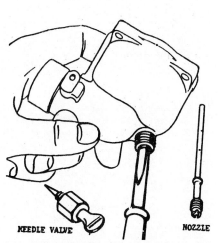

Fig. B&S4 — Remove main nozzle before separating upper and lower carburetor bodies.

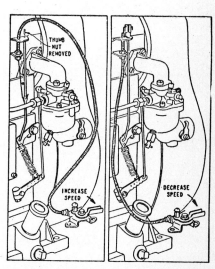

Fig. B&S6 — View showing mechanical governor linkage and remote governor controls.

233

CAUTION: The upper and lower bodies are locked together by the main nozzle. Be sure to remove power needle valve and main nozzle before attempting to separate upper body from lower body. See Fig. B&S4.

The fuel pump used on some engines is actuated by a lever which rides in a groove on the crankshaft. The lever should be greased at point shown in Fig. B&S5 before fuel pump is installed. The fuel pump diaphragm can be renewed.

GOVERNOR. The governor used is the gear driven mechanical type, with linkage as shown in Fig. B&S6. All slack due to wear must be removed from governor linkage to prevent "Hunting" or unsteady running. To adjust carburetor to governor linkage, loosen clamp on governor lever so lever will turn on governor shaft. Move carburetor throttle shaft to wide open position and turn governor shaft counterclockwise as far as possible. Then, tighten governor lever clamp.

Briggs & Stratton recommended operating speed range for those models is

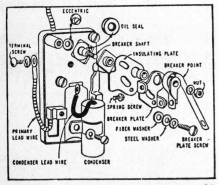

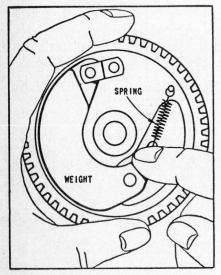

Fig. B&S7 — Exploded view of breaker box. Oil seal is installed with metal side out. See Fig. B&S15 also.

1800-3600 rpm. However, engine rpm may differ slightly depending on equipment in which engines are used. Equipment manufacturers recommendations should be followed in all cases.

MAGNETO. The breaker contact gap is 0.020 inch (0.508 mm) and condenser capacity is .18 to .24 mfd. The breaker mechanism (Fig. B&S7) is located externally on carburetor side of engine. The armature, coil and magnetic rotor are enclosed by the flywheel. This ignition system is called "Magnamatic Ignition." This system includes a centrifugal unit mounted on face of camshaft gear which provides automatic advance of ignition timing. To check freeness of advance weight action, place camshaft gear in position shown in Fig. B&S8 and press weight down. When weight is released, spring should return weight to its original position without binding. If weight does not return to its original position, renew and recheck as before.

Static timing of ignition is controlled by the position of magneto armature on magneto back plate. To adjust timing, first remove flywheel and breaker box cover. Adjust breaker contact gap to 0.020 inch (0.508 mm). Turn crankshaft in normal direction of rotation until breaker contacts just start to open. At this point, arrow on armature (X – Fig. B&S9) should register with arrow on rotor marked with model number of engine. If arrow on armature does not register with correct arrow on rotor, loosen the three armature mounting screws and rotate armature until correct register is obtained, then tighten screws. The armature air gap is nonadjustable, but when installing an armature, make certain it is as concentric as possible with magnetic rotor.

LUBRICATION. Crankcase capacity is 3 pints (1.4L) for Models 19 and 19D and 4 pints (1.9L) for Models 23 and 23D. Use SAE 30 oil when operating in

temperatures above 32°F (0°C) and SAE 10W oil when operating in temperatures below 32°F (0°C). Use high quality detergent oil having API classification SC, SD or SE. These engines are splash lubricated by a connecting rod dipper.

The engines are equipped with crankcase breathers with a sucker valve in breather body. The valve fiber disc or complete valve should be renewed if it does not operate properly.

REPAIRS

NOTE: When checking compression on models with "Easy Spin" starting, turn engine opposite normal direction of engine rotation. See CAMSHAFT paragraph.

CYLINDER HEAD. When removing cylinder head, be sure to note the position from which different length screws were removed. If they are not used in the same position when installing cylinder head, it will result in some screws bottoming in holes and not enough thread engagement on others. Install all screws finger tight, then tighten them with wrench in sequence shown in Fig. B&S10 to a torque of 190 in.-lbs. (21.5 N·m). Run engine about five minutes to allow it to warm up and retighten screws in same sequence.

CONNECTING ROD. Rod and piston assembly are removed from cylinder head end of block. The aluminum alloy connecting rod rides directly on the induction hardened crankpin. The rod should be rejected if crankpin hole is out-of-round over 0.0007 inch (0.0178 mm)

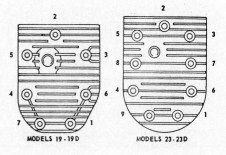

MODELS 19 - 19 D   MODELS 23 - 23 D

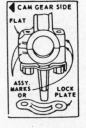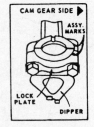

Fig. B&S11 — View showing connecting rod assembly index marks and oil dippers.

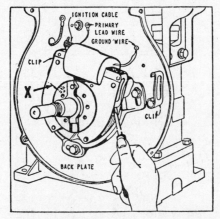

Fig. B&S9 — Arrow (X) on armature must align with appropriate number (as "19" for Model 19 engines, etc.) when points just start to open.

Fig. B&S8 — Method of checking advance weight action. Refer to text.

or piston pin hole is out-of-round over 0.0005 inch (0.0127 mm). The rod should also be rejected if either hole is scored or worn to rejection size of 1.001 inches (25.425 mm) on 19 and 19D or 1.189 inches (30.200 mm) on 23 and 23D for crankpin hole or 0.6735 inch (17.107 mm) on 19 and 19D or 0.736 inch (18.694 mm) on 23 and 23D for piston pin hole. Piston pins are available in 0.005 inch (0.127 mm) oversize.

Recommended clearance of rod to crankpin is 0.0015-0.0045 inch (0.0381-0.1143 mm) and rod to piston pin is 0.0015-0.002 inch (0.0381-0.051 mm). Tighten connecting rod bolts to a torque of 175-200 in.-lbs. (20-22 N·m). Refer to Fig. B&S11 for rod assembly index marks.

PISTON, PIN AND RINGS. Pistons in these models are aluminum alloy. If piston shows signs of wear, scoring or scuffing, it should be rejected. It should also be rejected if, after cleaning top ring groove, side clearance of a new ring installed in top groove exceeds 0.007 inch (0.178 mm).

Check piston pin by taking several measurements to find point of greatest wear. If a piston pin is 0.0005 inch (0.0127 mm) or more out-of-round, or is worn to rejection size of 0.6713 inch (17.051 mm) on 19 and 19D or 0.7338

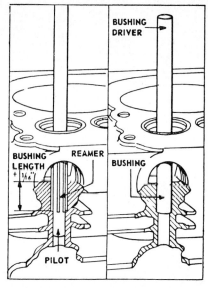

Fig. B&S14 — View showing valve guide being reamed and valve guide bushing installed.

inch (18.6385 mm) on 23 and 23D install a new pin. When piston pin holes in piston and connecting rod are worn beyond rejection size, are scored or are out-of-round over 0.0005 inch (0.0127 mm), the 0.005 inch (0.127 mm) oversize piston pin may be used if reaming piston and rod to 0.005 inch (0.127 mm) oversize cleans up worn or scored surfaces.

Reject piston rings having more than 0.030 inch (0.762 mm) end gap. End gap on new rings should be 0.010-0.018 inch (0.254-0.457 mm). If end gap on new

rings exceeds 0.018 inch (0.457 mm), it is an indication cylinder should be rebored. Install rings on piston as shown in Fig. B&S12 and stagger ring end gaps 90 degrees apart around piston.

If cylinder is more than 0.003 inch (0.076 mm) oversize or 0.0015 inch (0.0381 mm) out-of-round, it will be necessary to rebore it. Pistons and rings are available in standard size and oversizes. The standard bore size for these engines is 2.999-3.000 inches (76.175-76.2 mm).

CRANKSHAFT. The crankshaft is carried in two main bearings which may be either bushing or ball bearing type, or be one bushing and one ball bearing.

On engines having a bushing type main bearings, running clearance should be not less than 0.0015 inch (0.0381 mm) and not more than 0.0045 inch (0.1143 mm). Wear on both crankshaft and bushings will determine running clearance; therefore, both crankshaft and bushings must be checked. Renew crankshaft if worn to the following rejection sizes: Models 19 and 19D crankpin journal 0.9974 inch (25.334 mm), main bearing journal 1.180 inches (29.972 mm); Models 23 and 23D crankpin journal 1.1854 inches (30.109 mm), main bearing journal 1.3769 inches (34.973 mm). Maximum allowable out-of-round on journals is 0.0007 inch (0.0178 mm). If main bearing bushings are rough, scored or out-of-round 0.0007 inch (0.0178 mm) or more, renew main

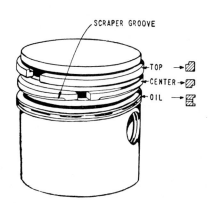

Fig. B&S12 — Install piston rings on piston as shown and stagger ring end gaps 90 degrees apart around piston.

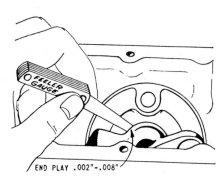

Fig. B&S13 — Checking end play between bearing plate and crankshaft thrust face.

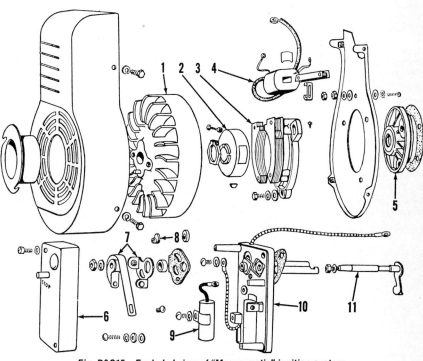

Fig. B&S15 — Exploded view of "Magna-matic" ignition system.

1. Engine flywheel	4. Coil assy.	7. Breaker points	9. Condenser
2. Magneto rotor	5. Bearing plate	8. Point gap adjusting	10. Breaker base
3. Magneto armature	6. Breaker box cover	cam	11. Breaker shaft

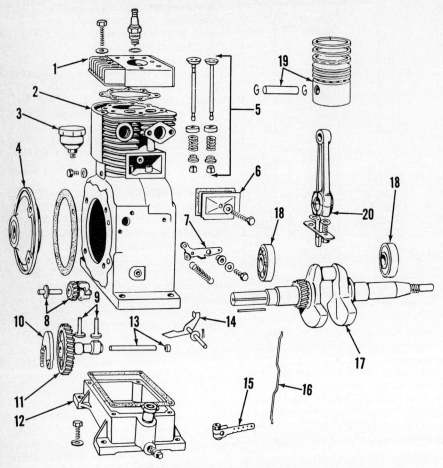

Fig. B&S16–Exploded view of main engine components.

1. Cylinder head	7. Governor control lever	11. Cam gear	17. Crankshaft
2. Cylinder assembly	8. Governor shaft and weight assembly	12. Engine base	18. Ball type main bearings
3. Crankcase breather	9. Valve tappets	13. Camshaft and plug	19. Piston, ring and pin assembly
4. Bearing plate	10. Spark advance weight and spring	14. Governor crank assembly	20. Connecting rod with oil slinger
5. Valves, springs, and keepers		15. Governor lever	
6. Tappet cover plate		16. Throttle link	

bearing support plates with factory reamed bushings. Main bearing bushing rejection sizes are as follows: 1.1843 inches (30.081 mm) for Models 19 and 19D and 1.3813 inches (35.085 mm) for Models 23 and 23D.

The recommended crankshaft end play is 0.002-0.008 inch (0.051-0.203 mm) and is measured as shown in Fig. B&S13. End play is controlled by use of different thickness gaskets between bearing plate and crankcase.

On engines equipped with ball bearing mains, check ball bearings for wear or roughness. When renewing ball bearing mains, press crankshaft out of old bearings. Expand new bearings by heating them in oil. Slide heated bearing in place with sealed side towards crankpin journal.

CAMSHAFT. On all models, camshaft and timing gear are an integral part and are referred to as the "cam gear". The cam gear turns on a stationary shaft which is referred to as the "camshaft." Reject camshaft if it is worn to a diameter of 0.49675 inch (12.6917 mm). Reject cam gear if lobes are worn to the following reject sizes: Models 19

and 19D, 1.115 inches (28.321 mm); Models 23 and 23D, 1.184 inches (30.073 mm).

On models equipped with "Easy Spin" starting, intake cam lobe is designed to hold intake valve slightly open on a part of compression stroke. Therefore, to check compression, engine must be turned backwards.

NOTE: On engines equipped with either a wind-up or rewind starter, blower housing must be removed in order to turn engine in reverse direction.

"Easy Spin" cam gears are identified by two holes drilled in web of the gear. Where part number of an older cam gear and an "Easy Spin" cam gear are the same (except for an "E" following "Easy Spin" part), gears may be interchanged. Align timing marks on cam gear and crankshaft gear on assembly.

VALVE SYSTEM. Always set valve clearance when engine is cold. Proper valve clearance is as follows: Models 19 and 19D intake valve 0.008 inch (0.203 mm) and exhaust valve 0.015 inch (0.381 mm); Models 23 and 23D intake valve 0.008 inch (0.203 mm) and exhaust valve 0.018 inch (0.457 mm). Valve clearance is adjusted by grinding end of valve stem squarely. Valves have a seat angle of 45 degrees and a seat width of 3/64 to 5/64-inch (1.2-2.0 mm).

Renewal of exhaust valve seat insert requires the use of special equipment which is available from Briggs & Stratton.

If valve guides are worn, they can be rebushed in the following manner. Use reamer (B&S #19183) to ream worn guide. See Fig. B&S14. Ream only 1/16 inch (1.6 mm) deeper than valve guide bushing (B&S #230655). Do not ream all the way through guide. Press in valve guide bushing until top end of bushing is flush with top end of valve guide. Use a soft metal driver so top end of bushing is not peened over. Valve guide bushings used in these engines are finish reamed to size at the factory so no further reaming is necessary and a standard valve can be used.

VALVE TIMING. When reinstalling cam gear, align timing mark on cam gear with timing mark on crankshaft gear. Valve to piston timing will then be correct.

BRIGGS & STRATTON

Model	No. Cyls.	Bore	Stroke	Displacement	Horsepower
140000 Series	1	2-¾ in. (69.8 mm)	2-⅜ in. (60.3 mm)	14.1 cu. in. (231 cc)	6 (4.5 kW)
170000 Series	1	3 in. (76.2 mm)	2-⅜ in. (60.3 mm)	16.79 cu. in. (275 cc)	7 (5.2 kW)
171000 Series	1	3 in. (76.2 mm)	2-⅜ in. (60.3 mm)	16.79 cu. in. (275 cc)	7 (5.2 kW)
190000 Series	1	3 in. (76.2 mm)	2-¾ in. (69.8 mm)	19.44 cu. in. (318 cc)	8 (6.0 kW)
191000 Series	1	3 in. (76.2 mm)	2-¾ in. (64.8 mm)	19.44 cu. in. (318 cc)	8 (6.0 kW)
251000 Series	1	3-7/16 in. (87.3 mm)	2-⅝ in. (66.7 mm)	24.36 cu. in. (399 cc)	10 (7.5 kW)
252000 Series	1	3-7/16 in. (87.3 mm)	2-⅝ in. (66.7 mm)	24.36 cu. in. (399 cc)	11 (8.2 kW)
253000 Series	1	3-7/16 in. (87.3 mm)	2-⅝ in. (66.7 mm)	24.36 cu. in. (399 cc)	11 (8.2 kW)

All engines in this section have aluminum cylinder blocks with aluminum cylinder bores.

MAINTENANCE

SPARK PLUG. Recommended spark plug for all models is a Champion J-8, Autolite A-71 or an AC GC46. Set electrode gap to 0.030 inch (0.762 mm) for all models.

NOTE: If a resistor type plug is necessary to reduce radio interference, use Champion XJ-8 or equivalent. Briggs & Stratton Corporation does not recommend cleaning spark plugs by abrasive blasting method as this may introduce some abrasive material into the engine which could cause extensive damage.

FLO-JET CARBURETORS. Two different float type carburetors are used. They are called a "two-piece" (Fig. B&S20) or a "one-piece" (Fig. B&S21) carburetor depending upon type of construction.

Float type carburetors are equipped with adjusting needle for both idle and power fuel mixtures. Refer to Fig. B&S22. Counter-clockwise rotation of adjusting needles richens the mixture. For initial starting adjustment, open idle mixture needle valve ½ to ¾ turn and main needle valve (power fuel mixture) 1½ turns on two-piece carburetor. On one-piece carburetor, open both needle valves 1⅛ turns. Start engine and when it is warm, make final adjustments as follows: Set engine control for desired operating speed, turn main needle clockwise until engine misses, and then turn it counter-clockwise just past smooth operating point until engine begins to run unevenly. Return speed control to idle position and adjust idle speed stop screw until engine idles at 1750 rpm. Then adjust idle needle valve until engine runs smoothly. Reset idle speed stop screw if necessary. The engine should then accelerate without

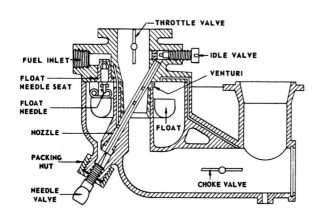

Fig. B&S20 — Cross-sectional view of typical B&S "two-piece" carburetor. Before separating upper and lower body sections, remove packing nut and power needle valve as a unit. Then, using special screwdriver, remove nozzle.

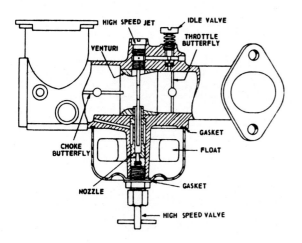

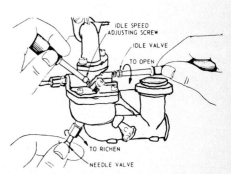

Fig. B&S21 — Cross-sectional view of typical B&S "one-piece" carburetor.

Fig. B&S22 — Adjustment points for typical B&S carburetor. Refer to text for adjustment procedure.

hesitation or sputtering. If it does not accelerate properly, turn main needle valve counter-clockwise slightly to provide a richer fuel mixture.

NOTE: The upper and lower bodies of two-piece float type carburetor are locked together by the main nozzle. Refer to cross-sectional view of carburetor in Fig. B&S20. Before attempting to separate upper body from lower body, loosen packing nut and unscrew nut and needle valve. Then, using special screwdriver (B&S tool #19061 or #19062), remove nozzle.

If a 0.002 inch (0.051 mm) feeler gage can be inserted between upper and lower bodies of two-piece carburetor as shown in Fig. B&S23, upper body is warped and should be renewed.

The float level on both float type carburetors should be within dimensions

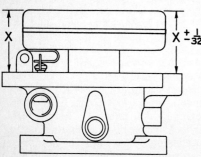

shown in Figs. B&S24. If not, bend tang on float as shown in Fig. B&S25 to adjust float level. If any wear is visible on inlet valve or inlet valve seat, install a new valve and seat assembly. On one-piece carburetors, inlet valve seat is machined in carburetor body and is not renewable.

Check throttle shaft for wear on all float type carburetors. If 0.010 inch (0.254 mm) or more free play (shaft to bushing clearance) is noted, install new throttle shaft and/or throttle shaft bushings. To remove worn bushings, turn a ¼-inch x 20 tap into bushing and pull bushing from body casting with a tap. Press new bushings into casting by using a vise and, if necessary, ream bushings with a 7/32-inch (5.5 mm) drill bit.

PUMP TYPE (PULSA-JET) CARBURETOR. The pump type (Pulsa-Jet) carburetor is basically a suction type carburetor incorporating a fuel pump to fill a constant level fuel sump in top of fuel tank. Refer to schematic view in

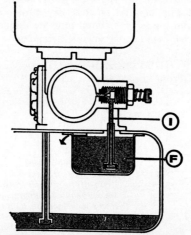

Fig. B&S26 — Fuel flow in Pulsa-Jet carburetor. Fuel pump incorporated in carburetor fills constant level sump below carburetor (F) and excess fuel flows back into tank. Fuel is drawn from sump through inlet (I) past fuel mixture adjusting needle by vacuum in carburetor.

Fig. B&S26. This makes a constant fuel-air mixture available to engine regardless of fuel level in tank.

Carburetor adjustment is accomplished by turning fuel mixture needle. Turning needle clockwise leans fuel-air mixture. To adjust carburetor, engine should be warm and running at approximately 3000 rpm at no-load. Turn needle valve clockwise until engine begins to lose speed; then, turn needle slowly counter-clockwise until engine begins to run unevenly from excessively rich fuel-air mixture. This should result in a correct adjustment for full load operation. Adjust idle speed to 1750 rpm.

To remove pump type carburetor, first remove carburetor and fuel tank as an assembly; then, remove carburetor from fuel tank. When reinstalling carburetor on fuel tank, use a new gasket or pump diaphragm as required and tighten retaining screws evenly. Fig. B&S27 shows an exploded view of pump unit.

The pump type carburetor has two fuel feed pipes; the long pipe feeds fuel into pump portion of carburetor from which fuel then flows to constant level fuel sump. The short pipe extends into constant level sump and feeds fuel into carburetor venturi via fuel mixture needle valve. Check valves are incorporated in the pump diaphragm. The pipe or screen housing can be renewed if fuel screen in lower end of pipe is broken or clogged and cannot be cleaned. If pipe is made of nylon, unscrew old pipe and install new pipe with a wrench. Be careful not to overtighten new pipe. If pipe is made of brass, clamp pipe lightly in a

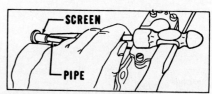

Fig. B&S28 — To renew screen housing on pump type carburetors with brass feed pipes, drive old screen housing from pipe as shown. To hold pipe, clamp lightly in a vise.

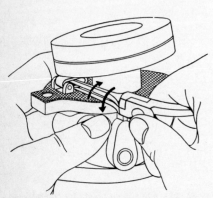

Fig. B&S24 — Float setting on both type carburetors should be within specifications as shown. Refer to Fig. B&S25 for adjustment.

Fig. B&S25 — Bend tang with needle nose pliers to adjust float setting.

Fig. B&S27 — View of Pulsa-Jet fuel pump. Note difference in old and new cups.

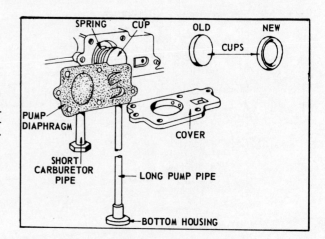

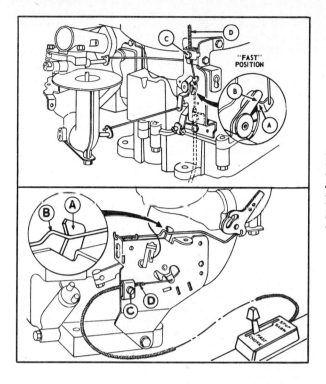

Fig. B&S29 — On Choke-A-Matic controls shown, choke actuating lever (A) should just contact choke link or shaft (B) when control is at "FAST" position. If not, loosen screw (C) and move control wire housing (D) as required.

vise and drive old screen housing from pipe with a small chisel as shown in Fig. B&S28. Drive a new screen housing onto pipe with a soft faced hammer.

NOTE: If soaking carburetor in cleaner for more than one-half hour, be sure to remove all nylon parts and "O" ring, if used, before placing carburetor in cleaning solvent.

CHOKE-A-MATIC CARBURETOR CONTROLS. Engines may be equipped with a control unit with which carburetor choke and throttle and magneto grounding switch are operated from a single lever (Choke-A-Matic carburetors).

To check operation of Choke-A-Matic carburetor controls, move control lever to "CHOKE" position; carburetor choke slide or plate must be completely closed. Then, move control lever to "STOP" position; magneto grounding switch should be making contact. With control lever in "RUN", "FAST", or "SLOW" position, carburetor choke should be completely open. On units with remote controls, synchronize movement of

remote lever to carburetor control lever by loosening screw (C – Fig. B&S29) and moving control wire housing (D) as required; then, tighten screw to clamp the housing securely. Refer to Fig. B&S30 to check remote control wire movement.

AUTOMATIC CHOKE (THERMOSTAT TYPE). A thermostat operated choke is used on some models equipped with two-piece carburetor. To adjust choke linkage, hold choke shaft so thermostat lever is free. At room temperature, stop screw in thermostat collar should be located midway between thermostat stops. If not, loosen stop screw, adjust collar and tighten stop screw. Loosen set screw (S – Fig. B&S31) on thermostat lever. Then, slide lever on shaft to insure free movement of choke unit. Turn thermostat shaft clockwise until stop screw contacts thermostat stop. While holding shaft in this position, move shaft lever until choke is open exactly 1/8-inch (3 mm) and tighten lever set screw. Turn thermostat shaft counter-clockwise until stop screw contacts thermostat stop as shown in Fig. B&S32. Manually open choke valve until it stops against top of choke link opening. At this time, choke valve should be open at least 3/32-inch (2 mm), but not more than 5/32-inch (4 mm). Hold choke valve in wide open position and check position of counterweight lever. Lever should be in a horizontal position with free end towards right.

FUEL PUMP. A fuel pump is available as optional equipment on some

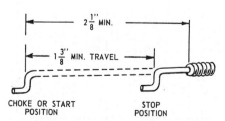

Fig. B&S30 — For proper operation of Choke-A-Matic controls, remote control wire must extend to dimension shown and have a minimum travel of 1 3/8 inches (35 mm).

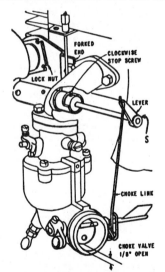

Fig. B&S31 — Automatic choke used on some models equipped with two-piece Flo-Jet carburetor showing unit in "Hot" position.

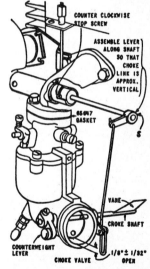

Fig. B&S32 — Automatic choke on two-piece Flo-Jet carburetor in "Cold" position.

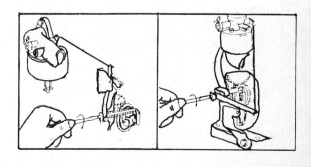

Fig. B&S33 — Adjust governor with throttle lever in high speed position. See text.

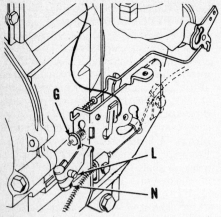

Fig. B&S34 — View of governor linkage used on horizontal crankshaft engines; refer to text for adjustment procedure.

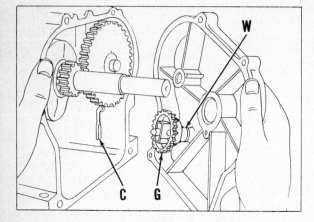

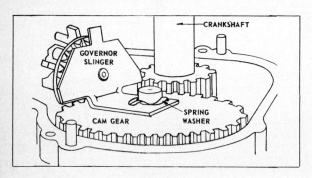

models. Refer to SERVICING BRIGGS & STRATTON ACCESSORIES section in this manual for fuel pump servicing information.

GOVERNOR. Engines are equipped with a gear driven mechanical governor. The governor unit is enclosed within the engine and is driven from camshaft gear. Governor unit and lubrication oil slinger are integral on all vertical crankshaft engines. All binding or slack due to wear must be removed from governor linkage to prevent "hunting" or unsteady operation. To adjust carburetor to governor linkage, loosen clamp bolt on governor lever. Move link end of governor lever until carburetor throttle shaft is in wide open position. Using a screwdriver, rotate governor

Fig. B&S35 — Installing crankcase cover on horizontal crankshaft Series 170000, 190000 and late 140000 with mechanical governor. Governor on Series 251000, 252000 and 253000 is similar. Governor crank (C) must be in position shown. A thrust washer (W) is placed between governor (G) and crankcase cover.

Fig. B&S36 — View showing Series 140000, 170000, 171000, 190000, 191000, 251000 and 252000 vertical crankshaft mechanical governor unit. Drawing is of lower side of engine with oil sump (engine base) removed.

lever shaft clockwise as far as possible, then tighten clamp bolt (Fig. B&S33).

Governor gear and weight unit can be removed when engine is disassembled. Refer to exploded views of engines in Figs. B&S48, B&S49, B&S50 and B&S51. Remove governor lever, cotter pin and washer from outer end of governor lever shaft. Slide governor lever out of bushing towards inside of engine. Governor gear and weight unit can now be removed. Renew governor lever shaft bushing in crankcase, if necessary, and ream new bushing after installation to 0.2385-0.239 inch (6.058-6.070 mm).

MAGNETO. The breaker point gap is 0.020 inch (0.508 mm) on all models. Condenser capacity on all models is 0.18-0.24 mfd.

On all models, breaker points and condenser are accessible after removing engine flywheel and breaker cover.

On some models, one breaker point is an integral part of ignition condenser and breaker arm is pivoted on a knife edge retained in a slot in pivot post. On these models, breaker contact gap is adjusted by moving condenser as shown in Fig. B&S37. On other models, breaker contact gap is adjusted by relocating position of breaker contact bracket; refer to Fig. B&S38.

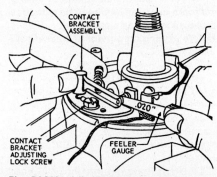

Fig. B&S38 — Adjusting breaker point gap on models having breaker points separate from condenser.

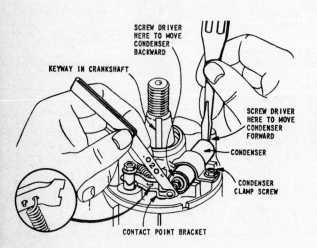

Fig. B&S37 — View showing breaker point adjustment on models having breaker point integral with condenser. Move condenser to adjust point gap.

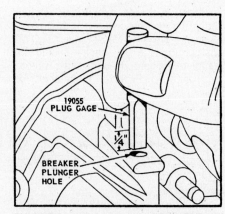

Fig. B&S39 — If B&S plug gage #19055 can be inserted in breaker plunger bore a distance of ¼-inch (6 mm) or more, bore is worn and must be rebushed.

On all models, breaker contact arm is actuated by a plunger held in a bore in engine crankcase and riding against a cam on engine crankshaft. Plunger can be removed after removing breaker points. Renew plunger if worn to a length of 0.870 inch (22.098 mm) or less. If breaker point plunger bore in crankcase is worn, oil will leak past plunger. Check bore with B&S plug gage #19055; if plug gage will enter bore ¼-inch (6 mm) or more, bore should be reamed and a bushing installed. Refer to Fig. B&S39 for method of checking bore and to Fig. B&S40 for steps in reaming bore and installing bushing if bore is worn. To ream bore and install bushing, it is necessary that breaker points, armature and ignition coil and crankshaft be removed.

When reassembling, adjust breaker point gap to 0.020 inch (0.508 mm) and set armature to flywheel air gap at 0.010-0.014 inch (0.254-0.356 mm) on two-leg armature or 0.016-0.019 inch (0.406-0.483 mm) on three-leg armature. Ignition timing is non-adjustable on these models.

LUBRICATION. Vertical crankshaft engines are lubricated by an oil slinger wheel on governor gear which is driven by camshaft gear (See 15 – Fig. B&S48 or B&S49.)

Horizontal crankshaft engines have a splash lubrication system provided by an oil dipper attached to connecting rod. Refer to Fig. B&S41 for view of various types of dippers used.

Use oils labeled "For Service SC, SD or SE only". (Use of higher or lower API classification oils is not recommended.) SAE-30 or 10W-30 oil is recommended for temperatures above 40°F (4°C), SAE 10W oil in temperatures between 40°F (4°C) and 0°F (–18°C) and SAE 5W-20 (or 10W oil diluted with 10% kerosene) for below 0°F (–18°C).

For engine crankcase oil capacity, refer to condensed specifications for tractor model.

CRANKCASE BREATHER. The crankcase breather is built into engine valve cover. A partial vacuum must be maintained in crankcase to prevent oil from being forced out through oil seals and gaskets or past breaker plunger and piston rings. Air can flow out of crankcase through the breather, but the one-way valve blocks return flow, maintaining the necessary vacuum. Breather mounting holes are offset one way. A vent tube connects breather to carburetor air horn for extra protection against dusty conditions.

REPAIRS

NOTE: When checking compression on models with "Easy-Spin" starting, turn engine opposite the direction of normal rotation. See CAMSHAFT paragraph.

CYLINDER HEAD. When removing cylinder head, be sure to note position from which each of the different length screws were removed. If they are not used in the same holes when reinstalling cylinder head, it will result in screws bottoming in some holes and not enough thread contact in others. Lubricate cylinder head screws with graphite grease before installation. Do not use sealer on head gasket. When installing cylinder head, tighten all screws lightly and then retighten them in sequence shown in Fig. B&S42 or B&S43 to a torque of 165 in.-lbs. (18.6 N·m). Note early models use eight cap screws to retain cylinder head while later models use nine cap screws. Run engine for 2 to 5 minutes to allow it to warm up and retighten head screws again following sequence and torque values mentioned above.

CONNECTING ROD. The connecting rod and piston are removed from cylinder head end of block as an assembly. The aluminum alloy connecting rod rides directly on the induction hardened crankpin. The rod should be rejected if crankpin hole is scored or out-of-round over 0.0007 inch (0.0178 mm) or if piston pin hole is scored or out-of-round over 0.0005 inch (0.0127 mm). Wear limit sizes are given in the following chart. Reject connecting rod if either crankpin or piston pin hole is worn to or larger than sizes given in the chart.

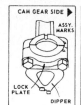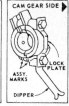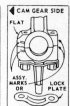

Fig. B&S41 — View of various types of lubricating oil dippers used on horizontal crankshaft engines.

REJECT SIZES FOR CONNECTING ROD

Basic Model	Crankpin Hole	*Piston Pin Hole
140000	1.0949 in. (27.8105 mm)	0.674 in. (17.1196 mm)
170000, 171000	1.0949 in. (27.8105 mm)	0.674 in. (17.1196 mm)
190000, 191000	1.1265 in. (28.6131 mm)	0.674 in. (17.1196 mm)
All Other Models	(1.2520 in.) (31.8008 mm)	(0.802 in.) (20.3708 mm)

*NOTE: Piston pins of 0.005 inch (0.127 mm) oversize are available for service. Piston pin hole in rod can be reamed to this size if crankpin hole is O.K.

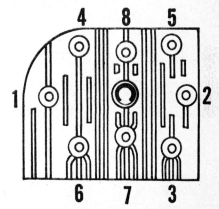

Fig. B&S42 — Tightening sequence on models with eight cylinder head cap screws. Long screws are used in positions 2, 3 and 7.

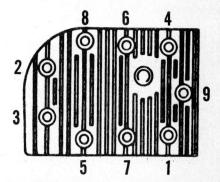

Fig. B&S43 — Tightening sequence on models with nine cylinder head cap screws. Long screws are used in positions 1, 7 and 9.

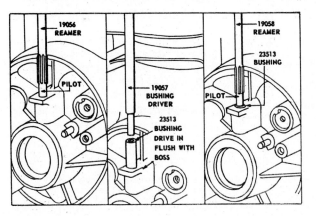

Fig. B&S40 — Views showing reaming plunger bore to accept bushing (left view), installing bushing (center) and finish reaming bore of bushing (right).

Tighten connecting rod cap screws to a torque of 165 in.-lbs. (18.6 N·m) on Models 140000, 170000, 171000, 190000 and 191000 and to 190 in.-lbs. (21.5 N·m) on all other models.

PISTON, PIN AND RINGS. Piston used in aluminum bore ("Kool-Bore") engine is not marked on top of piston. This chrome plated piston does not use an expander with the oil ring. Reject pistons showing visible signs of wear, scoring or scuffing. If, after cleaning carbon from top ring groove, a new top ring has a side clearance of 0.007 inch (0.178 mm) or more, reject the piston. Reject piston or hone piston pin hole to 0.005 inch (0.127 mm) oversize if pin hole is 0.0005 inch (0.0127 mm) or more out-of-round, or exceeds standard pin hole size.

Reject piston pin if pin is 0.0005 inch (0.0127 mm) or more out-of-round or if pin is worn to a diameter of 0.671 inch (17.043 mm) or smaller on Models 140000, 170000, 171000, 190000 and 191000 or to a diameter of 0.799 inch (20.294 mm) or smaller on all other models.

The piston ring end gap for new rings should be 0.010-0.025 inch (0.254-0.635 mm). Reject compression rings having an end gap of 0.035 inch (0.889 mm) or more and reject oil rings having an end gap of 0.045 inch (1.016 mm) or more.

Pistons and rings are available in standard size and oversizes.

A chrome ring set is available for slightly worn standard bore cylinders. Refer to note in CYLINDER paragraph.

CYLINDER. If cylinder bore wear is 0.003 inch (0.076 mm) or more or is 0.0025 inch (0.0635 mm) or more out-of-round, cylinder must be rebored to next larger oversize.

Standard bore size is 2.749-2.750 inches (69.825-69.850 mm) on Model 14000, 2.999-3.000 inches (76.175-76.200 mm) for Models 170000, 171000, 190000 and 191000 and 3.4365-3.4375 inches (87.287-87.312 mm) for all other models.

It is recommended that a hone be used for resizing cylinders. Operate hone at 300-700 rpm and with an up and down movement that will produce a 45 degree cross-hatch pattern. Clean cylinder after honing with oil or soap suds. Aproved hones are as follows: For aluminum bore, use Ammco No. 3956 for rough and finishing or Sunnen No. AN200 for rough and Sunnen AN500 for finishing.

A chrome piston ring set is available for slightly worn standard bore cylinders. No honing or cylinder deglazing is required for these rings. The cylinder bore can be a maximum of 0.005 inch (0.127 mm) oversize when using chrome rings.

CRANKSHAFT AND MAIN BEARINGS. Except where equipped with ball bearings, the main bearings are an integral part of crankcase and cover or sump. The bearings are renewable by reaming out crankcase and cover or sump bearing bores and installing service bushings. The tools for reaming crankcase and cover or sump, and for installing service bushings are available from Briggs & Stratton. If bearings are scored, out-of-round 0.007 inch (0.178 mm) or more, or are worn to or larger than reject sizes given below, ream bearings and install service bushings.

MAIN BEARING REJECT SIZES

Basic Model	Bearing Magneto	Bearing Drive
140000, 170000, 190000	1.006 in. (25.552mm)	1.185 in. (30.099 mm)
171000, 191000— Synchro Balanced	1.185 in. (30.099 mm)	1.185 in (30.099 mm)
All Other Models	1.383 in. (35.128 mm)	1.383 in. (35.128 mm)

Rejection sizes for crankshaft bearing journals are given in the following chart. Figures given for main bearing journals would apply to plain bearing applications only.

CRANKSHAFT REJECTION SIZES

Magneto Journal		
140000, 170000		0.0075 in. (25.3365 mm)
190000		0.9975 in. (25.3365 mm)
171000 Synchro Balanced		1.179 in. (29.946 mm)
191000 Synchro Balanced		1.179 in. (29.946 mm)
All Other Models		1.376 in. (34.950 mm)
Crankpin Journal		
140000, 170000		1.090 in. (27.686 mm)
190000		1.122 in. (28.499 mm)
171000 Synchro Balanced		1.090 in. (27.686 mm)
191000 Synchro Balanced		1.122 in. (28.499 mm)
All Other Models		1.247 in. (31.674 mm)
Drive End Journal		
140000, 170000		1.179 in. (29.946 mm)
190000		1.179 in. (29.946 mm)
171000 Synchro Balanced		1.179 in. (29.946 mm)
191000 Synchro Balanced		1.179 in. (29.946 mm)
All Other Models		1.376 in. (34.950 mm)

Ball bearing mains are a press fit on crankshaft and must be removed by pressing crankshaft out of bearing. Reject ball bearing if worn or rough. Expand new bearing by heating it in oil and install it on crankshaft with shield side towards crankpin journal.

Crankshaft end play should be 0.002-0.008 inch (0.051-0.203 mm). At least one 0.015 inch cover or sump gasket must be used. Additional cover gaskets of 0.005 and 0.009 inch thicknesses are available if end play is less than 0.002 inch (0.051 mm). If end play is over 0.008 inch (0.203 mm) metal shims are available for use on crankshaft.

Place shims between crankshaft gear and cover or sump on models with plain bearings or between magneto end of crankshaft and crankcase on ball bearing equipped models.

CAMSHAFT. The camshaft and camshaft gear are an integral part which rides in journals at each end of the camshaft. The camshaft and gear should be inspected for wear on journals, cam lobes and gear teeth. Rejection sizes for journals and cam lobes are given in the following chart.

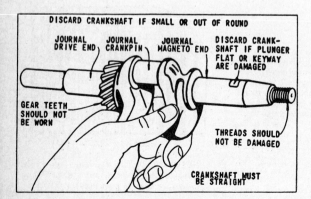

DISCARD CRANKSHAFT IF SMALL OR OUT OF ROUND

JOURNAL DRIVE END   JOURNAL CRANKPIN   JOURNAL MAGNETO END

DISCARD CRANKSHAFT IF PLUNGER FLAT OR KEYWAY ARE DAMAGED

GEAR TEETH SHOULD NOT BE WORN

THREADS SHOULD NOT BE DAMAGED

CRANKSHAFT MUST BE STRAIGHT

Fig. B&S44 — Inspection points on typical crankshaft.

CAMSHAFT REJECTION SIZES

Basic Model	Journal Reject Size	Lobe Reject Size
140000, 170000, 171000	0.4985 in. (12.662 mm)	0.977 in. (24.816 mm)
190000, 191000	0.4985 in. (12.662 mm)	0.977 in. (24.816 mm)
All Other Models	0.498 in. (12.649 mm)	1.184 in. (30.073 mm)

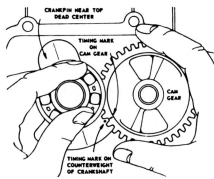

Fig. B&S45—Align timing marks on cam gear with mark on crankshaft counterweight on ball bearing equipped engines.

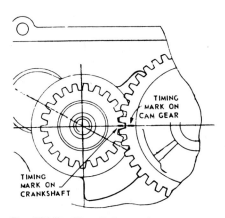

Fig. B&S46—Align timing marks on cam gear and crankshaft gear on plain bearing models.

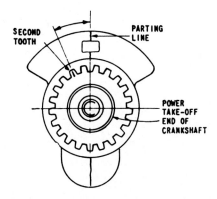

Fig. B&S47—Location of tooth to align with timing mark on cam gear if mark is not visible on crankshaft gear.

On models with "Easy-Spin" starting, intake cam lobe is designed to hold intake valve slightly open on a part of compression stroke. Therefore, to check compression, engine must be turned backwards.

"Easy-Spin" camshafts (cam gears) can be identified by two holes drilled in web of the gear. Where part number of an older cam gear and an "Easy-Spin" cam gear are the same (except for an "E" following "Easy-Spin" part number), the gears are interchangeable.

VALVE SYSTEM. Intake valve clearance is 0.005-0.007 inch (0.127-0.178 mm) and exhaust valve clearance is 0.009-0.011 inch (0.229-0.279 mm) when engine is cold. The valve seat angle is 45 degrees. Regrind or renew valve seat insert if seat width is 5/64-inch (2 mm) or wider. Regrind to width of 3/64 to 1/16-inch (1.2-1.6 mm). Obtain specified valve clearance by grinding end of valve stem squarely. Renew valve if margin is 1/64-inch (0.4 mm) or less after refacing.

The valve guides on all engines with aluminum blocks are an integral part of cylinder block. If flat end of valve guide plug gage can be inserted into valve guide for a distance of 5/16-inch (8 mm), guide is worn and should be reamed and a bushing installed. Reamers and

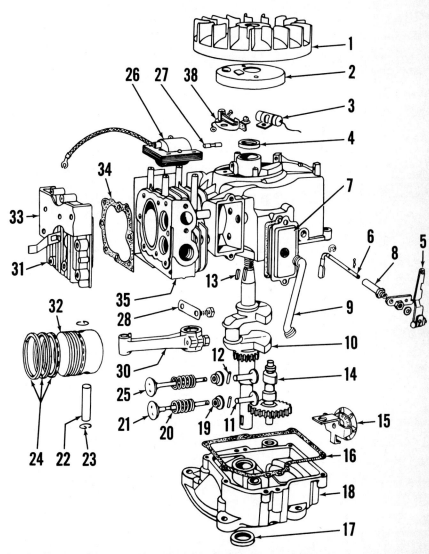

Fig. B&S48—Exploded view of typical vertical crankshaft engine assembly not equipped with Synchro-Balancer.

1. Flywheel
2. Breaker point cover
3. Condenser
4. Oil seal
5. Governor lever
6. Governor crank
7. Breather & valve cover
8. Bushing
9. Breather vent tube
10. Crankshaft
11. Tappets (cam followers)
12. Valve retaining pins
13. Flywheel key
14. Cam shaft & gear
15. Governor oil slinger assy.
16. Gasket (0.005, 0.009 or 0.015 in.)
17. Oil seal
18. Oil sump (engine base)
19. Valve spring retainer or "Rotocoil"
20. Valve spring
21. Exhaust valve
22. Piston pin
23. Retaining rings
24. Piston rings
25. Intake valve
26. Armature & coil assy.
27. Breaker plunger
28. Rod bolt lock
30. Connecting rod
31. Cylinder head
32. Piston
33. Air baffle
34. Head gasket
35. Cylinder block
38. Breaker points

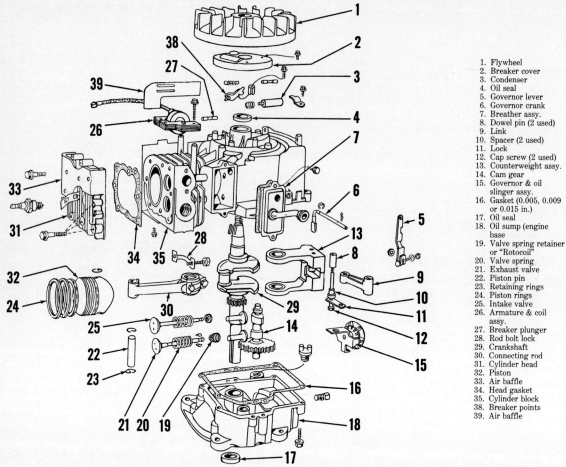

1. Flywheel
2. Breaker cover
3. Condenser
4. Oil seal
5. Governor lever
6. Governor crank
7. Breather assy.
8. Dowel pin (2 used)
9. Link
10. Spacer (2 used)
11. Lock
12. Cap screw (2 used)
13. Counterweight assy.
14. Cam gear
15. Governor & oil slinger assy.
16. Gasket (0.005, 0.009 or 0.015 in.)
17. Oil seal
18. Oil sump (engine base
19. Valve spring retainer or "Rotocoil"
20. Valve spring
21. Exhaust valve
22. Piston pin
23. Retaining rings
24. Piston rings
25. Intake valve
26. Armature & coil assy.
27. Breaker plunger
28. Rod bolt lock
29. Crankshaft
30. Connecting rod
31. Cylinder head
32. Piston
33. Air baffle
34. Head gasket
35. Cylinder block
38. Breaker points
39. Air baffle

Fig. B&S49 — Exploded view of Series 171000, 251000 or 252000 Synchro-Balanced vertical crankshaft engine assembly.

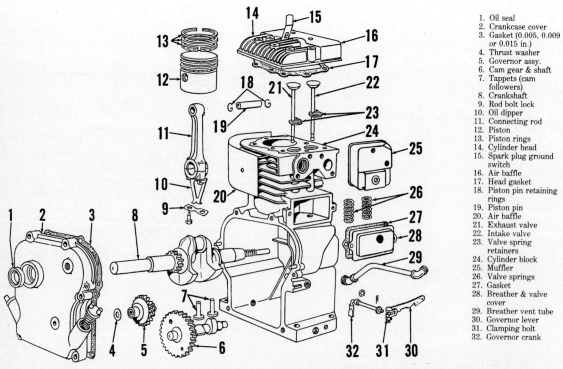

1. Oil seal
2. Crankcase cover
3. Gasket (0.005, 0.009 or 0.015 in.)
4. Thrust washer
5. Governor assy.
6. Cam gear & shaft
7. Tappets (cam followers)
8. Crankshaft
9. Rod bolt lock
10. Oil dipper
11. Connecting rod
12. Piston
13. Piston rings
14. Cylinder head
15. Spark plug ground switch
16. Air baffle
17. Head gasket
18. Piston pin retaining rings
19. Piston pin
20. Air baffle
21. Exhaust valve
22. Intake valve
23. Valve spring retainers
24. Cylinder block
25. Muffler
26. Valve springs
27. Gasket
28. Breather & valve cover
29. Breather vent tube
30. Governor lever
31. Clamping bolt
32. Governor crank

Fig. B&S50 — Exploded view of typical horizontal crankshaft engine assembly not equipped with Synchro-Balancer.

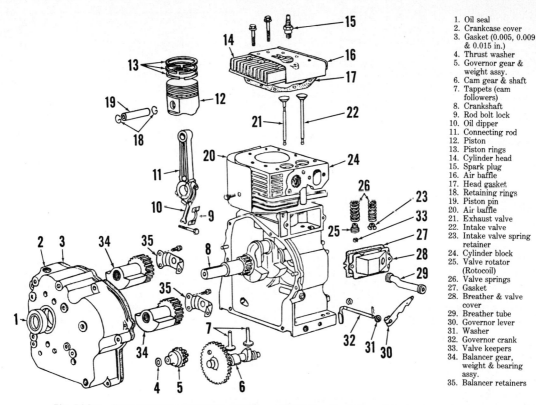

1. Oil seal
2. Crankcase cover
3. Gasket (0.005, 0.009 & 0.015 in.)
4. Thrust washer
5. Governor gear & weight assy.
6. Cam gear & shaft
7. Tappets (cam followers)
8. Crankshaft
9. Rod bolt lock
10. Oil dipper
11. Connecting rod
12. Piston
13. Piston rings
14. Cylinder head
15. Spark plug
16. Air baffle
17. Head gasket
18. Retaining rings
19. Piston pin
20. Air baffle
21. Exhaust valve
22. Intake valve
23. Intake valve spring retainer
24. Cylinder block
25. Valve rotator (Rotocoil)
26. Valve springs
27. Gasket
28. Breather & valve cover
29. Breather tube
30. Governor lever
31. Washer
32. Governor crank
33. Valve keepers
34. Balancer gear, weight & bearing assy.
35. Balancer retainers

Fig. B&S51 — Exploded view of 251000, 252000 or 253000 Synchro-Balanced horizontal crankshaft engines.

bushings are available from Briggs & Stratton. The part numbers are as follows:

Reamer No. 19183
Bushing Part No. 230655
Valve Guide Plug Gage No. 19151

Ream to only 1/16-inch (1.6 mm) deeper than length of valve guide bushing. Do not ream completely through valve guide. Press in bushing with soft driver as bushing is finish reamed at factory.

VALVE TIMING. On engines equipped with ball bearing mains, align timing mark on cam gear with timing mark on crankshaft counterweight as shown in Fig. B&S45. On engines with plain bearings, align timing marks on camshaft gear with timing mark on crankshaft gear (Fig. B&S46). If timing mark is not visible on crankshaft gear, align timing mark on camshaft gear with second tooth to the left of crankshaft counterweight parting line as in Fig. B&S47.

SYNCHRO-BALANCER (OSCILLATING). Some vertical crankshaft engines may be equipped with an oscillating Synchro-balancer. The balance weight assembly rides on eccentric journals on crankshaft and moves in opposite direction of piston. Refer to Fig. B&S52.

To disassemble balancer unit, first re-

move flywheel, engine base, cam gear, cylinder head and connecting rod and piston assembly. Carefully pry off crankshaft gear and key. Remove the two cap screws holding halves of counterweight together. Separate weights

and remove link, dowel pins and spacers. Slide weights from crankshaft. See Fig. B&S53.

To reassemble, install magneto side weight on magneto end of crankshaft. Place crankshaft (pto end up) in a vise as

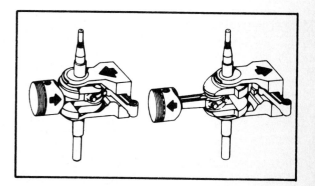

Fig. B&S52 — View showing operating principle of Synchro-Balancer used on Series 171000, 191000, 251000 and 252000 vertical crankshaft engines. Counterweight oscillates in opposite direction of piston.

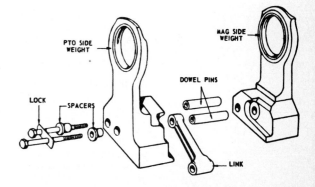

Fig. B&S53 — Exploded view of Synchro-Balancer assembly used on Series 171000, 191000, 251000 and 252000 vertical crankshaft engines. Counterweights ride on eccentric journals on crankshaft.

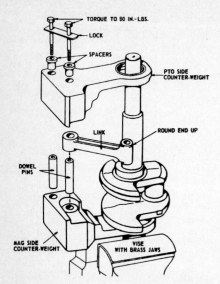

Fig. B&S54—Assemble balance units on crankshaft as shown. Install link with rounded edge on free end toward pto end of crankshaft.

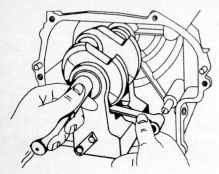

Fig. B&S55—When installing crankshaft and balancer assembly, place free end of link on anchor pin in crankcase.

shown in Fig. B&S54. Install both dowel pins and place link on pin as shown. Note rounded edge on free end of link must be up. Install pto side weight, spacers, lock and cap screws. Tighten

Fig. B&S56—View showing operating principle of Synchro-Balancer used on 251000, 252000 and 253000 horizontal crankshaft engines. Balancers rotate in opposite direction of crankshaft rotation.

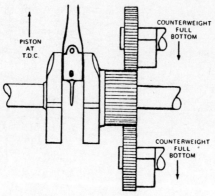

Fig. B&S57—View showing correct position of crankshaft and counterweights when timing balancers to crankshaft gear. Refer to text.

cap screws to 80 in.-lbs. (9 N·m) and bend up bolt lock ends. Install key and crankshaft gear with chamfer on inside of gear facing shoulder on crankshaft.

Install crankshaft and balancer assembly in crankcase, sliding free end of link on anchor pin as shown in Fig. B&S55. Reassemble engine.

SYNCHRO-BALANCER (ROTATING). Some horizontal crankshaft engines may be equipped with two gear driven counterweights in constant mesh with crankshaft gear. The gears, mounted in crankcase cover, rotate in

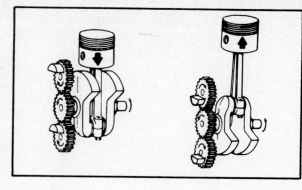

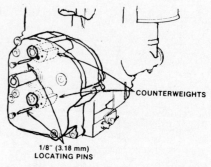

Fig. B&S58—To properly align counterweights, remove two small screws from crankcase cover and insert 1/8-inch (3 mm) diameter locating pins.

opposite direction of crankshaft. See Fig. B&S56.

To properly align counterweights when installing cover, remove two small screws from cover and insert 1/8-inch (3 mm) diameter locating pins through holes and into holes in counterweights as shown in Fig. B&S58.

With piston at TDC, install cover assembly. Remove locating pins, coat threads of timing hole screws with non-hardening sealer and install screws with fiber sealing washers.

NOTE: If counterweights are removed from crankcase cover, exercise care in handling or cleaning to prevent losing needle bearings.

BRIGGS & STRATTON

Model	No. Cyls.	Bore	Stroke	Displacement	Horsepower
243000 Series.........................	1	3-1/16 in. (77.8 mm)	3-1/4 in. (82.5 mm)	23.94 cu. in. (392 cc)	10 (7.5 kW)
300000 Series.........................	1	3-7/16 in. (87.3 mm)	3-1/4 in. (82.5 mm)	30.16 cu. in. (494 cc)	12 (8.9 kW)
302000 Series.........................	1	3-7/16 in. (87.3 mm)	3-1/4 in. (82.5 mm)	30.16 cu. in. (494 cc)	13 (9.7 kW)
320000 Series.........................	1	3-9/16 in. (90.5 mm)	3-1/4 in. (82.5 mm)	32.4 cu. in. (531 cc)	14 (10.4 kW)
325000 Series.........................	1	3-9/16 in. (90.5 mm)	3-1/4 in. (82.5 mm)	32.4 cu. in. (531 cc)	15 (11.2 kW)
326000 Series.........................	1	3-9/16 in. (90.5 mm)	3-1/4 in. (82.5 mm)	32.4 cu. in. (531 cc)	16 (11.9 kW)

All Briggs & Stratton engines covered in this section are of cast iron construction.

MAINTENANCE

SPARK PLUG. Recommended spark plug for all models is a Champion J-8, Autolite A-71 or an AC GC46. Set electrode gap to 0.030 inch (0.762 mm) for all models.

NOTE: If a resistor type plug is necessary to reduce ratio interference, use Champion XJ-8 or equivalent. Briggs & Stratton Corporation does not recommend cleaning spark plugs by abrasive blasting method as this may introduce some abrasive material into the engine which could cause extensive damage.

CARBURETOR. All models are equipped with Briggs & Stratton two-piece float type carburetors. Refer to Fig. B&S60 for cross-sectional view of typical unit.

Counter-clockwise rotation of both idle valve and needle valve will richen fuel mixture. For initial adjustment, open idle valve ¾ turn and open needle valve 1½ turns. Make final adjustment with engine running at normal operating temperature. Turn needle valve in until engine misses from lean mixture, then out past smooth operating point until engine runs unevenly due to rich mixture. Final adjustment should be midway between lean and rich adjustment points. After adjusting needle valve (main fuel adjustment), hold throttle at slow idle position and adjust idle stop screw so engine is running at 1200 rpm. While holding throttle against stop screw, adjust idle valve for smoothest idle performance. Then, if necessary, readjust idle stop screw to obtain 1200 rpm.

Before disassembling carburetor, check for warped body as follows: If a 0.002 inch (0.051 mm) feeler gage can be inserted as shown in Fig. B&S61, upper body is warped and should be renewed. If diametral play of throttle shaft in bushings exceeds 0.010 inch (0.254 mm), upper body should be rebushed and/or throttle shaft renewed.

To disassemble carburetor, proceed as follows: Remove idle mixture valve. Loosen power needle valve packing nut, then screw needle valve and packing nut out together. Using a narrow blunt screwdriver (B&S special tool #19061 or #19062), carefully remove nozzle taking care not to damage threads in lower carburetor body. Remainder of carburetor disassembly is evident after examination of unit.

If necessary to renew throttle shaft bushings, they can be removed by threading a ¼ inch x 20 tap into bushing, then pulling bushing from upper body. Press new bushings in with vise and ream with a 7/32-inch (5.5 mm) drill if throttle shaft binds. Check float level as shown in Fig. B&S62 and reassemble carburetor by reversing disassembly procedure.

Fig. B&S61—Checking carburetor for warped upper body. If a 0.002 inch (0.051 mm) feeler gage can be inserted between upper and lower bodies as shown, renew upper body.

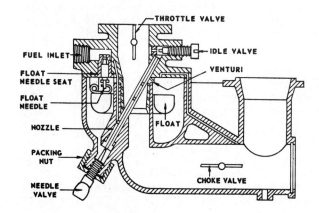

Fig. B&S60—Cross-sectional view of typical float type carburetor. Before separating upper and lower carburetor bodies, loosen packing nut and unscrew needle valve and packing nut. Then, using special screwdriver, remove nozzle.

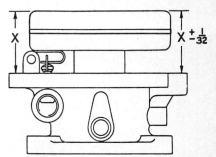

Fig. B&S62—Check carburetor float level as shown. Bend tang if necessary to adjust float level.

247

GOVERNOR. Engines are equipped with a gear driven mechanical governor. The governor unit is enclosed within the engine and is driven from camshaft gear. All binding or slack due to wear must be removed from governor linkage to prevent "hunting" or unsteady operation. To adjust carburetor to governor linkage, loosen clamp bolt on governor lever. Move link end of governor lever upward until carburetor throttle shaft is in wide open position. Using a screwdriver, rotate governor lever shaft counter-clockwise as far as possible, then tighten clamp bolt.

Briggs & Stratton recommended operating speed range for these models is 1200 rpm idle to 3800 rpm maximum. However, engine rpm may differ slightly depending on tractors in which engines are used. Tractor manufacturers recommendations should be followed in all cases.

Governor gear and weight unit can be removed when engine is disassembled. Remove governor lever, cotter pin and washer from outer end of governor lever shaft. Slide governor lever out of bushing towards inside of engine. Governor gear and weight unit can now be removed. Renew governor lever shaft bushing in crankcase, if necessary, and ream new bushing after installation to 0.2385-0.239 inch (6.058-6.070 mm).

MAGNETO. An exploded view of magneto is shown in Fig. B&S64. Breaker points (11) and condenser (10) are accessible after removing breaker box cover (8) located on carburetor side

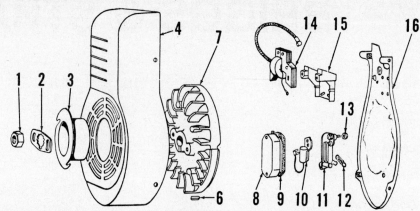

Fig. B&S64 – Exploded view of typical magneto ignition system. Position of armature is adjustable to time magneto armature with magneto rotor (flywheel) by moving armature mounting bracket (15) in slotted mounting holes. Refer to text and Figs. B&S65 and B&S66.

1. Flywheel nut	7. Flywheel	12. Breaker spring
2. Retainer	8. Breaker box cover	13. Locknut
3. Pulley	9. Gasket	14. Coil & armature assy.
4. Blower housing	10. Condenser	15. Armature bracket
6. Flywheel key	11. Breaker points	16. Backplate

of engine. Adjust breaker point gap to 0.020 inch (0.508 mm). Condenser capacity is 0.18-0.24 mfd.

Installation of new breaker points is made easier by turning engine so points are open to their widest gap before removing old points. For method of adjust-

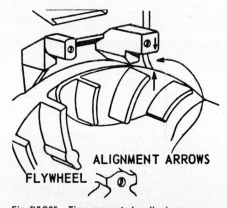

Fig. B&S65 – Time magneto by aligning arrow on armature core support with arrow on flywheel when breaker points are just starting to open.

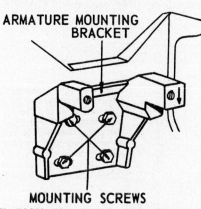

Fig. B&S66 – Magneto is timed by shifting armature mounting bracket on slotted mounting holes.

ing breaker point gap, refer to Fig. B&S 67.

NOTE: When installing points, apply Permatex or other sealer to retaining screw threads to prevent engine oil from leaking into breaker box.

Breaker points are actuated by plunger that rides against breaker cam on engine cam gear. The plunger and plunger bushing are renewable after removing engine cam gear and breaker points.

Magneto armature and ignition coil are mounted outside the engine flywheel. Adjust armature air gap to 0.010-0.014 inch (0.254-0.356 mm). If armature mounting bracket (15 – Fig. B&S64) has been loosened or removed, magneto edge gap (armature timing) must be adjusted as follows: First, be sure breaker point gap is adjusted to 0.020 inch (0.508 mm). Remove armature ignition coil assembly from mounting bracket and if available, con-

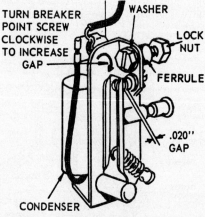

Fig. B&S67 – When adjusting breaker point gap, loosen locknut and turn screw clockwise to increase gap.

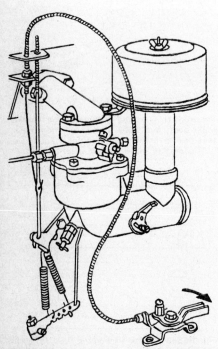

Fig. B&S63 – View showing typical governor remote control and carburetor to governor linkage.

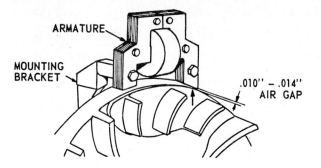

Fig. B&S68 — After armature mounting bracket is properly installed, install armature and coil assembly so there is a 0.010-0.014 inch (0.254-0.356 mm) air gap between armature and flywheel.

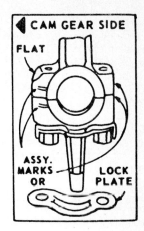

Fig. B&S70 — Drawing of lower end of 243000 series connecting rod showing clearance flat and assembly marks.

nect a static timing light across breaker points after disconnecting coil primary wire. Slowly turn flywheel in a clockwise direction until breaker points just start to open (timing light goes out). The arrow on flywheel should then be exactly aligned with arrow on armature mounting bracket; refer to Fig. B&S65. If not mark position of bracket, remove flywheel and shift bracket on slotted mounting holes (Fig. B&S66) to bring arrows into alignment.

NOTE: To simplify alignment of arrows, proceed as follows: Loosen, but do not remove engine flywheel; then, be sure engine is turned so breaker points are just starting to open and carefully slip flywheel off of crankshaft. Loosen mounting bracket retaining cap screws so bracket will slide on slotted mounting holes and carefully place flywheel back on crankshaft and drive key. Slide bracket to align timing arrow, carefully remove flywheel to avoid moving bracket and tighten bracket cap screws.

Reinstall flywheel and tighten flywheel nut to a torque of 144 ft.-lbs. (195 N·m). Reinstall armature and ignition coil and adjust armature air gap to 0.010-0.014 inch (0.254-0.356 mm). See Fig. B&S68.

LUBRICATION. All models are splash lubricated by oil dipper attached to lower end of connecting rod.

Use oils labeled "For Service SC, SD or SE only." (Use of higher or lower API classification oils is not recommended.) SAE-30 or 10W-30 oil is recommended for temperatures above 40°F (4°C), SAE 10W oil in temperatures between 40°F (4°C) and 0°F (−18°C) and SAE 5W-20 (or 10W oil diluted with 10% kerosene) for below 0°F (−18°C).

For engine crankcase oil capacity, refer to condensed specifications for tractor model.

REPAIRS

CYLINDER HEAD. When removing cylinder head, be sure to note position from which different length screws were removed. If they are not used in the same position when reinstalling cylinder

head, it will result in some screws bottoming in holes and not enough thread engagement on others. When installing cylinder head, tighten all screws lightly and then retighten them in sequence shown in Fig. B&S69 to a torque of 190 in.-lbs. (21.5 N·m).

Run engine about five minutes to allow it to warm up and retighten screws to 190 in.-lbs. (21.5 N·m using same sequence.

CONNECTING ROD. Rod and piston assembly are removed from cylinder head end of block. The aluminum alloy connecting rod rides directly on the induction hardened crankpin. The rod should be rejected if crankpin hole is out-of-round over 0.0007 inch (0.0178 mm) or piston pin hole is out-of-round over 0.0005 inch (0.0127 mm). The rod should also be rejected if either hole is scored or worn to rejection size of 1.314 inches (33.375 mm) for crankpin hole or 0.6735 inch (17.107 mm) (243000 series) or 0.8015 inch (20.358 mm) (all other models) for piston pin hole.

NOTE: If rod is otherwise serviceable except for piston pin hole, rod and piston can be reamed and a 0.005 inch (0.127 mm) oversize piston pin installed.

On 243000 series, install connecting rod with clearance flat (Fig. B&S70) toward cam gear side of crankcase. Tighten connecting rod cap screws to a torque of 190 in.-lbs. (21.5 N·m).

When assembling piston to connecting rod on 300000, 302000, 320000, 325000

and 326000 series, notch on top of piston and stamped letter "F" must be on same side as assembly marks on rod. See Fig. B&S71. Install assembly in cylinder with assembly marks to flywheel side of crankcase. Tighten connecting rod cap screws to a torque of 190 in.-lbs. (21.5 N·m).

PISTON, PIN AND RINGS. Piston is of aluminum alloy and is fitted with two compression rings and one oil ring. If piston shows visible signs of wear, scoring or scuffing, it should be renewed. Also, renew piston if side clearance of new ring in top ring groove exceeds 0.007 inch (0.178 mm). Reject piston or hone piston pin hole to 0.005 inch (0.127 mm) oversize if pin hole is 0.0005 inch (0.0127 mm) or more out-of-round or worn to a diameter of 0.673 inch (17.094 mm) on 243000 series or 0.801 inch (20.345 mm) on all other models.

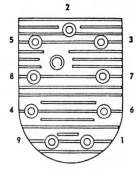

Fig. B&S69 — View showing cylinder head cap screw tightening sequence.

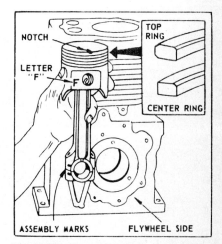

Fig. B&S71 — Assemble piston to connecting rod, on 300000, 302000, 320000, 325000 and 326000 series, with notch and stamped letter "F" on piston to the same side as assembly marks on rod. Install assembly in cylinder with assembly marks to flywheel side of crankcase.

Briggs & Stratton

ENGINE

Renew piston pin if 0.0005 inch (0.0127 mm) or more out-of-round or if worn to a diameter of 0.671 inch (17.043 mm) on 243000 series or 0.799 inch (20.294 mm) on all other models. A 0.005 inch (0.127 mm) oversize piston pin is available for service.

Reject piston rings having an end gap of 0.030 inch (0.762 mm) for compression rings and 0.035 inch (0.889 mm) for oil ring. If top ring has groove on inside, install with groove up. If second compression ring has groove on outside, install with groove down. Oil ring may be installed either side up. Piston and rings are available in standard size and oversizes. A chrome ring set is available for slightly worn standard bore cylinders. Refer to note in CYLINDER paragraph.

CYLINDER. Cylinder and crankcase are an integral iron casting. If cylinder is worn more than 0.003 inch, or is more than 0.0015 inch out-of-round, it should be rebored and next larger oversize piston and ring set installed.

The standard cylinder bore is 3.0615-3.0625 inches (77.762-77.787 mm) on

243000 series; 3.4365-3.4375 inches (87.287-87.312 mm) on 300000 and 302000 series; 3.5615-3.5625 inches (90.462-90.487 mm) on 320000, 325000 and 326000 series engines.

NOTE: A chrome piston ring set is available for slightly worn standard bore cylinders. No honing or cylinder deglazing is required for these rings. The cylinder bore can be a maximum of 0.005 inch (0.127 mm) oversize when using chrome rings.

CRANKSHAFT. The crankshaft is supported in two ball bearing mains. Check ball bearings for wear or roughness. If bearing is loose or noisy, renew the bearing. When renewing ball bearings, press crankshaft out of old bearings. Expand new bearings by heating them in oil to a maximum temperature of 325°F (160°C). Slide heated bearing in place with shield side towards crankpin journal.

Crankshaft end play should be 0.002-0.008 inch (0.051-0.203 mm). End play is controlled by use of different thickness shim gaskets between main bearing sup-

port plate and crankcase on magneto side of engine. End play can be checked by clamping dial indicator to crankshaft and resting indicator button against crankcase. Shim gaskets are available in thicknesses of 0.005, 0.009 and 0.020 inch for 243000 series engines and 0.005, 0.010 and 0.015 inch for all other engines.

On 300000, 302000, 320000, 325000 and 326000 series engines, tighten main bearing support plate cap screws to a torque of 85 in.-lbs. (9.6 N·m) on magneto end and 185 in.-lbs. (20.9 N·m) on pto end.

Renew crankshaft if crankpin is 0.0007 inch (0.0178 mm) or more out-of-round or if crankpin is worn to a diameter of 1.3094 inches (33.2587 mm).

CAM GEAR. The cam gear and lobes are an integral part. Renew cam gear if gear teeth are damaged or if cam lobes are worn to rejection point of 1.184 inches (30.073 mm) on 243000, 300000 and 302000 series engines. On 320000, 325000 and 326000 series engines, cam lobe rejection point is 1.215 inches

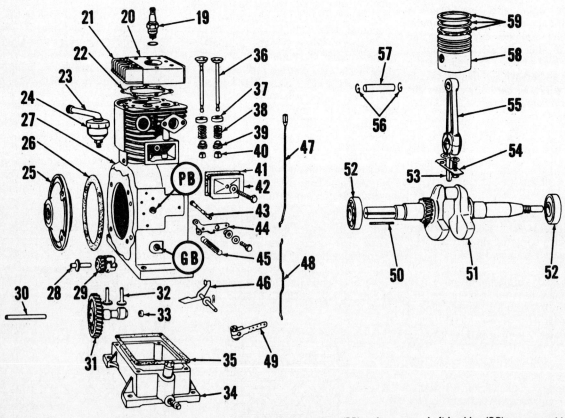

Fig. B&S72—Exploded view of 243000 series engine assembly. Breaker plunger bushing (PB) and governor shaft bushing (GB) are renewable in engine crankcase (27).

19. Spark plug
20. Air baffle
21. Cylinder head
22. Head gasket
23. Breather tube
24. Breather
25. Bearing plate
26. Gasket
27. Cylinder block
28. Governor shaft
29. Governor assy.
30. Camshaft
31. Cam gear
32. Valve lifters
33. Camshaft plug
34. Engine base
35. Gasket
36. Valves
37. Spring caps
38. Valve springs
39. Valve rotators
40. Keepers
41. Gasket
42. Valve spring cover
43. Breaker point plunger
44. Governor control lever
45. Governor spring
46. Governor lever shaft
47. Control rod
48. Link
49. Governor lever
50. Key
51. Crankshaft
52. Ball bearings
53. Oil dipper
54. Rod bolt lock
55. Connecting rod
56. Retaining rings
57. Piston pin
58. Piston
59. Piston rings

250

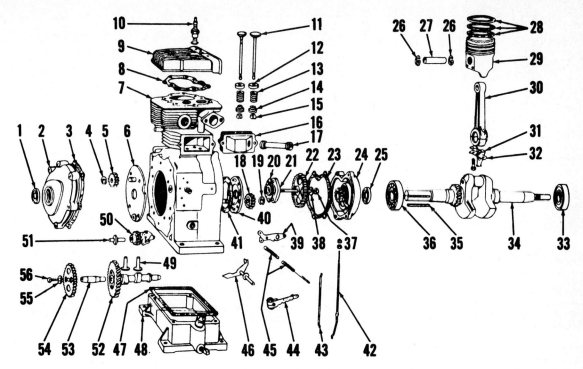

Fig. B&S73 — Exploded view of typical 300000, 302000, 320000, 325000 and 326000 series engine assembly.

1. Oil seal	12. Spring caps	23. Gasket
2. Cover & balance	13. Valve springs	24. Cover & balance
assy. (pto end)	14. Valve rotators	assy. (magneto end)
3. Gasket	15. Keepers	25. Oil seal
4. "E" ring	16. Breather assy.	26. Retaining rings
5. Idler gear	17. Breather tube	27. Piston pin
6. Bearing support	18. Idler gear	28. Piston rings
7. Cylinder block	19. "E" ring	29. Piston
8. Head gasket	20. Shim (0.005, 0.007	30. Connecting rod
9. Cylinder head	and 0.009 in.)	31. Oil dipper
10. Spark plug	21. Cam bearing	32. Rod bolt lock
11. Valves	22. Balance drive gear	33. Ball bearing
		34. Crankshaft

35. Key	45. Governor springs
36. Ball bearing	46. Governor lever shaft
37. Drive gear bolt	47. Gasket
38. Belleville washer	48. Engine base
39. Governor control	49. Valve lifters
lever	50. Governor assy.
40. Bearing support	51. Governor shaft
41. Shim (0.005, 0.010	52. Cam gear
and 0.015 in.)	53. Camshaft
42. Control rod	54. Balance drive gear
43. Link	55. Belleville washer
44. Governor lever	56. Drive gear bolt

(30.861 mm). Also, renew cam gear if journals are worn to a diameter of 0.4968 inch (12.6187 mm) on 243000 series engines. On all other engines, renew cam gear if journals are worn to diameter of 0.8105 inch (20.5867 mm) on

magneto end or 0.6145 inch (15.6083 mm) on pto end.

On 300000, 302000, 320000, 325000 and 326000 series, cam gear end play should be 0.002-0.008 inch (0.051-0.203 mm). End play is controlled by use of different thickness shims (20 – Fig. B&S73) between cam bearing (21) and crankcase. Shims are available in thicknesses of 0.005, 0.007 and 0.009 inch. Tighten cam gear bearing cap screws to a torque of 85 in.-lbs. (9.6 N·m).

Align timing marks on crankshaft gear and cam gear when reassembling engine.

VALVE SYSTEM. Valve clearance is adjusted by grinding end of valve stems squarely. Check clearance with engine cold. Intake valve clearance should be 0.007-0.009 inch (0.0178-0.229 mm) and exhaust valve clearance should be 0.017-0.019 inch (0.432-0.483 mm).

Valve face and seat angle is 45 degrees. Desired seat width is 3/64 to 1/16-inch (1.2-1.6 mm). Renew valve if margin is 1/64-inch (0.4 mm) or less after refacing.

Engines are equipped with an exhaust valve seat insert and an intake valve seat is available for service. Renewal of

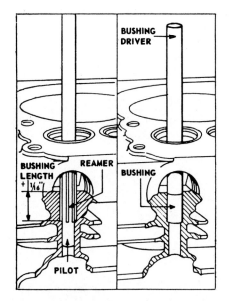

Fig. B&S74 — View showing valve guide being reamed and valve guide bushing installed.

Fig. B&S75 — Synchro-Balance weights rotate in opposite direction of crankshaft counterweights on 300000, 302000, 320000, 325000 and 326000 series engines.

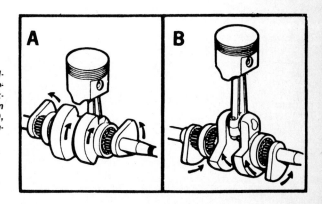

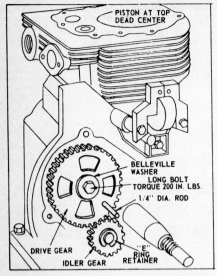

Fig. B&S76 — View showing drive gear (magneto end) being timed. With piston at TDC, insert ¼-inch (6 mm) rod through timing hole in gear and into locating hole in crankshaft bearing support plate.

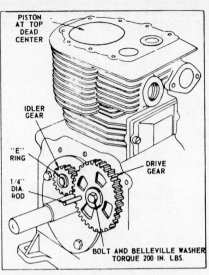

Fig. B&S77 — View showing drive gear (pto end) being timed. With piston at TDC, insert ¼-inch rod through timing hole in gear and into locating hole in crankshaft bearing support plate.

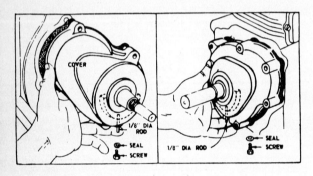

Fig. B&S78 — Insert ⅛-inch (3 mm) rod through timing hole in covers and into hole in balance weights when installing cover assemblies. Piston must be at TDC.

exhaust valve seat insert and installation of intake valve service seat requires the use of special equipment which is available from Briggs & Stratton.

If Briggs & Stratton plug gage #19151 can be inserted a distance of 5/16-inch (8 mm) or more into valve guide, guide should be rebushed with a service housing, Briggs & Stratton part #230655, as follows: Ream guide a depth of 1/16-inch (1.6 mm) longer than bushing with Briggs & Stratton reamer #19183; then, press bushing in flush with top of guide. Bushing is pre-sized and should not re-quire reaming for new standard size valve. See Fig. B&S74.

VALVE TIMING. When reassembling engine, align timing mark on cam gear with timing mark on crankshaft gear. Valve to piston timing will then be correct.

SYNCHRO-BALANCER. The 300000, 302000, 320000, 325000 and 326000 series engines are equipped with rotating balance weights at each end of the crankshaft. The balancers are geared to rotate in opposite direction of crankshaft counterweights. See Fig. B&S75. The balance weights, ball bearings and cover (2 and 24 – Fig. B&S73) are serviced only as assemblies.

The balancers are driven from idler gears (5 and 18) that are driven by gears (22 and 54). Drive gears (22 and 54) are bolted to camshaft. To time balancers, first remove cover and balancer assemblies (2 and 24). Position piston at TDC. Loosen bolts (37 and 56) until drive gears will rotate on cam gear and camshaft. Insert a ¼-inch (6 mm) rod through timing hole in each drive gear and into locating holes in main bearing support plates as shown in Figs. B&S76 and B&S77. With piston at TDC and ¼-inch (6 mm) rods in place, tighten drive gear bolts to a torque of 200 in.-lbs. (22.6 N·m). Remove the ¼-inch (6 mm) rods. Remove timing hole screws (Fig. B&S78) and insert ⅛-inch (3 mm) rods through timing holes and into hole in balance weights. Then, with piston at TDC, carefully slide cover assemblies into position.

Tighten cap screws in pto end cover to a torque of 200 in.-lbs. (22.6 N·m) and magneto end cover to 120 in.-lbs. (13.5 N·m). Remove the ⅛-inch (3 mm) rods. Coat threads of timing hole screws with Permatex and install screws with fibre sealing washers.

BRIGGS & STRATTON

SERVICING BRIGGS & STRATTON ACCESSORIES

REWIND STARTER

OVERHAUL. To renew broken rewind spring, proceed as follows: Grasp free outer end of spring (S–Fig. B&S80) and pull broken end from starter housing. With blower housing removed, remove tangs (T) and remove starter pulley from housing. Untie knot in rope (R) and remove rope and inner end of broken spring from pulley. Apply a small amount of grease on inner face of pulley, thread inner end of new spring through notch in starter housing, engage inner end of spring in pulley hub and place pulley in housing. Insert a ¾-inch square bar in pulley hub and turn pulley approximately 13½ turns in a counter-clockwise direction as shown in Fig. B&S81. Tie wrench to blower housing with wire to hold pulley so hole (H) in pulley is aligned with rope guide (G) in

housing as shown in Fig. B&S82. Hook a wire in inner end of rope and thread rope through guide and hole in pulley; then, tie a knot in rope and release pulley allowing spring to wind rope into pulley groove.

To renew starter rope only, it is not generally necessary to remove starter pulley and spring. Wind up spring and install new rope as outlined in preceding paragraph.

Two different types of starter clutches have been used; refer to exploded view of early production unit in Fig. B&S83 and exploded view of late production unit in Fig. B&S84. The outer end of late production ratchet (refer to cutaway

view in Fig. B&S85) is sealed with a felt and a retaining plug and a rubber ring is used to seal ratchet to ratchet cover.

To disassemble early type starter clutch unit, refer to Fig. B&S83 and proceed as follows: Remove snap ring (3) and lift ratchet (5) and cover (4) from starter housing (7) and crankshaft. Be careful not to lose steel balls (6). Starter housing (7) is also flywheel retaining nut; to remove housing, first remove screen (2) and using Briggs & Stratton flywheel wrench #19114, unscrew housing from crankshaft in counter-clockwise direction. When reinstalling housing, be sure spring washer (8) is placed

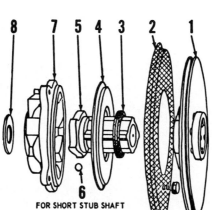

Fig. B&S82—Threading starter rope through guide (G) in blower housing and hole (H) in starter pulley with wire hooked in end of rope.

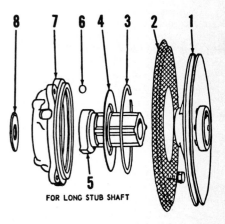

FOR LONG STUB SHAFT

Fig. B&S84—View of late production sealed starter clutch unit. Late unit can be used with "short stub shaft" only; refer to Fig. B&S86. Refer to Fig. B&S85 for cut-away view of ratchet (5).

1. Starter rope pulley
2. Rotating screen
3. Rubber seal
4. Ratchet cover
5. Starter ratchet
6. Steel balls
7. Clutch housing (flywheel nut)
8. Spring washer

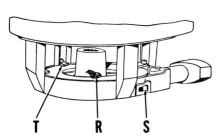

Fig. B&S80—View of rewind starter showing rope (R), spring end (S) and retaining tangs (T).

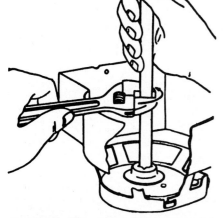

Fig. B&S81—Using square shaft and wrench to wind up rewind starter spring. Refer to text.

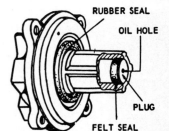

FOR SHORT STUB SHAFT

Fig. B&S83—Exploded view of early production starter clutch unit; refer to Fig. B&S86 for view of "long stub shaft." A late type unit (Fig. B&S85) should be installed when renewing "long" crankshaft with "short" (late production) shaft.

1. Starter rope pulley
2. Rotating screen
3. Snap ring
4. Ratchet cover
5. Starter ratchet
6. Steel balls
7. Clutch housing (flywheel nut)
8. Spring washer

RUBBER SEAL
OIL HOLE
PLUG
FELT SEAL

B&S85—Cut-away view showing felt seal plug in end of late production starter ratchet (5—Fig. B&S84).

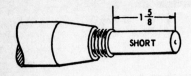

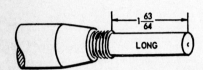

Fig. B&S86—Crankshaft with short stub (top view) must be used with late production starter clutch assembly. Early crankshaft (bottom view) can be modified by cutting off stub end to dimension shown in top view and beveling end of shaft to allow installation of late type clutch unit.

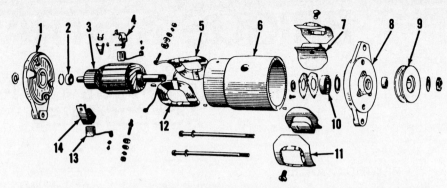

Fig. B&S89—Exploded view of Delco-Remy starter-generator unit used on some B&S engines.

1. Commutator end frame	4. Ground brush holder	8. Drive end frame	12. Field coil R.H.
2. Bearing	5. Field coil L.H.	9. Pulley	13. Brush
3. Armature	6. Frame	10. Bearing	14. Insulated brush holder
	7. Pole shoe	11. Field coil insulator	

on crankshaft with cup (hollow) side toward flywheel, then install starter housing and tighten securely. Reinstall rotating screen. Place ratchet on crankshaft and into housing and insert steel balls. Reinstall cover and retaining snap ring.

To disassemble late starter clutch unit, refer to Fig. B&S84 and proceed as follows: Remove rotating screen (2) and starter ratchet cover (4). Lift ratchet (5) from housing and crankshaft and extract steel balls (6). If necessary to remove housing (7), hold flywheel and unscrew housing in counter-clockwise direction using Briggs & Stratton flywheel wrench #19114. When installing housing, be sure spring washer (8) is in

place on crankshaft with cup (hollow) side toward flywheel, then tighten housing securely. Inspect felt seal and plug in outer end of ratchet; renew ratchet if seal or plug are damaged as these parts are not serviced separately. Lubricate felt with oil and place ratchet on crankshaft. Insert steel balls and install ratchet cover, rubber seal and rotating screen.

NOTE: Crankshafts used with early and late starter clutches differ; refer to Fig. B&S86. If renewing early (long) crankshaft with late (short) shaft, also install late type starter clutch unit. If renewing early starter clutch with late type unit, crankshaft must be shortened to dimension shown for short shaft in Fig. B&S86; also, hub of starter rope pulley must be shortened to ½-inch dimension shown in Fig. B&S87. Bevel end of crankshaft after

removing the approximate ⅜-inch from shaft.

When installing blower housing and starter assembly, turn starter ratchet so word "TOP" on ratchet is toward engine cylinder head.

12-VOLT STARTER-GENERATOR UNITS

The combination starter-generator functions as a cranking motor when starting switch is closed. When engine is operating and with starting switch open, unit operates as a generator. Generator output and circuit voltage for battery and various operating requirements are controlled by a current-voltage regulator. On units where voltage regulator is mounted separately from generator unit, do not mount regulator with cover down as regulator will not function in

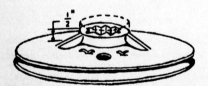

Fig. B&S87—When installing a late type starter clutch unit as replacement for early type, either install new starter rope pulley or cut hub of old pulley to dimension shown.

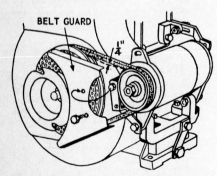

Fig. B&S88—View showing starter-generator belt adjustment on models so equipped. Refer to text.

Fig. B&S90—Exploded view of 110-volt AC starter motor. 12-volt DC starter motor is similar. See Fig. B&S 90A. Rectifier and switch unit (8) is used on 110-volt motor only.

1. Pinion gear
2. Helix
3. Armature shaft
4. Drive cap
5. Thrust washer
6. Housing
7. End cap
8. Rectifier & switch unit
9. Bolt
10. Nut

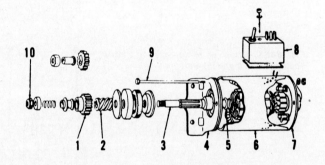

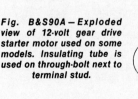

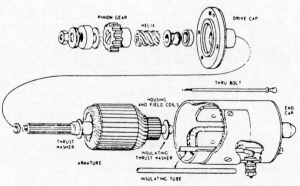

Fig. B&S90A—Exploded view of 12-volt gear drive starter motor used on some models. Insulating tube is used on through-bolt next to terminal stud.

this position. To adjust belt tension, apply approximately 30 pounds (14 kg) pull on generator adjusting flange and tighten mounting bolts. Belt tension is correct when a pressure of 10 pounds (44.5N) applied midway between pulleys will deflect belt ¼-inch (6 mm). See Fig. B&S88. On units equipped with two drive belts, always renew belts in pairs. A 50 amp-hour capacity battery is recommended Starter-generator units are intended for use in temperatures above 0°F (−18°C). Refer to Fig. B&S89 for exploded view of starter generator. Parts and service on starter-generator are available at authorized Delco-Remy service stations.

GEAR-DRIVE STARTERS

Two types of gear drive starters may be used, a 110-volt AC starter or a 12-volt DC starter. Refer to Fig. B&S90 or B&S90A for an exploded view of starter motors. A properly grounded receptacle should be used with power cord connected to 110-volt AC starter motor. A 32 amp-hour capacity battery is recommended for use with 12-volt DC starter motor.

To renew a worn or damaged flywheel ring gear, drill out retaining rivets using a 3/16-inch (4.7 mm) drill. Attach new ring gear using screws provided with new ring gear.

To check for correct operation of 110-volt AC starter motor, remove starter motor from engine and place motor in a vise or other holding fixture. Install a 0-5 amp ammeter in power cord to 110-volt AC starter motor. On 12-volt DC motor, connect a 12-volt battery to motor with a 0-50 amp ammeter in series with positive line from battery to starter motor. Connect a tachometer to drive end of starter. With starter activated on 110-volt motor, starter motor should turn at 5200 rpm minimum with a maximum current draw of 3½ amps. The 12-volt motor should turn at 6200 rpm minimum with a current draw of 16 amps maximum. If starter motor does not operate satisfactorily, check operation of rectifier or starter switch. if rectifier and starter switch are good, disassemble and inspect starter motor.

To check rectifier used on 110-volt AC starter motor, remove rectifier unit from starter motor. Solder a 10,000 ohm 1 watt resistor to DC internal terminals of rectifier as shown in Fig. B&S91. Connect a 0-100 range DC voltmeter to resistor leads. Measure voltage of AC outlet to be used. With starter switch in "OFF" position, a zero reading should be shown on DC voltmeter. With starter switch in "ON" position, the DC voltmeter should show a reading that is 0-14-volts lower than AC line voltage measured previously. If voltage drop exceeds 14-volts, renew rectifier unit.

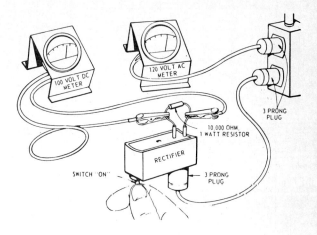

Fig. B&S91—View of test connections for 110-volt rectifier. Refer to text for procedure.

Disassembly of starter motor is self-evident after inspection of unit and referral to Fig. B&S90 or B&S 90A. Note position of through-bolts during disassembly so they can be installed in their original positions during reassembly. When reassembling motor, lubricate end cap bearings with SAE 20 oil. Be sure to match drive cap keyway to stamped key in housing when sliding armature into motor housing. Brushes may be held in their holders during installation by making a brush spreader tool from a piece of metal as shown in Fig. B&S92. Splined end of helix (2—Fig. B&S90) must be towards end of armature shaft as shown in Fig. B&S93. Tighten armature shaft nut to 170 in.-lbs. (19 N·m).

FLYWHEEL ALTERNATORS

4 Amp Non-Regulated Alternator

Some engines are equipped with 4 amp non-regulated flywheel alternator shown in Fig. B&S94. A solid state rectifier and 7½ amp fuse is used with this alternator.

If battery is run down and no output from alternator is suspected, first check 7½ amp fuse. If fuse is good, clean and tighten all connections. Disconnect charging lead and connect an ammeter as shown in Fig. B&S95. Start engine and check for alternator output. If ammeter shows no charge, stop engine, remove ammeter and install a test lamp

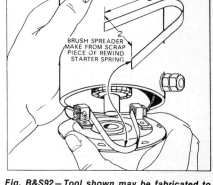

Fig. B&S92—Tool shown may be fabricated to hold brushes when installing motor end cap.

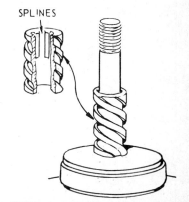

Fig. B&S93—Install helix on armature so splines of helix are to top as shown above.

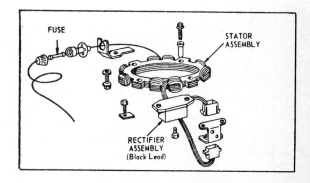

Fig. B&S94—Stator and rectifier assemblies used on 4 amp non-regulated flywheel alternator. Fuse is 7½ amp AGC or 3AG.

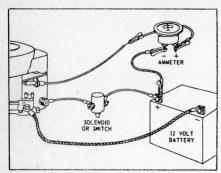

Fig. B&S95 — Install ammeter as shown for output test.

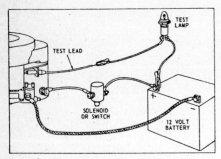

Fig. B&S96 — Connect a test lamp as shown to test for shorted stator or defective rectifier. Refer to text.

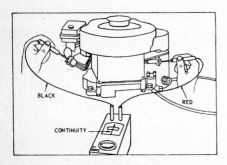

Fig. B&S97 — Use an ohmmeter to check condition of stator. Refer to text.

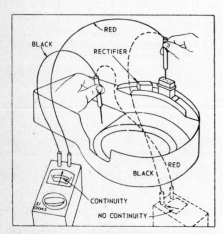

Fig. B&S98 — If ohmmeter shows continuity in both directions or in neither direction, rectifier is defective.

as shown in Fig. B&S96. Test lamp should not light. If it does light, stator or rectifier is defective. Unplug rectifier plug under blower housing. If test lamp goes out, rectifier is defective. If test lamp does not go out, stator is shorted.

If shorted stator is indicated, use an ohmmeter and check continuity as follows: Touch one test lead to lead inside of fuse holder as shown in Fig. B&S97. Touch the other test lead to each of the four pins in rectifier connector. Unless ohmmeter shows continuity at each of the four pins, stator winding is open and stator must be renewed.

If defective rectifier is indicated, unbolt and remove flywheel blower housing with rectifier. Connect one ohmmeter test lead to blower housing and other test lead to single pin connector in rectifier connector. See Fig. B&S98. Check for continuity, then reverse leads and again test for continuity. If tests show no continuity in either direction or continuity in both directions, rectifier is faulty and must be renewed.

7 Amp Regulated Alternator

A 7 amp regulated flywheel alternator is used with 12-volt gear drive starter motor on some models. The alternator is equipped with a solid state rectifier and regulator. An isolation diode is also used on most models.

If engine will not start, using electric start system, and trouble is not in starting motor, install an ammeter in circuit as shown in Fig. B&S100. Start engine manually. Ammeter should indicate charge. If ammeter does not show battery charging taking place, check for defective wiring and if necessary proceed with troubleshooting.

If battery charging occurs with engine running, but battery does not retain charge, then isolation diode may be defective. The isolation diode is used to prevent battery drain if alternator circuit malfunctions. After troubleshooting diode, remainder of circuit should be inspected to find reason for excessive battery drain. To check operation of diode, disconnect white lead of diode from fuse holder and connect a test lamp from diode white lead to negative terminal of battery. Test lamp should not light. If test lamp lights, diode is defective. Disconnect test lamp and disconnect red lead of diode. Test continuity of diode with ohmmeter by connecting leads of ohmmeter to leads of diode then reverse lead connections. The ohmmeter should show continuity in one direction and an open circuit in the other direction. If readings are incorrect then diode is defective and must be renewed.

To troubleshoot alternator assembly, proceed as follows: Disconnect white lead of isolation diode from fuse holder and connect a test lamp between positive terminal of battery and fuse holder on engine. Engine must not be started. With connections made, test lamp should not light. If test lamp does light, stator, regulator or rectifier is defective. Unplug rectifier-regulator plug under blower housing. If lamp remains lighted, stator is grounded. If lamp goes out, regulator or rectifier is shorted.

If previous test indicated stator is grounded, check stator leads for defects and repair if necessary. If shorted leads

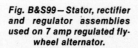

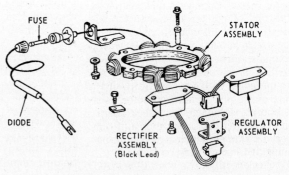

Fig. B&S99 — Stator, rectifier and regulator assemblies used on 7 amp regulated flywheel alternator.

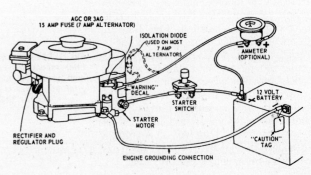

Fig. B&S100 — Typical wiring used on engines equipped with 7 amp flywheel regulator.

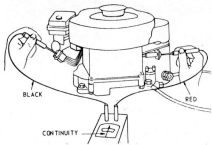

Fig. B&S101 — Use an ohmmeter to check condition of stator. Refer to text.

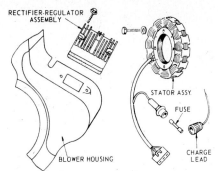

Fig. B&S103 — View of 10 amp flywheel alternator stator and rectifier-regulator used on some engines.

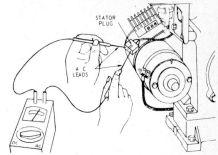

Fig. B&S105 — AC voltmeter is used to test stator.

are not found, renew stator. Check stator for an open circuit as follows: Using an ohmmeter, connect red lead to fuse holder as shown in Fig. B&S101 and black lead to one of the pins in rectifier and regulator connector. Check each of the four pins in the connector. The ohmmeter should show continuity at each pin, if not, then there is an open in stator and stator must be renewed.

To test rectifier, unplug rectifier and regulator connector plug and remove blower housing from engine. Using an ohmmeter check for continuity between connector pins connected to black wires and blower housing as shown in Fig. B&S102. Be sure good contact is made with metal of blower housing. Reverse ohmmeter leads and check continuity again. The ohmmeter should show a continuity reading for one direction only on each pin. If either pin shows a continuity reading for both directions, or if either pin shows no continuity for either direction, then rectifier must be renewed.

To test regulator unit, repeat procedure used to test rectifier unit except connect ohmmeter lead to pins connected to red wire and white wire. If ohmmeter shows continuity in either direction for red lead pin, regulator is defective and must be renewed. White lead pin should read as an open on ohm-

meter in one direction and a weak reading in the other direction. Otherwise, regulator is defective and must be renewed.

10 Amp Regulated Alternator

Engines may be equipped with a 10 amp flywheel alternator and a solid state rectifier-regulator. To check charging system, disconnect charging lead from battery. Connect a DC voltmeter between charging lead and ground as shown in Fig. B&S104. Start engine and operate at 3600 rpm. A voltmeter reading of 12 volts or above indicates alternator is functioning. If reading is less than 14 volts, stator or rectifier-regulator is defective.

To test stator, disconnect stator plug from rectifier-regulator. Operate engine at 3600 rpm and connect AC voltmeter leads to AC terminals in stator plug as shown in Fig. B&S105. Voltmeter reading above 20 volts indicates stator is good. A reading less than 20 volts indicates stator is defective.

To test rectifier-regulator, make certain charging lead is connected to battery and stator plug is connected to rectifier-regulator. Check voltage across battery terminals with DC voltmeter (Fig. B&S106). If voltmeter reading is 13.8 volts or higher, reduce battery voltage by connecting a 12 volt load lamp across battery terminals. When battery voltage is below 13.5 volts, start engine and operate at 3600 rpm. Voltmeter reading should rise. If battery is

fully charged, reading should rise above 13.8 volts. If voltage does not increase or if voltage reading rises above 14.7 volts, rectifier-regulator is defective and must be renewed.

Dual Circuit Alternator

A dual circuit alternator is used on some models. This system operates as two separate alternators. See Fig. B&S107. A single ring of magnets inside flywheel supplies magnetic field for both sets of windings on the stator. One alternator uses a solid state rectifier and provides 2 amps at 2400 rpm or 3 amps at 3600 rpm for battery charging current. The other alternator feeds alternating current directly to the lights. Since the two are electrically independent, use of the lights does not reduce charge going into battery.

Current for the lights is available only when engine is operating. Twelve volt lights with a total rating of 60 to 100 watts may be used. With a rating of 70 watts, voltage rises from 8 volts at 2400 rpm to 12 volts at 3600 rpm. Since output depends on engine speed, brightness of lights changes with engine speed.

The battery charging current connection is made through a 7½ amp fuse mounted in fuse holder. See Fig. B&S108. Current for lights is available at plastic connector below fuse holder. The 7½ amp fuse protects 3 amp charging alternator and rectifier from burnout due to reverse polarity battery connections. The 5 amp lighting alternator does not require a fuse.

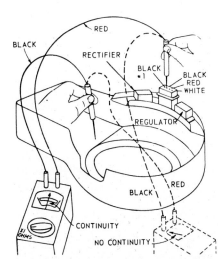

Fig. B&S102 — Be sure good contact is made between ohmmeter test lead and metal cover when checking rectifier and regulator.

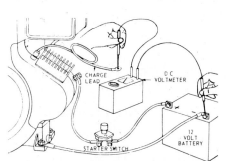

Fig. B&S104 — DC voltmeter is used to determine if alternator is functioning. Refer to text.

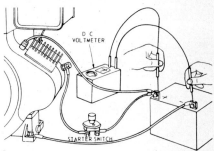

Fig. B&S106 — Check battery voltage with DC voltmeter. Refer to text for rectifier-regulator test.

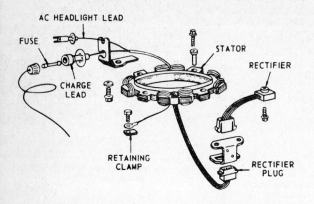

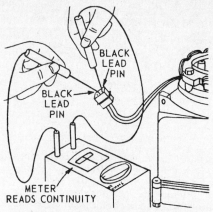

Fig. B&S107—Stator and rectifier assemblies used on dual circuit alternator. Fuse is 7½ amp AGC or 3AG.

Fig. B&S112—Checking charging coils for an "open". Meter should show continuity.

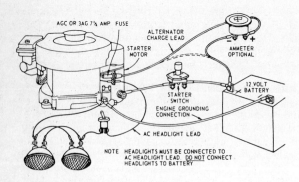

Fig. B&S108—Typical wiring used on engines equipped with the dual circuit flywheel alternator.

To check charging alternator output, install ammeter in circuit as shown in Fig. B&S109. Start engine and allow it to operate at a speed of 3000 rpm. Ammeter should indicate charge. If not, and fuse is known to be good, test for short in stator or rectifier as follows: Disconnect charging lead from battery and connect a small test lamp between battery positive terminal and fuse cap as shown in Fig. B&S110. DO NOT start engine. Test lamp should not light. If it does light, stator's charging lead is grounded or rectifier is defective. Unplug rectifier plug under blower housing. If test lamp goes out, rectifier is defective. If test lamp does not go out, stator charging lead is grounded.

If test indicates stator charging lead is grounded, remove blower housing, flywheel, starter motor and retaining clamp, then examine length of red lead for damaged insulation or obvious shorts in lead. If bare spots are found, repair with electrical tape and shellac. If short cannot be repaired, renew stator. Charging lead should also be checked for continuity as follows: Touch one lead of ohmmeter to lead at fuse holder and other ohmmeter lead to red lead pin in connector as shown in Fig. B&S111. If ohmmeter does not show continuity, charging lead is open and stator must be renewed. The charging coils should be

checked for continuity as follows: Touch ohmmeter test leads to the two black lead pins as shown in Fig. B&S112. If ohmmeter does not show continuity, charging coils are defective and stator must be renewed. Test for grounded charging coils by touching one test lead of ohmmeter to a clean ground surface on engine and the other test lead to each of the black lead pins as shown in Fig. B&S113. If ohmmeter shows continuity, charging coils are grounded and stator must be renewed.

To test rectifier, use an ohmmeter and check for continuity between each of the three lead pin sockets and blower housing. See Fig. B&S114. Reverse ohmmeter leads and check continuity again. Ohmmeter should show a continuity reading for one direction only on each lead socket. If any pin socket shows continuity reading in both directions or neither direction, rectifier is defective and must be renewed.

To test AC lighting alternator circuit, connect a load lamp to AC output plug and ground as shown in Fig. B&S115. Load lamp should light at full brillance at medium engine speed. If lamp does not light or is very dim at medium speeds, remove blower housing and flywheel. Disconnect ground end of AC coil

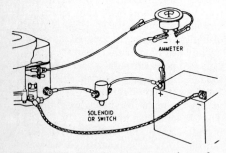

Fig. B&S109—Install ammeter as shown for charging output test.

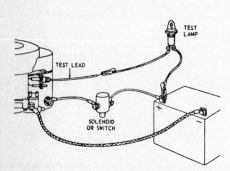

Fig. B&S110—Connect a test lamp as shown to test for short in stator or rectifier.

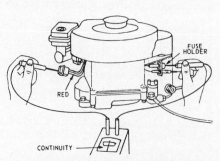

Fig. B&S111—Use an ohmmeter to check charging lead for continuity. Refer to text.

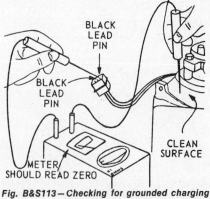

Fig. B&S113—Checking for grounded charging coils. Refer to text.

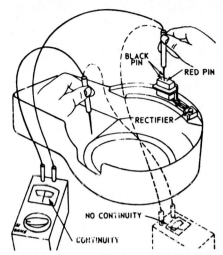

Fig. B&S114—If ohmmeter shows continuity in both directions or neither direction, rectifier is defective.

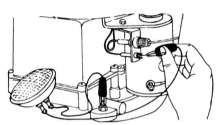

Fig. B&S115—Load lamp (GE #4001 or equivalent is used to test AC lighting circuit output.

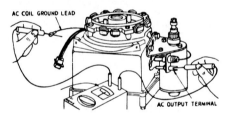

Fig. B&S116—Checking AC lighting circuit for continuity. Refer to text.

from retaining clamp screw (Fig. B&S107). Connect ohmmeter between ground lead of AC coil and AC output

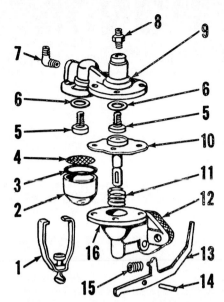

Fig. B&S117—Exploded view of diaphragm type fuel pump used on some B&S engines.

1. Yoke assy.	9. Fuel pump head
2. Filter bowl	10. Pump diaphragm
3. Gasket	11. Diaphragm spring
4. Filter screen	12. Gasket
5. Pump valves	13. Pump lever
6. Gaskets	14. Lever pin
7. Elbow fitting	15. Lever spring
8. Connector	16. Fuel pump body

terminal as shown in Fig. B&S116. Ohmmeter should show continuity. If not, stator must be renewed. Be sure AC ground lead is not touching a grounded surface, then check continuity from AC output terminal to engine ground. If ohmmeter indicates continuity, lighting coils are grounded and stator must be renewed.

FUEL PUMP

A diaphragm type fuel pump is used on some models. Refer to Fig. B&S117 for exploded view of pump.

To disassemble pump, refer to Figs. B&S117 and B&S118; then, proceed as follows: Remove clamp (1), fuel bowl (2), gasket (3) and screen (4). Remove

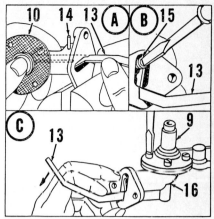

Fig. B&S118—Views showing disassembly and reassembly of diaphragm type fuel pump. Refer to text for procedure and to Fig. B&S117 for exploded view of pump and for legend.

screws retaining upper body (9) to lower body (16). Pump valves (5) and gaskets (6) can now be removed. Drive pin (14) out to either side of body (16), then press diaphragm (10) against spring (11) as shown in view A, Fig. B&S118, and remove lever (13). Diaphragm and spring (11 – Fig. B&S117) can now be removed.

To reassemble, place diaphragm spring in lower body and place diaphragm on spring, being sure spring enters cup on bottom side of diaphragm and slot in shaft is at right angle to pump lever. Then, compressing diaphragm against spring as in view A, Fig. B&S118, insert hooked end of lever into slot in shaft. Align hole in lever with hole in lower body and drive pin into place. Then, insert lever spring (15) into body and push outer end of spring into place over hook on arm of lever as shown in view B. Hold lever downward as shown in view C while tightening screws holding upper body to lower body. When installing pump on engine, apply a liberal amount of grease on lever (13) at point where it contacts groove in crankshaft.

HONDA

Model	Bore	Stroke	Displacement
G400	86 mm	70 mm	406 cc
	(3.4 in.)	(2.8 in.)	(24.8 cu. in.)

ENGINE IDENTIFICATION

Honda G400 series engine is a four-stroke, air-cooled, single-cylinder engine. Valves are located in cylinder block and crankcase casting. Model G400 engine develops 7.5 kW (10) horsepower at 3600 rpm. The "G" prefix indicates horizontal crankshaft model.

Engine model number decal is located on engine cooling shroud just above or beside rewind starter. Engine serial number is located as shown in Fig. HN1. Always furnish engine model and serial number when ordering service parts.

MAINTENANCE

SPARK PLUG. Recommended spark plug is Champion L92C.

Spark plug should be removed and cleaned at 100 hour intervals. Set electrode gap at 0.6-0.7 mm (0.024-0.028 in.).

NOTE: Caution should be exercised if abrasive type spark plug cleaner is used. Inadequate cleaning procedure may allow the abrasive cleaner to be deposited in engine cylinder causing rapid wear and premature failure of engine components.

CARBURETOR. Model G400 engine is equipped with a float type side draft carburetor (Fig. HN2). Idle fuel mixture is controlled by adjusting a pilot screw and high speed fuel mixture is controlled by a fixed main jet. Initial adjustment of pilot screw is two turns open from a lightly seated position. Recommended engine idle speed (tractor application) is 2200 rpm and maximum engine speed (un-loaded) is 3700-4000 rpm. Standard main jet size is #102.

Float level should be 8.6 mm (0.34 in.). To measure float level, invert carburetor throttle body with float assembly installed and measure from top of float to float bowl mating surface on carburetor throttle body. If dimension is not as specified, renew float.

FUEL FILTER. A fuel filter screen is located in sediment bowl below fuel shut-off valve. To remove sediment bowl, first shut off fuel. Unscrew threaded ring and remove ring, sediment bowl and gasket. Make certain gasket is in place during reassembly. To clean screen, fuel shut-off valve must be disconnected from the fuel line and unscrewed from fuel tank.

AIR FILTER. Engine is equipped with a dual element type air filter. Air filter should be removed and serviced at 20 hour intervals.

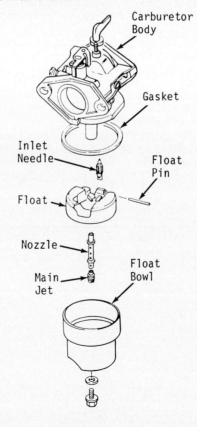

Fig. HN2 — Exploded view of carburetor used on Honda G400 engine.

To service air filter, remove wing nut, cover and withdraw elements. Separate foam outer element from paper element. Wash foam element in warm soapy water and thoroughly rinse. Allow element to air dry. Dip the dry foam element in clean engine oil and gently squeeze out excess oil.

Direct low air pressure from inside paper element toward the outside to remove all loose dirt and foreign material. Reassemble elements and reinstall.

GOVERNOR. The internal centrifugal flyweight governor assembly is located inside crankcase. Governor flyweights are attached to the camshaft gear.

To adjust governor, first stop engine and make certain all linkage is in good condition and tension spring (2 – Fig. HN4) is not stretched or damaged. Spring (4) must pull governor lever (3) toward throttle pivot (6).

Loosen clamp bolt (8) and turn governor shaft counterclockwise as far as possible while moving governor lever so throttle valve is at wide-open position. Tighten clamp bolt (8). Start and run engine until it reaches operating temperature. Adjust maximum speed screw (9) to obtain 3700-4000 rpm.

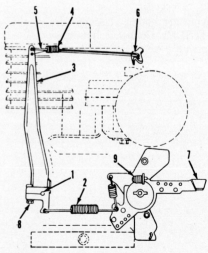

Fig. HN4 — View of external governor linkage.

1. Governor shaft
2. Tension spring
3. Governor lever
4. Spring
5. Carburetor-to-governor lever rod
6. Throttle pivot
7. Throttle lever
8. Clamp bolt
9. Maximum speed screw

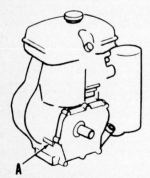

Fig. HN1 — View showing location of engine serial number (A).

IGNITION SYSTEM. Engines may be equipped with a breaker point ignition system or a transistorized ignition system. Refer to appropriate paragraph for ignition system being serviced.

Breaker Point Ignition System. Breaker point set and ignition coil are located behind the flywheel on all models. Breaker points should be checked at 300 hour intervals. Initial breaker point gap should be 0.3-0.4 mm (0.012-0.016 in.) and point gap should be varied to obtain 20 degrees BTDC timing setting.

NOTE: Timing tool 07974-8830001 is available from Honda Motor Company to allow timing adjustment with flywheel removed.

To check ignition timing, connect positive ohmmeter lead to engine stop switch wire and connect negative ohmmeter lead to engine ground. Rotate flywheel until ohmmeter just does register. "F" mark on flywheel should align with index mark on crankcase (Fig. HN5). If marks do not align, remove flywheel and adjust point gap opening. Reinstall flywheel or use special tool 07974-8830001 and repeat previous procedure to verify correct timing setting is obtained.

To check ignition coil, connect positive ohmmeter lead to spark plug wire and negative ohmmeter lead to coil laminations. Ohmmeter should register 6.6 ohms. When installing ignition coil, make certain coil is positioned correctly on locating pins.

Transistorized Ignition System. The transistorized ignition system coil is mounted on engine block. Air gap between ignition coil and outer edge of flywheel should be 0.2-0.6 mm (0.008-0.024 in.).

To test primary side of transistorized ignition coil, attach one ohmmeter test lead to coil laminations. Connect remaining ohmmeter test lead to the primary (thin black) coil lead wire. Refer to Fig. HN6. Resistance reading should be 0.7-0.9 ohms.

To test the secondary side of transistorized ignition coil, remove spark plug boot and attach one ohmmeter test lead to coil laminations. Connect remaining ohmmeter test lead to the terminal end of spark plug lead. Refer to Fig. HN7. Resistance reading should be 6300-7700 ohms.

VALVE ADJUSTMENT. Valves and seats should be refaced and stem clearance adjusted at 300 hour intervals. Refer to VALVE SYSTEM paragraphs in REPAIRS section for service procedure and specifications.

CYLINDER HEAD AND COMBUSTION CHAMBER. Cylinder head, combustion chamber and piston should be cleaned and carbon and lead deposits

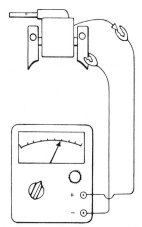

Fig. HN6—Check resistance on ignition coil primary side using an ohmmeter as shown. Refer to text.

removed at 300 hour intervals. Refer to CYLINDER HEAD paragraphs in REPAIRS section for service procedure.

LUBRICATION. Engine is splash lubricated and engine oil should be checked prior to each operating interval. Oil level should be maintained between reference marks on dipstick with dipstick just touching first threads. Do not screw dipstick in to check oil level.

Manufacturer recommends oil with an API service classification of SE or SF. Use SAE 10W-40 motor oil.

Oil should be changed after the first 20 hours of operation and at 100 hour intervals thereafter. Crankcase capacity is 1.2 L (1.27 qt.).

GENERAL MAINTENANCE. Check and tighten all loose bolts, nuts or clamps daily. Check for fuel or oil leakage and repair as necessary.

Clean dust, dirt, grease or any foreign material from cylinder head and cylinder block cooling fins at 100 hour intervals or more frequent if needed. Inspect fins for damage and repair as necessary.

REPAIRS

TIGHTENING TORQUES. Recommended tightening torque specifications are as follows:

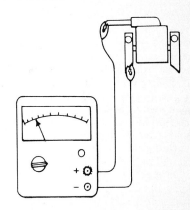

Fig. HN7—Check resistance on ignition coil secondary side using an ohmmeter as shown. Refer to text.

Fig. HN5—"F" mark on flywheel should align with timing mark on crankcase when breaker points just begin to open. Honda timing tool 07974-8830001 is used to adjust timing with flywheel removed.

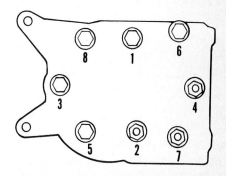

Fig. HN8—Loosen or tighten cylinder head bolts in sequence shown.

Spark plug . . . . .10-15 N·m
(7-11 ft.-lbs.)
Flywheel nut . . . . .108-118 N·m
(80-87 ft.-lbs.)
Cylinder head . . . . .31-37 N·m
(23-27 ft.-lbs.)
Tappet cover . . . . .8-12 N·m
(6-9 ft.-lbs.)
Crankcase cover . . . . .20-23 N·m
(15-17 ft.-lbs.)
Connecting rod . . . . .23-27 N·m
(17-20 ft.-lbs.)

CYLINDER HEAD. To remove cylinder head, first remove cooling shrouds. Clean engine to prevent entrance of foreign material. Loosen cylinder head cap screws in ¼-turn increments in sequence shown in Fig. HN8 until all cap screws are loose enough to remove by hand. Remove cylinder head.

Remove spark plug and clean carbon and lead deposits from cylinder head.

Reinstall cylinder head and new gasket. Tighten cylinder head cap screws to 31-37 N·m (23-27 ft.-lbs.) in sequence shown in Fig. HN8. Compression should be checked after cylinder head has been installed. Compression should be 588 kPa (85 psi).

CONNECTING ROD AND BEARING. Connecting rod is equipped with renewable type connecting rod bearing inserts. Piston and connecting rods are removed as an assembly after cylinder head has been removed and crankcase cover has been separated from crankcase. Remove the two connecting rod cap screws, lock plate, oil dipper plate and connecting rod cap. Push piston and connecting rod assembly out through the top of cylinder block. Remove snap rings and piston pin to separate piston from connecting rod.

Standard diameter for piston pin bore in connecting rod small end is 19.010-19.028 mm (0.7484-0.7491 in.). If dimension exceeds 19.8 mm (0.7512 in.), renew connecting rod.

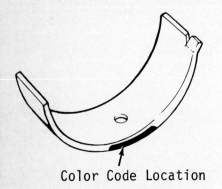

Color Code Location

Fig. HN10—Connecting rod bearing inserts are color coded and should be matched to the connecting rod and crankshaft identification numbers. Refer to text.

Standard connecting rod side play on crankpin journal is 0.15-0.40 mm (0.0059-0.0159 in.). If side play exceeds 1.0 mm (0.0394 in.), renew connecting rod.

Connecting rod bearing inserts are color coded (Fig. HN10) and connecting rod and crankshaft are stamped with an identification number (Figs. HN11 and HN12) which identify different connecting rod bearing bore sizes or crankshaft connecting rod journal sizes. Bearing inserts, connecting rod and crankshaft must be matched by referring to the CRANKSHAFT, MAIN BEARINGS AND SEALS paragraphs.

Assemble piston to connecting rod with the arrow mark on top of piston toward ribbed side of connecting rod. Install piston pin retaining rings with gaps opposite notch in piston pin bore of piston. Align connecting rod and cap match marks and install connecting rod so ribbed side is toward crankcase cover. Arrow stamped on piston top should be toward valve side of engine after installation. Install oil dipper and lock plate. Tighten connecting rod cap screws to 23-27 N·m (17-20 ft.-lbs.).

PISTON, PIN AND RINGS. Piston and connecting rod are removed as an assembly. Refer to CONNECTING ROD AND BEARING paragraphs for removal and installation procedure.

After separating piston from connecting rod, carefully remove piston rings and clean carbon and lead deposits from piston surface and piston ring lands.

CAUTION: Extreme care should be exercised when cleaning piston ring lands. Do not damage squared edges or widen piston ring grooves. If piston ring lands are damaged, piston must be renewed.

Measure piston diameter on piston thrust surface, 90 degrees from piston pin. Standard piston diameter is 85.97 mm (3.385 in.). If piston diameter is less than 85.85 mm (3.380 in.), renew piston.

Before installing piston rings, install piston in cylinder bore and use a suitable feeler gage to measure clearance between piston and cylinder bore. Standard clearance is 0.05 mm (0.002 in.). If clearance exceeds 0.25 mm (0.010 in.), renew piston and/or recondition cylinder bore.

Standard piston pin bore diameter is 19.002-19.008 mm (0.7481-0.7483 in.). If diameter exceeds 19.046 mm (0.7498 in.), renew piston.

Standard piston pin outside diameter is 18.994-19.000 mm (0.7478-0.7480 in.). If diameter is less than 18.97 mm (0.7469 in.), renew piston pin.

Standard piston ring-to-piston groove side clearance is 0.020-0.060 mm

(0.0008-0.0024 in.) for top ring and 0.010-0.050 mm (0.0004-0.0020 in.) for second ring. If clearance exceeds 0.15 mm (0.0059 in.) on both rings, then renew rings and/or piston.

Standard ring end gap for top or second piston ring is 0.2-0.4 mm (0.0079-0.0157 in.) with ring squarely installed in cylinder bore. If end gap exceeds 0.6 mm (0.023 in.), renew ring and/or recondition cylinder bore.

Standard ring end gap for the oil control ring is 0.2-0.3 mm (0.0079-0.0118 in.). If ring end gap exceeds 0.5 mm (0.020 in.), renew ring and/or recondition cylinder bore.

Install piston rings which are marked with marked side toward top of piston and stagger ring end gaps equally around circumference of piston.

CYLINDER AND CRANKCASE. Cylinder and crankcase are an integral casting. Standard cylinder bore diameter is 86.02 mm (3.387 in.). If bore diameter exceeds 86.10 mm (3.3898 in.) at any point, recondition cylinder bore.

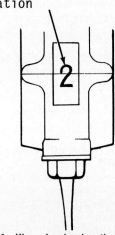

Connecting Rod Identification Number Location

Fig. HN11—View showing location of the connecting rod identification number. The number identifies connecting rod bearing bore size. Refer to text.

Crankshaft Identification Number Location

Fig. HN12—View showing location of the crankshaft identification number. The number identifies connecting rod journal size. Refer to text.

CRANKSHAFT, MAIN BEARINGS AND SEALS. Crankshaft is supported by ball bearing type main bearings on each end. To remove crankshaft, remove all cooling shrouds, flywheel, cylinder head and crankcase cover. Remove piston and connecting rod assembly. Carefully remove crankshaft and camshaft. Remove main bearings and crankshaft oil seals as necessary.

Crankshaft connecting rod journal diameters for G400 engines with serial number 1200001 to 1286491 is 36.968-36.976 mm (1.4554-1.4557 in.) for a crankshaft with "1" as the identification mark and 36.960-36.968 mm (1.4551-1.4554 in.) for a crankshaft with "2" as the identification number and 36.952-36.960 mm (1.4548-1.4551 in.) for crankshaft with "3" as the identification number. Crankshaft connecting rod journal diameters for G400 engines with serial number 1286492 and above are

36.976-36.984 mm (1.4557-1.4560 in.) for crankshaft with "O" as the identification mark, 36.968-36.976 mm (1.4554-1.4557 in.) for crankshaft with "1" as the identification mark and 36.960-36.968 mm (1.4551-1.4554 in.) for crankshaft with "2" as the identification mark.

Determine crankshaft and connecting rod identification numbers and refer to the chart shown in Fig. HN13 for engines with serial number 1200001 to 1286491 and to Fig. HN14 for engines with serial number 128492 and above to determine correct bearing insert by color code. For example, an engine with a serial number between 1200001 and 1286491 would use a bearing insert with a brown color code when installing a crankshaft with an identification number of "2" in conjunction with a connecting rod with an identification number of "3."

Main bearings are a light press fit on crankshaft and in bearing bores of crankcase and crankcase cover. It may be necessary to slightly heat crankcase or crankcase cover to reinstall bearings.

If main bearings are rough, loose, or loose fit on crankshaft journals or in

crankcase or crankcase cover, renew bearings.

If crankshaft oil seals have been removed, use a suitable seal driver to install new seals. Seals should be pressed in evenly until slightly below seal bore surface.

Make certain crankshaft gear and camshaft gear timing marks are aligned as shown in Fig. HN15 during crankshaft installation.

CAMSHAFT. Camshaft is supported at each end by bearings which are an integral part of crankcase or crankcase cover casting. Refer to CRANKSHAFT, MAIN BEARINGS AND SEALS paragraphs for camshaft removal procedure.

Standard camshaft lobe height is 38.46-38.72 mm (1.5142-1.5244 in.) for intake lobe and 38.49-38.75 mm (1.5154-1.5256 in.) for exhaust lobe. If intake or exhaust lobe is less than 38.3 mm (1.5079 in.), renew camshaft.

Standard camshaft bearing journal diameter is 17.766-17.784 mm (0.6994-0.7002 in.). If diameter is less than 17.716 mm (0.6975 in.), renew camshaft.

Make certain camshaft gear and crankshaft gear timing marks are aligned as shown in Fig. HN15 during installation.

ENGINE BALANCER. The engine balancer (Fig. HN16) is mounted on a stub shaft located in crankcase cover and is driven by an auxiliary gear pressed onto crankshaft. Bearing is pressed into balancer counterweight to a depth of 1.0 mm (0.4 in.) using Honda bearing driver 07945-8910000 (Fig. HN17).

To install engine balance weight and crankcase cover, position piston at TDC. Remove the 8 mm plug from crankcase cover and secure balancer by inserting

CONNECTING ROD IDENTIFICATION

CRANKSHAFT IDENTIFICATION	1	2	3
1	Pink	Yellow	Green
2	Yellow	Green	Brown
3	Green	Brown	Black

BEARING COLOR CODE

Fig. HN13 — On G400 engines with serial number 1200001 to 1286491, locate crankshaft and connecting rod identification numbers and use the appropriate color-coded bearing inserts. Refer to text.

CONNECTING ROD IDENTIFICATION

CRANKSHAFT IDENTIFICATION	1	2	3
O	Pink	Yellow	Green
1	Yellow	Green	Brown
2	Green	Brown	

BEARING COLOR CODE

Fig. HN14 — On G400 engines with serial number 1286492 and above, locate crankshaft and connecting rod identification numbers and use the appropriate color-coded bearing inserts. Refer to text.

Fig. HN15 — When installing crankshaft or camshaft, make certain timing marks on gears are aligned as shown.

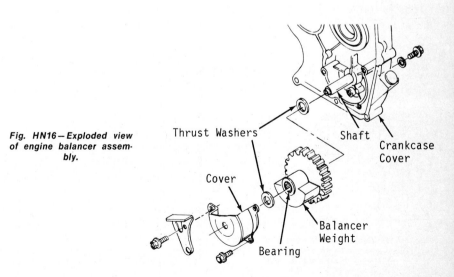

Fig. HN16 — Exploded view of engine balancer assembly.

Thrust Washers — Shaft — Crankcase Cover — Cover — Balancer Weight — Bearing

locating dowel rod as shown in Fig. HN18. Remove locating dowel rod after crankcase cover bolts are tightened to specified torque and install the 8 mm plug.

GOVERNOR. The internal centrifugal flyweight governor is located on camshaft gear. Refer to GOVERNOR paragraphs in MAINTENANCE section for external governor adjustments.

To remove governor assembly, remove external linkage, metal cooling shrouds and crankcase cover. The governor flyweight assembly is on camshaft gear.

When reassembling, make certain governor sliding sleeve and internal governor linkage is correctly positioned.

VALVE SYSTEM. Clearance between valve stem and valve tappet (cold) should be 0.08-0.16 mm (0.0031-0.0063 in.) for intake valve and 0.11-0.19 mm (0.0043-0.0075 in.) for exhaust valve.

On all models, valve clearance is adjusted by removing valve and grinding off end of stem to increase clearance or by renewing valve and/or grinding valve seat deeper to decrease clearance.

Valve face and seat angle is 45 degrees and standard valve seat width is 1.06 mm (0.0417 in.) for the intake valve and 1.414 mm (0.0557 in.) for the exhaust valve. If intake or exhaust valve seat width exceeds 2.0 mm (0.0787 in.), valve seat must be narrowed.

Standard valve spring free length for intake and exhaust valve springs is 42.7 mm (1.6811 in.). If spring length is 41.0 mm (1.6142 in.) or less, renew spring.

Standard valve stem diameter is 6.995-6.970 mm (0.2738-0.2744 in.) for intake valve stem and 6.910-6.925 mm (0.2720-0.2726 in.) for exhaust valve stem. If intake valve stem diameter is less than 6.91 mm (0.272 in.) or exhaust valve stem diameter is less than 6.89 mm (0.271 in.), renew valve.

Standard valve guide inside diameter is 7.000-7.015 mm (0.2756-0.2762 in.). If inside diameter of guide exceeds 7.07 mm (0.278 in.), guides must be renewed.

To remove and install valve guides, use the following procedure and refer to the sequence of illustrations in Fig. HN19. Cover tappet opening to prevent fragments from entering crankcase and use Honda driver 07942-8230000 to slightly drive valve guide down into valve chamber (A). Use a suitable cold chisel to fracture guide adjacent to guide bore (B). Drive remaining piece of guide into valve chamber (C) and remove from chamber. Place new guide on driver and start guide into guide bore (D). Alternate between driving guide into bore and measuring guide depth below cylinder head surface (E). Depth "X" in procedure (F) should be 32 mm (1.3 in.) for intake guide and 30 mm (1.2 in.) for exhaust valve. Finish ream intake and exhaust guides using Honda reamer 07984-6890100.

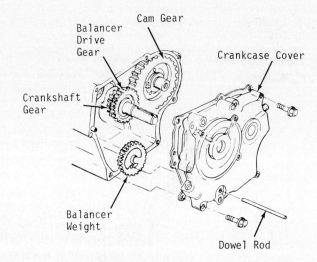

Fig. HN18 — When installing crankcase cover and balance gear assembly, a guide dowel rod must be used. Refer to text.

Fig. HN17 — Bearing is pressed into engine balance weight to a depth of 1.0 mm (0.4 in.) using Honda driver 07945-8910000.

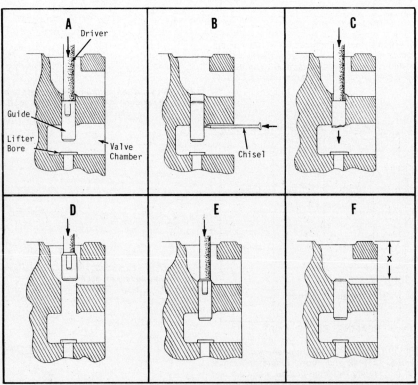

Fig. HN19 — View showing valve guide removal and installation sequence. Refer to text.

KOHLER

Model	No. Cyls.	Bore	Stroke	Displacement	Horsepower
K-161 (Early)	1	2-7/8 in. (73.0 mm)	2-1/2 in. (63.5 mm)	16.22 cu. in. (266 cc)	7 (5.2 kW)
K-161 (Late)	1	2-15/16 in. (74.6 mm)	2-1/2 in. (63.5 mm)	16.9 cu. in. (277 cc)	7 (5.2 kW)
K-181	1	2-15/16 in. (74.6 mm)	2-3/4 in. (69.8 mm)	18.6 cu. in. (305 cc)	8 (6.0 kW)
K-241	1	3-1/4 in. (82.5 mm)	2-7/8 in. (73.0 mm)	23.9 cu. in. (392 cc)	10 (7.5 kW)
K-301	1	3-3/8 in. (85.7 mm)	3-1/4 in. (82.5 mm)	29.07 cu. in. (476 cc)	12 (8.9 kW)
K-321	1	3-1/2 in. (88.9 mm)	3-1/4 in. (82.5 mm)	31.27 cu. in. (512 cc)	14 (10.4 kW)
K-341	1	3-3/4 in. (95.2 mm)	3-1/4 in. (82.5 mm)	35.89 cu. in. (588 cc)	16 (11.9 kW)

All engines are four-cycle, single cylinder, horizontal crankshaft type. All engines are equipped with ball bearing mains at each end of crankshaft and are splash lubricated. A side draft carburetor is used on all engines.

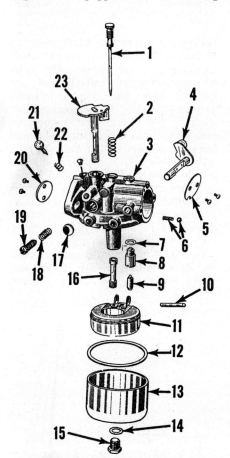

Fig. KO1—Exploded view of typical Carter Model N carburetor used on early production K-161, K-181, K-241 and K-301 engine.

1. Main fuel needle
2. Spring
3. Carburetor body
4. Choke shaft
5. Choke disc
6. Choke detent
7. Sealing washer
8. Inlet valve seat
9. Inlet valve
10. Float pin
11. Float
12. Gasket
13. Float bowl
14. Sealing washer
15. Retainer
16. Main jet
17. Plug
18. Spring
19. Idle stop screw
20. Throttle disc
21. Idle fuel needle
22. Spring
23. Throttle shaft

MAINTENANCE

SPARK PLUG. Recommended plug for Models K-241, K-301, K-321 and K-341 is Champion H-10. All other engines in this section use a Champion J-8 plug. Set electrode gap to 0.025 inch (0.635 mm) on all models.

An automotive diaphragm type fuel pump is used on some models. This pump is equipped with a priming lever. A fuel pump repair kit is available for this pump.

CARBURETOR. Early production K-161, K-181, K-241 and K-301 engines are equipped with a Carter model "N" side draft carburetor. Late production K-161, K-181, K-241 and K-301 and all K-321 and K-341 engines are equipped with Kohler side draft carburetors. Refer to appropriate paragraph for service information.

CARTER CARBURETOR. Refer to Fig. KO1 for exploded view of typical Model N Carter carburetor used on all engines so equipped. For initial adjustment, open idle fuel needle 1½ turns and open main fuel needle 2 turns. Make final adjustment with engine warm and running. Place engine under load and adjust main fuel needle for leanest setting that will allow satisfactory acceleration and steady governor operation. Then adjust idle needle for smoothest idle operation. As adjustments affect each other, adjustment sequence may have to be repeated.

To check float level, invert carburetor body casting and float assembly. There should be 13/64-inch (5.2 mm) clearance between free side of float and machined surface of body casting. If not, carefully bend float lever tang that contacts inlet

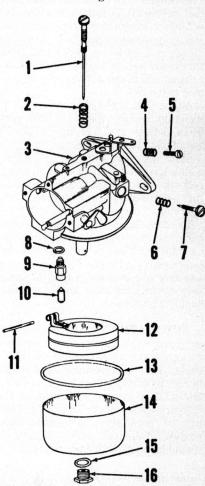

Fig. KO2—Exploded view of Kohler carburetor used on late production K-161, K-181, K-241 and K-301 engines. Carburetor used on K-321 and K-341 engines is similar.

1. Main fuel needle
2. Spring
3. Carburetor body assy.
4. Spring
5. Idle speed stop
6. Spring
7. Idle fuel needle
8. Sealing washer
9. Inlet valve seat
10. Inlet valve
11. Float pin
12. Float
13. Gasket
14. Float bowl
15. Sealing washer
16. Bowl retainer

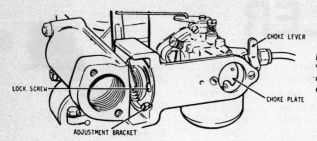

Fig. KO3—View showing "Thermostatic" automatic choke used on some engines equipped with Kohler or Carter carburetors.

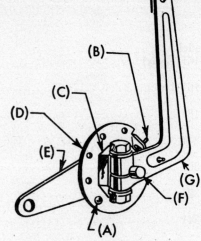

Fig. KO5—Drawing showing governor lever and related parts of Models K-161 and K-181.

A. Drive pin
B. Governor spring
C. Bushing nut
D. Speed control disc
E. Throttle bracket
F. Governor shaft
G. Governor lever

valve as necessary to provide correct measurement.

KOHLER CARBURETOR. Refer to Fig. KO2 for exploded view of Kohler carburetor. For initial adjustment, open main fuel needle 2 turns and open idle fuel needle 1¼ turns. Make final adjustment with engine warm and running. Place engine under load and adjust main fuel needle (1) to leanest mixture that will allow satisfactory acceleration and steady governor operation. If engine misses and backfires under load, mixture is too lean. If engine shows a sooty exhaust and is sluggish under load, mixture is too rich.

Adjust idle speed stop screw (5) to maintain an idle speed of 1000 rpm. Then, adjust idle fuel needle (7) for smoothest idle operation.

Since main fuel and idle fuel adjustments have some effect on each other, recheck engine operation and readjust fuel needles as necessary for smoothest operation.

To check float level, invert carburetor body and float assembly. There should be 11/64-inch (4.4 mm) clearance between machined surface of body casting and free end of float. Adjust as necessary by bending float lever tang that contacts inlet valve.

AUTOMATIC CHOKE. Some models equipped with Kohler or Carter carburetors are also equipped with an automatic choke. The "Thermostatic" type shown in Fig. KO3 may be used on either electric start or manual start models. The "Electric-Thermostatic" type (Fig. KO4) can be used only on electric start models. Automatic choke adjustment should be made with engine cold.

THERMOSTATIC TYPE. To adjust "Thermostatic" type, loosen lock screw (Fig. KO3) and rotate adjustment bracket as necessary to obtain correct amount of choking. Tighten lock screw. In cold temperature, choke should be closed. In room temperature, (70-75°F (21-24°C), choke should be partially open and choke lever should be in vertical position. Start engine and allow it to run until normal operating temperature is obtained. Choke should be fully open when engine is at normal operating temperature.

ELECTRIC-THERMOSTATIC TYPE. To adjust "Electric-Thermostatic type, refer to Fig. KO4 and move choke lever arm until hole in brass cross shaft is aligned with slot in bearings. Insert a No. 43 (0.089 inch diameter) drill through cross shaft as shown. Push drill through shaft until drill is engaged in notch in base of choke. Loosen clamp bolt on lever arm and move link end of lever arm upward until choke disc is closed to desired position. Tighten clamp bolt while holding lever arm in this position. Remove the drill. Choke should be fully closed when starting a cold engine and should be fully open when engine is running at normal operating temperature.

GOVERNOR. All models are equipped with a gear driven flyweight governor that is located inside engine crankcase. Maximum recommended governed engine speed is 3600 rpm on all engines. Recommended idle speed of 1000 rpm is controlled by adjustment of throttle stop screw on carburetor.

Before attempting to adjust engine governed speed, synchronize governor

linkage on all models as follows: On Models K-161 and K-181, loosen the bolt clamping governor arm (G – Fig. KO5) to governor cross shaft (F) and turn governor cross shaft counter-clockwise as far as possible. While holding cross shaft in this position, move governor arm away from carburetor to limit of linkage travel and tighten clamping bolt.

On Models K-241, K-301, K-321 and K-341, refer to Fig. KO7 and loosen governor arm hex nut. Rotate governor cross-shaft counter-clockwise as far as possible, move governor arm away from carburetor to limit of linkage travel, then tighten hex nut on arm.

To adjust maximum governed speed on Model K-241, K-301, K-321 and K-341, adjust position of stop so speed

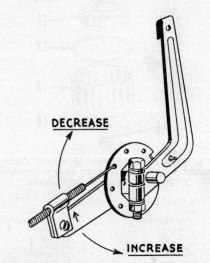

Fig. KO6—On Models K-161 and K-181, loosen bushing nut (C—Fig. KO5) and move throttle bracket as shown to change governed speed of engine.

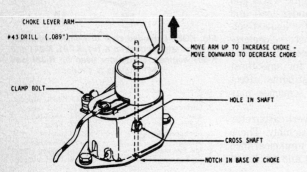

Fig. KO4—View of "Electric-Thermostatic" automatic choke used on some engines equipped with Kohler or Carter carburetors.

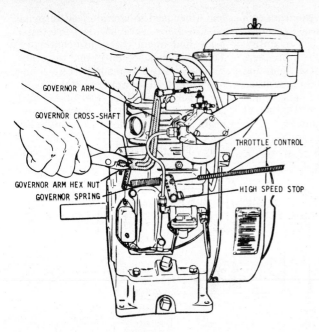

Fig. KO7— View showing governor adjusting points on K-241, K-301, K-321 and K-341 engines. Governor sensitivity is adjusted by moving governor spring to alternate holes.

control lever contacts stop at desired engine speed. On Models K-161 and K-181, loosen governor shaft bushing nut (C – Fig. KO5) and move throttle bracket (E) to increase or decrease governed speed. See Fig. KO6 for direction movement.

On Models K-241, K-301, K-321 and K-341, governor sensitivity is adjusted by moving governor spring to alternate holes in governor arm and speed lever.

On Model K-161 engines prior to S.N. 202305, governor shaft is supported by a snap ring. Later production K-161 engines and all other models in this section, inner end of governor shaft is supported in a needle bearing located in engine crankcase.

Governor unit is accessible after removing engine crankshaft and camshaft. The governor gear and flyweight assembly turns on a stub shaft pressed into engine crankcase. Renew gear and weight assembly if gear teeth or any part of assembly is excessively worn. Desired clearance of governor gear to stub shaft is 0.0025-0.0055 inch (0.0635-

0.1397 mm) for Models K-161 and K-181 and 0.0005-0.002 inch (0.0127-0.051 mm) for Models K-241, K-301, K-321 and K-341.

IGNITION AND TIMING. Three types of ignition systems used are as follows: Battery ignition, flywheel magneto ignition and solid state breakerless ignition. Refer to the following paragraphs for timing and service procedures.

BATTERY AND MAGNETO IGNITION. On engines equipped with either battery or magneto ignition systems, the breaker points are located externally on engine crankcase as shown in Fig. KO8.

The breaker points are actuated by a cam through a push rod. On early models, breaker cam is driven by the camshaft gear through an automatic advance mechanism as shown in Fig. KO9. At cranking speed, ignition occurs at 3° BTDC on Models K-161 and K-181 or 3° ATDC on early Models K-241 and K-301. At operating speeds, centrifugal

force of advance weights overcomes spring tension and advances timing of breaker cam so ignition occurs at 20° BTDC on all models.

Late Model K-161, K-181, K-241 and K-301 and all K-321 and K-341 engines are equipped with an automatic compression release (see CAMSHAFT paragraph) and do not have an automatic timing advance; ignition occurs at 20° BTDC at all engine speeds.

Nominal breaker point gap on all models is 0.020 inch (0.508 mm); however, breaker point gap should be varied to obtain exact ignition timing as follows:

With a static timing light, disconnect coil and condenser leads from breaker point terminal and attach one timing light lead to terminal and ground the other lead. Remove button plug from timing sight hole and turn engine until piston has just completed its compression stroke and "DC" mark (models with automatic timing advance) or "SP" mark (models with automatic compression release) on flywheel appears in sight hole. Loosen breaker point adjustment screw and adjust points to closed position (timing light will be on); then, slowly move breaker point base towards engine until timing light goes out. Tighten adjustment screw and check point setting by turning engine in normal direction of rotation until timing light goes on. Then, continue to turn engine very slowly until timing light goes out. The "DC" mark (models with automatic timing advance) or "SP" mark (models with automatic compression release) should now be in

Fig. KO9— View showing alignment marks on ignition breaker cam and camshaft gear on models with automatic timing advance.

Fig. KO8— Ignition breaker points are located externally on engine crankcase on all models equipped with magneto or battery ignition systems.

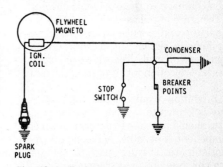

Fig. KO10— Typical wiring diagram of magneto ignition system used on manual start engines.

register with sight hole. Disconnect timing light leads, connect leads from coil and condenser to breaker point terminal and install breaker cover.

If a power timing light is available, more accurate timing can be obtained by adjusting the points with engine running. Breaker point gap should be adjusted so light flash causes "SP" timing mark (20° BTDC) to appear in sight hole. Engine should be running above 1500 rpm when checking breaker point setting with a power timing light on models with automatic timing advance.

Typical wiring diagrams of magneto ignition systems are shown in Figs. KO10 and KO11. Fig. KO12 is typical wiring diagram of battery ignition system.

SOLID STATE BREAKERLESS IGNITION. The breakerless-alternator ignition system uses solid state devices which eliminate the need for mechanically operated breaker points. Ignition timing is non-adjustable. The only adjustment is trigger module to flywheel trigger projection air gap. To adjust air gap, rotate flywheel until projection is adjacent to trigger module. Loosen trigger retaining screws and move trigger until an air gap of 0.010-0.015 inch (0.254-0.381 mm) is obtained. Make certain flat surfaces on trigger and projection are parallel, then tighten retaining screws. Refer to Fig. KO13 for typical wiring diagram of breakerless ignition system.

The breakerless ignition system includes four main components which are: Ignition winding (on alternator stator), trigger module, ignition coil assembly and special flywheel with trigger projection. The system also includes a conventional spark plug, high tension lead and ignition switch. The ignition winding is separate from battery charging AC windings on alternator stator.

The trigger module includes three diodes, a resistor, a sensing coil and magnet plus the SCR (electronic switch). The trigger module has two clip-on type terminals. See Fig. KO14. Terminal marked "A" must be connected to ignition winding on alternator stator. The "I" terminal must be connected to ignition switch. Improper connection will cause damage to the electronic devices.

The ignition coil assembly includes the capacitor and a pulse transformer arrangement similar to a conventional high tension coil. The flywheel has a special projection for triggering the ignition.

If ignition trouble exists and spark plug is known to be good, the following tests should be made to determine which component is at fault. A flashlight type continuity tester can be used to test ignition coil assembly and trigger module.

To test coil assembly, remove high tension lead (spark plug wire) from coil. Insert one tester lead in coil terminal and other tester lead to coil mounting bracket. Tester light should be on. Then, connect one tester lead to coil mounting bracket and other tester lead to ignition switch wire of coil. Tester light should be out. Renew ignition coil if either of the tests show wrong results.

To test trigger module, connect the tester lead to AC inlet (A–Fig. KO14) and other lead to ignition lead terminal (I). Check for continuity. Reverse tester leads and again check for continuity. Test light must be on in one test only. The second test is made by connecting one tester lead to trigger module mounting bracket and other lead to AC inlet (A). Check for continuity. Reverse tester leads and again check for continuity. Again, test light must be on in one test only. The third test is made by con-

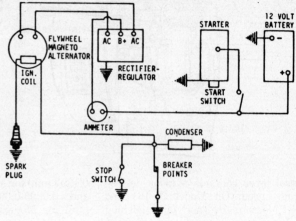
Fig. KO11—Typical wiring diagram of magneto-alternator ignition system used on models equipped with 12-volt starter.

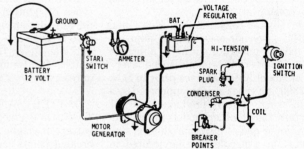
Fig. KO12—Typical wiring diagram of battery ignition system used on models equipped with 12-volt starter-generator.

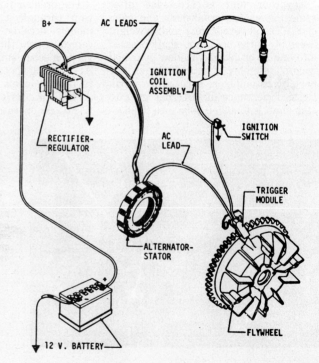
Fig. KO13—Typical wiring diagram of solid state breakerless-alternator ignition system used on models equipped with 12-volt starter.

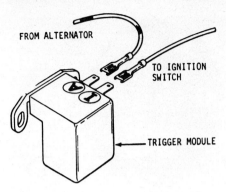

Fig. KO14 — Wires must be connected to trigger module as shown. Reversing connections will damage electronic devices.

necting POSITIVE lead of tester to (I) terminal of trigger and connect other tester lead to trigger module mounting bracket. Test light should be off. Rotate flywheel in normal direction of rotation. When trigger projection on flywheel passes trigger module, test light should turn on. Renew trigger module if any of the three tests show wrong results.

If ignition trouble still exists after ignition coil assembly and trigger module tests show they are good, ignition winding on alternator stator is faulty. In this event, renew stator.

LUBRICATION. All models are splash lubricated. Maintain crankcase oil level at full mark on dipstick, but do not overfill. For engine oil capacity refer to

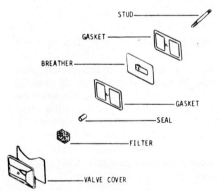

Fig. KO15 — Exploded view of crankcase breather assembly used on Models K-161 and K-181.

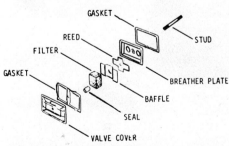

Fig. KO16 — Exploded view of crankcase breather assembly used on Models K-241, K-301, K-321 and K-341.

condensed specifications for tractor model. High quality detergent oil have API classification "SC", "SD", "SE" or "SF" is recommended.

Use SAE 30 oil in temperatures above 32°F (0°C), SAE 10W oil in temperatures between 32°F (0°C) and 0°F (–18°C) and SAE 5W-20 oil in below 0°F (–18°C) temperatures.

CRANKCASE BREATHER. Refer to Fig. KO15 and KO16. A reed valve is located at valve spring compartment to maintain a partial vacuum in crankcase and thus reduce leakage of oil at bearing seals. If a slight amount of crankcase vacuum is not present, reed valve is faulty or engine has excessive blow-by past rings and/or valves.

REPAIRS

TIGHTENING TORQUES. Recommended tightening torques are as follows:
Spark plug . . . . .22 ft.-lbs.
(29 N·m)
Connecting rod
K-161, K-181 . . . . *200 in.-lbs.
(22.6 N·m)
K-241, K-301, K-321,
K-341 . . . . *300 in.-lbs.
(33.9 N·m)
Cylinder head
K-161, K-181 . . . . *241 in.-lbs.
(27.1 N·m)
K-241, K-301, K-321,
K-341 . . . . *360 in.-lbs.
(40.7 N·m)
Flywheel retaining nut
Models with ⅝-inch nut . . . .60 ft.-lbs.
(81.3 N·m)
Models with ¾-inch nut . . .100 ft.-lbs.
(135.5 N·)
*With lubricated threads.

CONNECTING ROD. Connecting rod and piston unit is removed after removing oil pan and cylinder head. The aluminum alloy connecting rod rides directly on the crankpin. Connecting rod with 0.010 inch (0.254 mm) undersize crankpin bore is available for reground crankshaft. Oversize piston pins are also available on some models. Desired running clearances are as follows:
Connecting rod to
crankpin . . . . .0.001-0.002 in.
(0.025-0.051 mm)
Connecting rod to
piston pin
K-161, K-181 . . . . .0.0006-0.0011 in.
(0.0152-0.0279 mm)
K-241, K-301, K-321,
K-341 . . . . .0.0003-0.0008 in.
(0.0076-0.0203 mm)
Rod side play on
crankpin
K-161, K-181 . . . . . . .0.005-0.016 in.
(0.127-0.406 mm)

K-241, K-301, K-321,
K-341 . . . . .0.007-0.016 in.
(0.178-0.406 mm)

Standard crankpin diameter is 1.1855-1.1860 inches (30.1117-30.1244 mm) on Models K-161 and K-181; standard diameter on Models K-241, K-301, K-321 and K-341 is 1.4995-1.5000 inches (38.0873-38.1 mm).

Assemble piston on connecting rod so dot on top of piston is opposite match mark side of connecting rod. Dot on top of piston must be toward pto side of engine after installation. Make certain match marks (Fig. KO17) on rod and cap are aligned and are toward flywheel side of engine. Kohler recommends that connecting rod cap screws be tightened, then loosened and retightened to prevent possibility of screws tightening in threads instead of tightening cap to rod. Tighten connecting rod cap screws to a torque of 200 in.-lbs. (22.6 N·m) on Models K-161 and K-181 and 300 in.-lbs. (33.9 N·m) on Models K-241, K-301, K-321 and K-341.

NOTE: Torque valves for connecting rod cap screws are with lubricated threads.

PISTON, PIN AND RINGS. The aluminum alloy piston is fitted with two 0.093 inch (2.362 mm) wide compression rings and one 0.187 inch (4.750 mm) wide oil control ring. Renew piston if scored or if side clearance of new ring in piston top groove exceeds 0.006 inch (0.152 mm). Pistons and rings are available in standard size and oversizes.

Piston pin fit in piston bore should be from 0.0001 inch (0.0025 mm) interference to 0.0003 inch (0.0076 mm) loose on Models K-161 and K-181 and 0.0002-0.0003 inch (0.0051-0.0076 mm) loose on Models K-241, K-301, K-321 and K-341.

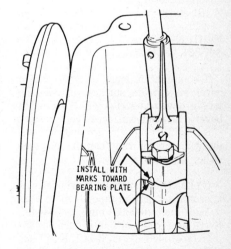

Fig. KO17 — When installing connecting rod and piston unit, be sure alignment marks on rod and cap are aligned and are facing towards flywheel side of engine.

Standard piston pin diameter is 0.6248 inch (15.8699 mm) on Models K-161 and K-181; 0.8592 inch (21.8237 mm) on Model K-241; 0.8753 inch (22.2326 mm) on Models K-301, K-321 and K-341. Piston pins are available in oversize of 0.005 inch on some models. Always renew piston pin retaining rings.

Recommended piston to cylinder bore clearance is as follows:

Measured at thrust side at bottom of skirt.

K-161, K-181 .... 0.0045-0.007 in.
(0.1143-0.178 mm)
K-241, K-301 .... 0.003-0.004 in.
(0.076-0.102 mm)
K-321, K-341 .... 0.0035-0.0045 in.
(0.0889-0.1143 mm)

Measured at thrust side just below oil ring.

K-161, K-181 .... 0.006-0.008 in.
(0.152-0.203 mm)
K-241 .... 0.0075-0.0085 in.
(0.1905-0.2159 mm)
K-301 .... 0.0065-0.0095 in.
(0.1651-0.2413 mm)
K-321, K-341 .... 0.007-0.010 in.
(0.178-0.254 mm)

Kohler recommends that piston rings always be renewed whenever they are removed. Piston ring specifications are as follows:

Ring End Gap
K-161, K-181 .... 0.007-0.017 in.
(0.178-0.432 mm)
K-241, K-301,
K-321, K-341 .... 0.010-0.020 in.
(0.254-0.508 mm)

Ring Side Clearance—
Compression Rings
K-161, K-181 .... 0.0025-0.004 in.
(0.0635-0.102 mm)
K-241, K-301,
K-321, K-341 .... 0.002-0.004 in.
(0.051-0.102 mm)

Ring Side Clearance—
Oil Control Ring
K-161, K-181 .... 0.001-0.0025 in.
(0.025-0.0635 mm)
K-241, K-301,
K-321, K-341 .... 0.001-0.003 in.
(0.025-0.076 mm)

If compression ring has a groove or bevel on outside surface, install ring with groove or bevel down. If groove or bevel is on inside surface of compression ring, install ring with groove or bevel up. Oil control ring can be installed either side up.

CYLINDER BLOCK. If cylinder wall is scored or bore is tapered more than 0.0025 inch (0.0635 mm) on Models K-161 and K-181 or 0.0015 inch (0.0381 mm) on Models K-241, K-301, K-321 and K-341, or out-of-round more than 0.005 inch (0.127 mm), cylinder should be bored to nearest suitable oversize. Standard cylinder bore is 2.875 inches

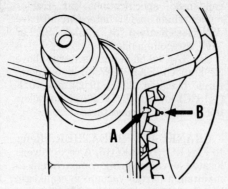

Fig. KO18—When installing crankshaft, make certain timing mark (A) on crankshaft is aligned with timing mark (B) on camshaft gear.

(73.025 mm) on early K-161 engines; 2.9375 inches (74.612 mm) on late K-161 and all K-181 engines; 3.251 inches (82.575 mm) on Model K-241; 3.375 inches (85.725 mm) on Model K-301; 3.500 inches (88.9 mm) on Model K-321; 3.750 inches (95.25 mm) on Model K-341.

CRANKSHAFT. Crankshaft is supported in two ball bearing mains on all models. Renew bearings if excessively loose or rough. Crankshaft end play should be 0.003-0.020 inch (0.076-0.508 mm) on K-241, K-301, K-321 and K-341 models, and 0.002-0.023 inch (0.051-0.584 mm) on other models. End play is controlled by thickness of bearing plate gasket. Gasket is available in 0.010 inch thickness. Install ball bearing mains with sealed side towards crankpin.

The crankpin journal may be ground to 0.010 inch (0.254 mm) undersize for use of undersize connecting rod if journal is scored or out-of-round. Standard crankpin diameter is 1.4995-1.500 inches (38.087-38.1 mm) on K-241, K-301, K-321 and K-341 engines and 1.1855-1.1860 inches (30.112-30.124 mm) on Models K-161 and K-181.

When installing crankshaft, align timing marks on crankshaft and camshaft gears as shown in Fig. KO18.

Fig. KO19—Views showing operation of camshaft with automatic compression release. In View 1, spring (C) has moved control lever (D) which moves cam lever (B) upward so tang (T) is above exhaust cam lobe. This tang holds exhaust valve open slightly on a portion of compression stroke to relieve compression while cranking engine. At engine speeds of 650 rpm or more, centrifugal force moves control lever (D) outward allowing tang (T) to move below lobe surface as shown in View 2.

NOTE: On models equipped with dynamic balancer, refer to DYNAMIC BALANCER paragraph for installation and timing of balancer gears. On all models, Kohler recommends crankshaft seals be installed in crankcase and bearing plate after crankshaft and bearing plate are installed. Carefully work oil seals over crankshaft and drive seals into place with hollow driver that contacts outer edge of seals.

Fig. KO20—View showing automatic compression release camshaft.

A. Camshaft gear
B. Cam lever
C. Spring
D. Control lever
1. Rivet
2. Steel washer
3. Copper washer

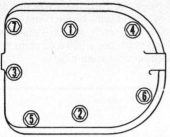

Fig. KO21—Tighten cylinder head cap screws to a torque of 240 in.-lbs. (27.1 N·m) on Models K-161 and K-181 in sequence shown.

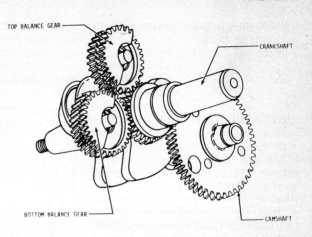

Fig. KO24—View showing components of dynamic balancer system used on some engines.

CAMSHAFT. The hollow camshaft and integral camshaft gear turn on a pin that is a slip fit in flywheel side of crankcase and a drive fit in closed side of crankcase. Remove and install pin from open side (bearing plate side) of crankcase. Desired camshaft to pin running clearance is 0.001-0.0035 inch (0.025-0.0889 mm). Desired camshaft end play of 0.005-0.010 inch (0.127-0.254 mm) is controlled by use of 0.005 and 0.010 inch thick spacer washers between camshaft and cylinder block at bearing plate side of crankcase.

On models equipped with automatic timing advance, the ignition spark advance weights, springs and weight pivot

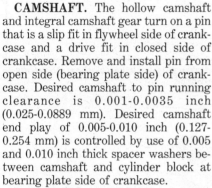

Fig. KO22—Use sequence shown above to tighten cylinder head cap screws to 360 in.-lbs (40.7 N·m) on Models K-241, K-301 and K-321.

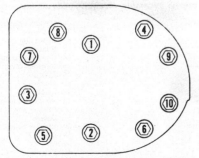

Fig. KO23—On Model K-341, tighten cylinder head cap screws evenly, in sequence shown, to a torque of 360 in.-lbs. (40.7 N·m).

pins are renewable separately from camshaft gear. When reinstalling camshaft in engine, be sure breaker cam is correctly installed. Spread the springs as shown in Fig. KO9 and install breaker cam on tangs of flyweights with timing marks on cam and camshaft gear aligned as shown.

Some engines may be equipped with an Automatic Compression Release Camshaft. Engines so equipped do not have a spark advance mechanism. See Figs. KO19 and KO20. To check compression on engines equipped with Automatic Compression Release, engines must be turned over at 650 rpm or higher to overcome compression release action. A reading can also be obtained by turning engine over in reverse direction with throttle wide open. Compression reading should be 110-120 psi (758-827 kPa) on an engine in top mechanical condition. When compression reading falls below 100 psi (689 kPa), it indicates leaking rings or valves.

CYLINDER HEAD. Always use a new head gasket when installing cylinder head. Tighten cylinder head cap screws evenly and in steps using the correct sequence shown in Fig. KO21, KO22 or KO23.

VALVE SYSTEM. Cam follower (valve tappet) gap cold is as follows:
Models K-161, K-181
Intake . . . . 0.006-0.008 in.
(0.152-0.203 mm)
Exhaust . . . . 0.015-0.017 in.
(0.381-0.432 mm)
Models K-241, K-301, K-321, K-341
Intake . . . . 0.008-0.010 in.
(0.203-0.254 mm)
Exhaust . . . . 0.017-0.020 in.
(0.432-0.508 mm)
Correct gap is obtained by grinding ends of valve stems on Models K-161 and K-181. Be sure to grind end square and remove all burrs from end of stem after grinding. Models K-241, K-301, K-321 and K-341 have adjustable cam followers.

The exhaust valve seats on a renewable seat insert on all models. The intake valve seats directly on machined seat in cylinder block on some models. On all Models K-321 and K-341 and some other models, a renewable intake valve seat insert is used. Valve face and seat angle is 45 degrees. Desired seat width is 1/32 to 1/16-inch (0.8-1.6 mm).

Valve guides are available for all models and after being pressed into block, guides must be reamed to obtain correct valve stem to guide clearance.

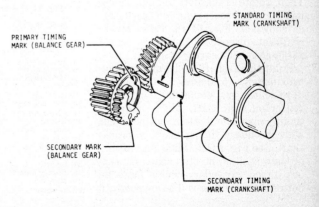

Fig. KO25—View showing timing marks for installing dynamic balance gears.

Valve stem to guide clearance for all models is as follows:

Intake . . . . 0.001-0.0025 in.
(0.025-0.0635 mm)
Exhaust . . . . 0.0025-0.004 in.
(0.0635-0.102 mm)

DYNAMIC BALANCER. A dynamic balance system (Fig. KO24) is used on some K-241 and K-301 engines and all K-321 and K-341 engines. The two balance gears, equipped with needle bearings, rotate on two stub shafts which are pressed into bosses on pto side of crankcase. Snap rings secure gears on stub shafts and shim spacers are used to control gear end play. The balance gears are driven by crankshaft in opposite direction of crankshaft rotation. Use following procedure to install and time dynamic balancer components.

To install new stub shafts, press shafts into special bosses in crankcase until they protrude 0.735 inch (18.669 mm) above thrust surface of bosses, if stub shaft boss is about 7/16-inch (11 mm) above main bearing boss. If stub shaft boss is only 1/16-inch (1.6 mm) above main bearing boss, press shaft in until end of shaft is 1.110 inch (28.194 mm) above stub shaft boss. See Fig. KO26.

To install top balance gear-bearing assembly, first place one 0.010 inch shim spacer on stub shaft and then slide top gear assembly on shaft. Timing marks must face flywheel side of crankcase. Install one 0.005, one 0.010 and one 0.020 inch shim spacers in this order, then install snap ring. Using a feeler gage, check gear end play. Proper end play of balance gear is 0.005-0.010 inch (0.127-0.254 mm). Add or remove 0.005 inch thick spacers as necessary to obtain correct end play.

NOTE: Always install the 0.020 inch thick spacer next to snap ring.

Install crankshaft in crankcase and align primary timing mark on top balance gear with standard timing mark on crankshaft. See Fig. KO25. With primary timing marks aligned, engage crankshaft gear 1/16-inch (1.6 mm) into narrow section of top balance gear. Then, rotate crankshaft to align timing marks on camshaft gear and crankshaft as shown in Fig. KO18. Press crankshaft into crankcase until it is seated firmly into ball bearing main.

Rotate crankshaft until crankpin is approximately 15 degrees past bottom dead center. Install one 0.010 inch shim spacer on stub shaft. Align secondary timing mark on bottom balance gear with secondary timing mark on crankshaft. See Fig. KO25. Slide gear assembly into position on stub shaft. If properly timed, secondary timing mark on bottom balance gear will be aligned with

standard timing mark on crankshaft after gear is fully on stub shaft. Install one 0.005 and one 0.020 inch shim spacer, then install snap ring. Check bottom balance gear end play and add or

remove 0.005 inch thick spacers as required to obtain proper end play of 0.005-0.010 inch (0.127-0.254 mm). Make certain the 0.020 inch shim spacer is used against snap ring.

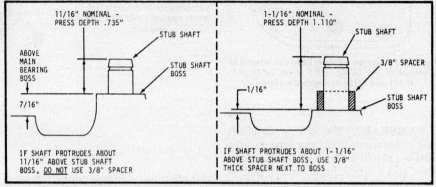

Fig. KO26 — Views showing correct dimensions used when pressing in new balancer stub shafts on models so equipped.

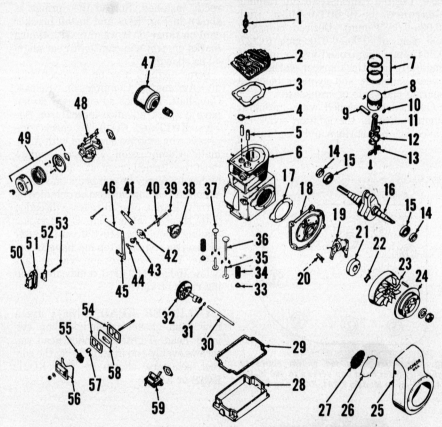

Fig. KO27 — Exploded view of Model K-181 basic engine assembly. Model K-161 is similar.

1. Spark plug
2. Cylinder head
3. Head gasket
4. Exhaust valve seat
5. Valve guide
6. Cylinder block
7. Piston rings
8. Piston
9. Piston pin
10. Retaining rings
11. Connecting rod
12. Rod cap
13. Rod bolt lock
14. Oil seal
15. Ball bearing
16. Crankshaft
17. Gasket
18. Bearing plate
19. Magneto
20. Condenser

21. Magneto rotor
22. Wave washer
23. Flywheel
24. Pulley
25. Shroud
26. Screen retainer
27. Screen
28. Oil pan
29. Gasket
30. Camshaft pin
31. Shim washer
32. Camshaft
33. Spring retainer
34. Valve spring
35. Valve tappet
36. Intake valve
37. Exhaust valve
38. Governor gear & weight assy.
39. Needle bearing

40. Governor shaft
41. Bracket
42. Speed disc
43. Bushing
44. Governor spring
45. Governor lever
46. Link
47. Muffler
48. Carburetor
49. Air cleaner assy.
50. Breaker cover
51. Gasket
52. Breaker points
53. Push rod
54. Gaskets
55. Filter
56. Valve cover
57. Breather seal
58. Reed plate
59. Fuel pump

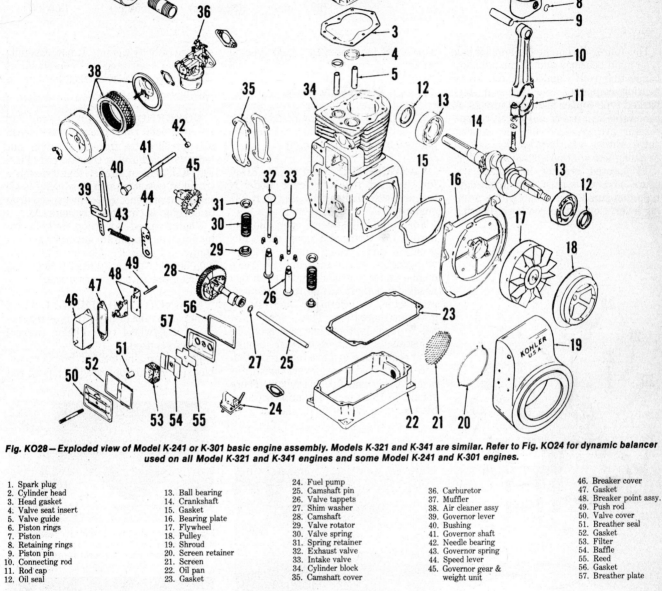

Fig. KO28—Exploded view of Model K-241 or K-301 basic engine assembly. Models K-321 and K-341 are similar. Refer to Fig. KO24 for dynamic balancer used on all Model K-321 and K-341 engines and some Model K-241 and K-301 engines.

1. Spark plug
2. Cylinder head
3. Head gasket
4. Valve seat insert
5. Valve guide
6. Piston rings
7. Piston
8. Retaining rings
9. Piston pin
10. Connecting rod
11. Rod cap
12. Oil seal

13. Ball bearing
14. Crankshaft
15. Gasket
16. Bearing plate
17. Flywheel
18. Pulley
19. Shroud
20. Screen retainer
21. Screen
22. Oil pan
23. Gasket

24. Fuel pump
25. Camshaft pin
26. Valve tappets
27. Shim washer
28. Camshaft
29. Valve rotator
30. Valve spring
31. Spring retainer
32. Exhaust valve
33. Intake valve
34. Cylinder block
35. Camshaft cover

36. Carburetor
37. Muffler
38. Air cleaner assy
39. Governor lever
40. Bushing
41. Governor shaft
42. Needle bearing
43. Governor spring
44. Speed lever
45. Governor gear &
    weight unit

46. Breaker cover
47. Gasket
48. Breaker point assy.
49. Push rod
50. Valve cover
51. Breather seal
52. Gasket
53. Filter
54. Baffle
55. Reed
56. Gasket
57. Breather plate

KOHLER

Model	No. Cyls.	Bore	Stroke	Displacement	Horsepower
K331	1	3-5/8 in. (92.1 mm)	3-1/4 in. (82.5 mm)	33.6 cu. in. (550 cc)	12.5 (9.3 kW)

This four-cycle engine has annular ball type main bearings and aluminum alloy connecting rod. Connecting rod lower bearing comprises two precision steel backed type copper lead shell inserts. A renewable seat insert and a positive type rotator are provided for the exhaust valve. Either a battery ignition system or a magneto ignition system with externally located breaker and automatic spark advance is used. The diaphragm type fuel pump is provided with a priming lever. Connecting rod lower bearing is pressure lubricated by a gear type oil pump.

MAINTENANCE

SPARK PLUG. Recommended plug is Champion J8 or equivalent. Electrode gap is 0.025 inch (0.635 mm).

CARBURETOR. Refer to Fig. KO30 for exploded view of Carter Model N carburetor similar to that used on K-331 engines.

For initial adjustment, open idle fuel needle 1½ turns and open main fuel needle 2 turns. Make final adjustment with engine warm and running. Place engine under load and adjust main fuel needle for leanest setting that will allow satisfactory acceleration and steady governor operation. Then, adjust idle needle for smoothest idle operation. As adjustments affect each other, adjustment sequence may have to be repeated.

To check float lever, invert carburetor body casting and float assembly. There should be 13/64-inch (5.2 mm) clearance between free side of float and machined surface of body casting. If not, carefully bend float lever tang that contacts inlet valve to provide correct float level measurement.

GOVERNOR. Maximum no-load speed is 3600 rpm. The governed speed is controlled by throttle position but length of carburetor throttle rod (TR – Fig. KO31) must be such that it matches travel of governor arm to which it is attached at one end. Excessive speed drop or surging is controlled by nuts (A).

Engine speed governor weights are mounted on a separate governor gear as shown in Fig. KO32. Governor gear has a 0.0005-0.0015 inch (0.0127-0.0381 mm) interference fit on governor shaft.

MAGNETO AND TIMING. Either a Bendix-Scintilla crankshaft type magneto or a flywheel type Phelon (Repco) magneto is used.

The externally located breaker contacts (KO33) are operated by a push rod

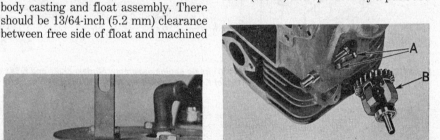

Fig. KO30 — Exploded view of typical Carter Model "N" carburetor.

1. Main fuel needle
2. Spring
3. Carburetor body
4. Choke shaft
5. Choke disc
6. Choke detent
7. Sealing washer
8. Inlet valve seat
9. Inlet valve
10. Float pin
11. Float
12. Gasket
13. Float bowl
14. Sealing washer
15. Retainer
16. Main jet
17. Plug
18. Spring
19. Idle stop screw
20. Throttle disc
21. Idle fuel needle
22. Spring
23. Throttle shaft

Fig. KO31 — View of carburetor adjustment points and variable speed governor linkage.

A. Sensitivity adjustment
B. Main fuel needle
C. Idle stop screw
D. Idle fuel needle
E. Choke lever
TR. Throttle rod

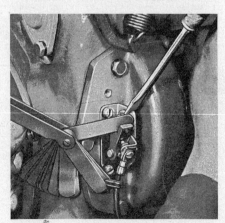

Fig. KO32 — View showing governor gear and flyweight assembly (B) removed from engine. Governor yoke is shown at (A).

Fig. KO33 — Ignition breaker points are located externally on engine crankcase for either magneto or battery ignition.

actuated by a removable cam located in and driven by a separate flyweight governor in gear end of camshaft as shown in Fig. KO34A. This governor varies the angular position of breaker cam in accordance with engine speed to provide automatic advance of ignition timing. Note assembly marks "A" and "B" which must be in register when assembling breaker cam to governor.

A timing inspection port is provided in the bearing plate and there are two timing marks on the flywheel. Satisfactory timing is obtained by adjusting breaker contact gap to 0.018-0.020 inch (0.457-0.508 mm). For precision timing, use a timing light and adjust breaker gap until the first or "SP" timing mark is centered in inspection port, engine running at high idle speed.

BATTERY IGNITION. Battery ignition is generally used on electric starting engines. An automotive type Delco-Remy coil and condenser are used with this system. However, since breaker points and adjustments are the same as with magneto ignition, refer to previous paragraph for adjustment procedure.

LUBRICATION. Engine is pressure lubricated by a gear type oil pump. High quality detergent type oil having API classification "SC", "SD", "SE" or "SF" should be used. Use SAE 30 oil in Summer; SAE 10 in Winter. For engine crankcase capacity, refer to condensed specifications for tractor model.

CRANKCASE BREATHER. A reed valve assembly is located in valve spring compartment to maintain a partial vacuum in crankcase and thus reduce leakage of oil at bearing seals. If a slight amount of crankcase vacuum is not present, reed valve is faulty or engine has

excessive blow-by past rings and/or valves.

REPAIRS

TIGHTENING TORQUES. Recommended tightening torque valves are as follows:

Spark plug . . . . .22 ft.-lbs.
(29.8 N·m)
Connecting rod . . . .See CONNECTING
ROD paragraph
Cylinder head . . . . .40 ft.-lbs.*
(54.2 N·m)
Flywheel nut. . . . . .100 ft.-lbs.
(135.5 N·m)
*With lubricated threads.

CONNECTING ROD. Connecting rod and piston unit is removed from above after removing cylinder head and oil pan (engine base). The aluminum alloy connecting rod is fitted with renewable crankpin bearing inserts, but rides directly on the piston pin. Refer to the following specifications:

Desired Clearances:
Rod to crankpin . . . . . .0.0003-0.0023 in.
(0.0076-0.0584 mm)
Rod to piston pin . . . . .0.0003-0.0008 in.
(0.0076-0.0203 mm)
Rod side play on
crankpin . . . . .0.007-0.011 in.
(0.178-0.279 mm)
Crankpin diameter is 1.873 inches (47.574 mm). Crankpin bearing inserts for connecting rod are available in undersizes of 0.002, 0.010 and 0.020 inch as well as standard size. If crankpin is only moderately worn, the 0.002 inch undersize bearing inserts can be installed. If crankpin is excessively worn, out-of-round or scored, crankpin can be reground for use with the 0.010 or 0.020 inch undersize bearing inserts. Piston pin is available in standard size and 0.005 inch oversize.

When reinstalling piston and connecting rod assembly, piston may be installed either way on connecting rod; but, match marks on connecting rod and cap must be aligned and be installed towards flywheel side of engine. See

Fig. KO34. Tighten connecting rod cap screws to a torque of 40 ft.-lbs. (54.2 N·m); then, loosen cap screws and retighten them to a torque of 35 ft.-lbs. (47.4 N·m).

PISTON RINGS, PIN AND PISTON. Two 3/32-inch (2.4 mm) compression rings and one 3/16-inch (1.6 mm) oil ring are fitted with end gap limits of 0.007-0.017 inch (0.178-0.432 mm). Side clearance of compression rings in grooves should be 0.0025-0.0045 (0.0635-0.1143 mm); oil ring 0.002-0.0035 inch (0.051 0.0889 mm). Rings of 0.010, 0.020 and 0.030 inch oversize are available.

The floating piston pin is retained in piston by a snap ring at each end. Recommended clearance of pin in the unbushed aluminum rod is 0.0003-0.0008 inch (0.0076-0.0203 mm); on piston bosses, 0.0001-0.0003 inch (0.0025-0.0076 mm). Oversize pin is available.

Aluminum alloy piston should have a clearance of 0.0005-0.0015 inch (0.0127-0.0381 mm) in cylinder bore measured at top of skirt thrust face below the ring belt. Reject piston if a new piston ring has 0.005 inch (0.127 mm) or more side clearance in top ring groove.

CYLINDER HEAD. Always use new head gasket when installing cylinder head. Tighten cylinder head cap screws evenly to a torque of 40 ft.-lbs. (54.2 N·m) using sequence shown in Fig. KO35.

CYLINDER BLOCK. If cylinder walls are scored or bore is tapered or out-of-round more than 0.005 inch (0.127 mm), cylinder should be resized to next standard oversize. Standard cylinder bore diameter is 3.625 inches (92.075 mm).

CAMSHAFT ASSEMBLY. Camshaft and gear assembly should have 0.001-0.0025 inch (0.025-0.0635 mm) running clearance on camshaft support

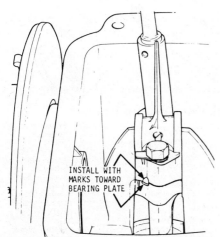

Fig. KO34—When installing connecting rod and piston unit, be sure alignment marks on rod and cap are aligned and are facing toward flywheel side of engine.

Fig. KO34A—View showing alignment marks on ignition breaker cam and camshaft gear. Spread springs as indicated by arrows and insert cam on drive tangs of weights.

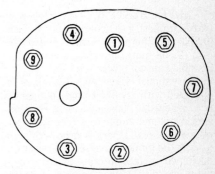

Fig. KO35—Tighten cylinder head cap screws evenly to a torque of 40 ft.-lbs. (54.2 N·m) using sequence shown.

pin. Similar clearance should exist between breaker cam and camshaft pin. Desired camshaft end play of 0.005-0.010 inch (0.127-0.254 mm) is controlled by spacer washers (44–Fig. KO37) which are available in thicknesses of 0.005 and 0.010 inch. Ignition advance cam weights are mounted on the face of cam gear. Check weights to make sure they work freely through their full travel. Ignition breaker cam should be installed with mark (A–Fig. KO34A) in register with mark (B) on cam gear.

Camshaft pin is a slip fit in open (flywheel) side of crankcase and a press fit in closed (pto) side of crankcase. Remove and install pin from open side of crankcase.

CRANKSHAFT. The crankshaft is supported in two ball bearing mains. Crankshaft end play should be 0.005-0.011 inch (0.127-0.279 mm). End play is controlled by thickness of gasket used between crankcase and bearing plate (closure plate). Gaskets are available in thicknesses of 0.005, 0.010 and 0.020 inch.

When installing crankshaft, align timing mark (A–Fig. KO36) on crankshaft with mark (B) on camshaft gear.

Crankcase gear (15–Fig. KO37) should have an interference fit of 0.001-0.0015 inch (0.025-0.0381 mm) on crankshaft. Install crankshaft main bearings in crankcase and bearing plate with shielded side of ball bearings toward inside of crankcase. Install oil seals with lips to inside of crankcase. Use a tapered protective sleeve or tape over crankshaft keyways to prevent damage to seals.

Oil transfer sleeve (13–Fig. KO37) is a press fit in crankcase between oil seal (12) and main bearing (14) at pto end of crankshaft. Oil clearance between transfer sleeve and crankshaft should be 0.001-0.0035 inch (0.025-0.0889 mm). Oil holes in sleeve must be aligned with oil passage in crankcase. Purpose of transfer sleeve is to conduct oil to drilled passage in crankshaft for lubrication of crankpin bearing.

VALVE SYSTEM. Cam follower (valve tappet) gap (cold) is 0.008 inch (0.203 mm) for intake valve and 0.020 inch (0.508 mm) for exhaust valve. Adjustable cam followers are used.

The exhaust valve on all engines is equipped with a valve rotator and seats in a renewable hardened alloy steel insert. On some engines, a renewable intake valve seat insert is used although usually the intake valve seats directly on machined surface in crankcase and cylinder casting. Desired valve seat width is 1/32-inch (0.8 mm). If valve seat width exceeds 1/16-inch (1.6 mm), narrow seat

Fig. KO36—When installing crankshaft, align marked tooth of crankshaft gear (A) with timing mark (B) on camshaft gear.

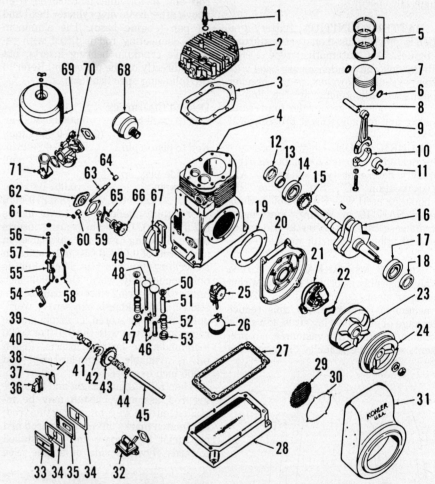

Fig. KO37—Exploded view of Model K-331 basic engine assembly.

1. Spark plug
2. Cylinder head
3. Head gasket
4. Cylinder block
5. Piston rings
6. Retaining rings
7. Piston
8. Piston pin
9. Connecting rod
10. Rod cap
11. Rod bearing
12. Oil seal
13. Oil transfer sleeve
14. Ball bearing
15. Crankshaft gear
16. Crankshaft
17. Ball bearing
18. Oil seal
19. Gasket (0.005, 0.010, & 0.020 in.)
20. Bearing plate
21. Magneto
22. Wave washer
23. Flywheel
24. Pulley
25. Oil pump
26. Oil strainer
27. Gasket
28. Oil pan
29. Screen
30. Screen retainer
31. Shroud
32. Fuel pump
33. Valve cover
34. Gaskets
35. Breather plate
36. Breaker cover
37. Breaker points
38. Push rod
39. Spacer
40. Breaker cam
41. Advance spring
42. Advance weight
43. Camshaft
44. Shim spacer
45. Camshaft pin
46. Valve tappets
47. Valve rotator
48. Exhaust valve
49. Intake valve
50. Spring seat
51. Valve guide
52. Valve spring
53. Spring retainer
54. Throttle arm
55. Control arm
56. Link
57. Governor spring
58. Throttle extension
59. Bushing
60. Needle bearing
61. Oil seal
62. Governor cover
63. Governor shaft
64. Needle bearing
65. Yoke
66. Governor gear & weight unit
67. Camshaft cover
68. Fuel pump
69. Air cleaner
70. Carburetor
71. Air intake elbow

using 30 and 60-degree cutters or stones; then, renew seating surface with 45-degree cutter or stone. Valve face and seat angle is 45 degrees.

Desired clearance for intake valve stem in guide is 0.0005-0.002 inch (0.0127-0.051 mm) and for exhaust valve stem in guide is 0.002-0.0035 inch (0.051-0.0889 mm). Renew valve guides if clearance of new valve stem in guide is excessive. Clearance of cam followers in bores of crankcase should be 0.0008-0.0023 inch (0.0203-0.0584 mm).

Free length of intake valve spring should be 2¼ inches (57 mm) and free length of exhaust valve spring should be 1-13/16 inches (46 mm). Renew spring if free length is not approximately equal to specified free length.

OIL PUMP. A gear type oil pump is used to supply lubricating oil under pressure to the connecting rod. A sudden drop in oil pressure may be caused by dirt or foreign particles in the oil pump. Sometimes it is possible to discon-

nect oil line to oil pressure gage and dislodge foreign material by forcing compressed air into the pump. Pump pressure is adjusted at factory. Should it be necessary to readjust oil pressure, turn screw in pump body to left to decrease pressure or to right to increase pressure. Seal screw with permatex or equivalent sealer when adjustment is completed.

When installing pump assembly, check pump drive gear for backlash and alignment with camshaft gear.

KOHLER
SERVICING KOHLER ACCESSORIES

RETRACTABLE STARTERS
Fairbanks-Morse or Eaton retractable starters are used on some Kohler engines. When servicing starters, refer to appropriate following paragraph.

Fairbanks-Morse

OVERHAUL. To disassemble starter, remove retainer ring, retainer washer, brake spring, friction washer, friction

shoe assembly and second friction washer as shown in Fig. KO50. Hold rope handle in one hand and cover in the other and allow rotor to rotate to unwind recoil spring preload. Lift rotor from cover, shaft and recoil spring.

NOTE: Check winding direction of recoil spring and rope for aid in reassembly. Remove recoil spring from cover and unwind rope from rotor.

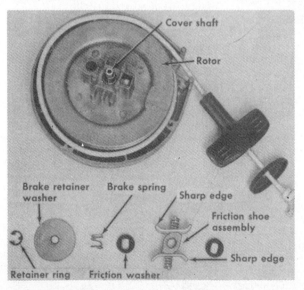

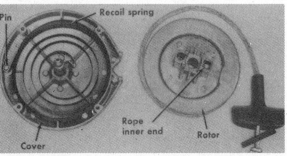

Fig. KO51—View showing recoil spring and rope installed for counter-clockwise starter operation.

When reassembling unit, lubricate recoil spring, cover shaft and its bore in rotor with Lubriplate or equivalent. Install rope in rotor and rotor to the shaft and engage recoil spring inner end hook. Preload recoil spring four turns and install middle flange and mounting flange. Check friction shoe sharp ends and renew if necessary. Install friction washers, friction shoe assembly, brake spring, retainer ring. Make certain friction shoe assembly is installed properly for correct starter rotation. If properly installed, sharp ends of friction shoe plates will extend when rope is pulled.

Starter operation can be reversed by winding rope and recoil spring in opposite direction and turning friction shoe assembly upside down. See Fig. KO51 for counter-clockwise assembly and Fig. KO52 for clockwise assembly.

Eaton

OVERHAUL. To disassemble starter, first release tension of rewind spring as follows: Hold starter assembly with pulley facing up. Pull starter rope until notch in pulley is aligned with rope hole in cover. Use thumb pressure to prevent pulley from rotating. Engage rope in notch of pulley and slowly release thumb pressure to allow spring to unwind until all tension is released.

When removing rope pulley, use extreme care to keep starter spring confined in housing. Check starter spring for breaks, cracks or distortion. If starter spring is to be renewed, carefully remove it from housing, noting direction of rotation of spring before removing. Exploded view of clockwise starter is shown in Fig. KO53.

Check the pawl, brake, spring, retainer and hub for wear and renew as

Fig. KO50—Fairbanks-Morse starter with friction shoe assembly removed.

necessary. If starter rope is worn or frayed, remove from pulley, noting direction it is wrapped on pulley. Renew rope and install pulley in housing, aligning notch in pulley hub with hook in end of spring. Use a wire bent to form a hook to aid in positioning spring on hub.

After securing pulley assembly in housing, align notch in pulley with rope bushing in housing. Engage rope in notch and rotate pulley at least two full turns in same direction it is pulled to properly preload starter spring. Pull rope to fully extended position. Release handle and if spring is properly preloaded, rope will fully rewind.

Before installing starter on engine, check teeth in starter driven hub (165 – Fig. KO54) for wear and renew hub if necessary.

12-VOLT STARTER-GENERATOR

The combination 12-volt starter-generator manufactured by Delco-Remy is used on some Kohler engines. The starter-generator functions as a cranking motor when starting switch is closed. When engine is operating and with starting switch open, unit operates as a generator. Generator output and circuit voltage for battery and various operating requirements are controlled by a current-voltage regulator.

Kohler recommends starter-generator belt tension be adjusted until about 10 pounds (44.5N) pressure applied midway between pulleys will deflect belt ¼-inch (6 mm).

To determine cause of abnormal operation, starter-generator should be given a "no-load" test or a "generator output" test. The generator output test can be performed with starter-generator on or off the engine. The no-load test must be made with starter-generator removed from engine. Refer to Fig. KO55 for exploded view of starter-generator assembly. Parts are available from Kohler as well as authorized Delco-Remy service stations.

Starter-generator and regulator service test specifications are as follows:

Starter-Generators 1101940, 1101970, 1101973, 1101980
Brush spring tension . . . . 24-32 oz.
(680-900g)

Field draw:
Amperes 1.52-1.62
Volts 12
Cold output:
Amperes .12
Volts 14
RPM 4950
No-load test:
Volts 11
Amperes, max. 18
Rpm., min. 2500
Rpm., max. 2900

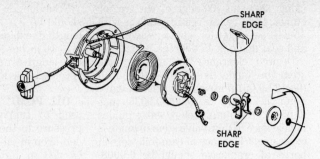

Fig. KO52 – For clockwise starter operation, reverse friction shoe assembly and wind rope and recoil spring in opposite direction.

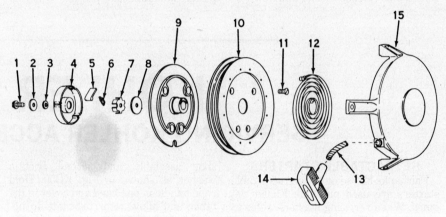

Fig. KO53 – Exploded view of Eaton retractable starter.

1. Retainer screw	6. Spring	11. Screw
2. Brake washer	7. Brake	12. Recoil spring
3. Spacer	8. Thrust washer	13. Rope
4. Retainer	9. Pulley hub	14. Handle
5. Pawl	10. Pulley	15. Starter housing

Starter-Generators 1101932, 1101948, 1101968, 1101972, 1101974
Brush spring tension . . . . 24-32 oz.
(680-900g)

Field draw:
Amperes 1.45-1.57
Volts 12
Cold output:
Amperes .10
Volts 14
Rpm 5450
No-load test:
Volts 11
Amperes, max. 17
Rpm., min. 2500
Rpm., max. 2900

Starter-Generators 1101951, 1101967
Brush spring tension . . . . 24-32 oz.
(680-900g)

Field draw:
Amperes 1.52-1.62
Volts 12
Cold output:
Amperes .15
Volts 14
Rpm 3400
No-load test:
Volts 11
Amperes, max. 14
Rpm., min. 1650
Rpm., max. 1950

Starter-Generator 1101996
Brush spring tension . . . . 24-32 oz.
(680-900g)

Field draw:
Amperes 1.52-1.62
Volts 12
Cold output:
Amperes .12
Volts 14
Rpm 4950
No-load test:
Volts 11
Amperes, max. 18
Rpm., min. 2500
Rpm., max. 2900

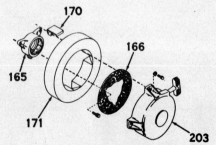

Fig. KO54 – View showing retractable starter and starter hub.

165. Starter hub	171. Air director
166. Screen	203. Retractable starter
170. Bracket	assy.

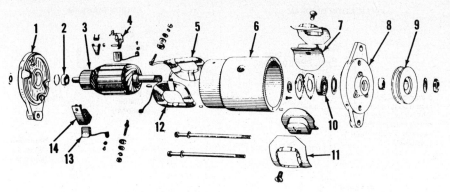

Fig. KO55—Exploded view of typical Delco-Remy starter-generator assembly.

1. Commutator end frame
2. Bearing
3. Armature
4. Ground brush holder
5. Field coil L.H.
6. Frame
7. Pole shoe
8. Drive end frame
9. Pulley
10. Bearing
11. Field coil insulator
12. Field coil R.H.
13. Brush
14. Insulated brush holder

Regulators 1118984, 1118988, 1118999

Ground polarity .... Negative
Cut-out relay:
  Air gap .... 0.020 in. (0.508 mm)
  Point gap ...... 0.020 in. (0.508 mm)

Closing voltage, range 11.8-14.0
  Adjust to 12.8
Voltage regulator:
  Air gap .... 0.075 in. (1.905 mm)
  Setting volts, range 13.6-14.5
  Adjust to 14.0

Regulator 1118985

Ground polarity .... Positive
Cut-out relay:
  Air gap .... 0.020 in. (0.508 mm)
  Point gap .... 0.020 in. (0.508 mm)
  Closing voltage, range 11.8-14.0
  Adjust to 12.8
Voltage regulator:
  Air gap .... 0.075 in. (1.905 mm)
  Setting volts, range 13.6-14.5
  Adjust to 14.0

12-VOLT GEAR DRIVE STARTERS

Two types of gear drive starters are used on Kohler engines. Refer to Figs. KO56 and KO57 for exploded views of starter motors and drives.

TWO BRUSH COMPACT TYPE. To disassemble starting motor, clamp mounting bracket in a vise. Remove through-bolts (H – Fig. KO56) and slide commutator end plate (J) and frame assembly (A) off armature. Then, clamp steel armature core in vise and remove Bendix drive retaining nut. Remove Bendix drive (E), drive end plate (F), thrust washer (D) and spacer (C) from armature (B).

Renew brushes if unevenly worn or worn to a length of 5/16-inch (8 mm) or less. To renew ground brush (K), drill out rivet, then rivet new brush lead to end plate. Field brush (P) is soldered to field coil lead.

Reassemble by reversing disassembly procedure. Lubricate bushings with a light coat of SAE 10 oil. Inspect Bendix drive pinion and splined sleeve for damage. If Bendix is in good condition, wipe clean and install completely dry. Tighten Bendix drive retaining nut to a torque of 130-150 in.-lbs. (14.7-17 N·m). Tighten through-bolts (H) to a torque of 40-55 in.-lbs. (4.5-6 N·m).

PERMANENT MAGNET TYPE. To disassemble starting motor, clamp mounting bracket in vise and remove through-bolts (19 – Fig. KO57). Carefully slide end cap (10) and frame (11) off armature. Clamp steel armature core in vise and remove nut (18), spacer (17), anti-drift spring (16), drive assembly (15), end plate (14) and thrust washer (13) from armature (12).

The two input brushes are part of terminal stud (6). The other two brushes (9) are secured with cap screws. When reassembling, lubricate bushings with American Bosch lubricant #LU3001 or equivalent. Do not lubricate starter drive. Use rubber band to hold brushes in position until started in commutator, then cut and remove rubber band. Tighten through-bolts to a torque of 80-95 in. lbs. (9-10.7 N·m) and nut (18) to a torque of 90-110 in.-lbs. (10.2-12.4 N·m).

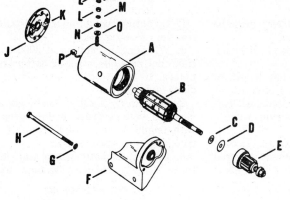

Fig. KO56—Exploded view of 2-brush compact gear drive starting motor.

A. Frame & field coil assy.
B. Armature
C. Spacer
D. Thrust washer
E. Bendix drive assy.
F. Drive end plate & mounting bracket
G. Lockwasher
H. Through-bolt
J. Commutator end plate
K. Ground brush
L. Terminal nuts
M. Lockwashers
N. Flat washer
O. Insulating washer
P. Field brush

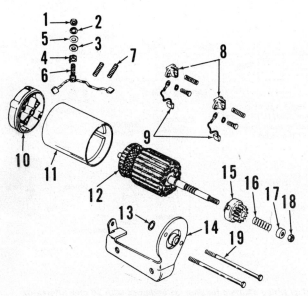

Fig. KO57—Exploded view of permanent magnet type starting motor.

1. Terminal nut
2. Lockwasher
3. Insulating washer
4. Terminal insulator
5. Flat washer
6. Terminal stud & input brushes
7. Brush springs (4 used)
8. Brush holders
9. Brushes
10. Commutator end cap
11. Frame & permanent magnets
12. Armature
13. Thrust washer
14. Drive end plate & mounting bracket
15. Drive assy.
16. Anti-drift spring
17. Spacer
18. Nut
19. Through-bolts

FLYWHEEL ALTERNATORS

3 AMP ALTERNATOR. The 3 amp alternator consists of three major components; a permanent magnet ring with five or six magnets on flywheel rim, a stator assembly and a diode in charging output lead. See Fig. KO58.

To avoid possible damage to charging system, the following precautions must be observed:

1. Negative post of battery must be connected to engine ground.

2. Prevent alternator leads (AC) from touching or shorting.

3. Remove battery or disconnect battery cables when recharging battery with battery charger.

4. Do not operate engine for any length of time without a battery in system.

5. Disconnect plug before electric welding is done on equipment powered by and in common ground with engine.

TROUBLESHOOTING. Trouble conditions and possible causes are as follows:

1. No output. Could be caused by:
   a. Faulty windings in stator.
   b. Defective diode.
   c. Broken lead wire.
2. No lighting. Could be caused by:
   a. Shorted stator wiring.
   b. Broken lead.

If "No output" condition is the trouble, run the following tests:

1. With engine running 3000 rpm, check battery voltage across battery terminals with a DC voltmeter. If 12.5 volts or less, stator or diode is defective.

2. Run engine at 3000 rpm and disconnect battery charging lead to ground. If 15 volts or more, stator is OK.

3. Disconnect battery charge lead from battery, measure resistance of lead to ground. Reverse ohmmeter leads and take another reading. One reading should be infinity ohms and the other reading should be about mid-scale with meter set at R x 1. If both readings are low, diode is shorted. If both readings are high, diode or stator is open.

4. Expose diode connections on battery charge lead. Check resistance on stator side of ground. Reading should be 1 ohm. If 0 ohms, winding is shorted. If infinity ohms, stator winding is open or lead wire is broken.

If "no lighting" is the trouble, use an AC voltmeter and measure open circuit voltage from lighting lead to ground with engine running at 3000 rpm. If 15 volts or more, stator is OK; if less than 15 volts, wiring may be shorted.

Check resistance of lighting lead to ground. If 0.5 ohms, stator is OK; 0 ohms, stator is shorted; infinity ohms, stator is open or lead is broken.

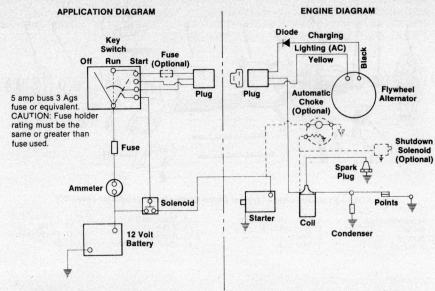

Fig. KO58 — Typical electrical wiring diagram for engines equipped with 3 amp alternator.

3/6 AMP ALTERNATOR. The 3/6 amp alternator has three major components: a permanent magnet ring with six magnets on flywheel rim, a stator assembly and two diodes located in battery charging lead and auxiliary load lead. See Fig. KO59.

To avoid possible damage to charging system, the following precautions must be observed:

1. Negative post to battery must be connected to engine ground.

2. Prevent alternator leads (AC) from touching or shorting.

3. Do not operate for any length of time without a battery in system.

4. Remove battery or disconnect battery cables when recharging battery with battery charger.

5. Disconnect plug before electric welding is done on equipment powered by and in common ground with engine.

TROUBLESHOOTING. Trouble conditions and their possible causes are as follows:

1. No output. Could be caused by:
   a. Faulty stator.
   b. Defective diode.
   c. Broken lead wire.
2. No lighting. Could be caused by:
   a. Shorted stator.
   b. Broken lead wire.

If "no output" condition is the trouble, run the following tests:

1. With engine running at 3000 rpm, check battery voltage across battery terminals. If 12.5 volts or less, stator or diode is defective.

2. Disconnect auxiliary load lead and measure voltage from lead to ground with engine running 3000 rpm. If 17 volts or more, stator is OK.

3. Disconnect battery charging lead from battery. Measure voltage from

Fig. KO59 — Typical electrical wiring diagram for engines equipped with 3/6 amp alternator.

APPLICATION DIAGRAM   ENGINE DIAGRAM

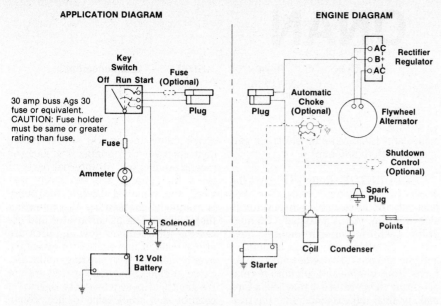

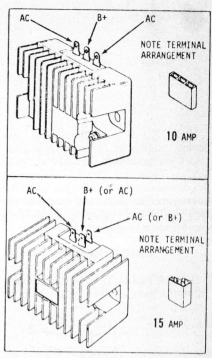

Fig. KO60—Typical electrical wiring diagram for engines equipped with 15 amp alternator and breaker point ignition. The 10 amp alternator is similar.

Fig. KO61—Rectifier-regulators used with 10 amp and 15 amp alternators. Although similar in appearance, units must not be interchanged.

charging lead to ground with engine running at 3000 rpm. If 17 volts or more, stator is OK.

4. Disconnect battery charge lead from battery and auxiliary load lead from switch. Measure resistance of both leads to ground. Reverse ohmmeter leads and take readings again. One reading should be infinity and the other reading should be about mid-scale with meter set at R x 1. If both readings are low, diode is shorted. If both readings are high, diode or stator is open.

5. Expose diode connections on battery charging lead and auxiliary load lead. Check resistance on stator side of diodes to ground. Readings should be 0.5 ohms. If reading is 0 ohms, winding is shorted. If infinity ohms, stator winding is open or lead wire is broken.

If "no lighting" is the condition, disconnect lighting lead and measure open circuit voltage with AC voltmeter from lighting lead to ground with engine running at 3000 rpm. If 22 volts or more, stator is OK. If less than 22 volts, wiring may be shorted.

Check resistance of lighting lead to ground. If 0.5 ohms, stator is OK; 0 ohms, stator is shorted; infinity ohms, stator is open or lead is broken.

ALTERNATOR AND RECTIFIER-REGULATOR (10 AND 15 AMP).
Either a 10 amp or 15 amp flywheel alternator is used on some engines. Alternator output is controlled by a solid state rectifier-regulator.

To avoid possible damage to alternator system, the following precautions

must be observed:

1. Negative post of battery must be connected to ground on engine.

2. Rectifier-regulator must be connected in common ground with engine and battery.

3. Disconnect leads at rectifier-regulator if arc welding is to be done on equipment in common ground with engine.

4. Remove battery or disconnect battery cables when recharging battery with battery charger.

5. Do not operate engine with battery disconnected.

6. Make certain AC leads are prevented from being grounded at all times.

OPERATION. Alternating current (AC) produced by the alternator is changed to direct current (DC) in rectifier-regulator unit. See Fig. KO60. Current regulation is provided by electronic devices which "sense" countervoltage created by battery to control or limit charging rate. No adjustments are possible on alternator charging system. Faulty components must be renewed. Refer to the following troubleshooting paragraph to help pinpoint faulty part.

TROUBLESHOOTING. Trouble conditions and their possible causes are as follows:

1. No output. Could be caused by:
  a. Faulty windings in stator.
  b. Defective diode(s) in rectifier.
  c. Rectifier-regulator not properly grounded.

2. Full charge-no regulation. Could be

caused by:
  a. Defective rectifier-regulator.
  b. Defective battery (unable to hold charge).

If "no output" condition is the trouble, disconnect B+ cable from rectifier-regulator (Fig. KO61). Connect a DC voltmeter between B+ terminal on rectifier-regulator and clean ground surface on engine. Start engine and operate at 3600 rpm. DC voltage should be above 14 volts. If reading is above 0 volts but less than 14 volts, check for defective rectifier-regulator or if reading is 0 volts, check for defective rectifier-regulator or defective stator as follows: Disconnect AC leads from rectifier-regulator, Connect an AC voltmeter to the two AC leads. With engine operating at 3600 rpm, check AC voltage. If reading is less than 20 volts (10 amp alternator) or 28 volts (15 amp alternator), stator is defective. If reading is more than 20 volts (10 amp alternator) or 28 volts (15 amp alternator), rectifier-regulator is defective.

If "full charge-no regulation" is the trouble, use a DC voltmeter and check B+ to ground with engine operating at 3600 rpm. If reading is over 14.7 volts, rectifier-regulator is defective. If reading is under 14.7 volts and over 14.0 volts, alternator and rectifier-regulator are satisfactory and battery is probably defective (unable to hold charge).

ONAN

Model	No. Cyls.	Bore	Stroke	Displacement
NB	1	3-9/16 in.	3 in.	30 cu. in.
		(90.5 mm)	(76.2 mm)	(492 cc)

Model NB is a single-cylinder, air-cooled, engine of "L"-head configuration. Cylinder bore is vertical and crank-shaft is horizontal. This model develops 6.5 horsepower at 1800 rpm and 12.0 horsepower at 3600 rpm. Compression ratio is 7:1 and engine is splash-lubricated from a two quart oil sump.

MAINTENANCE

SPARK PLUG. This engine calls for a 14 mm Champion H-8 spark plug or

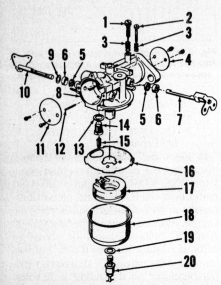

Fig. O1—Exploded view of carburetor used on NB model engine.

1. Idle mixture needle
2. Throttle stop screw
3. Spring
4. Throttle plate
5. Seal
6. Seal retainer
7. Throttle shaft
8. Body
9. Washer
10. Choke shaft
11. Choke plate
12. Float pin
13. Washer
14. Fuel inlet valve
15. Needle valve
16. Gasket
17. Float
18. Float bowl
19. Washer
20. Main jet

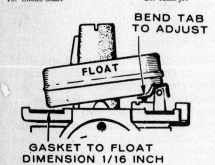

BEND TAB TO ADJUST

FLOAT

GASKET TO FLOAT DIMENSION 1/16 INCH

Fig. O2—Float level on Model NB carburetor should be 1/16-inch (1.6 mm) measured from gasket.

equivalent. Required plug electrode gap is 0.025 inch (0.635 mm).

CARBURETOR. Refer to Fig. O1 for details of carburetor construction. Set inlet valve of disassembled carburetor as shown in Fig. O2. A 1/16-inch (1.6 mm) drill is useful for measurement of float setting. To adjust carburetor, back main and idle fuel mixture needles out 1 to 1½ turns. Start engine and run until normal operating temperature is reached before making final adjustments. Idle mixture screw should be adjusted for smooth running at recommended idle speed which should be set using throttle stop screw. Main fuel mixture should be set with engine running under load. Turn screw inward until engine loses speed, then back out again until engine handles load without laboring. If it is difficult or impractical to operate engine under load, set main fuel mixture for even acceleration from idle speed to rated rpm. Use a tachometer or revolution counter for exact setting of rpm recommendations set forth in CONDENSED SPECIFICATIONS at beginning of section covering tractor to be serviced.

FUEL PUMP. NB engines are equipped with mechanical fuel pumps of

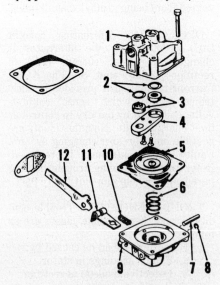

Fig. O3—Exploded view of early fuel pump used on Model NB engines.

1. Upper body
2. Gaskets
3. Valves
4. Valve retainer
5. Diaphragm
6. Spring
7. Pin
8. Snap ring
9. Lower body
10. Spring
11. Spring
12. Lever

styles shown in Fig. O3 or O4, dependent upon whether engine is of early or recent production. All internal parts of these fuel pumps are separately serviced. Performance check of fuel pump is routinely checked by disconnecting fuel delivery line at carburetor and observing for adequate flow and pressure at open end of line while turning engine over by hand or with starting motor. Because engines mounted on tractors are frequently exposed to dusty operating conditions, it is advisable to check condition of fuel line from tank to pump as well. Be sure lines and any in-line filters used are in good condition.

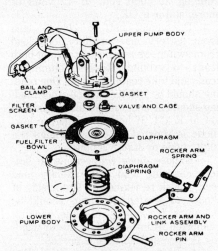

Fig. O4—Exploded view of new style mechanical fuel pump on current NB models.

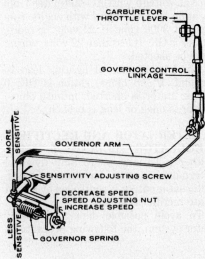

Fig. O5—Governor controls for Model NB. Refer to text for adjustment procedure.

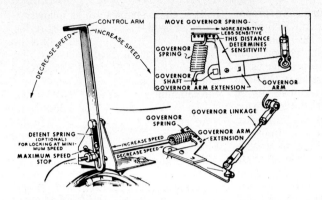

Fig. O6—ONAN variable speed governor. Note adjustment points and refer to text.

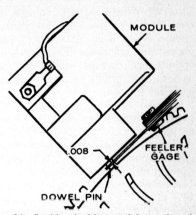

Fig. O8—Position ignition module so there is 0.008 inch (0.203 mm) gap between trigger pin and module pin.

GOVERNOR. Occasional adjustment of tractor engine governors is required to maintain idle and high operating speed within acceptable limits. Worn parts, binding linkages, dirt and improper connections can all contribute to unsatisfactory operation.

Certain general principles apply to all mechanical governor service:

When engine is halted, throttle plate is held wide open. Engine is restarted at wide open throttle.

Control linkage is adjusted by turning threaded ball joint on rod to shorten or lengthen link from governor arm to throttle lever. See Fig. O5.

Engine rpm under load is dependent upon tension of governor spring. See adjusting nut on governor spring stud as shown in Fig. O5 to make corrections.

Governor sensitivity is actual rapidity of response to changes in load or power demand. Sensitivity (or quickness of response) is increased as spring is moved closer to governor arm pivot point and decreased as spring is moved farther away. Note sensitivity adjustment screw function in Fig. O5. When governor is over-sensitive, engine will surge or "hunt". The opposite condition results in an unresponsive, sluggish engine. See Figs. O5 and O6 for applications.

Perform actual adjustment as follows:

Be sure carburetor and ignition system are adjusted to specifications. Refer to Fig. O16 in REPAIRS section, following and be sure governor drive assembly on camshaft and compression relief are fully operational.

Now, in sequence, disconnect throttle linkage at carburetor end (Fig. O5 or O6). Place throttle control in full speed position and hold throttle lever in wide open position. Adjust length of control linkage by turning threaded rod so link stud will fit easily in its hole in throttle lever. Reattach linkage.

Carefully check for binding, then proceed to adjust sensitivity, slow idle rpm and specified high idle and full load rpm after engine is running and warmed up. See REPAIRS section if governor drive does not operate normally.

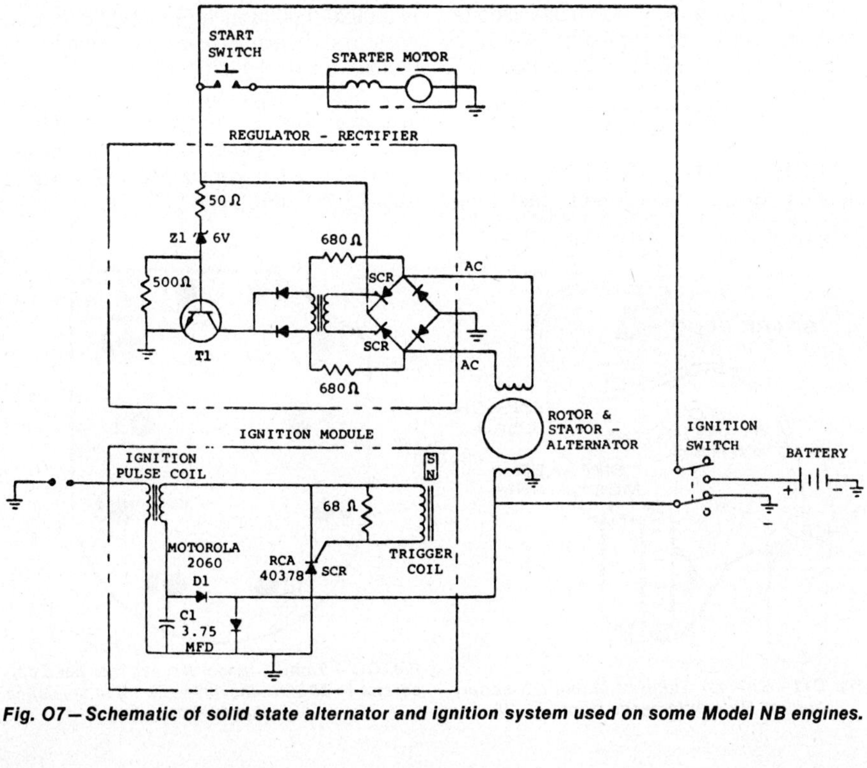

IGNITION. All types of ignition used on Model NB engines are considered. Refer to appropriate following paragraph.

SOLID STATE BREAKERLESS IGNITION. Some tractors are equipped with a capacitor discharge ignition system and a solid state regulator-rectifier. Only moving part is the revolving flywheel with its charging magnets and a trigger pin on its circumference. See Fig. O7 for system circuit diagram.

Operation of capacitive discharge system is as follows: Current generated by coil at flywheel passes through diode (D1 – Fig. O7) and is stored in capacitor (C1). As trigger pin of flywheel passes trigger coil in module, SCR (silicon controlled rectifier) is energized through its gate and capacitor (C1) will discharge through the ignition coil to generate a high voltage spark at the spark plug.

Ignition timing is non-adjustable. To properly energize trigger coil, gap between trigger pin on flywheel and pin of ignition module should be set at 0.008 inch (0.203 mm) as shown in Fig. O8. To adjust, loosen module mounting bolts and position module so correct gap is obtained. Recheck gap after tightening module.

Regulator-rectifier operation is as follows: When battery (Fig. O7) is not up to full charge, SCR's in bridge rectifier circuit shown in Fig. O7 are turned on allowing rectifying of alternating current from alternator to provide DC to charge the battery. When battery reaches full charge, zener diode (Z1) passes current to allow transistor to operate. When transistor (T1) passes current by its switching action, gate voltage is removed from SCR's of bridge rectifier and charging current ceases to flow to

Fig. O7—Schematic of solid state alternator and ignition system used on some Model NB engines.

battery. When battery voltage decreases due to use such as cranking engine, zener diode (Z1) will stop passing current, transistor (T1) will cease to operate and current will be switched back through bridge rectifier to battery as SCR's turn on.

In order to check regulator-rectifier output, orange wire must be disconnected from its terminal on rectifier and a DC voltmeter connected between this open terminal and ground. With engine running at high rpm, voltage should be 14.5 volts or more. If voltage is less than 14.5, alternator output must be checked. To do so, disconnect green wires from regulator-rectifier and connect an AC voltmeter across open ends of these wires. At high engine rpm, AC voltage should reach or exceed 20 volts. If voltage is less, alternator stator is defective and should be renewed. If alternator voltage is correct and regulator-rectifier voltage is deficient, regulator-rectifier is defective. It is normal to renew regulator-rectifier as a unit, however, in some cases individual parts may be serviced. Parts sources should be checked.

MAGNETO IGNITION. Breaker point gap for magneto equipped NB engines is 0.020 inch (0.508 mm). Adjust gap after turning engine by hand about ¼ turn past TDC when points are fully open. Be sure points are in serviceable condition with mating surfaces in proper alignment. Renew if defective. Ignition timing is set for 22° BTDC against flywheel index mark on compression stroke. Most accurate procedure is to connect a continuity test lamp between external breaker box terminal and a good ground on engine to determine exactly when points open. Shift breaker box upward to retard spark timing or downward to advance. Tighten breaker box mounting screws securely after adjustment. See Fig. O9 for wiring layout for magneto ignition. Fig. O10 provides a view of breaker box. Note that magneto coil assembly of this system is **grounded.**

BATTERY IGNITION. Ignition timing and breaker point service for this system is identical to that used for magneto system which precedes. Check differences between Fig. O9 and Fig. O11 and note that in battery ignition system, coil is not grounded. Refer to FLYWHEEL ALTERNATOR section following for service to optional 20 amp alternator system.

LUBRICATION. Engine lubricating oils approved by manufacturer for this model must meet requirements of API service classification SE or SE/CC. Manufacturer specifies that DS (CD) oils not be used. Oil change interval should be shortened when unit is operated in extremely dusty conditions. Crankcase breathers should be serviced and cleaned regularly for continuous engine protection. Crankcase capacity is 2 quarts (1.9L).

Some NB engines were fitted with gear type oil pumps. Pump parts are not serviced, so in the unlikely event of failure, entire pump must be renewed.

REPAIRS

TIGHTENING TORQUES. Recommended torque values for fastening bolts in these engines are as follows:

Cylinder head ....29-31 ft.-lbs.
　　　　　　　　　　(39.3-42 N·m)
Rear bearing plate ....30-35 ft.-lbs.
　　　　　　　　　　(40.7-47.4 N·m)
Connecting rod
　Aluminum ....24-26 ft.-lbs.
　　　　　　　　　　(32.5-35.2 N·m)
　Forged ....27-29 ft.-lbs.
　　　　　　　　　　(36.6-39.2 N·m)
Flywheel
　Zinc or aluminum ....30-35 ft.-lbs.
　　　　　　　　　　(40.7-47.4 N·m)
　Cast iron ....40-45 ft.-lbs.
　　　　　　　　　　(54.2-61 N·m)
Oil base ....38-43 ft.-lbs.
　　　　　　　　　　(51.5-58.2 N·m)
Gearcase cover ....14-18 ft.-lbs.
　　　　　　　　　　(19-24.3 N·m)
Spark plug ....15-20 ft.-lbs.
　　　　　　　　　　(20.3-27 N·m)
Starter mounting ....25-30 ft.-lbs.
　　　　　　　　　　(33.9-40.6 N·m)

CYLINDER HEAD. Removable cylinder head should be torqued down in 5-10 ft.-lbs. (7-13 N·m) steps to value shown in table preceding, when engine is cold. Use tightening sequence shown in Fig. O12 and re-torque when engine has been run-in.

CONNECTING ROD. Rod and piston are removed together from top end of cylinder bore. Use a ridge reamer first if ridge at top of bore is prominent. Aluminum connecting rod used on some NB models is fitted directly to crankpin journal. Forged connecting rods have precision bearing inserts. Crankpin diameter is 1.6252-1.6260 inch (41.280-41.300 mm). Connecting rod bearing clearance is 0.0020-0.0033 inch (0.051-0.0838 mm) with rod bearing inserts available on 0.002, 0.010, 0.020 and 0.030 inch undersizes. Aluminum connecting rods are available in undersizes of 0.010, 0.020 and 0.030 inch. Bearing side clearance required is from 0.002 to 0.016 inch (0.051-0.406 mm).

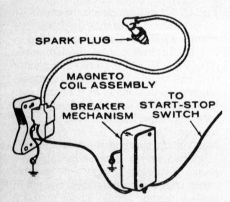

Fig. O9—External wiring for magneto ignition system used on Model NB.

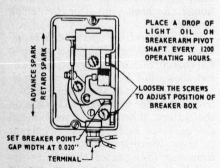

Fig. O10—View of ignition breaker box used on Model NB. Timing and point adjustment procedure is typical.

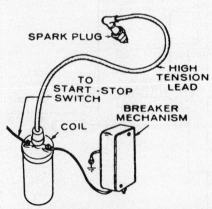

Fig. O11—External wiring of Model NB battery ignition. Note differences from Fig. O9.

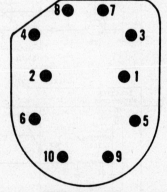

Fig. O12—Tighten Model NB cylinder head cap screws to 29-31 ft.-lbs. (39-42 N·m) in sequence shown above.

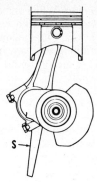

Fig. O13—Be sure oil slinger (S) is installed in position shown on Model NB.

Correct fitting of renewed rods or bearings calls for use of plastigage for accurate measurement. Witness marks on rods and caps should be matched and installed facing toward camshaft. In some cases, witness marks may be substituted for by numbers. If so, these should be installed to face camshaft.

PISTON, PIN AND RINGS. Two compression rings and one oil control ring are used. Required piston ring end gap is 0.010-0.020 inch (0.254-0.508 mm). Standard honed cylinder bore is 3.5625-3.5635 inches (90.4875-90.5129 mm) with a standard piston diameter of 3.56000-3.5610 inches (90.424-90.449 mm). Clearance of piston in cylinder bore, measured at right angles to piston pin just below oil ring groove is 0.0015-0.0035 inch (0.0381-0.0889 mm). Oversize pistons and rings for rebored cylinders are available at 0.010, 0.020, 0.030 and 0.040 inch for this engine.

Side clearance of new piston rings in grooves should be from 0.002 to 0.008 inch (0.051-0.203 mm). Renew piston if larger figure is exceeded. Both compression ring grooves are 0.0955-0.0965 inch (2.426-2.451 mm) wide and oil control ring groove measures 0.1880-0.1890 inch (4.775-4.800 mm) in new piston. Compression rings in renewal sets are installed with legend "TOP" (or other mark to indicate taper of ring) toward head of piston. Oil rings are furnished with a ribbon type expander only. No side rails are used. Stagger ring end gaps by one-third circumference from one another before refitting piston in engine bore.

Piston pins, 0.7500-0.7502 inch (19.050-19.055 mm) diameter, are a light push fit into bores of piston bosses. Piston pins, oversized by 0.002 inch are available, and should be installed if standard pin drops through dry bore of used piston of its own weight. Refit snap rings at opposite ends of piston pin bore to retain.

If cylinder requires boring, it should be honed to about 0.002 inch (0.05 mm) under finish bore diameter using 100-grit stones and finish-honed to final diameter with 300-grit stones. Be sure honing leaves a cross-hatch pattern distinctly visible in finished cylinder bore. Iron liners which are precision-cast into aluminum cylinder blocks are not renewable.

CRANKSHAFT, BEARINGS AND SEALS. Two renewable sleeve-type main bearings are used to support crankshaft in this engine. See Fig. O14 for details. These are precision bearings, not to be line-reamed. Main bearing journal diameter of crankshaft is 1.9992-2.0000 inches (50.7797-50.8 mm), and specified bearing clearance is 0.0025-0.0038 inch (0.0635-0.0965 mm). Under-size bearings are available with diameters reduced by 0.002, 0.010, 0.020 and 0.030 inch. Recommended crankshaft end play is 0.006-0.012 inch (0.152-0.305 mm). Crankshaft end play is checked by feeler gage measurement between crank shoulder and thrust washer after rear main bearing plate is reinstalled and torqued to specifications. Shims are fitted between bearing plate and thrust washer to make this adjustment. It is accepted as good practice to turn crankshaft during bearing plate installation to ensure free movement.

For easier fitting of renewal main bearings, best procedure is to heat crankcase and rear bearing plate to expand bearing bores and to chill-shrink new bearing sleeves before insertion. Be sure oil holes in bearings are aligned with oil supply holes in bores in which they are fitted.

Renewal of front oil seal requires removal of timing gear cover. Bearing plate must be removed for removal of rear crankshaft oil seal. Lip of seal is installed facing inward. Seal must be pressed into bottom against shoulder of bearing plate bore. Two types of gear cover oil seals have been used, one being thicker than the other. Be sure to determine which is furnished from parts stock. Older style (thicker) seal is pressed in so seal is 31/32-inch (24.6 mm) from gear cover mounting surface. Newer type seal is pressed in so seal is 1-7/64 inch (28.2 mm) from gear cover mounting surface. Use a seal protector or shim stock to prevent seal damage when installing gear cover and bearing plate.

CAMSHAFT AND GOVERNOR. Camshaft drive gear is a press fit on

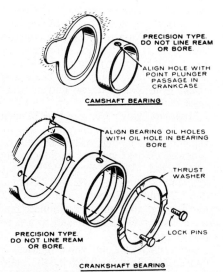

Fig. O14—Precision main and camshaft bearings used on Model NB engine. See text.

Fig. O15—Exploded view of crankshaft and camshaft assemblies used on Model NB engine.

1. Piston
2. Piston rings
3. Piston pin
4. Snap ring
5. Connecting rod
6. Drive gear
7. Crankshaft
8. Crankshaft gear
9. Washer
10. Snap ring
11. Connecting rod cap
12. Oil slinger
13. Flywheel
14. Snap ring
15. Governor cup
16. Flyballs (5)
17. Camshaft gear
18. Center pin
19. Thrust washer
20. Compression release
21. Pin
22. Camshaft

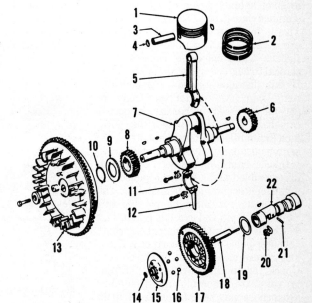

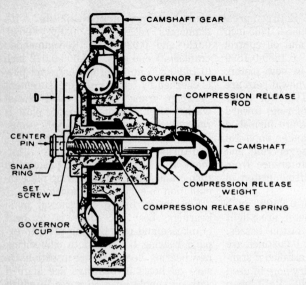

- CAMSHAFT GEAR
- GOVERNOR FLYBALL
- COMPRESSION RELEASE ROD
- CAMSHAFT
- COMPRESSION RELEASE WEIGHT
- COMPRESSION RELEASE SPRING
- CENTER PIN
- SNAP RING
- SET SCREW
- GOVERNOR CUP

Fig. O16 — View of camshaft, governor and compression release on Model NB. Distance (D) should be 7/32-inch (5.5 mm) as outlined in text.

camshaft. To remove gear, camshaft must first be completely removed from engine block. To do so, first remove cylinder head, timing gear cover, fuel pump, valves and tappets and large washer (9–Fig. O15) fitted outside crankshaft gear (8) after removing snap ring (10). Sleeve type precision bearings (see Fig. O14) and fitted into block bores at opposite ends of camshaft. No reaming is required if these bearings are renewed. Only standard sizes are available and clearance to camshaft journal should be 0.0015 to 0.0030 inch (0.0381-0.076 mm). Front (gear) end bearing is pressed in flush with outer surface of block. Rear bearing is pressed in flush with bottom of counterbore. This counterbore serves as a recess for a soft plug which seals rear of block.

Refer to Fig. O16 for view of governor weight unit assembly which fits into face of camshaft gear. Distance (D) is measured from outer face of governor cup to inner side of snap ring when cup is held in snug against governor flyballs. This distance must be 7/32-inch (5.5 mm). This is total outward travel which governor cup is allowed under pressure of flyballs when engine is running; it is critical to correct operation of governor. If this distance exceeds 7/32-inch (5.5 mm), camshaft center pin may be carefully pressed further into its bore in camshaft. If distance is less than 7/32-inch (5.5 mm), carefully grind off face of center bushing or flyball cup retainer.

In case camshaft has been completely disassembled and center pin pulled out, a new center pin must be installed. This new center pin must be pressed into camshaft so pin end extends **EXACTLY ¾-INCH** (19 mm) from end of camshaft. If center pin is installed correctly, flyball and governor movement will be correct. Check for specified 7/32-inch (5.5 mm) travel after completing assembly. Governors may have five or ten flyballs.

Tractor engines, which require a wider speed range usually have five.

IMPORTANT: When reinstalling gear cover, check length of roll pin which engages bushed hole in governor cup. This pin must extend exactly 25/32-inch (19.8 mm) from gear cover mating surface. Be sure tip of pin engages governor cup when installed.

COMPRESSION RELEASE. Fig. O16 also shows compression release mechanism used in NB engines. Additional assembly detail is shown in Fig. O15. Function of compression release is to hold exhaust valve open by about 0.020 inch (0.508 mm) during starting. Release lever retracts as centrifugal force throws weight outward, valve becomes properly seated and functions normally as engine runs. No adjustment of compression release is required.

TIMING GEARS. Engine timing gears must be renewed as a set, even if only one is damaged or defective. Removal of camshaft gear is covered in CAMSHAFT AND GOVERNOR par-

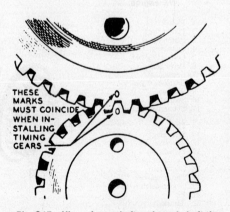

THESE MARKS MUST COINCIDE WHEN INSTALLING TIMING GEARS

Fig. O17 — View of camshaft and crankshaft timing marks.

agraph preceding. When removing cam gear from camshaft, take care not to disturb center pin. Fit a hollow tool over pin and carefully press camshaft out of gear bore. If ¾-inch (19 mm) depth setting of camshaft center pin is altered, pin must be pulled out of camshaft and renewed. Crankshaft gear may be removed by use of a conventional gear puller or by threading a pair of jack screws into tapped holes in gear to press against crank shoulder.

When new gears have been pressed on camshaft and crankshaft, be sure "O" marks on gear faces are in register to insure correct valve timing. See Fig. O17.

VALVE SYSTEM. "L"-head valve configuration is used. Valve tappet clearances are set by self-locking adjustment screws after removal of valve compartment cover. A 7/16-inch open end wrench will fit adjustment screw while a 9/16-inch wrench holds tappet from turning. Renew tappet if threads do not hold firm. Engine should be cold when valves are adjusted.

Set intake valve to 0.010 inch (0.254 mm) and exhaust valve to 0.014 inch (0.356 mm) with both valves closed and mark on flywheel aligned with "TC" mark on gear cover. Because of compression release feature of this engine, set exhaust valve clearance to 0.020 inch (0.508 mm) when making compression test, then reset to specified 0.014 inch (0.356 mm).

Face angle of valves is 44 degrees and valve seats are ground to 45 degrees to provide an interference angle of 1 degrees. Use of lapping compound is not recommended as it is likely to destroy sharp, clean edge between valve and seat furnished by this interference angle.

Renewable stellite seat is used for exhaust valve. Special ONAN tools are available for removal of these hardened seats. Best procedure for installing new exhaust inserts after recess in block is cleared is to heat block uniformly to about 300°F (150°C) and to chill-shrink new insert for fitting. New seats are available in standard size and in oversizes.

Minimum valve margin is 1/32-inch (0.8 mm). When this margin is lost by repeated machining, valve should be renewed or heat will not be adequately transferred. Valve seat width after grinding should be 1/32 to 3/64-inch (0.8-1.2 mm). Remove only enough metal when machining to eliminate pits from valve face and seat and to assure proper seating.

Stem clearance in valve guides is 0.0010-0.0025 inch (0.025-0.0635 mm) for intake valves and 0.0025-0.0040 inch (0.0635-0.102 mm) for exhaust valves.

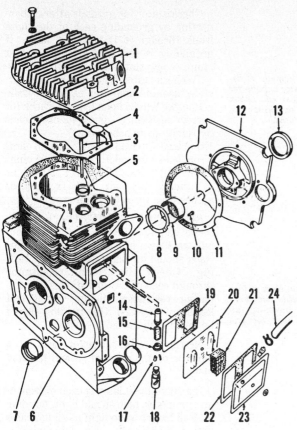

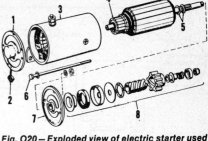

Fig. O18—Exploded view of crankcase assembly used on Model NB engine.

1. Cylinder head
2. Head gasket
3. Exhaust valve
4. Intake valve
5. Valve seat
6. Cylinder block
7. Bearing
8. Washer
9. Bearing
10. Lock pin
11. Gasket
12. Bearing plate
13. Seal
14. Valve guide
15. Valve spring
16. Spring retainer
17. Valve keepers
18. Tappet
19. Gasket
20. Baffle
21. Breather element
22. Gasket
23. Valve cover
24. Breather hose

Fig. O20 — Exploded view of electric starter used on Model NB engine.

1. End cap
2. Brush
3. Housing
4. Armature
5. Spacers
6. Bolt
7. Drive end cap
8. Drive assy.

Renewal valves and valve guides are offered only in standard size. Valve stem guides are removed and installed from within valve chamber. Press or drive with care.

Valve springs should be checked for squareness, free height and tension under compression. Do not re-use springs which are apparently distorted or damaged or which do not measure 1.662 inches (42.215 mm) in free height or which register less than 71-79 pounds (316-351N) pressure when compressed to 1-3/8 inch (35 mm) height.

Condition of valve rotators (5A–Fig. O19) used on exhaust valves in place of conventional valve spring retainers should be checked whenever cylinder head is removed. To do so, turn engine over slowly by hand observing if valve head rotates a slight amount every time valve is lifted from seat. When held open, valve should rotate freely in one direction only. Renew defective rotators.

STARTER. 12-volt electric starter used with this engine is shown in Fig. O20. Some useful service details: Armature end play should be 0.005-0.015 inch (0.127-0.381 mm). Adjust by use of spacers (5–Fig. O20). Tighten through-bolts (6) to a torque value of 35-44 in.-lbs. (4-5 N·m), armature end nut to 170-220 in.-lbs. (19-25 N·m). Brush spring tension should be 17-25 ounces (482-709 g).

No-load test specifications:
Volts 11.8
Amperes. 25
Rpm 8000

FLYWHEEL ALTERNATOR. Some NB engines may be equipped with an op-

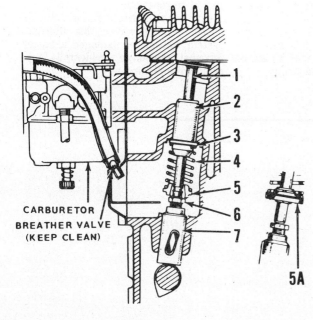

CARBURETOR
BREATHER VALVE
(KEEP CLEAN)

Fig. O19—Arrangement of valve train components on Model NB engine.

1. Valve
2. Valve guide
3. Gasket (intake only)
4. Valve spring
5. Spring retainer
5A. Rotator (exhaust only)
6. Adjuster
7. Tappet

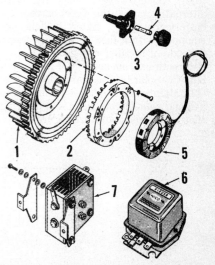

Fig. O21—Typical flywheel alternator. Appearance of stator (5) may differ and on some models, regulator (6) and rectifier (7) are combined in one unit.

1. Flywheel
2. Rotor
3. Fuse holder
4. Fuse
5. Stator & leads
6. Regulator
7. Rectifier assy.

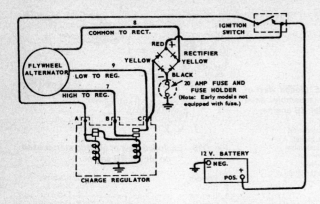

Fig. O22 – Schematic of fly-wheel alternator circuits for location of test and check points. Refer to text for procedures.

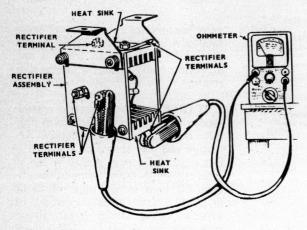

Fig. O23 – Test each of four diodes in rectifier using Volt-Ohmmeter hook-up as shown. See text for procedure.

Check stator for grounds after disconnecting by grounding each of the three leads through a 12-volt test lamp. If grounding is indicated by lighted test lamp, renew stator assembly.

To check stator for shorts or open circuits, use an ohmmeter of proper scale connected across open leads to check for correct resistance values. Identify leads by reference to schematic.

From lead 7 to lead 8 . . . . 0.25 ohms
From lead 8 to lead 9 . . . . 0.95 ohms
From lead 9 to lead 7 . . . . 1.10 ohms

Variance by over 25% from these values calls for renewal of stator.

RECTIFIER TESTS. Use an ohmmeter connected across a pair of terminals as shown in Fig. O23. All rectifier leads should be disconnected when testing. Check directional resistance through each of the four diodes by comparing resistance reading when test leads are reversed. One reading should be much higher than the other.

NOTE: Forward-backward ratio of a diode is on the order of several hundred ohms.

If a 12-volt test lamp is used instead of an ohmmeter, bulb should light, but dimly. Full bright or no light at all indicates that diode being tested is defective.

Voltage regulator may be checked for high charge rate by installing a jumper lead across regulator terminals (B and C – Fig. O22). With engine running, battery charge rate should be about 8 amps. If charge rate is low, then alternator or its wiring is defective.

If charge rate is correct (near 8 amps), defective regulator or its power circuit is indicated. To check, use a 12-volt test lamp to check input at regulator terminal (A). If lamp lights, showing adequate input, regulator is defective and should be renewed.

Engine should not be run with battery disconnected; however, this alternator system will not be damaged if battery terminal should be accidentally separated from binding post.

tional flywheel alternator. Flywheel-mounted permanent magnet rotor provides a rotating magnetic field to induce AC voltage in fixed stator coils. Current is then routed through a two-step mechanical regulator to a full-wave rectifier which converts this regulated alternating current to direct current for battery charging. Later models are equipped with a fuse between negative (−) side of rectifier and ground to protect rectifier from accidental reversal of battery polarity. See schematic, Fig. O22. Maintenance services are limited to keeping components clean and insuring that wire connections are secure.

TESTING. Check alternator output by connecting an ammeter in series between positive (+), red terminal of rectifier and ignition switch. Refer to Fig. O22. At 1800 engine rpm, a discharged battery should cause about 8 amps to register on a meter so connected. As battery charge builds up, current should decrease. Regulator will switch from high charge to low charge at about 14½ volts with low charge current of about 2 amps. Switch from low charge to high charge occurs at about 13 volts. If output is inadequate, test as follows:

Check rotor magnetism with a piece of steel. Attraction should be strong.

TECUMSEH

MEDIUM FRAME MODELS

Model	No. Cyls.	Bore	Stroke	Displacement	Horsepower
VM70	1	2-15/16 in. (74.6 mm)	2-17/32 in. (64.3 mm)	17.16 cu. in. (281 cc)	7 (5.2 kW)
VM80	1	3-1/16 in. (77.8 mm)	2-17/32 in. (64.3 mm)	18.65 cu. in. (305 cc)	8 (5.9 kW)
VM100	1	3-3/16 in. (80.9 mm)	2-17/32 in. (64.3 mm)	20.2 cu. in. (331 cc)	10 (7.5 kW)
HM70	1	2-15/16 in. (74.6 mm)	2-17/32 in. (64.3 mm)	17.16 cu. in. (281 cc)	7 (5.2 kW)
HM80	1	3 1/16 in. (77.8 mm)	2-17/32 in. (64.3 mm)	18.65 cu. in. (305 cc)	8 (5.9 kW)
HM100	1	3-3/16 in. (80.9 mm)	2-17/32 in. (64.3 mm)	20.2 cu. in. (331 cc)	10 (7.5 kW)

HEAVY FRAME MODELS

Model	No. Cyls.	Bore	Stroke	Displacement	Horsepower
VH70	1	2-3/4 in. (69.8 mm)	2-17/32 in. (64.3 mm)	15.0 cu. in. (246 cc)	7 (5.2 kW)
VH80	1	3-5/16 in. (84.1 mm)	2-3/4 in. (69.8 mm)	23.75 cu. in. (389 cc)	8 (5.9 kW)
VH100	1	3-5/16 in. (84.1 mm)	2-3/4 in. (69.8 mm)	23.75 cu. in. (389 cc)	10 (7.5 kW)
HH70	1	2-3/4 in. (69.8 mm)	2-17/32 in. (64.3 mm)	15.0 cu. in. (246 cc)	7 (5.2 kW)
HH80	1	3-5/16 in. (84.1 mm)	2-3/4 in. (69.8 mm)	23.75 cu. in. (389 cc)	8 (5.9 kW)
HH100	1	3-5/16 in. (84.1 mm)	2-3/4 in. (69.8 mm)	23.75 cu. in. (389 cc)	10 (7.5 kW)
HH120	1	3-1/2 in. (88.9 mm)	2-7/8 in. (73 mm)	27.66 cu. in. (453 cc)	12 (8.9 kW)

Engines must be identified by complete model number, including specification number in order to obtain correct repair parts. Numbers on early models are located on a name plate or tag. Numbers on later models are stamped in blower housing. It is important to transfer ID tags from original engine to replacement short block so unit can be identified later.

Medium frame engines have aluminum blocks with cast iron sleeves. Heavy frame engines have cast iron cylinder and block assemblies. Early VH70 and HH70 engines were identified as V70 and H70. Models VH and VM are vertical crankshaft engines and HM and HH models have horizontal crankshafts.

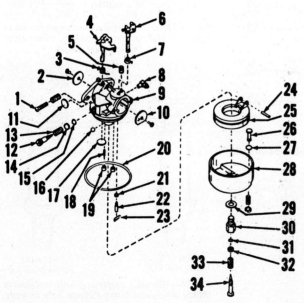

Fig. T1—Exploded view of Tecumseh carburetor.

1. Idle speed screw
2. Throttle plate
3. Return spring
4. Throttle shaft
5. Choke stop spring
6. Choke shaft
7. Return spring
8. Fuel inlet fitting
9. Carburetor body
10. Choke plate
11. Welch plug
12. Idle mixture needle
13. Spring
14. Washer
15. "O" ring
16. Ball plug
17. Welch plug
18. Pin
19. Cup plugs
20. Bowl gasket
21. Inlet needle seat
22. Inlet needle
23. Clip
24. Float shaft
25. Float
26. Drain stem
27. Gasket
28. Bowl
29. Gasket
30. Bowl retainer
31. "O" ring
32. Washer
33. Spring
34. Main fuel needle

MAINTENANCE

SPARK PLUG. Recommended spark plug is Champion J-8 or equivalent. Set electrode gap to 0.030 inch (0.762 mm). Spark plug should be removed, cleaned and adjusted periodically. Renew plug if electrodes are burned and pitted or if porcelain is cracked. If frequent plug fouling is experienced, check for following conditions:

a. Carburetor setting too rich
b. Partially closed choke
c. Clogged air filter
d. Incorrect spark plug
e. Poor grade of gasoline
f. Too much oil or crankcase breather clogged

CARBURETOR. Tecumseh or Walbro float type carburetors may be used. Adjustment and service procedures for each type carburetor is outlined in the following paragraphs.

TECUMSEH CARBURETOR. Clockwise rotation of idle mixture needle (12–Fig. T1) and main fuel adjusting needle (34) leans the mixture. Initial adjustment of both needles is 1 turn open. Final adjustment is made with engine running at normal operating temperature. Adjust main fuel needle for smoothest operation at high speed. Then, adjust idle mixture needle for smoothest engine idle. Adjust idle speed stop screw (1) for engine idle speed of 1800 rpm.

When overhauling, check adjusting needles for excessive wear or other damage. Inlet fuel needle (22) seats against a Vitron rubber seat (21) which is pressed into carburetor body. Remove rubber seat before cleaning carburetor in a commercial cleaning solvent. The seat should be installed grooved side first. See Fig. T2.

NOTE: Some later models have a Viton tipped inlet needle (Fig. T3) and a brass seat.

Install throttle plate (2–Fig. T1) with the two stamped lines facing out and at 12 and 3 o'clock position. The 12 o'clock line should be parallel to throttle shaft and to top of carburetor. Install choke plate (10) with flat side towards bottom of carburetor. Float setting should be 7/32-inch (5.5 mm), measured with body and float assembly in inverted position, between free end of float and rim on carburetor body. Fuel fitting (8) is pressed into body. When installing fuel inlet fitting, start fitting into bore; then, apply a light coat of "Loctite" (grade A) to shank and press fitting into position.

WALBRO CARBURETOR. To adjust, refer to Fig. T4 and proceed as follows: Turn both fuel adjusting needles (9 and 33) in finger tight, then back idle mixture needle (9) out 1¾ turns and main fuel needle (33) out 2 turns. Make final adjustment with engine warm and running. Adjust main fuel needle until engine runs smoothly at normal operating speed. Back out idle speed stop screw (7), hold throttle to slowest idle speed possible without stalling and adjust idle mixture needle for smoothest idle performance. Readjust idle speed screw so engine idle speed is 1800 rpm.

Float setting for Walbro carburetors is ⅛-inch (3 mm) on horizontal crankshaft engines and 3/32-inch (2.4 mm) on vertical crankshaft engines when measured with carburetor in inverted position, between free side of float and body casting rim. See H–Fig. T5. Float travel should be 9/16-inch (14 mm) as measured at free end of float. Bend lip of float tang to adjust float level.

NOTE: If carburetor has been disassembled and main nozzle (19–Fig. T4) removed, do not reinstall nozzle; obtain and install a new service nozzle. Refer to Fig. T6.

GOVERNOR. A mechanical flyweight type governor is used on all models. Governor weight and gear assembly is

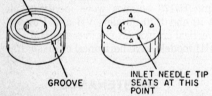

INSERT THIS FACE FIRST
GROOVE
INLET NEEDLE TIP SEATS AT THIS POINT

Fig. T2–The Viton seat used on some Tecumseh carburetors must be installed correctly to operate properly. All metal needle is used with seat shown.

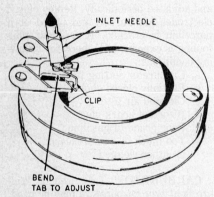

INLET NEEDLE
CLIP
BEND TAB TO ADJUST

Fig. T3–View of float and fuel inlet valve needle. The valve needle shown is equipped with resilient tip and a clip. Bend tab shown to adjust float height.

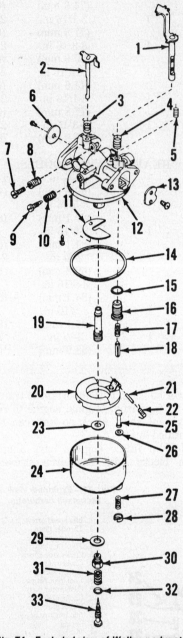

Fig. T4–Exploded view of Walbro carburetor.

1. Choke shaft
2. Throttle shaft
3. Throttle return spring
4. Choke return spring
5. Choke stop spring
6. Throttle plate
7. Idle speed stop screw
8. Spring
9. Idle mixture needle
10. Spring
11. Baffle
12. Carburetor body
13. Choke plate
14. Bowl gasket
15. Gasket
16. Inlet valve seat
17. Spring
18. Inlet valve
19. Main nozzle
20. Float
21. Float shaft
22. Spring
23. Gasket
24. Bowl
25. Drain stem
26. Gasket
27. Spring
28. Retainer
29. Gasket
30. Bowl retainer
31. Spring
32. "O" ring
33. Main fuel adjusting needle

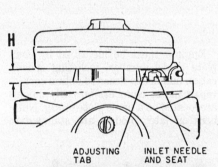

H
ADJUSTING TAB
INLET NEEDLE AND SEAT

Fig. T5–Float height (H) should be measured as shown on Walbro float carburetors. Bend adjusting tab to adjust height.

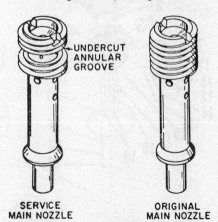

UNDERCUT ANNULAR GROOVE
SERVICE MAIN NOZZLE
ORIGINAL MAIN NOZZLE

Fig. T6–The main nozzle originally installed is drilled after installation through hole in body. Service main nozzles are grooved so alignment is not necessary.

driven by camshaft gear and rides on a renewable shaft which is pressed into engine crankcase or crankcase cover. Press governor shaft in until shaft end is located as shown in Fig. T7, T8, T9 or T10.

To adjust governor lever position on vertical crankshaft models, refer to Fig. T11. Loosen clamp screw on governor lever. Rotate governor lever shaft counter-clockwise as far as possible. Move governor lever to the left until throttle is fully open, then tighten clamp screw.

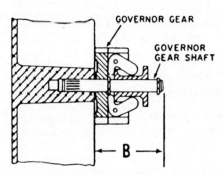

Fig. T7—View showing installation of governor shaft and governor gear and weight assembly on Models HH80, HH100 and HH120. Dimension (B) is 1 inch (25.4 mm).

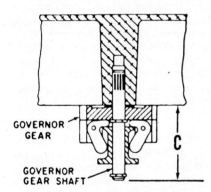

Fig. T8—Governor gear and shaft installation on Models VH80 and VH100. Dimension (C) is 1 inch (25.4 mm).

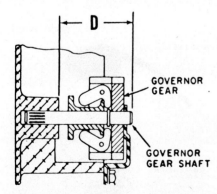

Fig. T9—Correct installation of governor shaft and gear and weight assembly on Models HH70, HM70, HM80 and HM100. Dimension (D) is 1-3/8 inches (34.9 mm) on Models HM70, HM80 and HM100 or 1-17/64 inches (32.1 mm) on Models HH70.

On horizontal crankshaft models, loosen clamp screw on lever, rotate governor lever shaft clockwise as far as possible. See Fig. T12. Move governor lever clockwise until throttle is wide open, tighten clamp screw.

For external linkage adjustments, refer to Figs. T13 and T14. Loosen screw (A), turn plate (B) counter-clockwise as far as possible and move lever (C) to the left until throttle is fully open. Tighten screw (A). Governor spring must be hooked in hole (D) as shown. Adjusting screws on bracket shown in Figs. T13 and T14 are used to adjust fixed or variable speed settings.

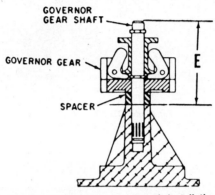

Fig. T10—Governor gear and shaft installation on Models VH70, VM70, VM80 and VM100. Dimension (E) is 1-19/32 inches (40.5 mm).

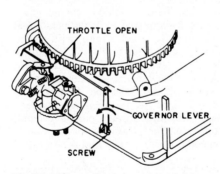

Fig. T11—When adjusting governor linkage on Models VH70, VM70, VM80 or VM100, loosen clamp screw and rotate governor lever shaft and lever counter-clockwise as far as possible.

Fig. T12—On Models HH70, HM70, HM80 and HM100, rotate governor lever shaft and lever clockwise when adjusting linkage.

MAGNETO IGNITION. Tecumseh flywheel type magnetos are used on some models. On Models VM70, HM70, VM80, HM80, VM100, HM100, HH70 and VH70, breaker points are enclosed

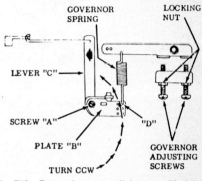

Fig. T13—External governor linkage on Models VH80 and VH100. Refer to text for adjustment procedure.

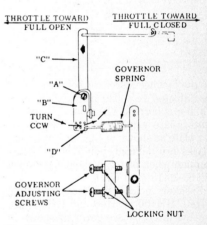

Fig. T14—External governor linkage on Models HH80, HH100 and HH120. Refer to text for adjustment procedure.

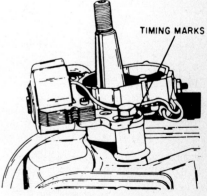

Fig. T15—On Models VM70, VH70, HM70, HH70, VM80, HM80, VM100 and HM100 equipped with magneto ignition, adjust breaker point gap to 0.020 inch (0.508 mm) and align timing marks as shown.

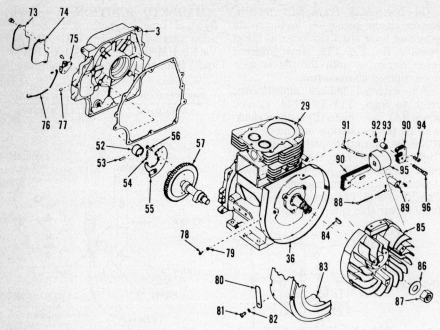

Fig. T16 — Exploded view of magneto ignition components used on Models HH80, HH100 and HH120. Timing advance and breaker points used on engines equipped with battery ignition are identical.

3. Crankcase cover	57. Camshaft assy.	88. Condenser wire
29. Cylinder block	73. Breaker box cover	89. Condenser
36. Blower air baffle	74. Gasket	90. Armature core
52. Breaker cam	75. Breaker points	91. High tension lead
53. Push rod	76. Ignition wire	92. Washer
54. Spring	77. Pin	93. Spacer
55. Timing advance weight	78. Screw	94. Screw
56. Rivet	79. Clip	95. Coil
	80. Ground switch	96. Screw
	81. Screw	
	82. Washer	
	83. Blower housing	
	84. Flywheel key	
	85. Flywheel	
	86. Washer	
	87. Nut	

by the flywheel. Breaker point gap must be adjusted to 0.020 inch (0.508 mm). Timing is correct when timing mark on stator plate is in line with mark on bearing plate as shown in Fig. T15. If timing marks are defaced, points should start to open when piston is 0.085-0.095 inch (2.159-2.413 mm) BTDC.

Breaker points on Models HH80, VH80, HH100, VH100 and HH120 are located in crankcase cover as shown in Fig. T16. Timing should be correct when points are adjusted to 0.020 inch (0.508 mm) gap. To check timing with a continuity light, refer to Fig. T17. Remove "pop" rivets securing identification plates to blower housing. Remove plate to expose timing port hole. Connect continuity light to terminal screw (78 – Fig. T16) and suitable engine ground. Rotate engine clockwise until piston is on compression stroke and timing mark

is just below stator laminations as shown in Fig. T17. At this time, points should be ready to open and continuity light should be on. Rotate flywheel until mark just passes under edge of laminations. Points should open and light should be out. If not, adjust points slightly until light goes out. The points are actuated by push rod (53 – Fig. T16) which rides against breaker cam (52). Breaker cam is driven by a tang on advance weight (55). When cranking, spring (54) holds advance weight in retarded position (TDC). At operating speeds, centrifugal force overcomes spring pressure and weight moves cam to advance ignition so spark occurs when piston is at 0.095 inch (2.413 mm) BTDC.

An air gap of 0.006-0.010 inch (0.152-0.254 mm) should be between flywheel and stator laminations. To adjust gap, turn flywheel magnet into position under coil core. Loosen holding screws and place shim stock or feeler gage between coil and magnet. Press coil against gage and tighten screws.

BATTERY IGNITION. Models HH80, HH100 and HH120 may be equipped with a battery ignition. Delco-Remy 1115222 coil and 1965489 condenser are externally mounted while points are located in crankcase cover. See Fig. T18. Points should be adjusted to 0.020 inch (0.508 mm) gap. To check timing, disconnect primary wire between coil and points and follow same procedure as described in MAGNETO IGNITION section.

SOLID STATE IGNITION (WITHOUT ALTERNATOR). The Tecumseh solid state ignition system shown in Fig. T19 may be used on some models not equipped with flywheel alternator. This system does not use ignition breaker points. The only moving part of the system is the rotating flywheel with charging magnets. As flywheel magnet passes

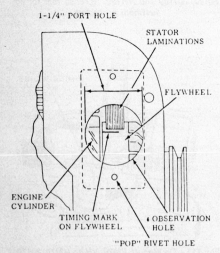

Fig. T17 — On Models HH80, HH100 and HH120, remove identification plate to observe timing mark on flywheel through port hole in blower housing.

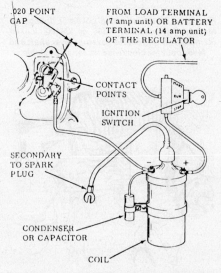

Fig. T18 — Typical battery ignition wiring diagram used on some HH80, HH100 and HH120 engines.

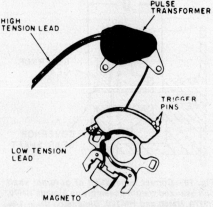

Fig. T19 — View of solid state ignition system used on some models not equipped with flywheel alternator.

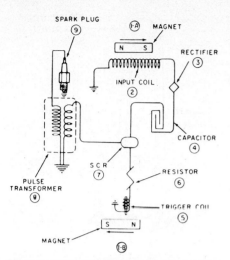

Fig. T20 — Diagram of solid state ignition system used on some models.

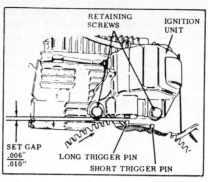

Fig. T22 — Adjust air gap between long trigger pin and ignition unit to 0.006-0.010 inch (0.152-0.254 mm).

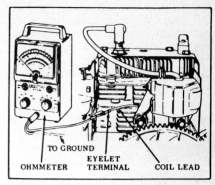

Fig. T24 — View showing an ohmmeter connected for resistance test of ignition generator coil.

position (1A – Fig. T20), a low voltage AC current is induced into input coil (2). Current passes through rectifier (3) converting this current to DC. It then travels to capacitor (4) where it is stored. The flywheel rotates approximately 180 degrees to position (1B). As it passes trigger coil (5), it induces a very small electric charge into the coil. This charge passes through resistor (6) and turns on the SCR (silicon controlled rectifier) switch (7). With SCR switch closed, low voltage current stored in capacitor (4) travels to pulse transformer (8). Voltage is stepped up instantaneously and current is discharged across electrodes of spark plug (9), producing a spark before top dead center.

Some units are equipped with a second trigger coil and resistor set to turn SCR switch on at a lower rpm. This second trigger pin is closer to the flywheel and produces a spark at TDC for easier starting. As engine rpm increases, the first (shorter) trigger pin picks up the small electric charge and turns SCR switch on, firing spark plug BTDC.

If system fails to produce a spark to spark plug, first check high tension lead Fig. T19. If condition of high tension lead is questionable, renew pulse trans-

former and high tension lead assembly. Check low tension lead and renew if insulation is faulty. The magneto charging coil, electronic triggering system and mounting plate are available only as an assembly. If necessary to renew this assembly, place unit in position on engine. Start retaining screws, turn mounting plate counter-clockwise as far as possible, then tighten retaining screw to a torque of 5-7 ft.-lbs. (7-9.5 N·m).

SOLID STATE IGNITION (WITH ALTERNATOR). The Tecumseh solid state ignition system used on some models equipped with flywheel alternator does not use ignition breaker points. The only moving part of the system is the rotating flywheel with charging magnets and trigger pins. Other components of system are ignition generator coil and stator assembly, spark plug and ignition unit.

The long trigger pin induces a small charge of current to close the SCR (silicon controlled rectifier) switch at engine cranking speed and produces a spark at TDC for starting. As engine rpm increases, the first (shorter) trigger pin induces the current which produces a spark when piston is 0.095 inch (2.413 mm) BTDC.

Test ignition system as follows: Hold high tension lead 1/8-inch (3 mm) from spark plug (Fig. T21), crank engine and check for a good blue spark. If no spark is present, check high tension lead and coil lead for loose connections or faulty insulation. Check air gap between long trigger pin and ignition unit as shown in Fig. T22. Air gap should be 0.006-0.010 inch (0.152-0.254 mm). To adjust air gap, loosen the two retaining screws and move ignition unit as necessary, then tighten retaining screws.

NOTE: The long trigger pin should extend 0.250 inch (6.35 mm) and the short trigger pin should extend 0.187 inch (4.75 mm), measured as shown in Fig. T23. If not, remove flywheel and drive pins in or out as required.

Remove coil lead from ignition terminal and connect an ohmmeter as shown in Fig. T24. If series resistance test of ignition generator coil is below 400 ohms, renew stator and coil assembly (Fig. T25). If resistance is above 400 ohms, renew ignition unit.

LUBRICATION. On Models VH70, VM70, VM80 and VM100, a barrel and plunger type oil pump (Fig. T26 or T27) driven by an eccentric on camshaft, pressure lubricates upper main bearing and connecting rod journal. When installing early type pump (Fig. T26), chamfered side of drive collar must be

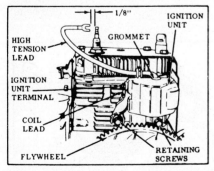

Fig. T21 — View of solid state ignition unit used on some models equipped with flywheel alternator. System should produce a good blue spark 1/8-inch (3 mm) long at cranking speed.

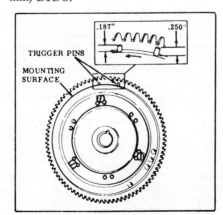

Fig. T23 — Remove flywheel and drive trigger pins in or out as necessary until long pin is extended 0.250 inch (6.35 mm) and short pin is extended 0.187 inch (4.75 mm) above mounting surface.

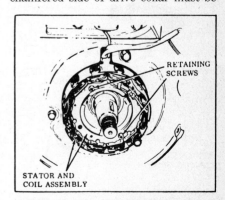

Fig. T25 — Ignition generator coil and stator serviced only as an assembly.

Tecumseh

ENGINE

against thrust bearing surface on camshaft gear. When installing late type pump, place side of drive collar with large flat surface shown in Fig. T27 away from camshaft gear.

An oil slinger (59–Fig. T28), installed on crankshaft between gear and lower

Fig. T26—View of early type oil pump used on Models VH70, VM70 and VM80. Chamfered face of drive collar should be towards camshaft gear.

Fig. T27—Install late type oil pump so large flat surface on drive collar is away from camshaft gear.

Fig. T28—Oil slinger (59) on Models VH80 and VH100 must be installed on crankshaft as shown.

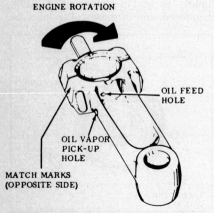

Fig. T29—Connecting rods used on Models VH80 and VH100 have two oil holes.

bearing is used to direct oil upward for complete engine lubrication on Models VH80 and VH100. A tang on slinger hub, when inserted in slot in crankshaft gear, correctly positions slinger on crankshaft as shown in Fig. T28.

Splash lubrication system on all other models is provided by use of an oil dipper on connecting rod. See Figs. T30 and T31.

Use only high quality, detergent motor oil having API classification SC, SD or SE. SAE 30 oil is recommended for operating in temperatures above 32°F (0°C) and SAE 10W for operating in temperatures below 32°F (0°C).

REPAIRS

TIGHTENING TORQUE. Recommended tightening torques are as follows:

Models VM70, HM70, VM80, HM80, VM100, HM100, HH70, VH70
Cylinder Head . . . . .180 in.-lbs.
(20.3 N·m)
Connecting Rod . . . . 120 in.-lbs.
(13.5 N·m)
Crankcase Cover . . . . 110 in.-lbs.
(12.4 N·m)
Ball Bearing Retainer
Nut .20 in.-lbs.
(2.3 N·m)

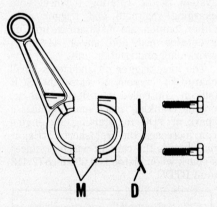

Fig. T30—Connecting rod assembly used on Models VH70, VM70, VM80, VM100, HH70, HM70, HM80 and HM100. Note position of oil dipper (D) and match marks (M).

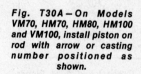

Fig. T30A—On Models VM70, HM70, HM80, HM100 and VM100, install piston on rod with arrow or casting number positioned as shown.

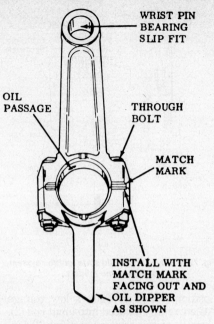

Fig. T31—Connecting rod assembly used on Models HH80, HH100 and HH120.

Flywheel Nut . . . . .440 in.-lbs.
(49.7 N·m)
Spark Plug . . . . .250 in.-lbs.
(28.2 N·m)
Magneto Stator Mounting . . . .75 in.-lbs.
(8.5 N·m)
Carburetor Mounting . . . . . . .60 in.-lbs.
(6.8 N·m)

Models HH80, VH80, HH100, VH100, HH120
Cylinder Head . . . . .200 in.-lbs.
(22.6 N·m)
Connecting Rod . . . . 110 in.-lbs.
(12.4 N·m)
Crankcase Cover . . . . 110 in.-lbs.
(12.4 N·m)
Bearing Retainer . . . . 110 in.-lbs.
(12.4 N·m)
Flywheel Nut . . . . .650 in.-lbs.
(73.5 N·m)
Spark Plug . . . . .250 in.-lbs.
(28.3 N·m)
Magneto Stator Mounting . . . .85 in.-lbs.
(9.6 N·m)
Carburetor Mounting . . . . . . .85 in.-lbs.
(9.6 N·m)

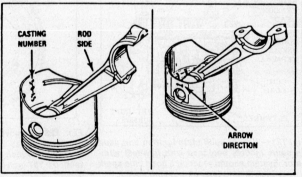

CONNECTING ROD. Piston and connecting rod assembly is removed from cylinder head end of engine. The aluminum alloy rod rides directly on the crankshaft. Running clearance is not adjustable. Crankpin diameter is 1.1865-1.1870 inches (30.137-30.150 mm) on Models VM70, HM70, VM80, HM80, VM100, HM100, HH70 and VH70 and 1.3750-1.3755 inches (34.925-34.938 mm) on all other models.

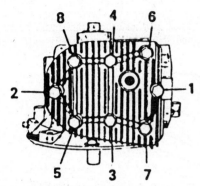

Fig. T32—On Models VM70, HM70, VH70 and HH70, tighten cylinder head cap screws evenly to a torque of 180 in.-lbs. (20 N·m) using tightening sequence shown.

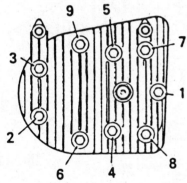

Fig. T33—Tighten cylinder head cap screws on Models HM80, VM80, HM100 and VM100 in sequence shown to a torque of 180 in.-lbs. (20 N·m).

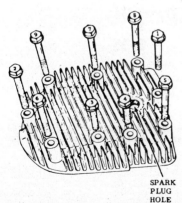

Fig. T34—View showing cylinder head cap screw tightening sequence used on early HH80, HH100 and HH120 engines. Tighten cap screws to a torque of 200 in.-lbs. (22.6 N·m). Note type and length of cap screws.

Connecting rods are equipped with match marks and on some models pistons are marked for correct assembly. See Figs. T29, T30, T30A and T31. Install rod on all models so marks are toward pto end of crankshaft. Use new self-locking nuts or rod bolt lock each time rod is installed.

CYLINDER HEAD. When removing cylinder head, be sure to note location of different length cap screws for aid in correct assembly. Always install new head gasket and tighten cap screws evenly in sequence shown in Figs. T32, T33, T34 or T35. Refer to TIGHTENING TORQUE section for correct torque values.

PISTON, PIN AND RINGS. Aluminum alloy piston is fitted with two compression rings and one oil control ring. Ring end gap on all models should be 0.010-0.020 inch (0.254-0.508 mm). Side clearance of new rings in ring grooves of a new piston should be 0.002-0.0035 inch (0.051-0.0889 mm) on Models HH80, HH100, HH120; 0.0025-0.003 inch (0.0635-0.076 mm) on Models VH80 and VH100; 0.002-0.003 inch (0.051-0.076 mm) on Models VM70, HM70, HM80, VM80, HH70, VH70; 0.002-0.005 inch (0.051-0.127 mm) on Models VM100 and HM100. Piston rings and pistons are available in standard size and oversizes of 0.010 and 0.020 inch for Models VM70, HM70, VM80, HM80, VM100, HM100, HH70 and VH70 or in standard size and oversizes of 0.010, 0.020, 0.030 and 0.040 inch for all other models.

The top compression ring must be installed with inside chamfer to top of piston. If second compression ring has a notch on outside of ring, install ring with notch towards bottom of piston skirt. Oil

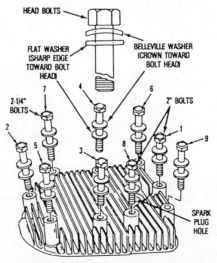

Fig. T35—Flat washers and Belleville washers are used on cylinder head cap screws on late HH80, HH100 and HH120 and all VH80 and VH100 engines. Tighten cap screws in sequence shown to a torque of 200 in.-lbs. (22.6 N·m).

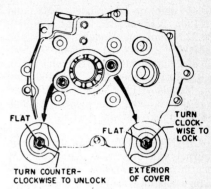

Fig. T36—View showing bearing locks on Models HM70, HH70, HM80 and HM100 equipped with ball bearing main. Locks must be released before removing crankcase cover. Refer to Fig. T37 for interior view of cover and locks.

ring can be installed either side up. Stagger ring gaps about 90 degrees around piston.

Piston skirt clearance in cylinder, measured at thrust side of piston just below oil ring, should be 0.010-0.012 inch (0.254-0.305 mm) on Model HH120; 0.006-0.008 inch (0.152-0.203 mm) on HH80 and HH100; 0.003-0.004 inch (0.076-0.203 mm) on VH80 and VH100; 0.0045-0.006 inch (0.1143-0.152 mm) on all other models.

Piston pin diameter is 0.6248-0.6250 inch (15.870-15.875 mm) on Models VM70, HM70, VM80, HM80, VM100, HM100, HH70 and VH70 or 0.6873-0.6875 inch (17.457-17.462) on all other models. Piston pin clearance should be 0.0001-0.0008 inch (0.0025-0.0203 mm) in rod and 0.0002-0.0005 inch (0.0051-0.0127 mm) in piston. If excessive clearance exists, both piston and pin must be renewed as pin is not available separately.

CYLINDER. If cylinder is scored or if taper or out-of-round exceeds 0.005 inch (0.127 mm), cylinder should be rebored to next suitable oversize. Standard cylinder bore is 2.9375-2.9385 inches (74.6125-74.6379 mm) on Models VM70 and HM70; 3.062-3.063 inches (77.775-77.800 mm) on early Models VM80 and HM80; 3.125-3.126 inches (79.375-

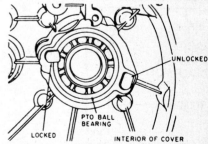

Fig. T37—Interior view of crankcase cover and ball bearing locks used on Models HM70, HH70, HM80 and HM100.

79.400 mm) on late Models VM80 and HM80; 3.187-3.188 inches (80.950-80.975 mm) on Models VM100 and HM100; 2.750-2.751 inches (69.850-69.875 mm) on Models HH70 and VH70; 3.312-3.313 inches (84.125-84.150 mm) on Models HH80, VH80, HH100 and VH100; 3.500-3.501 inches (88.900-88.925 mm) on Model HH120.

CRANKSHAFT. Crankshaft main journals ride directly in aluminum alloy bearings in crankcase and mounting flange (engine base) on vertical crankshaft engines or in two renewable steel backed bronze bushings. On some horizontal crankshaft engines, crankshaft rides in a renewable sleeve bushing at flywheel end and a ball bearing or bushing at pto end. Models HH80, VH80, HH100, VH100 and HH120 are equipped with taper roller bearings at both ends of crankshaft.

Normal running clearance of crankshaft journals in aluminum bearings or bronze bushings is 0.0015-0.0025 inch (0.0381-0.0635 mm). Renew crankshaft if main journals are more than 0.001

inch (0.025 mm) out-of-round or if crankpin is more than 0.0005 inch (0.0127 mm) out-of-round.

Check crankshaft gear for wear, broken tooth or loose fit on crankshaft. If gear is damaged, remove from crankshaft with an arbor press. Renew gear pin and press new gear on shaft making certain timing mark is facing pto end of shaft.

On models equipped with ball bearing at pto end of shaft, refer to Figs. T36 and T37 before attempting to remove crankcase cover. Loosen locknuts and rotate protruding ends of lock pins counter-clockwise to release bearing and remove cover. Ball bearing will remain

on crankshaft. When reassembling, turn lock pins clockwise until flats on pins face each other, then tighten locknuts to 20 in.-lbs. (2.3 N·m).

Crankshaft end play on Models VM70, HM70, VM80, HM80, VM100, HM100, HH70 and VH70 should be 0.0005-0.027 inch (0.127-0.686 mm), and is controlled by washers (25 and 27 – Fig. T40) or (35 and 37 – Fig. T41).

To remove tapered roller bearings (30 and 51 – Fig. T42 or T43) from crankshaft on Models HH80, VH80, HH100, VH100 and HH120, use a suitable puller. Bearings will be damaged during removal and new bearings must be installed. Heat bearings in oil to approxi-

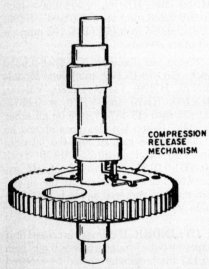

Fig. T38 – View of Insta-matic Ezee-Start compression release camshaft assembly used on all models except HH80, HH100 and HH120.

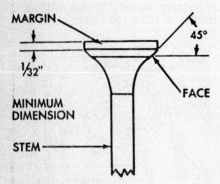

Fig. T39 – Valve face angle should be 45 degrees. Minimum valve head margin is 1/32-inch (0.8 mm).

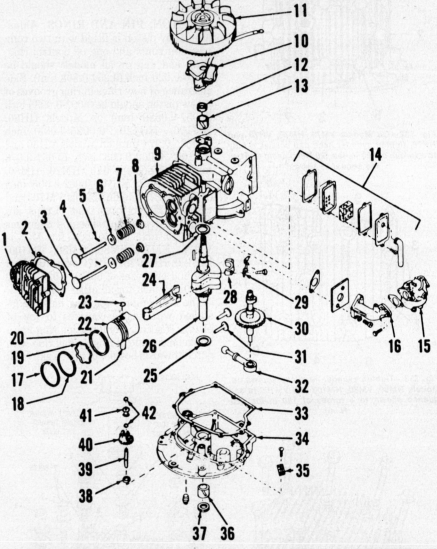

Fig. T40 – Exploded view of vertical crankshaft engine typical of Models VH70, VM70, VM80 and VM100. Renewable bushings (13 and 36) are not used on Models VM70, VM80 and VM100.

1. Cylinder head
2. Head gasket
3. Exhaust valve
4. Intake valve
5. Pin
6. Spring cap
7. Valve spring
8. Spring cap
9. Cylinder block
10. Magneto
11. Flywheel
12. Oil seal
13. Crankshaft bushing
14. Breather assy.
15. Carburetor
16. Intake pipe
17. Top compression ring
18. Second compression ring
19. Oil ring expander
20. Oil control ring
21. Piston pin
22. Piston
23. Retaining ring
24. Connecting rod
25. Thrust washer
26. Crankshaft
27. Thrust washer
28. Rod cap
29. Rod bolt lock
30. Camshaft assy.
31. Valve lifters
32. Oil pump
33. Gasket
34. Mounting flange (engine base)
35. Oil screen
36. Crankshaft bushing
37. Oil seal
38. Spacer
39. Governor shaft
40. Governor gear assy.
41. Spool
42. Retaining rings

mately 300°F ((150°C), then quickly slide bearings into position. Bearing cup (12) is a press fit in crankcase cover or engine base. Bearing cup (31) is a slip fit in block (29). To adjust crankshaft bearings, first assemble crankshaft assembly, piston and rod and crankcase cover or engine base. Tighten all bolts to correct torque value. Install bearing retaining cap (35) without shim gaskets (32), steel washers (33) or "O" ring (58). Tighten screws finger tight. Use a feeler gage to measure gap between bearing retainer flange and block. If no measurable clearance exists, install 0.010 inch steel washer between bearing retainer and cup until such clearance is obtained. If clearance does not exceed 0.007 inch (0.178 mm), no shim gasket (32) will be required and when retainer cap screws are tightened to correct torque, bearing preload will be 0.001-0.007 inch (0.025-0.178 mm). If clearance measures more than 0.007 inch (0.178 mm), subtract 0.001 inch (0.025 mm) from measurement to allow for preload; this will give actual distance to be shimmed. Since shim gaskets compress approximately ⅓ their thickness, shim pack should be 1½ times actual distance. Shim gaskets are available in thicknesses of 0.003-0.004, 0.004-0.005 and 0.005-0.007 inch. Remove bearing retainer, install "O" ring (58) and desired shim gaskets and reinstall retainer. Tighten cap screws to 110 in.-lbs. (12 N·m). Crankshaft seal should be installed to 0.025 inch (0.635 mm) below surface.

Crankshaft dimensions are as follows:

Main Journal Diameter
VH70, HH70
 Flywheel and pto
 ends..............0.9985-0.9990 in.
                   (25.362-25.375 mm)
VM70, HM70, VM80,
HM80, VM100, HM100
 Flywheel end .....0.9985-0.9990 in.
                   (25.362-25.375 mm)
 Pto end ....1.1870-1.1875 in.
                   (30.150-30.162 mm)
HH80, VH80, HH100,
VH100, HH120
 Flywheel and pto
 ends..............1.1865-1.870 in.
                   (30.137-30.150 mm)

Crankpin Journal Diameter
HH80, VH80, HH100,
VH100, HH120 ......1.3750-1.3755 in.
                   (34.925-34.938 mm)
All other models .....1.1860-1.1865 in.
                   (30.124-30.137 mm)

CAMSHAFT. The camshaft and camshaft gear are an integral part which rides on journals at each end of shaft. Renew camshaft if gear teeth are worn or if bearing surfaces are worn or scored. Cam lobe nose to heel diameter should be 1.3045-1.3085 inches (33.134-33.236 mm) on Models HH80, VH80, HH100 and HH120 or 1.263-1.267 inches (32.080-32.182 mm) on all other models. Camshaft journal diameter is 0.6235-0.6240 inch (15.837-15.850 mm). Maximum allowable clearance between camshaft journal and bearing is 0.003 inch (0.076 mm).

Medium frame engines and Models VH70 and VH80 are equipped with Insta-matic Ezee-Start compression release camshaft (Fig. T38). Check compression release parts for binding, or excessive wear or other damage. If any parts are damaged or worn, renew com-

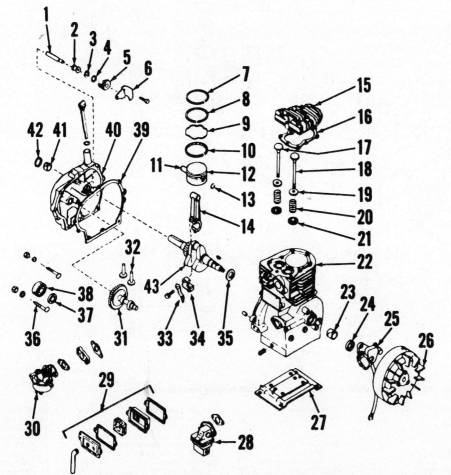

1. Governor shaft
2. Spool
3. Washer
4. Retaining ring
5. Gear & flyweight assy.
6. Bracket
7. Top compression ring
8. Second compression ring
9. Oil ring expander
10. Oil control ring
11. Piston pin
12. Piston
13. Retaining ring
14. Connecting rod
15. Cylinder head
16. Head gasket
17. Exhaust valve
18. Intake valve
19. Spring cap
20. Valve spring
21. Spring retainer
22. Cylinder block
23. Crankshaft bushing
24. Oil seal
25. Magneto
26. Flywheel
27. Mounting plate
28. Fuel pump
29. Breather assy.
30. Carburetor
31. Camshaft assy.
32. Valve lifter
33. Rod bolt lock
34. Rod cap
35. Thrust washer
36. Bearing lock pin
37. Thrust washer
38. Ball bearing
39. Gasket
40. Crankcase cover
41. Bushing
42. Oil seal
43. Crankshaft

Fig. T41 — Exploded view of horizontal crankshaft engine typical of Models HH70, HM70, HM80 and HM100. Engines may be equipped with crankshaft bushing (41) or ball bearing (38) at pto end of shaft.

plete camshaft assembly. Compression release parts are not serviced separately.

On Models HH80, HH100 and HH120, timing advance unit should be inspected and any worn or damaged parts renewed. Refer to Fig. T43 for exploded view of timing advance (52 through 56).

On all models, when installing camshaft, align timing mark on cam gear with mark on crankshaft gear. Timing mark on crankshaft gear is a chamfered tooth.

VALVE SYSTEM. On Models HH80, VH80, HH100, VH100 and HH120, valve tappet gap with engine cold is 0.010 inch (0.254 mm) for intake and 0.020 inch (0.508 mm) for exhaust. Valve tappet gap on all other models

with engine cold is 0.010 inch (0.254 mm) for both valves. To obtain correct gap, grind valve stem end off squarely. Valve seat angle width is 3/64-inch (1.2 mm) on all models. When valve head margin is less than 1/32-inch (0.8 mm), renew valve. See Fig. T39.

Valve guides are non-renewable on all models. If excessive clearance exists, valve guide should be reamed and a new valve with oversize stem installed. Ream guide to 0.344-0.345 inch (8.738-8.763 mm) on Models HH80, VH80, HH100, VH100 and HH120 and to 0.3432-0.3442 inch (8.717-8.743 mm) on all other models.

Valve spring free length should be 1.885 inches (47.88 mm) on Models HH80, VH80, HH100, VH100 and HH120. Valve spring free length should

be 1.562 inches (39.67 mm) on all other models.

DYNA-STATIC BALANCER. The Dyna-Static engine balancer operates by means of a pair of counterweighted gears driven by crankshaft to counteract the unbalance caused by counterweights on crankshaft. The balancer used on medium frame engine is similar to those used on heavy frame models. On medium frame models, balancer gears are held in position on the shafts by a bracket bolted to crankcase or engine base (Fig. T44). Snap rings are used on heavy frame models to retain balancer gears on shafts.

The renewable balancer gear shafts are pressed into crankcase cover or engine base. On medium frame models,

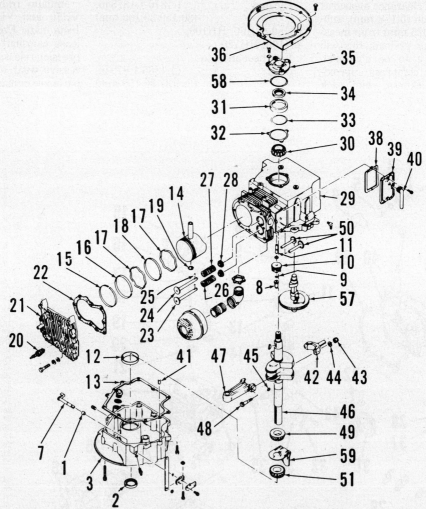

Fig. T42 — Exploded view of Model VH80 or VH100 vertical crankshaft engine.

1. Governor arm bushing	12. Bearing cup	21. Cylinder head	32. Shim gasket	44. Washer
2. Oil seal	13. Gasket	22. Head gasket	33. Steel washer (0.010 in.)	45. Crankshaft gear pin
3. Mounting flange (engine base)	14. Piston & pin assy.	23. Exhaust valve	34. Oil seal	46. Crankshaft
7. Governor arm	15. Top compression ring	24. Intake valve	35. Bearing retainer cap	47. Connecting rod
8. Thrust spool	16. Second compression ring	25. Pin	36. Blower air baffle	48. Rod bolt
9. Snap ring	17. Ring expanders	26. Exhaust valve spring	38. Gasket	49. Crankshaft gear
10. Governor gear & weight assy.	18. Oil control ring	27. Intake valve spring	39. Breather	50. Valve lifters
11. Governor shaft	19. Retaining ring	28. Spring cap	40. Breather tube	51. Bearing cone
	20. Spark plug	29. Cylinder block	42. Rod cap	57. Camshaft assy.
		30. Bearing cone	43. Self-locking nut	58. "O" ring
		31. Bearing cup		59. Oil slinger

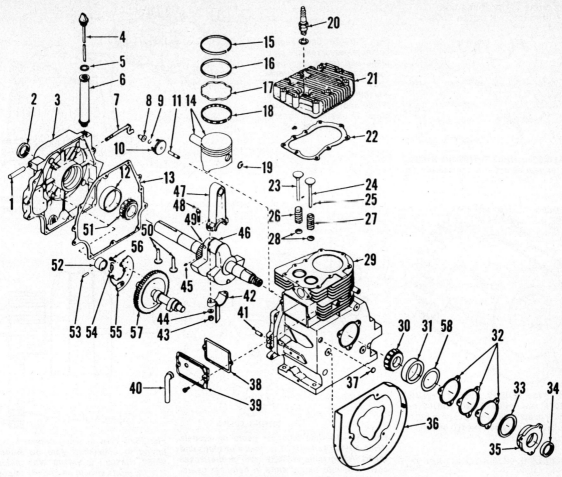

Fig. T43—Exploded view of Model HH80, HH100 or HH120 horizontal crankshaft engine.

1. Governor arm bushing
2. Oil seal
3. Crankcase cover
4. Dipstick
5. Gasket
6. Oil filler tube
7. Governor arm
8. Thrust spool
9. Snap ring
10. Governor gear & weight assy.
11. Governor shaft
12. Bearing cup

13. Gasket
14. Piston & pin assy.
15. Top compression ring
16. Second compression ring
17. Oil ring expander
18. Oil control ring
19. Retaining ring
20. Spark plug
21. Cylinder head
22. Head gasket
23. Exhaust valve

24. Intake valve
25. Pin
26. Exhaust valve spring
27. Intake valve spring
28. Spring cap
29. Cylinder block
30. Bearing cone
31. Bearing cup
32. Shim gaskets
33. Steel washer (0.010 in.)
34. Oil seal

35. Bearing retainer cap
36. Blower air baffle
37. Plug
38. Gasket
39. Breather assy.
40. Breather tube
41. Dowel pin
42. Rod cap
43. Self-locking nut
44. Washer
45. Crankshaft gear pin
46. Crankshaft

47. Connecting rod
48. Rod bolt
49. Crankshaft gear
50. Valve lifters
51. Bearing cone
52. Breaker cam
53. Push rod
54. Spring
55. Timing advance weight
56. Rivet
57. Camshaft assy.
58. "O" ring

press shaft into cover or engine base until a distance of 1.757-1.763 inches (44.628-44.780 mm) exists between shaft bore boss and edge of step cut on shafts as shown in Fig. T46. Heavy frame model shafts should be pressed until a distance of 1.7135-1.7185 inches (43.523-43.650 mm) exists between cover boss and the outer edge of snap ring groove as shown in Fig. T47.

All balancer gears are equipped with renewable cage needle bearings. See Figs. T48 and T49. Using tool #670210, press new bearings into gears until cage is flush to 0.015 inch (0.381 mm) below edge of bore.

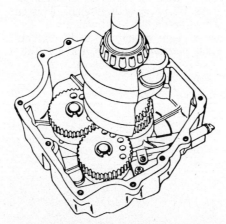

Fig. T44—View showing Dyna-Static balancer gears installed in Model VM80 or VM100 engine base. Balancer gears are identically located in Model HM80 or HM100 crankcase cover. Note location of washers between gears retaining bracket.

Fig. T45—View showing Dyna-Static balancer gears installed in Model HH80, HH100 or HH120 crankcase cover. Note gear retaining snap rings.

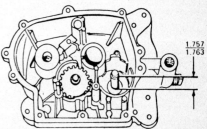

Fig. T46—On Models HM80, VM80, HM100 and VM100, balancer gear shafts must be pressed into cover or engine base so a distance of 1.757-1.763 inches (44.628-44.780 mm) exists between shaft bore boss and edge of step cut as shown.

MEASURE FROM COVER BOSS
TO RING GROOVE OUTER EDGE

1.7135
1.7185

Fig. T47—On Models HH80, HH100 and HH120, press balancer gear shafts into cover to dimension shown.

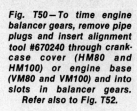

Fig. T50—To time engine balancer gears, remove pipe plugs and insert alignment tool #670240 through crankcase cover (HM80 and HM100) or engine base (VM80 and VM100) and into slots in balancer gears. Refer also to Fig. T52.

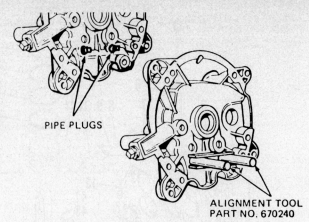

PIPE PLUGS

ALIGNMENT TOOL
PART NO. 670240

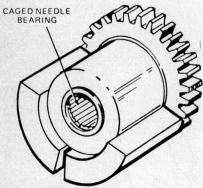

CAGED NEEDLE BEARING

Fig. T48—Using tool #670210, press new needle bearings into Model HM80, VM80, HM100 or VM100 balancer gears until bearing cage is flush to 0.015 inch (0.381 mm) below edge of bore.

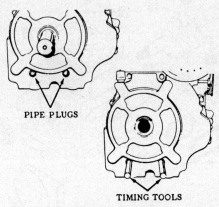

PIPE PLUGS

TIMING TOOLS

Fig. T51—To time balancer gears on Models HH80, HH100 and HH120, remove pipe plugs and insert timing tools #670239 through crankcase cover and into timing slots in balancer gears. Refer also to Fig. T53.

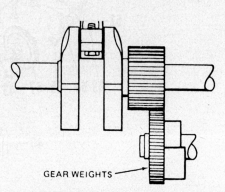

GEAR WEIGHTS

Fig. T52—View showing correct balancer gear timing to crankshaft gear on Models HM80, VM80, HM100 and VM100. With piston at TDC, weights should be directly opposite.

PRESS BEARINGS IN FLUSH TO .015 BELOW

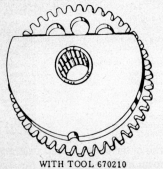

WITH TOOL 670210

Fig. T49—On Models HH80, HH100 and HH120, needle bearings are installed flush to 0.015 inch (0.381 mm) below edge of bore. Note tool alignment notch at lower side of balancer.

When reassembling engine, balancer gears must be timed with crankshaft for correct operation. Refer to Figs. T50 and T51 and remove pipe plugs. Insert alignment tool #670240 through crankcase cover of Models HM80 and HM100 or engine base of Models VM80 and VM100 and into timing slots in balancer gears. On Models HH80, HH100 and HH120, insert timing tool #670239 through cover and into balancer gears. Then, on all models, turn crankshaft to place piston at TDC and carefully install engine base or cover with balancer gears. When correctly assembled, piston should be on TDC and weights on balancer gears should be in directly opposite position. See Figs. T52 and T53.

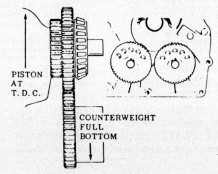

PISTON AT T.D.C.

COUNTERWEIGHT FULL BOTTOM

Fig. T53—On Models HH80, HH100 and HH120, balancer gears are correctly timed to crankshaft when piston is at TDC and weights are at full bottom position.

TECUMSEH

Model	No. Cyls.	Bore	Stroke	Displacement	Horsepower
OH120	1	3-1/8 in. (79.4 mm)	2-3/4 in. (69.8 mm)	21.1 cu. in. (346 cc)	12 (8.9 kW)
OH140	1	3-5/16 in. (84.1 mm)	2-3/4 in. (69.8 mm)	23.75 cu. in. (389 cc)	14 (10.4 kW)
OH160	1	3-1/2 in. (88.9 mm)	2-7/8 in. (73.0 mm)	27.66 cu. in. (453 cc)	16 (11.9 kW)
HH140	1	3-5/16 in. (84.1 mm)	2-3/4 in. (69.8 mm)	23.75 cu. in. (389 cc)	14 (10.4 kW)
HH150	1	3-1/2 in. (88.9 mm)	2-7/8 in. (73.0 mm)	27.66 cu. in. (453 cc)	15 (11.2 kW)
HH160	1	3-1/2 in. (88.9 mm)	2-7/8 in. (73.0 mm)	27.66 cu. in. (453 cc)	16 (11.9 kW)

Engines must be identified by complete model number, including specification number in order to obtain correct repair parts. It is important to transfer ID tags from original engine to replacement short block so unit can be identified later.

All models in this section are heavy frame cast iron engines and are valve-in-head, horizontal crankshaft type.

MAINTENANCE

SPARK PLUG. A Champion L-7 or equivalent spark plug is used. Set electrode gap to 0.030 inch (0.762 mm). Spark plug should be removed, cleaned and adjusted periodically. Renew plug if electrodes are burned and pitted or if porcelain is cracked.

CARBURETOR. A Walbro Model LM float type carburetor is used. To adjust carburetor, refer to Fig. T55 and proceed as follows: Turn idle mixture screw (9) clockwise until lightly seated, then back out 1¾ turns. Turn main fuel adjusting needle (27) clockwise until lightly seated, then back out 2¾ turns. Start and operate engine until normal operating temperature is reached. Then, readjust main fuel needle, if necessary, until engine runs smoothly and evenly under operating conditions.

Adjust idle speed screw (8) until engine idle speed of 1200 rpm is obtained. Readjust idle mixture needle (9), if necessary, until engine idles smoothly.

To check float setting, hold carburetor and float assembly in inverted position. A distance of 0.275-0.315 inch (7.0-8.0 mm) should exist between float and center boss measured as shown in Fig. T56. Carefully bend adjusting tab on float to adjust float setting. A Viton seat (12 – Fig. T55) is used with fuel inlet valve (13). The renewable seat must be installed grooved side first in bore so inlet valve will seat at smooth side. See Fig. T57.

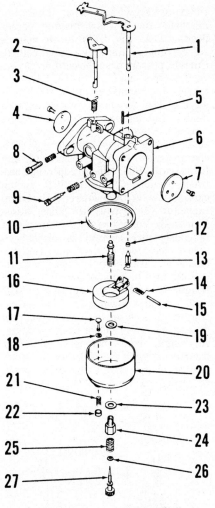

Fig. T55 – Exploded view of typical Walbro carburetor used on all models.

1. Choke shaft
2. Throttle shaft
3. Throttle return spring
4. Throttle plate
5. Choke stop spring
6. Carburetor body
7. Choke plate
8. Idle speed stop screw
9. Idle mixture needle
10. Bowl gasket
11. Main nozzle
12. Inlet valve seat
13. Inlet valve
14. Float spring
15. Float shaft
16. Float
17. Drain stem
18. Gasket
19. Gasket
20. Bowl
21. Spring
22. Retainer
23. Gasket
24. Bowl retainer
25. Spring
26. "O" ring
27. Main fuel adjusting needle

If main nozzle (11 – Fig. T55) is removed and is the original type (Fig. T58), obtain and install a new service

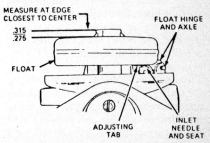

Fig. T56 – Float setting should be measured as shown. Bend adjusting tab to adjust float setting.

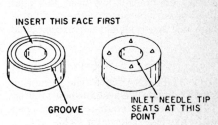

Fig. T57 – The Viton inlet fuel valve seat must be installed grooved side first.

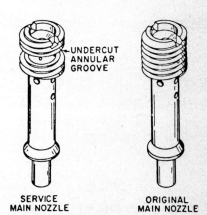

Fig. T58 – The main nozzle originally installed is drilled after installation through hole in body. Service main nozzles are grooved so alignment is not necessary.

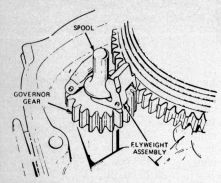

Fig. T59 — View showing governor assembly installed in crankcase. Governor gear is driven by camshaft gear.

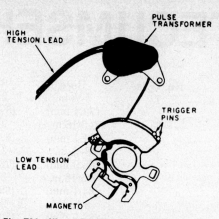

Fig. T61 — View of solid state ignition system used on engine not equipped with flywheel alternator.

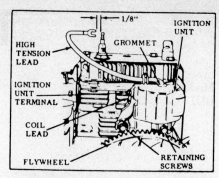

Fig. T63 — View of solid state ignition unit used on engine equipped with flywheel alternator. System should produce a good blue spark ⅛-inch (3 mm) long at cranking speed.

nozzle. The service nozzle will have an undercut annular groove in threaded area as shown in Fig. T58.

GOVERNOR. A mechanical flyweight type governor is used on all models. Governor gear, flyweights and shaft are serviced only as an assembly. Refer to Fig. T59 for view showing governor assembly installed in crankcase. Governor gear is driven by camshaft gear.

To adjust external governor linkage, refer to Fig. T60 and proceed as follows: Loosen screw (A), turn plate (B) counter-clockwise as far as possible and move governor lever (C) to the left until throttle is in wide open position. Tighten screw (A). Governor spring must be hooked in hole (D) as shown. Adjusting screws on bracket are used to adjust fixed or variable speed settings. Engine high idle speed should not exceed 3600 rpm.

SOLID STATE IGNITION (WITHOUT ALTERNATOR). The Tecumseh solid state ignition system shown in Fig. T61 is used on engines not equipped with flywheel alternator. This system does not use ignition breaker points. The only moving part of the system is the

rotating flywheel with charging magnets. As flywheel magnet passes position (1A – Fig. T62), a low voltage AC current is induced into input coil (2). Current passes through rectifier (3) converting this current to DC. It then travels to capacitor (4) where it is stored. The flywheel rotates approximately 180 degrees to position (1B). As it passes trigger coil (5), it induces a very small electric charge into the coil. This charge passes through resistor (6) and turns on the SCR (silicon controlled rectifier) switch (7). With SCR switch closed, low voltage current stored in capacitor (4) travels to pulse transformer (8). Voltage is stepped up instantaneously and current is discharged across electrodes of spark plug (9), producing a spark before top dead center.

Units may be equipped with a second trigger coil and resistor set to turn SCR switch on at a lower rpm. This second trigger pin is closer to flywheel and produces a spark at TDC for easier starting. As engine rpm increases, the first (shorter) trigger pin picks up the small electric charge and turns SCR switch on, firing spark plug BTDC.

If system fails to produce a spark to spark plug, first check high tension lead (Fig. T61). If condition of high tension lead is questionable, renew pulse transformer and high tension lead assembly. Check low tension lead and renew if insulation is faulty. The magneto charging coil, electronic triggering system and mounting plate are available only as an assembly. If necessary to renew this assembly, place unit in position on engine. Start retaining screws, turn mounting plate counter-clockwise as far as possible, then tighten retaining screws to a torque of 5-7 ft.-lbs. (7-9 N·m).

SOLID STATE IGNITION (WITH ALTERNATOR). The Tecumseh solid state ignition system used on engines equipped with flywheel alternator does not use ignition points. The only moving part of the system is the rotating flywheel with charging magnets and trigger pins. Other components of the system are ignition generator coil and stator assembly, spark plug and ignition unit.

The long trigger pin induces a small charge of current to close SCR (silicon controlled rectifier) switch at engine cranking speed and produces a spark at TDC for starting. As engine rpm increases, the first (shorter) trigger pin induces the current which produces a spark when piston is BTDC.

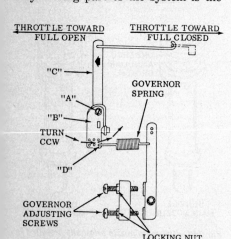

Fig. T60 — Typical external governor linkage. Refer to text for adjustment procedures.

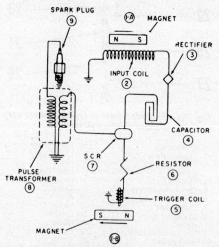

Fig. T62 — Operational diagram of solid state ignition system.

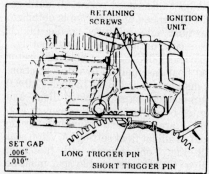

Fig. T64 — Adjust air gap between long trigger pin and ignition unit to 0.006-0.010 inch (0.152-0.254 mm).

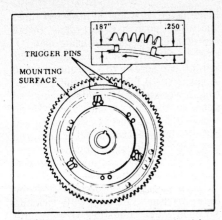

Fig. T65—Remove flywheel and drive trigger pins in or out as necessary until long pin is extended 0.250 (6.35 mm) inch and short pin is extended 0.187 inch (4.75 mm) above mounting surface.

Test ignition system as follows: Hold high tension lead 1/8-inch (3 mm) from spark plug (Fig. T63), crank engine and check for a good blue spark. If no spark is present, check high tension lead and coil lead for loose connections or faulty insulation. Check air gap between long trigger pin and ignition unit as shown in Fig. T64. Air gap should be 0.006-0.010 inch (0.152-0.254 mm). To adjust air gap, loosen the two retaining screws and move ignition unit as necessary, then tighten retaining screws.

NOTE: The long trigger pin should extend 0.250 inch (6.35 mm) and the short trigger pin should extend 0.187 inch (4.75 mm), measured as shown in Fig. T65. If not, remove flywheel and drive pins in or out as required.

Remove coil lead from ignition terminal and connect an ohmmeter as shown in Fig. T66. If series resistance test of ignition generator coil is below 400 ohms, renew stator and coil assembly (Fig. T67). If resistance is above 400 ohms, renew ignition unit.

LUBRICATION. Splash lubrication is provided by use of an oil dipper on connecting rod cap. See Fig. T68.

Use only high quality, detergent motor oil having API classification SC, SD or SE. SAE 30 oil is recommended for operating in temperatures above 32°F (0°C) and SAE 10W for operating in temperatures below 32°F (0°C).

REPAIRS

TIGHTENING TORQUES. Recommended tightening torques are as follows:

Cylinder head	220 in.-lbs. (24.8 N·m)
Connecting rod	110 in.-lbs. (12.4 N·m)
Crankcase cover	65-110 in.-lbs. (7.3-12.4 N·m)
Bearing retainer	65-110 in.-lbs. (7.3-12.4 N·m)
Flywheel nut	600-660 in.-lbs. (67.8-74.6 N·m)
Spark plug	270-360 in.-lbs. (30.5-40.7 N·m)
Stator mounting	60-84 in.-lbs. (6.8-9.5 N·m)
Carburetor to inlet pipe	48-72 in.-lbs. (5.4-8.1 N·m)
Inlet pipe to head	72-96 in.-lbs. (8.1-10.8 N·m)
Rocker arm housing to head	80-90 in.-lbs. (9.0-10.1 N·m)
Rocker arm shaft screw	180-220 in.-lbs. (20.3-24.8 N·m)
Rocker arm cover	15-20 in.-lbs. (1.7-2.2 N·m)

CONNECTING ROD. The aluminum alloy connecting rod rides directly on the crankpin. Piston and connecting rod assembly is removed from above after removing rocker arm housing, cylinder head, crankcase cover and connecting rod cap.

Crankpin diameter is 1.3750-1.3755 inches (34.925-34.938 mm) and running clearance of connecting rod to crankpin should be 0.001-0.0015 inch (0.025-0.381 mm). Renew connecting rod if clearance is excessive. If crankpin is scored, out-

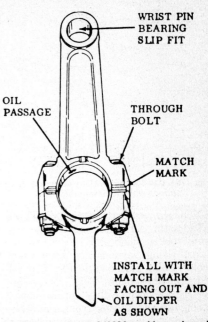

Fig. T68—Connecting rod assembly used on all models. Note oil dipper on rod cap and match marks.

of-round or excessively worn, crankshaft must be renewed. Connecting rod is available in standard size only. Standard diameter of piston pin hole in connecting rod is 0.6876-0.6881 inch (17.465-17.478 mm). Renew connecting rod if piston pin hole is excessively worn.

When installing piston and connecting rod assembly, make certain match marks on connecting rod and rod cap (Fig. T68) are aligned and marks are facing pto end of shaft. Always renew self-locking nuts on connecting rod bolts and tighten nuts to a torque of 110 in.-lbs. (12 N·m).

CYLINDER HEAD AND VALVE SYSTEM. To remove cylinder head and/or valves, first unbolt and remove blower housing and valve cover and breather assembly. Turn crankshaft until piston is at top dead center of compression stroke. Refer to Fig. T69,

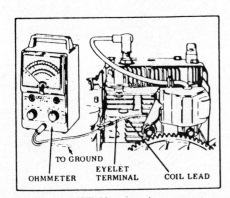

Fig. T66—View showing ohmmeter connected for resistance test of ignition generator coil.

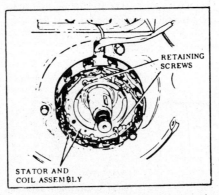

Fig. T67—Ignition generator coil and stator is serviced only as an assembly.

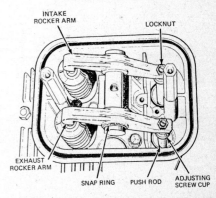

Fig. T69—View showing rocker arms used on all models. Slotted adjusting screws were used on early production engines. Later engines have adjusting nut on screw below rocker arm.

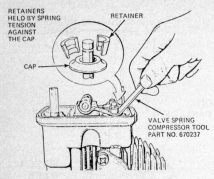

Fig. T70—Use tool #670237 to compress valve springs while removing retainers.

loosen locknuts on rocker arms and back off adjusting screws. Remove snap rings from rocker shaft and remove rocker arms. Using valve spring compressor tool #670237 as shown in Fig. T70, remove valve retainers. Then, remove upper spring cap, valve spring, lower spring cap and "O" ring from each valve. Remove the three cap screws, washers and "O" rings from inside rocker arm housing and carefully lift off housing. Push rods and push rod tubes can now be withdrawn. Unbolt and remove carburetor and inlet pipe assembly from cylinder head. Remove cylinder head cap screws and lift off cylinder head, taking care not to drop intake and exhaust valves.

Standard inside diameter of both guides is 0.312-0.313 inch (7.925-7.950

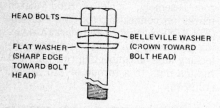

Fig. T71—Install Belleville washer and flat washer on cylinder head cap screws as shown.

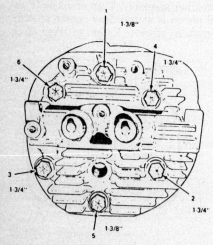

Fig. T72—Tighten cylinder head cap screws evenly to a torque of 220 in.-lbs. (24.8 N·m) using tightening sequence shown. Note location of different length cap screws.

mm). If excessive clearance exists between valve stem and guide, ream guide to 0.343-0.344 inch (8.712-8.737 mm) and install 1/32-inch (0.8 mm) oversize valve, or renew valve guides. To renew valve guides, remove and submerge head in large pan of oil. Heat on a hot plate until oil begins to smoke, about 15-20 minutes. Remove head from pan and place head on arbor press with valve seats facing up. Use a drift punch ½-inch (13 mm) in diameter to press guides out.

CAUTION: Be sure to center punch. DO NOT allow punch to contact head when pressing guides out.

To install new guides, place guides in freezer or on ice for 30 minutes prior to installation. Submerge head in pan of oil. Heat on hot plate until oil begins to smoke, about 15-20 minutes. Remove head and place, gasket surface down, on a 6 x 12 inch piece of wood. Using snap rings to locate both guides, insert silver color guide in intake side and brass colored guide in exhaust side. It may be necessary to use a rubber or rawhide mallet to fully seat snap rings. DO NOT use a metal hammer or guide damage will result. Allow head to cool and reface both valve seats.

Valve spring free length should be 1.915 inches (48.64 mm) and springs should test 25.6-28.6 pounds (113.9-127.2 N) when compressed to a length of 1.550 inches (39.37 mm). Renew springs if coils are rusted, pitted or cracked, or if springs fail to meet specifications.

Valves seat directly in cylinder head. Valve seat angle is 46 degrees and valve face angle is 45 degrees. Valve seat width should be 0.042-0.052 inch (1.07-1.32 mm). Renew valve when valve head margin is less than 0.060 inch (1.52 mm) after valve is refaced.

Use new head gasket and reinstall cylinder head and valves. Make certain Belleville washer and flat washer are installed on cylinder head cap screws as shown in Fig. T71 and the two short cap screws, 1-⅜ inches (35 mm), are installed in correct holes as shown in Fig. T72. Tighten cylinder head cap screws evenly to a torque of 220 in.-lbs. (24.8 N·m) using sequence shown in Fig. T72.

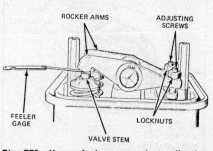

Fig. T73—Use a feeler gage when adjusting valve clearance. Refer to text for adjustment procedure.

Place new "O" rings on push rod tubes and install push rods and tubes. Install rocker arm housing and using new "O" rings on the three mounting cap screws, tighten cap screws to a torque of 80-90 in.-lbs. (9.0-10.1 N·m). Install new "O" ring, lower spring cap, valve spring and upper spring cap on each valve. Using tool #670237, compress valve spring and install retainers. Install rocker arms and secure them with snap rings.

To adjust valve clearance, make certain piston is positioned at TDC of compression stroke and proceed as follows: Refer to Fig. T73 and with locknuts loosened, turn adjusting screws until correct valve clearance is measured with feeler gage as shown. Valve clearance (cold) should be 0.005 inch (0.127 mm) for intake valve and 0.010 inch (0.254 mm) for exhaust valve. Tighten locknuts to secure adjusting screws.

NOTE: Slotted adjusting screws were used on early production engines, while later engines have adjusting nut on screw below rocker arm. Locknuts are above rocker arms on all models.

Reinstall valve cover and breather assembly, carburetor and inlet pipe assembly and blower housing.

PISTON, PIN AND RINGS. Aluminum alloy piston is fitted with two compression rings and one oil control ring. Recommended end gap for all rings is 0.010-0.020 inch (0.254-0.508 mm). Side clearance of new rings in ring grooves of new piston is 0.0015-0.0035 inch (0.038-0.089 mm). Maximum allowable (wear limit) piston ring side clearance is 0.006 inch (0.152 mm). Compression ring groove width of new piston is 0.095-0.096 inch (2.413-2.438 mm) and oil ring groove width (new) is 0.188-0.189 inch (4.775-4.800 mm). Piston rings and piston are available in standard size and oversizes.

The top compression ring must be installed with inside chamfer to top of piston. If second compression ring has a

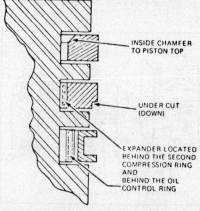

Fig. T74—Cross-sectional view showing correct installation of piston rings.

notch on outside of ring, install ring with notch toward bottom end of piston. Oil ring can be installed either side up. See Fig. T74. Stagger ring end gaps about 90 degrees around piston.

Piston skirt clearance in cylinder, measured at thrust side of piston just below oil ring should be 0.010-0.012 inch (0.254-0.305 mm).

Piston pin diameter is 0.6873-0.6875 inch (17.457-17.462 mm). Piston pin clearance should be 0.0001-0.0008 inch (0.0025-0.0203 mm) in rod and 0.0002-0.0005 inch (0.0051-0.0127 mm) in piston. If clearance is excessive, both piston and pin must be renewed as pin is not serviced separately.

CYLINDER. If cylinder is scored or if taper or out-of-round exceeds 0.005 inch (0.127 mm), cylinder should be rebored to next suitable oversize. Standard cylinder bore is 3.125-3.126 inches (79.375-79.400 mm) on Model OH120, 3.312-3.313 inches (84.125-84.150 mm) on Models HH140 and OH140 and 3.500-3.501 inches (88.900-88.925 mm) on all other models. Pistons and rings are available in standard size and oversizes.

CAMSHAFT. The camshaft and camshaft gear are an integral part which rides on journals at each end of camshaft. The camshaft is equipped with a compression release mechanism. See Fig. T75. Check compression release parts for binding, excessive wear or other damage. If any parts are excessively worn or damaged, renew complete camshaft assembly. Parts are not serviced separately for compression release mechanism.

Renew camshaft if gear teeth are excessively worn or if bearing surfaces or lobes are worn or scored. Camshaft lobe nose-to-heel diameter should be 1.3117-1.3167 inches (33.3172-33.4442 mm).

Diameter of camshaft journals is 0.6235-0.6240 inch (15.8369-15.8496 mm). Maximum allowable clearance between camshaft journal and bearing bore is 0.003 inch (0.076 mm).

When installing camshaft, align timing mark on camshaft gear with timing mark (chamfered tooth) on crankshaft gear. This will provide correct valve timing.

CRANKSHAFT. The crankshaft is supported by tapered roller bearings (20 and 54–Fig. T76). Use a suitable puller to remove bearings. Bearings will be damaged during removal and new bearings must be installed when reassembling. Heat bearings in oil to approximately 300°F (150°C), then quickly slide bearings into position on crankshaft. Bearing cup (55) in a press fit in crankcase cover (62) and must be pressed in against shoulder. Bearing cup (19) is a slip fit in cylinder block (21). To adjust crankshaft bearings, assemble engine to the point where cylinder block, crankshaft assembly, piston and connecting rod assembly and crankcase cover are assembled and all bolts are tightened to correct torque values given in TIGHTENING TORQUES paragraph. With bearing cup (19) installed in cylinder block, install bearing retainer cap (15) without shim gaskets (17), steel washers (16) or "O" ring (18). Tighten cap screws finger tight. Using a feeler gage, measure gap between bearing retainer flange and cylinder block. If no measurable clearance exists, install 0.010 inch steel washers (as required) between bearing retainer (15) and bearing cup (19) until such clearance is obtained. If measured

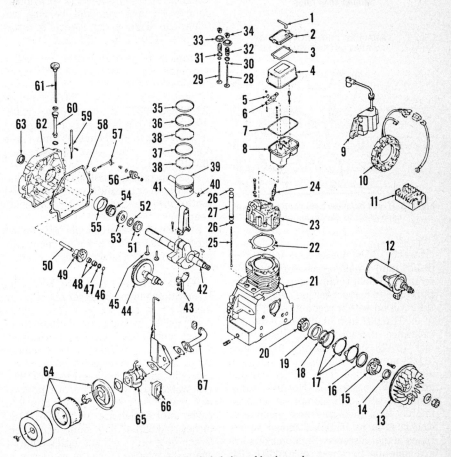

Fig. T76—Exploded view of basic engine.

1. Breather tube	35. Top compression ring	51. Crankshaft gear
2. Breather	36. Second compression ring	52. Spacer
3. Gasket	37. Oil control ring	53. Balancer drive gear
4. Valve cover	38. Ring expanders	54. Bearing cone
5. Snap ring	39. Piston & pin assy.	55. Bearing cup
6. Rocker arm (2 used)	40. Retaining ring	56. Governor assy.
7. Seal ring	41. Connecting rod	57. Governor arm
8. Rocker arm housing	42. Crankshaft	58. Gasket
9. Ignition unit	43. Rod cap	59. Oil filler tube extension
10. Stator assy.	44. Camshaft assy.	60. Oil filler tube
11. Regulator-rectifier	45. Valve lifters	61. Dipstick
12. Starter motor	46. Snap ring	62. Crankcase cover
13. Flywheel	47. Thrust washer	63. Oil seal
14. Oil seal	48. Needle bearings	64. Air cleaner assy.
15. Bearing retainer cap	49. Dyna-Static balancer	65. Carburetor
16. Steel washer (0.010 in.)	50. Balancer shaft	66. Fuel pump
17. Shim gaskets		67. Inlet pipe
18. "O" ring	19. Bearing cup	
19. Bearing cup	20. Bearing cone	
	21. Cylinder block	
	22. Head gasket	
	23. Cylinder head	
	24. Spark plug	
	25. Push rod	
	26. "O" ring	
	27. Push rod tube	
	28. Intake valve	
	29. Exhaust valve	
	30. "O" ring	
	31. Lower spring cap	
	32. Valve spring	
	33. Upper valve cap	
	34. Valve retainers	

Fig. T75—View of Insta-matic Ezee-Start compression release camshaft assembly.

COMPRESSION RELEASE MECHANISM

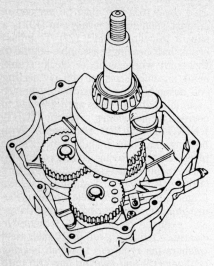

Fig. T77—View showing Dyna-Static balancer gears installed in crankcase cover. Note gear retaining snap rings.

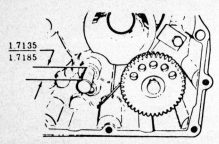

MEASURE FROM COVER BOSS
TO RING GROOVE OUTER EDGE

1.7135
1.7185

Fig. T78—Press balancer gear shafts into crankcase cover to dimension shown.

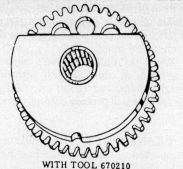

PRESS BEARINGS IN FLUSH TO .015 BELOW

WITH TOOL 670210

Fig. T79—Using tool #670210, press new needle bearings into balancer gears until bearing cage is flush to 0.015 inch (0.381 mm) below edge of bore. Note tool alignment notch at lower side of balancer.

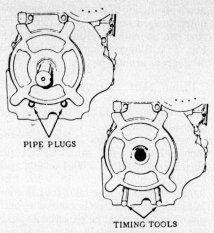

PIPE PLUGS

TIMING TOOLS

Fig. T80—To time engine balancer gears, remove pipe plugs and insert timing tools #670239 through crankcase cover and into slots in balancer gears. Refer also to Fig. T81.

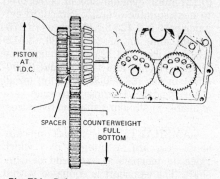

PISTON AT T.D.C.

SPACER   COUNTERWEIGHT FULL BOTTOM

Fig. T81—Balancer gears are correctly timed to crankshaft when piston is at TDC and weights are at full bottom position.

clearance does not exceed 0.007 inch (0.178 mm) no shim gasket (17) will be required. When retainer cap screws are tightened to correct torque, bearing preload will be within recommended range of 0.001-0.007 inch (0.025-0.178 mm). If clearance measures more than 0.007 inch (0.178 mm), subtract 0.001 inch (0.025 mm) from measured clearance to allow for preload. This will give actual distance to be shimmed. However, since shim gaskets will compress approximately 1/3 of their thickness, shim pack thickness to be installed should be 1½ times actual distance. Shim gaskets are available in thickness of 0.003-0.004, 0.004-0.005 and 0.005-0.007 inch. Re-

move bearing cap, install "O" ring and thickness of shim gaskets previously determined and reinstall bearing retainer cap. Tighten cap screws to a torque of 65-110 in.-lbs. (7.3-12.4 N·m).

Crankshaft seat diameter for roller bearings is 1.1865-1.1870 inches (30.1371-30.1498 mm). Crankpin journal diameter is 1.3750-1.3755 inches (34.9250-34.9377 mm). Renew crankshaft if crankpin is scored or is tapered or worn over 0.002 inch (0.051 mm) or is out-of-round more than 0.0005 inch (0.0127 mm).

When installing crankshaft, align timing mark on crankshaft gear (chamfered tooth) with timing mark on camshaft gear.

Crankshaft oil seals should be installed flush to 0.025 inch (0.635 mm) below surface, with lips on seals facing inward.

DYNA-STATIC BALANCER. The Dyna-Static engine balancer operates by means of a pair of counterweighted gears driven by the crankshaft to counteract unbalance caused by counterweights on crankshaft. The balancer gears are held in position on balancer shafts by snap rings. See Fig. T77. The renewable balancer shafts are pressed into crankcase cover. Press shafts into cover until a distance of 1.7135-1.7185 inches (43.523-43.650 mm) exists between boss on cover and outer edge of snap ring groove on shafts as shown in Fig. T78.

Balancer gears are equiped with renewable caged needle bearings. See Fig. T79. Using tool #670210, press new bearings into balancer gears until bearing cage is flush to 0.015 inch (0.381 mm) below edge of bore.

When reassembling engine, balancer gears must be timed with crankshaft for correct operation. To time balancer gears, refer to Fig. T80 and remove pipe plugs. Insert timing tools #670239 through crankcase cover and into timing slots in balancer gears. Then, turn crankshaft to place piston at TDC position and carefully install crankcase cover with balancer gears. When correctly assembled, piston should be exactly at TDC and weights should be at full bottom position. See Fig. T81.

TECUMSEH
SERVICING TECUMSEH ACCESSORIES

12 VOLT STARTING AND CHARGING SYSTEMS

Some Tecumseh engines may be equipped with 12-volt electrical systems.

Refer to the following paragraphs for servicing Tecumseh electrical units and 12-volt Delco-Remy starter-generator used on some models.

12-VOLT STARTER MOTOR (BENDIX DRIVE TYPE). Refer to Fig. T85 or T86 for exploded view of 12-volt starter motor and Bendix drive unit used on some engines. To identify starter, refer to service number stamped on end cap.

When assembling starter motor in Fig. T85, use spacers (15) of varying thicknesses to obtain an armature end play of 0.005-0.015 inch (0.127-0.381 mm). Tighten armature nut (1) to 100 in.-lbs. (11.3 N·m) on motor numbers 29965, 32468, 32468A, 32468B and 33202, to 130-150 in.-lbs. (14.7-16.9 N·m) on motor number 32510 and to 170-220 in.-lbs. (19.2-24.8 N·m) on motor number 32817. Tighten through-bolts to 30-35 in.-lbs. (3.4-3.9 N·m) on motor numbers 29965, 32468 and 32468A, to 35-44 in.-lbs. (3.9-5.0 N·m) on motor number 32817 and to 45-50 in.-lbs. (5.0-5.6 N·m) on motor number 32510.

To perform no-load test for starter motors 29965, 32468 and 32468A, use a fully charged 6-volt battery. Maximum current draw should not exceed 25 amps at 6 volts. Minimum rpm is 6500.

No-load test for Models 32468B and 33202 requires a fully charged 12-volt battery. Maximum current draw should not exceed 25 amps at 11.8 volts. Minimum rpm is 8000.

No-load test for starter motors 32510 and 32817 must be performed with a 12-volt battery. Maximum current draw should not exceed 25 amps at 11.5 volts. Minimum rpm is 8000.

Disassembly and reassembly of starter motors 33605, 33606 and 33835 is evident after inspection of unit and referral to Fig. T86. Note that stops on through-bolts (14) are used to secure brush card (10) in housing (9).

Through-bolts must be installed with stops toward end cover (15).

Maximum current draw with starter on engine should not exceed 55 amps at a minimum of 850 rpm for starters 33605 and 33606 or 70 amps at a minimum of 600 rpm for starter 33835. Cranking test should not exceed 10 seconds.

ALTERNATOR CHARGING SYSTEMS. Flywheel alternators are used on some engines for the charging system. The generated alternating current is converted to direct current by two rectifiers on rectifier panel (Figs. T87 and T88) or regulator-rectifier (Fig. T89).

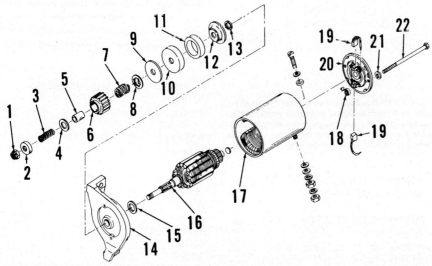

Fig. T85 — Exploded view of 12-volt starter motor Model No. 32817. Other starter motors are similar except as shown in Fig. T86. Spacer (15) is available in different thicknesses to adjust armature end play.

1. Nut
2. Pinion stop
3. Spring
4. Washer
5. Anti-drift sleeve
6. Pinion gear
7. Screw shaft
8. Stop washer
9. Thrust washer
10. Cushion cup
11. Rubber cushion
12. Thrust washer
13. Thrust bushing
14. Drive end cap
15. Spacer washer
16. Armature
17. Frame & field coil assy.
18. Brush spring
19. Brushes
20. End cap
21. Washer
22. Bolt

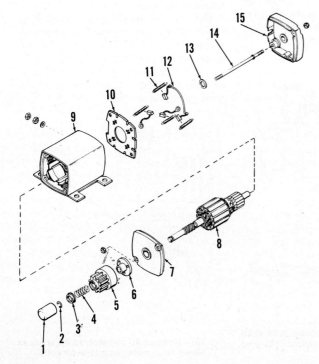

Fig. T86 — Exploded view of 12-volt starter motor used on some models.

1. Dust cover
2. Snap ring
3. Spring retainer
4. Anti-drift spring
5. Gear
6. Engaging nut
7. Drive end plate
8. Armature
9. Frame & field coil assy.
10. Brush card
11. Brush spring
12. Brushes
13. Thrust washer
14. Through-bolts
15. Commutator end plate

The system shown in Fig. T87 has a maximum charging output of about 3 amps at 3600 rpm. No current regulator is used on this low output system. The rectifier panel includes two diodes (rectifiers) and a 6 amp fuse for overload protection.

The system shown in Fig. T88 has a maximum output of 7 amps. To prevent overcharging battery, a double pole switch is used in low output position to reduce output to 3 amps for charging battery. Move switch to high output position (7 amps) when using accessories.

The system shown in Fig. T89 has a maximum output of 7 amps on engine of 7 hp; 10 or 20 amps on engines of 8 hp and larger. This system uses a solid state regulator-rectifier which converts generated alternating current to direct current for charging the battery. The regulator-rectifier also allows only required amount of current flow for existing battery conditions. When battery is fully charged, current output is decreased to prevent overcharging battery.

TESTING. On models equipped with rectifier panel (Figs. T87 or T88), remove rectifiers and test them with either a continuity light or an ohmmeter. Rectifiers should show current flow in one direction only. Alternator output can be checked using an induction ampere meter over positive lead wire to battery.

On models equipped with regulator-rectifier (Fig. T89), check system as follows: Disconnect B+ lead and connect a DC voltmeter as shown in Fig. T90. With engine running near full throttle, voltage should be 14.0-14.7. If voltage is above 14.7 or below 14.0 but above 0, regulator-rectifier is defective. If voltmeter reading is 0, regulator-rectifier or alternator coils may be defective. To test alternator coils, connect an AC voltmeter to AC leads as shown in Fig. T91. With engine running at near full throttle, check AC voltage.

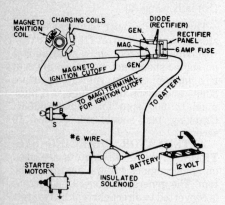

Fig. T87 — Wiring diagram of typical 3 amp alternator and rectifier panel charging system.

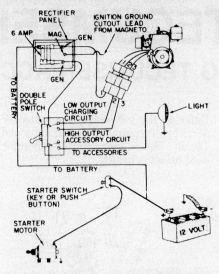

Fig. T88 — Wiring diagram of typical 7 amp alternator and rectifier panel charging system. The double pole switch in one position reduces output to 3 amps for charging or increases output to 7 amps in other position to operate accessories.

If voltage is less than 20.0 volts, alternator is defective.

MOTOR-GENERATOR. The combination motor-generator (Fig. T92) functions as a cranking motor when starting switch is closed. When engine is operating and starting switch is open, unit operates as a generator. Generator output and circuit voltage for battery and various accessories are controlled by current-voltage regulator.

To determine cause of abnormal operation, motor-generator should be given a "no-load" test or a "generator output" test. The generator output test can be performed with a motor-generator on or off the engine. The no-load test must be made with motor-generator removed from engine.

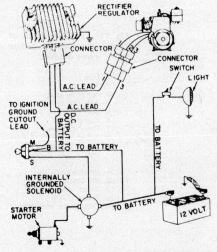

Fig. T89 — Wiring diagram of typical 7, 10 or 20 amp alternator and regulator-rectifier charging system.

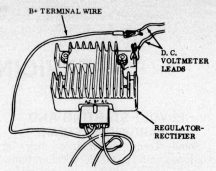

Fig. T90 — Connect DC voltmeter as shown when checking regulator-rectifier.

Motor-generator test specifications are as follows:

Motor-Generator Delco-Remy No. 1101980
Brush spring tension . . . . 24-32 oz.
(680-900g)
Field draw,
 Amperes 1.52-1.62
 Volts 12
Cold output,
 Amperes 12
 Volts 14
 Rpm 4950
No-load test,
 Amperes (max.) 18
 Volts 11
 Rpm (min.) 2500
 Rpm (max.) 2900

CURRENT-VOLTAGE REGULATORS. Two types of current-voltage regulators are used with motor-generator system. One is a low output unit which delivers a maximum of 7 amps. The high output unit delivers a maximum of 14 amps.

The low output (7 amp) unit is identified by its four connecting terminals (three on one side of unit and one on underside of regulator). The battery ignition coil has a 3 amp draw. This leaves a maximum load of 4 amps which may be used on accessory lead.

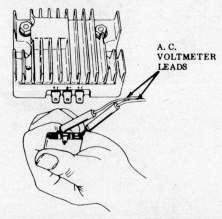

Fig. T91 — Connect AC voltmeter to AC leads as shown when checking alternator coils.

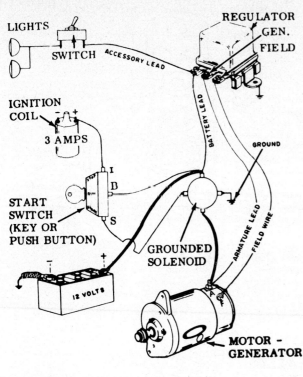

Fig. T92 — Wiring diagram of typical 14 amp output current-regulator and motor-generator system. The 7 amp output system is similar.

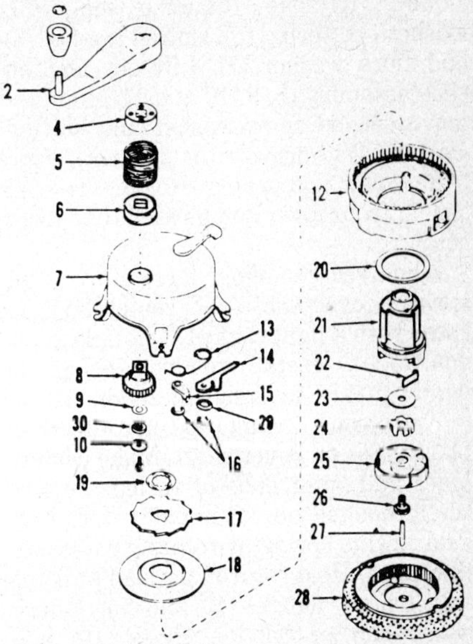

Fig. T93 — Exploded view of ratchet starter used on some engines.

2. Handle	18. Spring cover
4. Clutch	19. Retaining ring
5. Clutch spring	20. Hub washer
6. Bearing	21. Starter hub
7. Housing	22. Starter dog
8. Wind gear	23. Brake washer
9. Wave washer	24. Brake
10. Clutch washer	25. Retainer
12. Spring & housing	26. Screw (left hand thread)
13. Release dog spring	27. Centering pin
14. Release dog	28. Hub & screen
15. Lock dog	29. Spacer washers
16. Dog pivot retainers	30. Lockwasher
17. Release gear	

The high output (14 amp) unit has only three connecting terminals (all on side of unit). So with a 3 amp draw for battery ignition coil, a maximum of 11 amps can be used for accessories.

Regulator service test specifications are as follows:

Regulator Delco-Remy No. 1118988 (7 amp)

Ground polarity . . . . .Negative
Cut-out relay,
  Air gap. . . . . .0.020 in. (0.5 mm)
  Point gap . . . . .0.020 in. (0.5 mm)
  Closing voltage, range 11.8-14.0
  Adjust to 12.8
Voltage regulator,
  Air gap. . . . . .0.075 in. (1.9 mm)
  Setting volts, range. 13.6-14.5
  Adjust to 14.0

Regulator Delco-Remy No. 1119207 (14 amp)

Ground polarity . . . . .Negative
Cut-out relay,
  Air gap. . . . . .0.020 in. (0.5 mm)
  Point gap . . . . .0.020 in. (0.5 mm)
  Closing voltage, range 11.8-13.5
  Adjust to 12.8
Voltage regulator,
  Air gap. . . . . .0.075 in. (1.9 mm)
  Voltage setting @ degrees F.
  14.4-15.4 @ 65°
  14.2-15.2 @ 85°
  14.0-14.9 @ 105°
  13.8-14.7 @ 125°
  13.5-14.3 @ 145°
  13.1-13.9 @ 165°
Current regulator,
  Air gap. . . . . .0.075 in. (1.9 mm)
  Current setting 13-15

WIND-UP STARTER

RATCHET STARTER. On models equipped with ratchet starter, refer to Fig. T93 and proceed as follows: Move release lever to "RELEASE" position to remove tension from main spring. Remove starter assembly from engine. Remove left hand thread screw (26), retainer hub (25), brake (24), washer (23) and six starter dogs (22). Note position of starter dogs in hub (21). Remove hub (21), washer (20), spring and housing (12), spring cover (18), release gear (17) and retaining ring (19) as an assembly. Remove retaining ring, then carefully separate these parts.

CAUTION: Do not remove main spring from housing (12). The spring and housing are serviced only as an assembly.

Remove snap rings (16), spacer washers (29), release dog (14), lock dog (15) and spring (13). Winding gear (8), clutch (4), clutch spring (5), bearing (6)

and crank handle (2) can be removed after first removing retaining screw and washers (10, 30 and 9).

Reassembly procedure is reverse of disassembly. Centering pin (27) must align screw (26) with crankshaft center hole.

REWIND STARTERS

FRICTION SHOE TYPE. To disassemble starter, refer to Fig. T94 and proceed as follows: Hold starter rotor (12) securely with thumb and remove the four screws securing flanges (1 and 2) to cover (15). Remove flanges and release thumb pressure enough to allow spring to rotate pulley unit spring (13) is un-

Fig. T94 — Exploded view of typical friction shoe rewind starter assembly.

1. Mounting flange
2. Flange
3. Retaining ring
4. Washer
5. Spring
6. Slotted washer
7. Fibre washer
8. Spring retainer
9. Spring
10. Friction shoe
11. Actuating lever
12. Rotor
13. Rewind spring
14. Centering pin
15. Cover
16. Rope
17. Roller

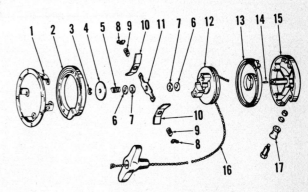

wound. Remove retaining ring (3), washer (4), spring (5), slotted washer (6) and fibre washer (7). Lift out friction shoe assembly (8, 9, 10 and 11), then remove second fibre washer and slotted washer. Withdraw rotor (12) with rope from cover and spring. Remove rewind spring from cover and unwind rope from rotor.

When reassembling, lubricate rewind spring, cover shaft and center bore in rotor with a light coat of "Lubriplate" or equivalent. Install rewind spring so windings are in same direction as removed spring. Install rope on rotor, then place rotor on cover shaft. Make certain inner and outer ends of spring are correctly hooked on cover and rotor. Preload rewind spring by rotating rotor two full turns. Hold rotor in preload position and install flanges (1 and 2). Check sharp end of friction shoes (10) and sharpen or renew as necessary. Install washers (6 and 7), friction shoe assembly, spring (5), washer (4) and retaining ring (3). Make certain friction shoe assembly is installed properly for correct starter rotation. If properly installed, sharp ends of friction shoes will extend when rope is pulled.

Remove brass centering pin (14) from cover shaft, straighten pin if necessary, then reinsert pin ⅓ of its length into cover shaft. When installing starter on engine, centering pin will align starter with center hole in end of crankshaft.

DOG TYPE. Two dog type starters may be used as shown in Fig. T95 and Fig. T96. Disassembly and assembly of both types is similar. To disassemble starter shown in Fig. T95, remove starter from engine and while holding pulley remove rope handle. Allow recoil spring to unwind. Remove starter components in order shown in Fig. T95 noting position of dog (6) and direction spring (3) is wound. Be careful when removing recoil spring (3). Reassemble by reversing disassembly procedure. Turn pulley six turns before passing rope through cover so spring (3), is preloaded. Tighten retainer screw (9) to

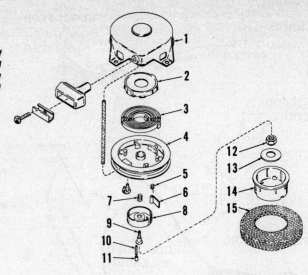

Fig. T95 — Exploded view of typical dog type recoil starter assembly. Some units of similar construction use three starter dogs (6).

1. Cover
2. Keeper
3. Recoil spring
4. Pulley
5. Spring
6. Dog
7. Brake spring
8. Retainer
9. Screw
10. Centering pin
11. Sleeve
12. Nut
13. Washer
14. Cup
15. Screen

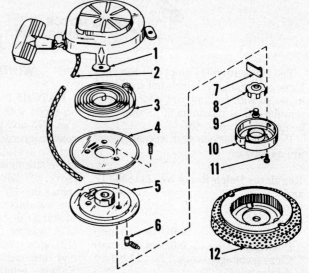

Fig. T96 — Exploded view of dog type recoil starter used on some models. Refer to Fig. T95 for view of other dog type recoil starter.

1. Cover
2. Rope
3. Rewind spring
4. Pulley half
5. Pulley half & hub
6. Retainer spring
7. Starter dog
8. Brake
9. Brake screw
10. Retainer
11. Retainer screw
12. Hub & screen assy.

45-55 in.-lbs. (5.08-6.21 N·m).

To disassemble starter shown in Fig. T96, pull starter rope until notch in pulley half (5) is aligned with rope hole in cover (1). Hold pulley and prevent from rotating. Engage rope in notch and allow pulley to slowly rotate so recoil spring will unwind. Remove components as shown in Fig. T96. Note direction recoil spring is wound being careful when removing spring from cover. Reassemble by reversing disassembly procedure. Preload recoil spring by turning pulley two turns with rope.

WISCONSIN

Model	No. Cyls.	Bore	Stroke	Displacement	Horsepower
TR-10D............................	1	3-1/8 in. (79.4 mm)	2-5/8 in. (66.7 mm)	20.2 cu. in. (331 cc)	10 (7.5 kW)
TRA-10D..........................	1	3-1/8 in. (79.4 mm)	2-5/8 in. (66.7 mm)	20.2 cu. in. (331 cc)	10 (7.5 kW)
TRA-12D..........................	1	3-1/2 in. (88.9 mm)	2-7/8 in. (73.0 mm)	27.66 cu. in. (453 cc)	12 (8.9 kW)
S-10D............................	1	3-1/4 in. (82.5 mm)	3 in. (76.2 mm)	24.89 cu. in. (408 cc)	10.5 (7.8 kW)
S-12D............................	1	3-1/2 in. (88.9 mm)	3 in. (76.2 mm)	28.86 cu. in. (473 cc)	12.5 (9.3 kW)
S-14D............................	1	3-3/4 in. (95.2 mm)	3 in. (76.2 mm)	33.1 cu. in. (542 cc)	14 (10.4 kW)

MAINTENANCE

SPARK PLUG. Recommended spark plug is a Champion D-16J, AC C86 or equivalent. Set electrode gap at 0.030 inch (0.762 mm). Tighten spark plug to a torque of 28-30 ft.-lbs. (38-41 N·m).

CARBURETOR. Zenith Model 68-7 carburetor is used on engine Models TR-

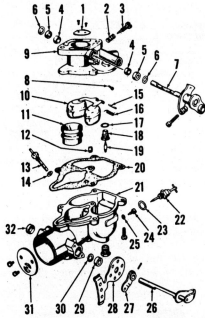

Fig. W1—Zenith 68-7 carburetor is used on Model TR-10D and TRA-10D engines.

1. Throttle plate
2. Spring
3. Idle mixture needle
4. Bushing
5. Seal
6. Retainer
7. Throttle shaft
8. Idle jet
9. Throttle body
10. Float
11. Venturi
12. Well vent
13. Discharge nozzle
14. Gasket
15. Float shaft
16. Float spring
17. Gasket
18. Inlet valve seat
19. Inlet valve
20. Gasket
21. Fuel bowl
22. Main fuel needle
23. Gasket
24. Main jet
25. Gasket
26. Choke shaft
27. Choke lever
28. Bracket
29. Retainer
30. Seal
31. Choke plate
32. Plug

10D and TRA-10D. See Fig. W1 for exploded view, Fig. W2 for cross-sectional view and Fig. W3 for location of adjustment points on carburetor.

TRA-12D engine is fitted with a Walbro LME-35 carburetor shown in exploded view in Fig. W4. Engine Models S-10D, S-12D and S-14D use a Zenith Model 1408 carburetor as shown in Fig. W5.

Float setting procedures for these carburetors varies. Measure float level of Zenith 68-7 carburetor as shown in Fig. W6. Bend float arm to obtain required height of 1-5/32 inches (29.4 mm).

See Fig. W7 for proper setting of float level of Walbro LME-35 carburetor. Space between free end of float and gasket surface should be 5/32-inch (4.0 mm).

Fig. W8 shows proper measurement procedure for checking float level of Zenith Model 1408 carburetors. Use a narrow blade depth gage as shown and be sure no pressure is on needle pin. Remove float when bending tab to make adjustment; do not try to adjust with

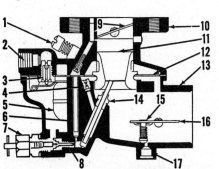

Fig. W2—Zenith 68-7 carburetor shown in cross-section.

1. Idle mixture needle
2. Fuel inlet
3. Float needle valve
4. Fuel well vent
5. Float
6. Idle fuel passage
7. Main jet adjusting needle
8. Main jet
9. Throttle plate
10. Throttle body
11. Venturi
12. Gasket
13. Fuel bowl
14. Main discharge jet
15. Poppet valve
16. Choke plate
17. Intake drain

float in place. Correct dimension is 7/8-inch (22.2 mm) as shown.

Refer to Fig. W3 for adjustment points of Model 68-7 carburetor and for initial setting, open both idle and main mixture needles by 1-1/4 turns each. Make final and trim adjustments after engine is warm. Use this same procedure to set Walbro carburetor. Idle mixture needle is shown at (9 – Fig. W4) with idle speed screw (7) and main fuel needle (33).

Model 1408 carburetor calls for initial setting of idle mixture at 1-1/2 turns open (5 – Fig. W9) and 2-1/4 turns open of main jet (18). Set idle speed (7) for 1000-1200 rpm.

FUEL PUMP. See Fig. W10 for exploded view of fuel pump used on some models. Repair kit (Wisconsin #LQ-28) is available from parts outlets and provides all parts marked (*) for service when renewal is needed.

GOVERNOR. All models are equipped with a mechanical governor of centrifugal flyweight design. Governor gear and weight assembly is driven by the

Fig. W3 – View of Zenith 68-7 carburetor to show adjustment point locations.

IN. Idle mixture needle
IS. Idle speed adjustment
MJ. Main jet adjustment

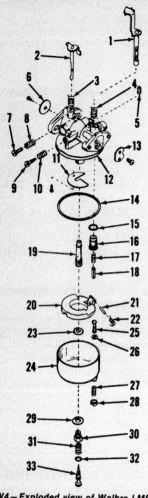

Fig. W4 — Exploded view of Walbro LME-35 carburetor used on TRA-12D engine.

1. Choke shaft
2. Throttle shaft
3. Throttle spring
4. Choke spring
5. Choke stop spring
6. Throttle plate
7. Idle speed screw
8. Spring
9. Idle mixture needle
10. Spring
11. Baffle
12. Carburetor body
13. Choke plate
14. Bowl gasket
15. Gasket
16. Inlet valve seat
17. Spring
18. Inlet valve
19. Main nozzle
20. Float
21. Float shaft
22. Spring
23. Gasket
24. Bowl
25. Drain stem
26. Gasket
27. Spring
28. Retainer
29. Gasket
30. Bowl retainer
31. Spring
32. "O" ring
33. Main fuel needle

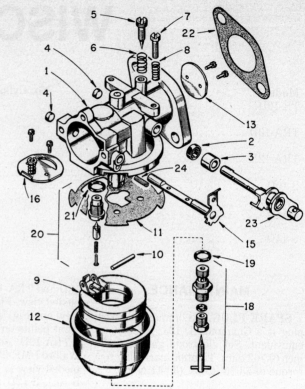

Fig. W5 — Exploded view of Zenith 1408 carburetor as used on engine Models S-10D, S-12D and S-14D.

1. Carburetor body
2. Throttle shaft seal
3. Seal retainer
4. Cup plugs
5. Idle fuel needle
6. Spring
7. Idle speed stop screw
8. Spring
9. Float assy.
10. Float pin
11. Gasket
12. Fuel bowl
13. Throttle disc
15. Choke shaft
16. Choke disc
18. Main jet needle assy.
19. Washer
20. Inlet valve & seat assy.
21. Gasket
22. Gasket
23. Throttle shaft
24. Choke lever friction spring

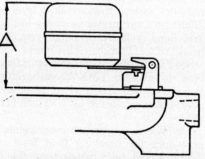

Fig. W6 — To measure float level of Zenith 68-7 carburetor, dimension "A" should be 1-5/32 inches (29.4 mm). Carefully bend float arm to adjust.

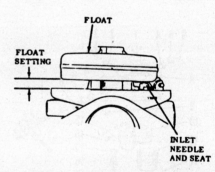

Fig. W7 — Float setting of Walbro carburetor calls for 5/32-inch (4 mm) space between free end of float and gasket surface as shown.

camshaft gear. Figs. W11 and W12 show operating parts of each type used and identify models which pertain.

Note thrust of governor weights in governor style shown in Fig. W11 is transmitted through a sliding pin to a vane which imparts rotary motion to governor shaft and lever. Governor shown in Fig. W12 has a movable thrust sleeve which transmits flyweight pressure to governor cross shaft so as to rotate governor lever. See Fig. W13 for typical linkage.

In order to correctly set governed speeds, use of a tachometer or revolution counter to accurately measure crankshaft rpm is necessary. Refer to appropriate table (I or II) corresponding to engine model being serviced to determine proper governor lever hole for attaching governor spring to set required speed.

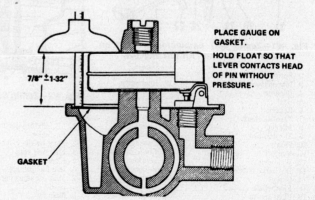

Fig. W8 — Measure for 7/8-inch (22 mm) float setting of Zenith 1408 carburetor as shown. See text.

7/8" ±1-32"

PLACE GAUGE ON GASKET.

HOLD FLOAT SO THAT LEVER CONTACTS HEAD OF PIN WITHOUT PRESSURE.

GASKET

Be sure correct parts are used in governor linkages. It will be noted in tables that for full range of adjustment, different lengths of adjusting screws are specified. TR and TRA models (Table I) also may call for different governor springs for setting higher or lower governed speeds. Authorized WISCONSIN parts service should be consulted.

Special Note: All TR-10D engines manufactured prior to S.N. 3909152 were set for full throttle operation. With governor lever in hole number 2, no-load rpm of 3800 will provide 3450 rpm under load.

Table I—Models TRA-10D, TRA-12D, TR10D
Use Lever Spring Hole Number and Set No-Load Rpm:

Desired Rpm Under Load	TRA-10D**		TRA-12D	
2000	1	2520	3	2230
2100	1	2580	4	2430
2200	1	2610	4	2515
2300	1	2690	4	2590
2400	1	2740	4	2660
2500	1	2800	4	2750
2600	1	2890	4	2810
2700	1	2935	5	3020
2800	2	3065	5	3100
2900	2	3160	5	3180
*3000	3	3230	5	3260
*3100	3	3300	5	3325
*3200	3	3380	6	3535
*3300	3	3460	6	3620
*3400	4	3615	6	3700
*3500	4	3690	6	3790
*3600	5	3850	6	3860

**Applies to TR-10 engines S.N. 3909152 and after.
2000-2900 rpm, TRA-10D uses 3-5/8 inch adjusting screw; TRA-12D uses 5-5/8 inch adjusting screw.
3000 rpm (*) and higher, TRA-10D uses 5 inch adjusting screw; TRA-12D uses 5-1/4 inch adjusting screw.

Table II—Models S-10D, S-12D, S-14D

Desired Rpm Under Load	Hole Number	Adjust No-Load Rpm To:
1600	1	1760
1800	2	1975
1900	2	2040
2000	2	2120
2100	3	2260
2200	3	2340
2300	3	2400
2400	4	2580
2500	4	2650
*2600	4	2720
*2700	4	2810
*2800	5	2910
*2900	5	3010
*3000	6	3150
*3100	6	3230
*3200	7	3360
*3300	7	3455
*3400	7	3520
*3500	7	3590
*3600	7	3680

1600-2500 rpm, use 3-15/16 inch adjusting screw.
2600 rpm (*) and higher, use 3-5/8 inch adjusting screws.

GOVERNOR SETTING. (MODELS TR-10D AND TRA-12D). Refer to Fig. W11 and to table I. Position governor lever (4—Fig. W11) on governor (fulcrum) shaft (7) with control rod connected between governor lever and throttle lever and with governor spring attached in correct hole of governor

lever as specified in table. Then, with carburetor throttle held wide open, loosen governor lever clamp so fulcrum shaft (7) can be turned independently of governor lever (4). Rotate fulcrum shaft counter-clockwise until internal governor vane (8) is in contact with flyweight thrust pin. Tighten clamp screw on governor lever (4), and on Model TR-10D engine, install idle return spring from breather tube to governor lever. Check no-load rpm using a tachometer. Regulate governor spring tension by means of the adjusting screw until required no load rpm is set.

(MODELS S-10D, S-12D and S-14D). Refer to Fig. W12 and to Table II. Loosen locknut (1—Fig. W12) and remove lower end of throttle rod (2) from governor lever (6). Hold throttle in wide open position and turn governor lever (6) as far clockwise as possible. Adjust length of rod (2) by turning its threaded end in or out of carburetor throttle lever until lower end will enter hole in governor lever. Reinstall retainer clip (14) and retighten nut (1). Use a tachometer to check no-load rpm.

If governor appears over-sensitive or if not responsive under load, check for correct spring and linkage components and be sure parts are not binding and are properly assembled.

Fig. W13 shows typical governor control linkage. That illustrated is used on Models S-10D, S-12D and S-14D. Variable speed control may take the form of a control handle attached to control disc (CD—Fig. W13) or a remote control assembly which consists of a throttle

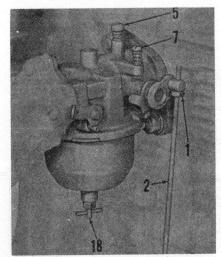

Fig. W9—View of carburetor adjustment points and throttle linkage of Model 1408 carburetor. See Text for procedure.

1. Nut	7. Idle speed adjustment
2. Throttle rod	screw
5. Idle fuel needle	18. Main fuel needle

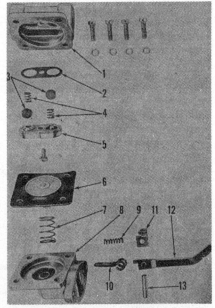

Fig. W10—Exploded view of fuel pump used on these Wisconsin engines. Renewable service parts are marked (*).

1. Pump head	
2. Valve gasket*	8. Mounting bracket
3. Valve (2)*	9. Rocker arm spring
4. Springs (2)*	10. Linkage
5. Valve plate & seats	11. Spring clip
6. Diaphragm*	12. Rocker arm
7. Spring*	13. Rocker arm pin

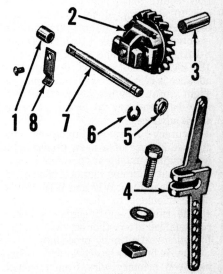

Fig. W11—Exploded view of governor assembly typical of that used on Models TR-10D, TRA-10D and TRA-12D.

1. Spacer	5. Oil seal
2. Gear/flyweight assy.	6. Retaining ring
3. Governor shaft	7. Fulcrum shaft
4. Governor lever	8. Vane

lever, conveniently mounted, which is connected by a Bowden cable to the control disc. If engine is equipped with variable speed controls, be sure they do not over-ride or cause binding in governor linkages.

MAGNETO IGNITION. Either Fairbanks-Morse or Wico flywheel magnetos are used. The breaker box is an integral part of the crankcase and points and condenser contained therein are interchangeable for either Wico or Fairbanks-Morse magnetos. However, should service replacement of flywheel or stator plate become necessary, both parts must be of the same manufacture.

See Fig. W14 for typical magneto ignition wiring diagram. Refer to IGNITION TIMING paragraph for breaker point adjustment.

BATTERY IGNITION. Engines equipped with battery ignition system use a conventional 12-volt ignition coil. Breaker points are the same as used with magneto ignition and are located in breaker box on crankcase. See Fig. W15 for typical battery ignition wiring diagram. Refer to IGNITION TIMING paragraph for point adjustment.

IGNITION TIMING. Ignition timing for engines equipped with either magneto ignition or battery ignition is as follows:

Breaker points and condenser are accessible when breaker box cover is removed. See Figs. W17 and W18. Models TR-10D and TRA-10D call for a point gap setting of 0.020 inch (0.508 mm). Models S-10D, S-12D and S-14D with conventional (magneto or battery) ignition require that points be set to 0.023 inch (0.584 mm). Model TRA-12D has breakerless (CD) ignition as standard; it is optional on Models S-10D, S-12D and S-14D. Fixed running spark advance is 18° BTDC on all models. Because this advance is regulated by point opening, a slight variation in breaker point setting may be necessary to obtain accurate spark advance.

Accuracy of spark timing can be checked by use of a neon timing light with engine running at operating speed. Placement of timing marks is shown for all models in Figs. W17 and W18. If it is not convenient to check timing with engine running, or if engine is being reassembled after other service, use the following static timing procedure.

Remove breaker box cover and disconnect coil primary wire from terminal stud at breaker box. Remove spark plug and place thumb over plug hole in cylinder head, then rotate flywheel clockwise by turning starting sheave until cylinder compression is felt against thumb. Continue to turn until timing

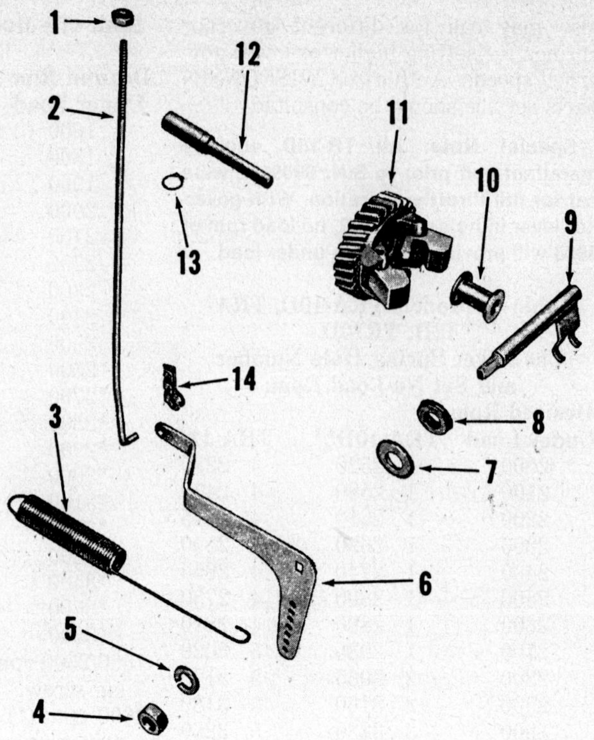

Fig. W12 — Governor mechanism as used on Models S-10D, S-12D and S-14D. Refer to text for service information.

1. Locknut
2. Throttle rod
3. Governor spring
4. Nut
5. Lockwasher
6. Governor lever
7. Flat washer
8. Oil seal
9. Cross (fulcrum) shaft
10. Thrust sleeve
11. Gear weight assy.
12. Shaft
13. Snap ring
14. Clip

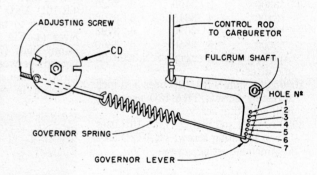

Fig. W13 — Typical governor adjustment and controls. Major speed changes are made by shifting holes in governor lever and minor adjustments on speed adjusting screw. In some cases, a control handle or remote control cable may be attached to control disc (CD) for variable speed control. See text and speed chart.

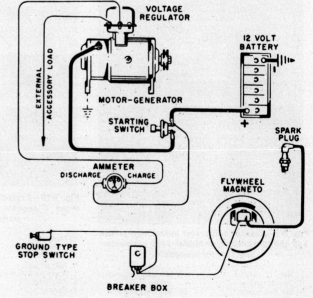

Fig. W14 — Typical magneto ignition wiring layout. Motorgenerator for electric starting with battery and charging circuit also shown. Refer to text.

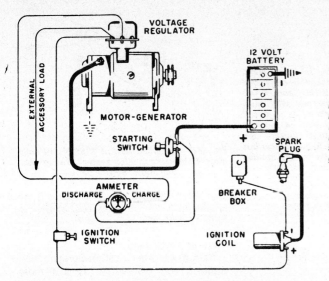

Fig. W15 — Typical battery ignition wiring diagram. Note by comparison with Fig. W14 how ignition system is tied in with motor-generator and battery circuits. See text.

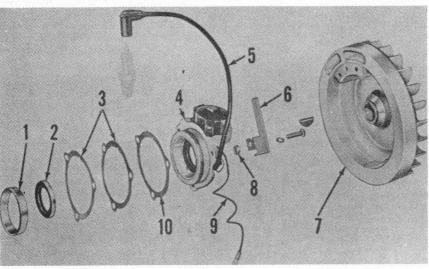

Fig. W16 — Typical flywheel magneto assembly. Note that crankshaft end play is adjusted by shims (3) which are offered in thickness of 0.005, 0.010, 0.015 and 0.20 inch. Flywheel must be pulled for access to magneto stator plate.

1. Bearing cup
2. Oil seal
3. Shims
4. Stator plate assy.
5. Spark plug lead
6. Wire clip
7. Flywheel
8. Spacer
9. Breaker point lead
10. Stator plate gasket

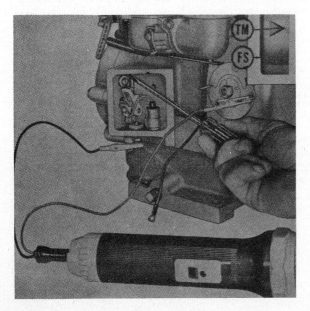

Fig. W17 — On Models TR-10D and TRA-10D, timing mark (TM) should be aligned with timing pointer on flywheel shroud (FS) as light goes out. Refer to text for static timing technique.

marks are aligned. Connect a continuity timing light, Wisconsin Motor part #DF-81-S1, or equivalent, as shown in Figs. W17 or W18. Then loosen lockscrew of ignition points baseplate just enough so plate can be moved. Fit a screwdriver into adjusting slots and turn to close points so light will come on, then back off until light just goes off. Tighten lockscrew securely. Make a final check by turning flywheel counter-clockwise until light goes on, then rotate flywheel clockwise and stop immediately when light goes out. At this point, advance timing mark on flywheel should line up with pointer or hole in shroud.

Disconnect and remove timing light and reconnect coil primary lead to breaker box stud. Reinstall cover.

SOLID STATE IGNITION (Models TRA-12D, S-10D, S-12D and S-14D). Breakerless capacitive-discharge (CD) ignition is offered on these models (standard on TRA-12D) for ease of starting and simplified maintenance. No adjustments are required. Only three parts assemblies are used: A magnet ring (fitted to and part of flywheel), a stator (containing trigger coil, rectifier diode and a silicon-controlled rectifier) mounted on bearing plate at flywheel end of engine and a special ignition coil.

In operation, an alternating current (AC) is generated in wire-wound coil poles of stator by passage of rotating flywheel magnets. Resulting AC passes to diode rectifier in stator which converts AC to DC. This direct current is then stored in a capacitor where it remains until further rotation of flywheel passes a permanent magnet over trigger coil section of stator which will generate a minute current to "trigger" or activate silicon-controlled rectifier (SCR) to switch the much heavier current stored in the capacitor into primary windings of the ignition coil. Now, by induction, this voltage is multiplied in secondary windings and discharged across spark plug electrode gap to ignite a fuel mixture charge in the engine combustion chamber. Elimination of electrical arcing at breaker points and wear of parts due to friction provides greatly increased service life in such a system when compared to conventional battery or magneto ignition.

TIMING CHECK – BREAKERLESS IGNITION. Design of this system does not allow for adjustment or alteration of spark timing, however, timing should be checked to determine if automatic advance is operating properly or to establish possible cause of ignition malfunction. Note in Fig. W20 that mounted positions of magnet ring in flywheel and stator on bearing plate assembly are fixed so as to be non-adjustable.

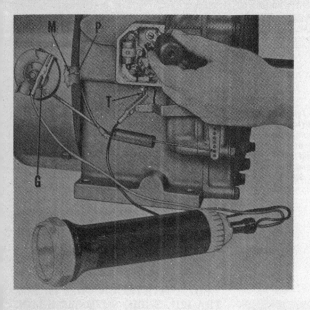

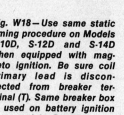

Fig. W18—Use same static timing procedure on Models S-10D, S-12D and S-14D when equipped with magneto ignition. Be sure coil primary lead is disconnected from breaker terminal (T). Same breaker box is used on battery ignition models. See text.

    G. Ground connection
    M. Timing mark
    P. Timing pointer
    T. Breaker terminals

Fig. W20—Exploded view of WISCONSIN solid state breakerless ignition system to show relationship of service parts.

1. Flywheel & magnet ring
2. Ignition coil
3. Ignition switch assy.
4. Bearing plate assy.
5. Stator & trigger coil assy.

To check timing, a conventional neon timing light will serve. During cranking, spark is retarded to 10-12° BTDC and will advance to line up 18° BTDC mark on flywheel rim with timing pointer when engine is running at 1000 rpm. When checking running advance, which is 20° BTDC at 2500 rpm, timing mark will appear about ⅛-inch (3 mm) above pointer.

TROUBLESHOOTING. If cause for poor or no performance appears to be in ignition system, proceed as follows:

Inspect wiring, both primary and secondary leads, for grounding or for loose or dirty connections. A test light or ohmmeter continuity check will show if high resistance or broken conductors are the problem.

Remove, inspect condition, and if convenient, test spark plug. Be sure to measure electrode gap if plug is reinstalled.

To test for system output, fit a short section of bare wire into spark plug lead boot and hold exposed tip of this wire about ⅛-inch (3 mm) from cylinder head while cranking engine. Observe spark for condition. A weak spark (thin and yellow) or no spark indicates a defective stator. Since stator is without external test terminals, no electrical tests are feasible and evaluation is entirely based upon performance.

Failure of other system components, ignition coil or switch, is a remote possibility. If doubtful, these items may be isolated by disconnecting wire leads and tested with an ohmmeter. Resistance from coil secondary socket to case (ground) should be 4000-6000 ohms. Coil primary winding resistance is too low for significant measurement, however, this winding should be tested for continuity. Switch should make and break circuit sharp and clean without high resistance in closed position.

If parts are available, substitution of new units, spark plug, coil or stator, followed by performance check is most reliable.

LUBRICATION. An oil dipper on connecting rod provides a splash lubrication system on all models. Use high quality detergent engine oil with a minimum API classification of "SD" or "SE". As seasonal temperatures vary, observe the following: Between 40°F (4°C) and 120°F (49°C), use SAE 30 weight oil. From 15°F (–9°C) to 40°F (4°C), use SAE 20W. From 0°F (–18°C) to 15°F (–9°C), use SAE 10W. Below 0°F (–18°C), use SAE 5W-20. Oil level should be checked for every eight hours of operation and changed every fifty hours. Crankcase capacity is one quart (0.9L) for Models TR-10D, TRA-10D and TRA-12D. Use two quarts (1.9L) in Models S-10D, S-12D and S-14D. When dipstick reads at "low" mark, add approximately ½-pint (0.2L) to restore proper oil level.

CRANKCASE BREATHER. A reed type breather valve is located at valve spring compartment. This one-way valve maintains a slight vacuum in the crankcase and helps prevent oil leakage of breaker point push rod and crankshaft oil seals. If a slight amount of crankcase vacuum is not present when engine is operating, clean and inspect breather valve. If breather valve is in satisfactory condition, check engine for

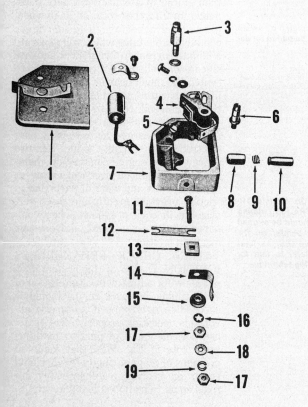

Fig. W19—Exploded view of breaker box assembly used on magneto and battery ignition models of S-10D, S-12D and S-14D engines.

  1. Box cover
  2. Condenser
  3. Mounting stud
  4. Breaker points
  5. Terminal screw
  6. Breaker pivot
  7. Breaker box
  8. Bushing
  9. Spring
10. Push pin
11. Terminal stud
12. Terminal strip
13. Insulator
14. Ground strip
15. Insulator
16. Lockwasher
17. Nuts
18. Flat washer
19. Lockwasher

excessive blow-by past piston rings and/or valves.

REPAIRS

TIGHTENING TORQUES. Recommended tightening torques are as follows:

Models TR-10D, TRA-10D, TRA-12D

Gear Cover . . . . 8 ft.-lbs.
(11 N·m)

Stator Plate . . . . 8 ft.-lbs.
(11 N·m)

Connecting Rod Cap . . . . 22 ft.-lbs.
(30 N·m)

Spark Plug . . . . 28-30 ft.-lbs.
(38-41 N·m)

Flywheel Nut . . . . 50-55 ft.-lbs.
(68-75 N·m)

Cylinder Head (see CYLINDER HEAD paragraph)

Models S-10D, S-12D, S-14D

Gear Cover . . . . 18 ft.-lbs.
(24 N·m)

Stator Plate . . . . 18 ft.-lbs.
(24 N·m)

Connecting Rod Cap . . . . 22 ft.-lbs.
(30 N·m)

Spark Plug . . . . 28-30 ft.-lbs.
(38-41 N·m)

Flywheel Nut . . . . 50-55 ft.-lbs.
(68-75 N·m)

Cylinder Block Nuts . . . . . . 42-50 ft.-lbs.
(57-68 N·m)

Compartment Cap Screw (see Fig. W34) . . . . 32 ft.-lbs.
(43 N·m)

Cylinder Head (see CYLINDER HEAD paragraph)

CYLINDER HEAD. Always install a new head gasket when installing cylinder head. Be sure to note different lengths and styles of studs and cap screws for correct reinstallation. Lubricate threads.

Cylinder heads should be torqued in three stages: On Models TR-10D, TRA-10D and TRA-12D, torque first to 10 ft.-lbs. (14 N·m), then to 14 ft.-lbs. (19 N·m) and finally to 18 ft.-lbs. (24 N·m). On Models S-10D, S-12D and S-14D, stages for tightening are 16 ft.-lbs. (22 N·m), 24 ft.-lbs. (33 N·m) and 32 ft.-lbs. (43 N·m). A criss-cross pattern for tightening is preferred over a rotation pattern around circumference of cylinder head.

CONNECTING ROD. Connecting rod is removed along with piston from top end of cylinder bore as shown in Fig. W21 or W22. Models TR-10D, TRA-10D and TRA-12D have a crankpin diameter of 1.3755-1.3760 inches (34.938-34.950 mm). Rod bearing clearance for all TR and TRA models is 0.0005-0.0015 inch (0.0127-0.0381 mm) and side clearance is 0.009-0.016 inch (0.229-0.406 mm). Crankpin diameter for Models S-10D, S-12D and S-14D is 1.4984-1.4990 inches (38.059-38.075 mm) and clearance of insert type rod bearing is 0.0005-0.0015 inch (0.0127-0.0381 mm). Side clearance on "S" model engines is 0.004-0.013 inch (0.102-0.330 mm). New rods with crankpin bearing end of 0.010, 0.020 and 0.030 inch undersize are available for all

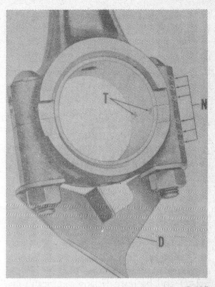

Fig. W23—Install connecting rod cap (S-10D, S-12D and S-14D) so tangs (T) of bearing inserts are on same side. Numbers (N) on rod end and cap should also be aligned and installed toward gear cover side of crankcase. Oil dipper (D) open side also faces outward. See text.

TR and TRA models. Bearing inserts (shells) for S-10D, S-12D and S-14D are available in undersizes as well as standard size.

Piston pin to connecting rod clearance

Fig. W24—Section view showing proper arrangement of piston rings. In this typical view, top ring may not be chamfered inside as shown, however, all rings are marked with "TOP" or pit mark for correct installation. See text.

Fig. W21—Piston (P) is removed from top. Oil dipper (D) provides lubrication for horizontal crankshaft engines. Note placement of connecting rod index arrow at (A), location of governor shaft (GS) and that camshaft gear is fitted with a compression release (CR), typical of "TR" and "TRA" models.

Fig. W22—Open view of typical S-10D, S-12D or S-14D engine. Compare to Fig. W21, and note difference in placement of governor shaft, style of oil dipper and that cylinder and crankcase are separate castings. Flywheel should be left in place to balance crankshaft when gear cover is removed.

Fig. W25—Location of cylinder-crankcase specification number on all "TR" and "TRA" models.

is 0.0002-0.0008 inch (0.0051-0.0203 mm) on all models except S-10D, S-12D and S-14D which are fitted with renewable bushings calling for clearance of 0.0005-0.0011 inch (0.0127-0.0279 mm). Oversize piston pins are available for some engines.

When installing piston and connecting rod assembly on models which are not equipped with renewable bearing inserts, TR-10D, TRA-10D and TRA-12D, align index arrows (A – Fig. W21) on rod end and cap. Arrows must face toward open end of crankcase. On all engines which are furnished with separate oil dipper (Fig. W22), install dipper so connecting rod cap screws are accessible from open end of crankcase. Refer to Fig. W23 when assembling cap to connecting rod on Models S-10D, S-12D and S-14D and be sure fitting tangs (T) are on same side as shown. Stamped numbers (N) and oil dipper (D) should face open side of crankcase.

PISTON, PIN AND RINGS. All engines are fitted with one chrome faced compression ring, one scraper ring and an oil control ring. Typical ring arrangement is shown in Fig. W24. Top side of all rings is marked "TOP" or bears a pit mark for correct installation. Ring end gaps should be spaced at 120 degree intervals from each other during reassembly.

When fitting pistons, clearance between skirt of cam ground piston and cylinder wall should be measured at right angle to piston pin. Required clearance for Models TR-10D and TRA-10D is 0.004-0.0045 inch (0.102-0.1143 mm) and for Models TRA-12D, S-10D and S-12D it is 0.0025-0.003 inch (0.0635-0.076 mm). Clearance for Model S-14D should be 0.0025-0.004 inch (0.0635-0.102 mm).

Ring end gaps of all models should measure 0.010-0.020 inch (0.254-0.508 mm). Side clearance of piston rings in grooves is as follows: For Models TR-10D, TRA-10D and TRA-12D, top (compression) ring should have a clearance of 0.002-0.0035 inch (0.051-0.0889 mm), second (scraper) ring calls for 0.001-0.0025 inch (0.025-0.0635 mm) and oil ring clearance is 0.002-0.0035 inch (0.051-0.0889 mm). For Models S-10D, S-12D and S-14D, top ring requires 0.002-0.004 inch (0.051-0.102 mm), second ring 0.002-0.004 inch (0.051-0.102 mm) and oil ring 0.0015-0.0035 inch (0.0381-0.0889 mm).

Renewal pistons and rings are available in oversize as well as standard. Tri-Chrome ring sets may also be used, and for long-term heavy duty service, are recommended.

Floating type piston pin is retained in bores by snap rings. Fit, for all models,

Fig. W26 – Dial indicator set up for checking crankshaft end play. Refer to text. Correct reading should be 0.001-0.004 inch (0.025-0.102 mm) measured with engine cold.

should be from zero to 0.0008 inch (0.0203 mm) tight. See CONNECTING ROD paragraph for fit of piston pin to small end of connecting rod. Renewal piston pins for Models S-10D, S-12D and S-14D are available in standard and 0.005 and 0.010 inch oversize. Larger oversizes of 0.020 inch and 0.030 inch are offered for other models.

CYLINDER. Cylinder and crankcase are a one-piece casting for Models TR-10D, TRA-10D and TRA-12D. See Fig. W25. When cylinder bores of these models are worn to exceed 0.005 inch (0.127 mm), they should be rebored to accept next available oversize piston. Be sure to check parts availability at this point of overhaul process. Other models, S-10D, S-12D and S-14D, have separate castings for cylinder and crankcase as can be seen in Fig. W22. Cylinder assembly should be removed and

Fig. W27 – Locate timing mark (A) on camshaft gear between two marked teeth (B) of crankshaft gear. View is typical of all "TR" and "TRA" series.

rebored when wear exceeds 0.005 inch (0.127 mm). If entire cylinder block must be renewed due to extensive damage, new valves, seats, guides, springs, retainers and rotators are all furnished as part of complete assembly. When reassembling cylinder to crankcase, use a new gasket and tighten retaining stud nuts to a torque value of 42-50 ft.-lbs. (57-68 N·m). A cap screw is concealed within valve spring compartment. See Fig. W34 and tighten this cap screw to 32 ft.-lbs. (43 N·m). Refer to PISTON, PIN AND RINGS paragraph for information relating to oversize renewal parts.

CRANKSHAFT. On all models, crankshaft rides in two tapered roller

Fig. W28 – View of timing marks lined up in Models S-10D, S-12D and S-14D. In current production, camshaft gear will support a compression release as shown in Fig. W31. Camshaft thrust spring (S) and governor thrust sleeve (10) must be in place before replacement of gear cover. Use heavy grease to hold camshaft thrust ball in cover hole during installation.

bearings. Removal of crankshaft is from gear cover end of crankcase.

CAUTION: When crankshaft removal is planned, be sure to loosen and remove flywheel nut from crankshaft and loosen flywheel from crankshaft tapered end before removing gear cover and its bearing from opposite end so crankshaft will be fully supported from heavy shock during flywheel removal. Leave flywheel loose on tapered shaft end to balance crankshaft during removal of gera cover.

Crankshaft end play on all models is 0.001-0.004 inch (0.025-0.102 mm) with engine cold. Adjustment is made by varying number of shims in shim pack between crankcase and stator plate (main bearing support) at flywheel end of crankshaft. To check, use a dial indicator mounted as shown in Fig. W26. If new tapered roller main bearings have been installed, it will be necessary to firmly bump crankshaft ends with a heavy soft hammer to insure that bear-

ings are fully seated before adjusting end play. Be sure camshaft and crankshaft timing marks are in proper register as shown in Figs. W27 and W28 and check tightening torque values for gear cover at beginning of the REPAIRS section. Figs. W29 and W30 show seal protectors which should be used and are identified by model.

In case of severe wear or scoring of crankpin journal, regrind to fit next undersize connecting rod or for proper undersize connecting rod bearing inserts, depending upon model. Refer to CONNECTING ROD paragraph. Should it be necessary to renew crankshaft, part number will be found stamped in counterweight toward tapered shaft end.

GOVERNOR GEAR AND WEIGHT ASSEMBLY. Governor gear and weight assemblies rotate on a shaft which is a press fit in a bore of crankcase. Exploded views are shown in Figs.

W11 and W12. On Models TR-10D, TRA-10D and TRA-12D, shaft (3 – Fig. W11) has had its depth in block held by a snap ring beginning with production serial number 3909152. Models S-10D, S-12D and S-14D require end play of 0.003-0.005 inch (0.076-0.127 mm) be maintained on governor gear shaft between gear and its snap ring retainer. See Fig. W32 for measurement technique to be used on these models. Press-fitted shaft is driven in or out of bore to make adjustment. On models with straight governor lever and governor gear mounted above cam gear, note in Fig. W33 that upper end of governor lever must tilt toward engine so governor vane will not be fouled or interfere with flyweights as gear cover is installed. On Models S-10D, S-12D and S-14D, governor thrust sleeve must be in place as shown in Fig. W34 when gear cover is placed in position.

CAMSHAFT AND TAPPETS. Camshafts, all models, ride in unbushed bores in crankcase and gear cover. Camshaft end play is controlled by a thrust spring (See Figs. W33 and W34) fitted into shaft hub which centers upon a steel ball fitted into a socket in gear cover; during assembly, this ball is easily held in place by a coating of heavy grease. Cam followers (valve tappets) are removed downward from their bores in block after camshaft has been removed. During removal or installation of camshaft, place block on its side as shown in Fig. W35 to prevent tappets from dropping out.

Models TR-10D, TRA-10D and TRA-12D have a tappet body diameter of 0.309-0.310 inch (7.848-7.874 mm) with a clearance of 0.002-0.006 inch (0.051-0.152 mm) in block bores. Tappet diameter for Models S-10D, S-12D and S-14D is 0.6235-0.6245 inch (15.837-15.862 mm) with clearance of 0.0005-0.0025 inch (0.0127-0.0635 mm) required. These larger tappets in "S"

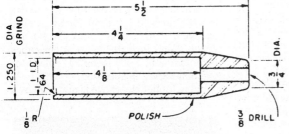

SLEEVE FOR ASSEMBLING GEAR COVER WITH OIL SEAL ON TO CRANKSHAFT

Fig. W29 – Dimensions of seal protector sleeve to be used on Models TR-10D, TRA-10D and TRA-12D.

SLEEVE FOR ASSEMBLING GEAR COVER WITH OIL SEAL, ON TO CRANKSHAFT.

Fig. W30 – Seal protector sleeve to be used on Models S-10D, S-12D and S-14D is fabricated to dimensions shown.

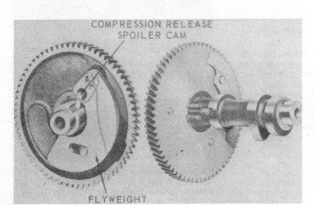

Fig. W31 – View of both sides of camshaft gear to show compression release assembly installed. See text.

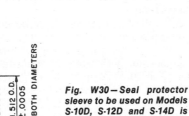
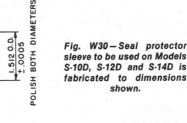

Fig. W32 – Use of feeler gage to measure end play of governor gear on shaft; snap ring must be correctly seated. See text.

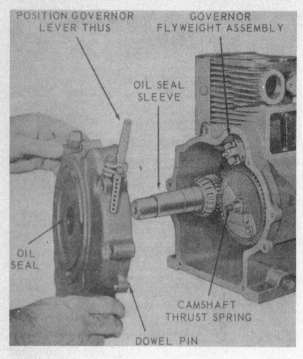

Fig. W33 — Replacement of gear cover on TR-10D, TRA-10D and TRA-12D engines, all integral cylinder-crankcase models. Note that governor flyweight assembly, camshaft thrust spring and oil seal protector are in place. Be sure governor lever is tilted as shown. Governor thrust ball is greased in place in its cover recess.

Fig. W35 — Place engine on its side as shown to prevent tappets dropping from block bores when camshaft is removed.

series engines are threaded, adjustable type.

On models equipped with a compression release type camshaft (Fig. W31), a spoiler cam holds exhaust valve slightly open during part of compression stroke while cranking. Reduced compression pressure allows for faster cranking speed at lower effort. When crankshaft reaches about 650 rpm during cranking, centrifugal force swings flyweight on front of cam gear to turn spoiler cam to inoperative position allowing exhaust valve to seat and restore full compression. Whenever camshaft is removed, compression release mechanism should be checked for damage to spring or excessive wear on spoiler cam. Flyweight and spoiler cam must move easily with no binding.

See Figs. W27 and W28 to set timing marks in register during reassembly.

VALVE SYSTEM. For all models, valve face and seat angle is 45 degrees for both valves. As indicated by letter "D" suffix to model numbers, all engines in this section are furnished with renewable stellite exhaust valve seat inserts and stellite-faced exhaust valves. Models S-10D, S-12D and S-14D also have renewable insert-type intake valve seats (not stellite) while others have their intake valves seated directly in cylinder block. Valve rotators are installed on all exhaust valves.

All valves are fitted in renewable guides pressed into cylinder block. Press or drive down (toward valve spring chamber) for both removal and installation. Tool #DF-72 guide driver is available from WISCONSIN. Internal chamfered end of guide is installed DOWN. Inside diameter of all valve guides is 0.312-0.313 inch (7.925-7.950 mm).

Diameter of valve stems is 0.310-0.311 inch (7.874-7.899 mm) for all intake valves and 0.309-0.310 inch (7.848-7.874 mm) for exhaust valves except for Models S-10D, S-12D and S-14D whose exhaust valve stems measure 0.308-0.309 inch (7.823-7.848 mm). Maximum allowable stem clearance in valve guides is 0.006 inch (0.152 mm) for all models except S-10D, S-12D and S-14D for which 0.005 inch (0.127 mm) clearance for intake and 0.007 inch (0.178 mm) for exhaust valves is specified.

Valve tappet clearance is adjusted by a

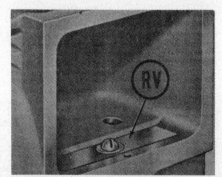

Fig. W36 — Reed-type breather valve located in valve spring compartment of Models TR-10D, TRA-10D and TRA-12D.

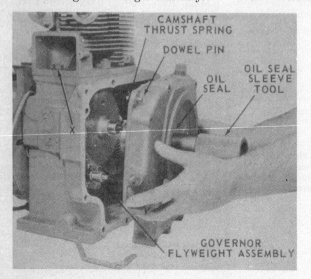

Fig. W34 — Installation of gear cover on S-10D, S-12D and S-14D engines. Note cap screw (X) in valve compartment, referred to in text. Protect cover oil seal with sleeve tool as shown and be sure thrust sleeve is in place on governor shaft. See TIGHTENING TORQUES.

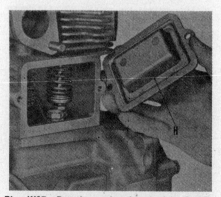

Fig. W37 — Breather valve for models S-10D, S-12D and S-14D is located in valve spring compartment cover. Drain hole (H) must be kept open.

self-locking cap screw in tappet body of Models S-10D, S-12D and S-14D. Setting for these models, engine cold, is 0.007 inch (0.178 mm) for intake valves and 0.016 inch (0.406 mm) for exhaust valves.

Tappet clearance for all other engine models is adjusted by careful grinding of valve stems. Cold clearance is 0.006 inch (0.152 mm) for intake valves and 0.012

inch (0.305 mm) for exhaust valves except for exhaust valve of Model TRA-12D which calls for a clearance of 0.015 inch (0.381 mm).

Manufacturer specifies that all reground valves be lapped in for proper seating.

Valve spring compartments have reed-type breather valves of types shown in Figs. W36 and W37. Action of

these valves during engine operation maintains a partial vacuum in engine crankcase to prevent internal pressure build-up which could cause oil leaks at seals and gaskets. If oil fouling occurs in ignition breaker box, condition of breather valve should be checked as a highly possible cause. These reed valve assemblies should be kept clean and renewed whenever found to be inoperable.

WISCONSIN
SERVICING WISCONSIN ACCESSORIES

12-VOLT STARTER-GENERATOR

The combination 12-volt starter-generator manufactured by Delco-Remy is used on some Wisconsin engines. The starter-generator functions as a cranking motor when starting switch is closed. When engine is operating and with starting switch open, unit operates as a generator. Generator output and circuit voltage for battery and various operating requirements are controlled by a current-voltage regulator.

To determine cause of abnormal operation, starter-generator should be given a "no-load" test or a "generator output" test. Generator output test can be performed with starter-generator on or off the engine. The no-load test must be made with starter-generator removed from engine. Refer to Fig. W38 for exploded view of starter-generator assembly. Parts are available from Wisconsin as well as authorized Delco-Remy service stations.

Starter-generator and regulator service test specifications are as follows:

Starter-Generator 1101696
Brush spring tension . . . . 22-26 oz.
                             (624-737 g)
Field draw:
  Amperes 1.43-1.54
  Volts 12
Cold output:
  Amperes 10
  Volts 14
  Rpm 5750
No-load test:
  Volts 11
  Amperes, max 17
  Rpm, min 2350
  Rpm, max 2850

Starter-Generator 1101870
Brush spring tension . . . . 22-26 oz.
                             (624-737 g)
Field draw:
  Amperes 1.52-1.62
  Volts 12
Cold output:
  Amperes 12
  Volts 14
  Rpm 4950

No-load test:
  Volts 11
  Amperes, max 18
  Rpm, min 2500
  Rpm, max 2900

Starter-Generators 1101871 & 1101972
Brush spring tension . . . . 24-32 oz.
                             (624-737 g)
Field draw:
  Amperes 1.43-1.54
  Volts 12
Cold output:
  Amperes 10
  Volts 14
  Rpm 5450
No load test:
  Volts 11
  Amperes, max 17
  Rpm, min 2500
  Rpm, max 3000

Regulators 1118791 & 1118985
Ground polarity . . . . Positive
Cut-out relay:
  Air gap . . . . 0.020 in. (0.5 mm)
  Point gap . . . . 0.020 in. (0.5 mm)
  Closing voltage, range 11.8-14.0
  Adjust to 12.8
Voltage regulator:
  Air gap . . . . 0.075 in. (1.9 mm)
  Setting voltage, range 13.6-14.5
  Adjust to 14.0

Regulators 1118983 & 1118984
Ground polarity . . . . Negative
Cut-out relay:
  Air gap . . . . 0.020 in. (0.5 mm)
  Point gap . . . . 0.020 in. (0.5 mm)
  Closing voltage, range 11.8-14.0
  Adjust to 12.8
Voltage regulator:
  Air gap . . . . 0.075 (1.9 mm)
  Setting voltage, range 13.6-14.5
  Adjust to 14.0

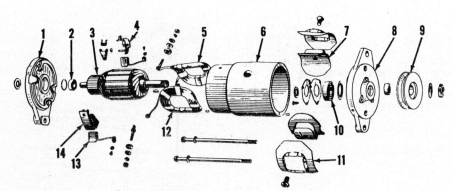

Fig. W38 — Exploded view of typical Delco-Remy starter-generator.

1. Commutator end frame
2. Bearing
3. Armature
4. Ground brush holder
5. Field coil L.H.
6. Frame
7. Pole shoe
8. Drive end frame
9. Pulley
10. Bearing
11. Field coil insulator
12. Field coil R.H.
13. Brush
14. Insulated brush holder

12-VOLT GEAR DRIVE STARTER

Some einges may be equipped with a 12-volt gear drive starting motor manufactured by Prestolite. Test specifications are as follows:

Prestolite MGD4102A

Volts 12
Brush spring tension . . . . 42-66 oz.
(1190-1870g)

No-load test
Volts 10
Amperes 38
Rpm 10000

Refer to Fig. W39 for exploded view of starting motor and drive. Bendix drive (15) is available only as an assembly. Thrust washers (7, 8, 9, 12 and 13) are available in a service package.

To disassemble starting motor, remove the two through-bolts and commutator end cover (1). Remove brushes and springs from brush holder and remove holder assembly (3). Carefully withdraw frame and field coil assembly (6) from armature. Clamp steel core of armature in vise and remove Bendix drive retaining nut (16). Remove Bendix drive assembly (15), drive end plate (14) and thrust washers from armature (10).

Renew brush springs if heat damage is evident and renew brushes if excessively worn. Input brush (4) is integral with terminal stud and field brush (5) lead is soldered to field coil.

When reassembling, apply a light coat of oil to bushings. Do not lubricate Ben-

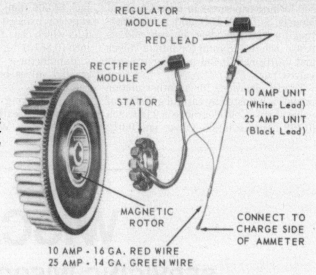

Fig. W40—View of 10 or 25 amp flywheel alternator charging system used on some engines.

dix drive assembly. Parts are available from Wisconsin as well as authorized Prestolite service stations.

FLYWHEEL ALTERNATOR

Some engines may be equipped with either a 10 amp or 25 amp flywheel alternator. See Fig. W40. To avoid possible damage to alternator system, the following precautions must be observed:

1. Negative post of battery must be connected to ground on engine.
2. Connect booster battery properly (positive to positive and negative to negative.)
3. Do not attempt to polarize alternator.
4. Do not ground any wires from stator or modules which terminate at connectors.
5. Do not operate engine with battery disconnected.

6. Disconnect battery cables when charging battery with a battery charger.

OPERATION. Alternating current (AC) produced by the alternator is changed to direct current (DC) in the rectifier module. See Fig. W41. Current regulation is provided by the regulator module which "senses" counter-voltage created by the battery to control or limit charging rate. No adjustments are possible on alternator charging system. Faulty components must be renewed. Refer to following troubleshooting paragraph to help pin point faulty component.

TROUBLESHOOTING. Trouble conditions and their possible causes are as follows:

1. Full charge—no regulation. Could be caused by:
   a. Faulty regulator module
   b. Defective battery

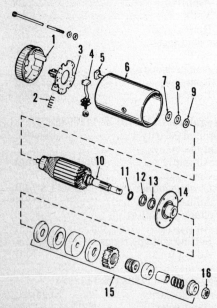

Fig. W39—Exploded view of typical Prestolite gear drive starting motor.

1. Commutator end cover
2. Brush spring (2 used)
3. Brush holder assy.
4. Input brush
5. Field brush
6. Frame & field coil assy.
7. Washer (0.031 in.)

8. Washer (0.23 in)
9. Washer (0.045 in.)
10. Armature
11. "O" ring
12. Washer (0.042 in.)
13. Washer (0.031 in.)
14. Drive end plate
15. Bendix drive assy.
16. Nut

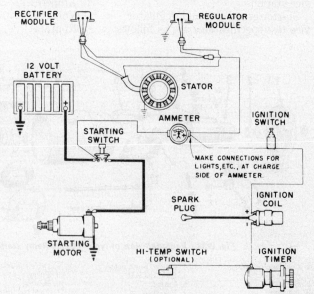

Fig. W41—Typical wiring diagram for ignition, starting and alternator charging systems used on some engines.

2. Low or no charge. Could be caused by:
   a. Faulty windings in stator
   b. Faulty rectifier module
   c. Regulator module not properly grounded or regulator module defective.

If "full-charge – no regulation" is the trouble, use a DC voltmeter and check battery voltage with engine operating at full rpm. If battery voltage is over 15.0 volts, regulator module is not functioning properly. If battery voltage is under 15.0 volts and over 14.0 volts, alternator, rectifier and regulator are satisfactory and battery is probably defective (unable to hold charge).

If "low" or "no charge" is the trouble, check battery voltage with engine operating at full rpm. If battery voltage is more than 14.0 volts, place a load on battery to reduce voltage to below 14.0 volts. If charge rate increases, alternator charging system is functioning properly and battery was fully charged. If charge rate does not increase, plug in a new rectifier module and retest. If charge increases, permanently install new rectifier module. If charge rate does not increase, stop engine and unplug all connectors between modules and stator. Start engine and operate at 2400 rpm. Using an AC voltmeter, check voltage between each of the black stator leads and ground. If either of the two voltage readings is zero or there is more than 10% difference between readings, the stator is faulty and should be renewed.

METRIC CONVERSION TABLE

INCHES FRACT.	DECIMALS	MM
	.000 04	.001
	.000 39	.01
	.001	.025
	.000 78	.02
	.001 18	.03
	.001 57	.04
	.001 97	.05
	.002	.051
	.002 36	.06
	.002 5	.0635
	.002 76	.07
	.002 95	.075
	.003	.0762
	.003 15	.08
	.003 54	.09
	.003 94	.1
	.004	.1016
	.005	.1270
	.007 87	.2
	.009 84	.25
	.01	.254
	.011 81	.3
1/64	.015 63	.3969
	.015 75	.4
	.019 69	.5
	.02	.508
	.023 62	.6
	.025	.635
	.027 56	.7
	.029 5	.75
	.03	.762
1/32	.031 25	.7938
	.031 5	.8
	.035 43	.9
	.039 37	1.0
	.04	1.016
	.043 31	1.1
3/64	.046 87	1.191
	.047 24	1.2
	.049 21	1.25
	.05	1.27
	.051 18	1.3
	.055 12	1.4
	.059 06	1.5

INCHES FRACT.	DECIMALS	MM
	.06	1.524
(1/16)	.062 5	1.5875
	.062 99	1.6
	.066 93	1.7
	.07	1.778
	.07087	1.8
	.075	1.905
5/64	.078 13	1.9844
	.078 74	2.0
	.08	2.032
	.082 68	2.1
	.086 61	2.2
	.088 58	2.25
	.09	2.286
	.090 55	2.3
3/32	.093 75	2.3812
	.094 49	2.4
	.098 43	2.5
	.1	2.54
	.102 36	**2.6**
	106 30	2.7
	.108 27	2.75
7/64	.109 37	2.7781
	.11	2.794
	.110 24	2.8
	.114 17	2.9
	.118 11	**3.0**
	.12	3.048
	.12 05	3.1
(1/8)	.125	3.175
	.125 98	3.2
	.127 96	3.25
	.129 92	3.3
	.13	3.302
	.133 86	3.4
	.137 80	**3.5**
	.14	3.556
9/64	.140 63	3.5719
	.141 73	3.6
	.145 67	3.7
	.149 61	3.8
	.15	3.810
	.153 54	3.9

INCHES FRACT.	DECIMALS	MM
5/32	.156 25	3.9688
	.157 48	**4.0**
	.16	4.064
	.161 42	4.1
	.165 35	4.2
	.169 29	4.3
	.17	4.318
11/64	.171 88	4.3656
	.173 23	4.4
	.177 17	4.5
	.18	4.572
	.181 10	4.6
	.185 04	4.7
(3/16)	.187 5	4.7625
	.188 98	4.8
	.19	4.826
	.192 91	4.9
	.196 85	**5.0**
	.2	5.08
	.200 79	5.1
13/64	.203 13	5.1594
	.204 72	5.2
	.208 66	5.3
	.21	5.334
	.216 60	5.4
	.216 54	5.5
7/32	.21875	5.5562
	.22	5.588
	.220 47	5.6
	.224 41	5.7
	.228 35	5.8
	.23	5.842
	.232 28	5.9
15/64	.234 38	5.9531
	.236 22	**6.0**
	.24	6.096
	.240 16	6.1
	.244 09	6.2
	.248 03	6.3
(1/4)	.25	6.35
	.251 97	6.4
	.255 91	6.5
	.259 84	6.6
	.26	6.604

INCHES FRACT.	DECIMALS	MM
	.263 78	6.7
17/64	.265 63	6.7469
	.267 72	6.8
	.27	6.858
	.271 65	6.9
	.275 59	7.0
	.279 53	7.1
	.28	7.112
9/32	.281 25	7.1438
	.283 46	7.2
	.287 40	7.3
	.29	7.366
	.291 34	7.4
	.295 28	7.5
19/64	.296 88	7.5406
	.299 21	7.6·
	.30	7.62
	.303 15	7.7
	.307 09	7.8
	.31	7.874
	.311 02	7.9
(5/16)	.312 5	7.9375
	.314 96	**8.0**
	.318 90	8.1
	.32	8.128
	.322 83	8.2
	.326 77	8.3
21/64	.328 13	8.3344
	.33	8.382
	.330 71	8.4
	.334 65	8.5
	.338 58	8.6
	.34	8.636
	.342 52	8.7
11/32	.343 75	8.7312
	.346 46	8.8
	.35	8.89
	.350 39	8.9
	.354 33	9.0
	.358 27	9.1
23/64	.359 38	9.1281
	.36	9.144
	.362 20	9.2
	.366 14	9.3

INCHES FRACT.	DECIMALS	MM		INCHES FRACT.	DECIMALS	MM		INCHES FRACT.	DECIMALS	MM		INCHES FRACT.	DECIMALS	MM
	.37	9.398			.54	13.716			.708 66	**18.0**			.877 95	22.3
	.370 08	9.4			.543 31	13.8			.71	18.034			.88	22.352
	.374 02	9.5		35/64	.546 88	13.8906			.712 60	18.1			.881 89	22.4
(3/8)	.375	9.525			.547 24	13.9			.716 53	18.2			.885 83	22.5
	.377 95	9.6			.55	13.970		23/32	.718 75	18.2562			.889 76	22.6
	.38	9.652			.551 18	**14.0**			.72	18.288			.89	22.606
	.381 89	9.7			.555 12	14.1			.720 47	18.3		57/64	.890 63	22.6219
	.385 83	9.8			.559 05	14.2			.724 41	18.4			.893 70	22.7
	.389 76	9.9			.56	14.224			.728 35	18.5			.897 64	22.8
	.39	9.906		(9/16)	.562 50	14.2875			.73	18.542			.90	22.860
25/64	.390 63	9.9219			.562 99	14.3			.732 28	18.6			.901 57	22.9
	.393 70	**10.0**			.566 93	14.4		47/64	.734 38	18.6531			.905 51	23.0
	.397 64	10.1			.57	14.478			.736 22	18.7		29/32	.906 25	23.0188
	.40	10.16			.570 87	14.5			.74	18.796			.909 49	23.1
	.401 57	10.2			.574 80	14.6			.740 16	18.8			.91	23.114
	.405 51	10.3		37/64	.578 13	14.6844			.744 09	18.9			.913 38	23.2
13/32	.406 25	10.3188			.578 74	14.7			.748 03	19.0			.917 32	23.3
	.409 45	10.4			.58	14.732		(3/4)	.75	19.050			.92	23.368
	.41	10.414			.582 68	14.8			.751 97	19.1			.921 26	23.4
	.413 39	10.5			.586 61	14.9			.755 90	19.2		59/64	.921 88	23.4156
	.417 32	10.6			.59	14.986			.759 84	19.3			.925 20	23.5
	.42	10.668			.590 55	15.0			.76	19.304			.929 13	23.6
	.421 26	10.7		19/32	.593 75	15.0812			.763 78	19.4			.93	23.622
27/64	.421 88	10.7156			.594 49	15.1		49/64	.765 63	19.4469			.933 07	23.7
	.425 20	10.8			.598 42	15.2			.767 72	19.5			.937 01	23.8
	.429 13	10.9			.60	15.24			.77	19.558		(15/16)	.937 50	23.8125
	.43	10.992			.602 36	15.3			.771 65	19.6			.94	23.876
	.433 07	11.0			.606 30	15.4			.775 59	19.7			.940 94	23.9
	.437 01	11.1		39/64	.609 38	15.4781			.779 53	19.8			.944 88	**24.0**
(7/16)	.437 5	11.1125			.61	15.494			.78	19.812			.948 82	24.1
	.44	11.176			.610 24	15.5		25/32	.781 25	19.8438			.95	24.130
	.440 94	11.2			.614 17	15.6			.783 46	19.9		61/64	.952 75	24.2
	.444 88	11.3			.618 11	15.7			.787 40	**20.0**			.953 13	24.2094
	.488 82	11.4			.62	15.748			.79	20.066			.956 69	24.3
	.45	11.430			.622 05	15.8			.791 34	20.1			.96	24.384
	.452 76	11.5		(5/8)	.625	15.875			.795 27	20.2			.960 63	24.4
29/64	.453 13	11.5094			.625 98	15.9		51/64	.796 88	20.2406			.964 57	24.5
	.456 69	11.6			.629 92	**16.0**			.799 21	20.3			.968 50	24.6
	.46	11.684			.63	16.002			.80	20.320		31/32	.968 75	24.6062
	.450 63	11.7			.633 86	16.1			.803 15	20.4			.97	24.638
	.464 57	11.8			.637 79	16.2			.807 09	20.5			.972 44	24.7
	.468 50	11.9			.64	16.256			.81	20.574			.976 38	24.8
(15/32)	.468 75	11.9062		41/64	.640 63	16.2719		(13/16)	.811 02	20.6			.98	24.892
	.47	11.938			.641 73	16.3			.812 50	20.6375			.980 31	24.9
	.472 44	**12.0**			.645 67	16.4			.814 96	20.7			.984 25	25.0
	.476 38	12.1			.649 61	16.5			.818 90	20.8		63/64	.984 38	25.0031
	.48	12.192			.65	16.510			.82	20.828			.988 19	25.1
	.480 31	12.2			.653 54	16.6			.822 83	20.9			.99	25.146
	.484 25	12.3		21/32	.656 25	16.6688			.826 77	21.0			.922 12	25.2
31/64	.484 38	12.3031			.657 48	16.7		53/64	.828 13	21.0344			.996 06	25.3
	.488 19	12.4			.66	16.764			.83	21.082		(1")	1.000 00	25.4000
	.49	12.446			.661 42	16.8			.830 71	21.1		1-1/4	1.25	31.75
	.492 13	12.5			.665 35	16.9			.834 64	21.2		1-1/2	1.50	38.1
	.496 06	12.6			.669 29	17.0			.838 58	21.3		1-3/4	1.75	44.45
(1/2)	.50	12.7			.67	17.018			.84	21.336		2"	2.000	50.8
	.503 94	12.8		43/64	.671 88	17.0656			.842 52	21.4		2-1/2	2.5	63.5
	.507 87	12.9			.673 23	17.1		27/32	.843 75	21.4312		3"	3.000	76.2
	.51	12.954			.677 16	17.2			.846 46	21.5		3-1/2	3.5	88.9
	.511 81	13.0			.68	17.272			.85	21.590			3.937	100.00
33/64	.515 63	13.0969			.681 10	17.3			.850 39	21.6		4"	4.000	101.6
	.515 75	13.1			.685 04	17.4			.854 33	21.7		4-1/2	4.5	114.3
	.519 68	13.2		(11/16)	.687 50	17.4625			.858 27	21.8		5"	5.000	127.0
	.52	13.208			.688 98	17.5		55/64	.859 38	21.8281		6"	6.000	152.4
	.523 62	13.3			.69	17.526			.86	21.844		7"	7.000	177.8
	.527 56	13.4			.692 91	17.6			.862 20	21.9		8"	8.000	203.2
	.53	13.462			.696 85	17.7			.866 14	22.0		8-1/2	8.5	215.9
17/32	.531 25	13.4938			.70	17.78			.87	22.098		9"	9.000	228.6
	.531 50	13.5			.700 79	17.8			.870 08	22.1		10"	10.000	254.00
	.535 43	13.6		45/64	.703 13	17.8594			.874 01	22.2		11"	11.000	279.4
	.539 37	13.7			.704 72	17.9		(7/8)	.875	22.225		12"	12.000	304.8

TRACTOR MANUFACTURERS' ADDRESSES

ALLIS-CHALMERS
See Deutz-Allis

ARIENS
Ariens Company
655 West Ryan Street
Brillion, WI 54110
(414) 756-2141

BARON
See Simplicity

BOLENS
Bolens International
215 South Park
Port Washington, WI 53074
(414) 284-5521

BROADMOOR
See Simplicity

CASE/INGERSOLL
Ingersoll Equipment Co.
119 South 1st Street
Winneconne, WI 54986
(414) 582-4455

CHARGER
See Wheel Horse

COMMANDO
See Wheel Horse

CUB CADET CORP.
Division of MTD
P.O. Box 36900
Cleveland, OH 44136
(216) 273-4550

DEUTZ-ALLIS
Deutz Corp.
7385 Ponce de Leon Circle
Atlanta, GA 30340
(404) 449-6140

ENGINEERING PRODUCTS CO.
Engineering Products Co.
P.O. Box 1510
Waukesha, WI 53187
(414) 547-5557

INTERNATIONAL HARVESTER
See Cub Cadet Corp.

JACOBSEN
Jacobsen, Division of Textron, Inc.
1721 Packard Avenue
Racine, WI 53403-9988
(414) 637-6711

JIM DANDY
See Engineering Products Co.

JOHN DEERE
Deere & Company
John Deere Road
Moline, IL 61265
(309) 752-8000

FORD
Ford New Holland, Inc.
500 Diller Avenue
New Holland, PA 17557
(717) 354-1121

GILSON
Lawn Boy Product Group
P.O. Box 152
Plymouth, WI 53073
(414) 893-1011

GRAVELY
Gravely Corporation
One Gravely Lane
Clemmons, NC 27012
(919) 766-4721

HOMESTEADER
See Deutz-Allis

HONDA
American Honda Motor Co., Inc.
100 West Alondra Blvd.
Gardena, CA 90247
(213) 327-8280

LANDLORD
See Simplicity

LAWN RANGER
See Wheel Horse

MTD
MTD Products, Inc.
5965 Grafton Road
P.O. Box 36900
Cleveland, OH 44136
(216) 225-2600

POWER KING
See Engineering Products Co.

RAIDER
See Wheel Horse

RANGER
See Wheel Horse

SERF
See Simplicity

SIMPLICITY
Simplicity Manufacturing Co.
500 North Spring Street
Port Washington, WI 53074
(414) 284-5535

SOVEREIGN
See Simplicity

SPECIAL
See Engineering Products Co.

SPEEDEX
Speedex Tractor Co.
367 North Freedom Street
Ravenna, OH 44266
(216) 297-1484

WESTERN AUTO
Western Auto
2107 Grand
Kansas City, MO 64108
(816) 346-4000

WHEEL HORSE
Wheel Horse Lawn &
  Garden Tractors
P.O. Box 2649
South Bend, IN 46680
(219) 291-3112

WHITE
White Outdoor Products
2625 Butterfield Road
Oak Brook, IL 60521
(312) 887-0110

WIZARD
See Western Auto

WORK HORSE
See Wheel Horse

YARD-MAN
See MTD

YEOMAN
See Simplicity

ENGINE MANUFACTURERS' ADDRESSES

BRIGGS & STRATTON
Briggs & Stratton Corp.
P.O. Box 702
Milwaukee, WI 53201
(414) 259-5618

HONDA
See Honda under Tractor
  Manufacturer's Addresses

KAWASAKI
Kawasaki Motors Corp.,
  Engine Div.
P.O. Box 504
Shakopee, MN 55379
(612) 445-6060

KOHLER
Kohler Co., Engine Div.
Highland Drive
Kohler, WI 53044
(414) 457-4441

ONAN
Onan
1400 73rd Avenue NE
Minneapolis, MN 55432
(612) 574-5000

TECUMSEH
Tecumseh Products Co.
900 North Street
Grafton, WI 53024
(414) 377-2700

WISCONSIN
Teledyne Total Power
P.O. Box 181160
Memphis, TN 38181-1160
(901) 365-3600

NOTES

NOTES